An understanding of the behavior of a material depends on a knowledge of its structure. Depending on the property to be understood, the material must be examined at one, or more, of three levels. It may be sufficient to examine its microstructure, or it may be necessary to take a deeper look into the geometric arrangement of its atoms, or perhaps it may even be necessary to probe further into the interaction among its atomic orbitals.

The structure
and properties
of materials

The structure and properties of materials

A. T. DiBenedetto
Associate Professor of
Chemical Engineering
Washington University

McGraw-Hill Book Company
New York
St. Louis
San Francisco
Toronto
London
Sydney

The Structure and Properties of Materials

Preface

Since I have been teaching in the general area of materials, I have always been able to say with complete certainty that it is very important for an engineer to be knowledgeable in "materials science." To the obvious question, *"What should I know about materials science?"* I have never had a very definite answer. To some people, the term "materials science" means the systematizing and formulating of the laws governing the behavior and properties of all states of matter (i.e., gases, liquids, solids, plasmas, and any other defined state that one wishes to imagine); others prefer to limit the term to merely the solid state. Most texts in this area are devoted primarily to solid materials.

The primary aim of this text is to promote an understanding of the relationship between the molecular structure of a material and the manner in which the material reacts to its environment (i.e., its physical properties). The emphasis is strongly on organic polymers simply because this is my major field of interest and because it is my conviction that this particular group of materials is of special interest to other chemical engineers. I have retained the more general title of "Structure and Properties of Materials" because I very much want to characterize the interdisciplinary nature of the subject. There is a great deal of technique and theory that has been developed to understand the behavior of gases, salt crystals, dielectric crystals, and metals that is also applicable to much more complicated materials such as ceramics, plastics, and composite structures. The general approach is thus to develop the basic concepts with as simple a structure as possible and then try to indicate how these techniques might be used to promote a better understanding of a complex organic polymer. Although the appeal is primarily toward chemical engineers, I think there is enough similarity in the problems of all classes of materials to retain a general interest to all engineers.

The text is divided into three major parts. The first part deals with the fundamental concepts in physics and chemistry which form the basis for a materials science. The second describes the nature and formation of solid structures with an emphasis on how the older and more complete studies on simple crystals are utilized to explain the behavior of polymers. The third describes the interrelationships between the molecular properties of materials and a variety of measurable physical properties.

The part on fundamentals consists of four chapters. In the first chapter it is pointed out that the molecules of any system will interact because of attractive and repulsive intermolecular forces. The nature of dispersive, electrostatic, inductive, and short-range forces are therefore discussed. The second chapter is a summary of the basic equations of statistical mechanics. The primary aim is to indicate the connection between the intermolecular forces that hold aggregates of atoms together and the thermodynamic properties of such a system. In the third chapter, the natural consequence of intermolecular forces, namely, chemical bonding, is considered. Electronic binding in atoms and the formation of simple molecules are considered. The quantitative principles developed in the third chapter are then utilized in Chapter 4 to discuss qualitatively the formation of complex organic molecules.

The second part consists of the next five chapters and is called Structure of Engineering Materials. In the fifth chapter, the geometry of simple crystals is discussed. The basic crystal lattices are listed, and the use of x-ray diffraction techniques for elucidating structure is described. The chapter closes with a discussion of the relationship between the geometry and chemical bonding. In the sixth and seventh chapters we temporarily break away from a completely molecular approach to see how materials are formed into complex polycrystalline solids. The sixth chapter is concerned with the nucleation and freezing of metals and the types of imperfections that arise in the process. The seventh chapter is a brief survey of the principles of alloy formation. Several specific alloys are separately discussed because of their industrial importance. In the eighth and ninth chapters we turn our attention to polymeric materials. The coverage on the properties of individual polymer molecules and the geometry of polymer crystals parallels the coverage in Chapter 5 on simple crystals. The chapter closes with a brief discussion of chemical bonding in polymer crystals. The ninth chapter parallels the sixth and seventh chapters by discussing the formation and structure of complex polycrystalline masses.

The third part of this text consists of the final six chapters, on the properties of engineering materials. The primary aim is to interrelate the molecular properties of the materials with observable physical properties. Considerable experimental data are included and discussed in "molecular" terms. In most cases the discussion is qualitative, but at a high enough level to get a sophisticated understanding of the response of the material to its environment. The tenth chapter quantitatively develops thermodynamic equations for simple crystals by relating the energy of the system to the atomic vibrations within the solid. The application of this idea to complex polymeric structures is then discussed, and empirical relationships are presented. The eleventh chapter is concerned with the mechanical properties of metallic solids. The relationships between deformation and imperfection in the atomic structure are considered first and are followed by analysis of the important properties of creep, fracture, and fatigue. The twelfth chapter parallels the eleventh by considering the mechanical properties of polymeric materials. In this case the main emphasis is on viscoelasticity rather than elasticity and plastic deformation.

The next two chapters consider the electromagnetic properties of materials. In Chapter 13, electrical conductivity is discussed from both a classical and a quantum-mechanical viewpoint. The differences between conductors, semiconductors, and insulators are discussed by bringing in the zone concepts of electron behavior. The dielectric and magnetic properties of materials are considered in Chapter 14. Special emphasis is on how particles respond to alternating fields. The conditions for dielectric breakdown are also discussed. The fifteenth chapter describes the chemical properties of materials. For metals, the emphasis is on oxidation and corrosion resistance because of the industrial importance of these phenomena. For organic materials the emphasis is on thermal stability and solvent compatibility, since these are often the limiting factors in commercial use of polymers. The final chapter is a brief discussion of properties that are related to the surface characteristics of the material.

The level of material is set for the junior or senior engineering student with some background in physical chemistry. The discussions of organic and inorganic substances have been sufficiently well separated that a one-semester introductory course may emphasize either inorganics or organics at the expense of the other. It has thus been recognized that non-chemical engineers may not wish to emphasize organic materials as much as this text does.

There are a number of points of view that may be satisfied by using this text in an introductory course. Four outlines for one-semester courses with different emphasis are suggested below:

Solid-state physics–oriented:
Chapters 1, 2, 3, 4, 5, 8, 10, 13, 14

Engineering–oriented:
Chapters 1, 3, 5, 6, 7, 9, 11, 12, 15, 16

Metals–oriented:
Chapters 1, 3, 5, 6, 7, 11, 13, 15 (corrosion), 16

Polymers–oriented:
Chapters 1, 3, 4, 8, 9, 12, 14, 15 (compatibility)

The author wishes to thank the University of Wisconsin and specifically the Department of Chemical Engineering for making available the time and facilities for preparing this manuscript. Special gratitude is extended to Professor R. A. Ragatz of the University of Wisconsin, who encouraged and stimulated the use of new ideas and approaches in the department's engineering materials courses. It was the development of these courses that stimulated the growth of this manuscript. Special thanks is also extended to Professor R. Byron Bird of the University of Wisconsin for his critical examination of the original classroom notes which served as the rough draft of this text. His imaginative advice immensely improved the content and organization of the final text. Thanks are also extended to Mrs. Yvonne Conklin, whose patience in typing and retyping was a tremendous help at all stages of the manuscript. The help of the draftsmen on the staff of the University of Wisconsin Engineering Experiment Station for their preparation of all of the original drawings is also acknowledged. Finally, acknowledgment must be given to all of the authors whose texts and publications have become an inseparable part of my own thinking. Although I have tried my best to formally acknowledge individual contributions, it is not always possible to determine where my words leave off and someone else's begin.

A. T. DiBenedetto

Notes about units

This text covers electrical, mechanical, and thermal properties of matter. In all texts of this nature it is often confusing when one utilizes a wide variety of units and unit systems. The first thought was to uniformly use *one* system, such as the mks system of units, but this very quickly led to a number of undesirable features. For one, it was often necessary to use uncommon units for quantities such as density (kilograms per cubic meter, kg/m^3) and another was that it often happened that unwieldy numbers resulted (10^{10} joules/kg mole).

Rather than dogmatically hold to one set of units, it was decided to drastically limit the number of units used and at the same time try to stay consistent with common scientific usage. *The general rule was that mks units would be used unless they were extremely inconvenient or not consistent with general usage in scientific literature.*

The units that have been utilized are given in the accompanying table.

Parameter	Unit and conversions
Length	Meters, centimeters, angstroms, inches 1 m = 100 cm = 10^{10} Å (Atomic dimensions are generally reported in angstrom units.)
Mass	Kilograms, grams 1 kg = 1,000 g
Time	Seconds
Standard gravity	9.80665 kg-m/sec²
Force	Newtons, kilograms of weight, pound of force 1 newton = 1 kg-m/sec² = 0.2248 lb_f 1 kg_w = (1 kg)(9.80665 m/sec²) = 9.80665 newtons
Energy	Kilocalories, joules 1 joule = 1 newton-m 1 kcal = 4,186 joules

The joule is the basic unit of energy in the mks system, but the units of kilocalories per gram-mole are universally used for describing bond strengths and thermodynamic properties. In general, the units of kilocalories per gram mole are used in this text with joules per kilogram-mole often reported in parentheses. For the same reason, pounds per square inch were chosen over newtons per square meter as a unit of strength.

Density	Grams per cubic centimeter, kilograms per cubic meter 1 g/cm³ = 1,000 kg/m³ (The cgs unit is normally the most convenient and is generally used in this text.)

Electromagnetism:
  Unit charge
  Unit potential
	
	Coulomb
	Volt
	ϵ_0 = ⅑ × 10^{-9} farads/m
	1 farad = 1 coul/volt
	$(\mu_0)_M$ = 10^{-7} henry/m
	1 henry = 1 volt-sec²/coul
	1 joule = 1 volt-coul

CONTENTS

Introduction

The fundamentals of materials science are not new or unique but rather are merely the application of principles of physics and chemistry to aggregates of atoms and molecules. The most basic research in materials science is really just the research work of physicists and chemists. The most dramatic event in the history of this field has been the development of semiconductor devices such as transistors. This latter invention, in fact, has pretty much dominated the thinking of those who have developed the logic of a separate materials science. The transistor is certainly an ideal example of the logical evolution from scientific thought, to inventiveness, to a major technology. As always, empiricism led the way with the use of galena and, later, selenium crystals as point-contact rectifiers. The theoretical explanation of their behavior by N. F. Mott and others, in the mid-1930s, then led to the scientific investigation of silicon, germanium, and other "semiconducting" crystals. The purely scientific explanations of the behavior of these materials by J. Bardeen and others soon led to the development of transistor devices. Over the past twenty years there have been revolutionary changes in the electronics industry as a result of this invention. Miniaturization, new electronic equipment, computing devices, and information-processing systems have all been very highly developed. Simultaneously, further research has been stimulated in the areas of crystal growing, purification of materials, dislocation theory, and diffusional processes, to name a few.

An equally important advance has been the development of transition-metal catalysts for the polymerization of sterically regulated organic polymers. The first important developments occurred in the mid-1950s when K. Ziegler produced polymers of ethylene with highly linear structures. At about the same time, G. Natta synthesized polymers of alkyl and aryl monosubstituted ethylenes (such as propylene and styrene) which had stereo-regular structures. The importance of this work was that for the first time a catalyst-monomer system was developed in which it was possible to produce a specific stereoisomer of a given material. It thus became possible to control the molecular structure of a polymeric material. A tremendous outpouring of research soon extended these techniques by creating many new catalysts for a wide variety of polymerizable monomers. Commercial development has been very rapid and has already led to the large-volume production of many new plastics, fibers, and synthetic rubbers. To a certain extent, one may now "tailor-make" a product with a specific set of physical properties. The impact on the polymer industry has been immense in terms of the wide variety of new products now available. In the United States in 1965, for example, 365 million pounds of polypropylene, at a minimum price of about $0.20 per pound, were produced by seven major chemical companies. Considering that the polymer industry is already a multibillion dollar industry, one can easily imagine that this kind of an advancement can have a significant impact on the economy of the world.

The next example illustrates the importance of combining different classes of materials in order to produce a different type of structure. The development of the organo-silicone products has been more artistic than theoretical, but has resulted in some very significant contributions to technology. Chemists have known how to produce chemicals with silicon-to-carbon bonds [such as di-methyldichlorosilane $(CH_3)_2SiCl_2$] for over fifty years. During the 1940s, especially during World War II, a special need developed for varnishes, greases, and elastomers that were more temperature-resistant than the common hydrocarbon materials. Polymer chemists at Mellon Institute, to name one research group, learned how to produce silicone polymers from monomers like di-methyldichlorosilane. The main chain of such a polymer is basically inorganic (Si   Si), while the side groups may be organic ($—CH_3$ for example). Thus a

$$\underset{O}{\diagdown\diagup}$$

"hybrid" material was designed which had some of the important properties of both inorganic and organic structures. In the present state of the art, fluids, greases, rubbers, and hard materials may all be produced on a commercial scale. Their uses include pressure-sensitive adhesives, damping fluids, coatings, gaskets, sealing compounds, insulators, and lubricants, to name a few. Perhaps the most interesting application of silicones, and the one that could have the greatest value to humanity, is the use of silicone products in medicine. Since these materials do not age for long periods of time and will not react with body tissue, they have been used for plastic surgery, for heart valves, for catheters, and for coating on implants in the body.

These three significant developments in materials science illustrate the breadth of this field. One should have a fairly sophisticated appreciation of solid-state physics to understand the interrelation between properties and molecular structure and, at the same time, have a familiarity with theoretical chemistry and reaction kinetics in order to understand chemical synthesis. An appreciation of the "state of the art," or the technology of things ranging from the casting of metals to organo-silicone chemistry, is also necessary. "Important" engineering materials range from single crystals of semiconductors, metals, organic polymers, ceramics, metallo-organic composites, and ceramo-metallic composites to an uncountable number of mixtures, alloys, and copolymers. The all-encompassing nature of this field should be very apparent.

The engineer, although he may not be a materials specialist, should have an insight into what molecular and environmental factors are important in determining how a solid will react to change. Since there is such a rapidly growing list of both commercially available materials and new applications, it is no longer possible to just study the properties of steel, concrete, and a few other widely used materials and observe how they react under certain conditions; the nature of the available materials is too varied and this would not prepare one to face the expanding possibilities of new applications. Since all matter is composed of atoms and molecules, the ideal situation is to be able to deduce the physical properties of a given substance a priori from its molecular structure and, conversely, to obtain fundamental information about molecular structure from observations of macroscopic properties. When dealing with even the simplest solid materials, this becomes a very difficult task. The present state of the field is such that a few structure-insensitive properties of simple solids can be handled quantitatively. On the other hand, by using a few simple models and applying well-known concepts to the solid state, a broad, qualitative understanding may be obtained.

In the following chapters, materials are classified according to the kinds of molecules that make up their structure and according to the manner in which they react to their environment. The aim of the text is to understand the relation between structure and properties.

Part A
Atoms and molecules

1
Intermolecular forces

1.1
Introduction

All matter, regardless of its state, is composed of the same fundamental particles. A material consists of many atoms, each of which is formed by the interaction of the fundamental particles. Most of the mass of each atom is concentrated in a small region of space, called the nucleus, and consists of neutrons, protons, and other "heavy" particles [5,8]. The remaining volume of the atom consists of a distribution of negative charge, visualized as a cloud of moving electrons which surrounds the nucleus. The density of this cloud at any point is a measure of the probability of finding an electron at that point. In an isolated atom the cloud thins out rapidly beyond a radius of 1 to 5 Å but actually persists for very large distances from the central nucleus.

In almost every instance, it is satisfactory to consider the electron cloud as being completely contained within a sphere of radius 1 to 5 Å. Since the diameter of a nucleus is of the order of 10^{-4} Å, 10^{-12} to 10^{-15} of the volume of an atom contains very nearly all the mass. Appendix A is a list of all the known elements along with their atomic weights in units of grams per gram atom. (A "gram atom" of material consists of 6.023×10^{23} atoms of the element in question.) Figure 1.1 is a schematic drawing of a hydrogen atom in its normal state. The nucleus is represented by the point in the center and the electronic distribution by the shaded area. The density of the shaded area is proportional to the density of the electronic cloud. The distribution curve in Fig. 1.1 shows that the quantity $4\pi r^2 \mid \Psi(r) \mid^2$, which is the relative probability of finding an electron at a distance r from the nucleus, reaches a maximum at $r = 0.529$ Å and fades away to nearly zero beyond 3 Å. A more complete description of atoms and molecules will be presented in Chap. 3.

States of matter (i.e., gases, liquids, and solids) are aggregates of atoms. If we were able to describe the forces that hold these atoms (or molecules) together exactly, we would then be able to predict many of the properties of the material. We shall see that this goal has been realized for dilute gases and that we can come pretty close for very simple crystals. We shall also see that we can make some rough approximations for complex materials and come up with some interesting qualitative information.

We should be aware that the atomic nature of a material determines many of its physical properties. For example, helium is a gas at normal pressure and temperature because the interatomic attraction of helium atoms for one

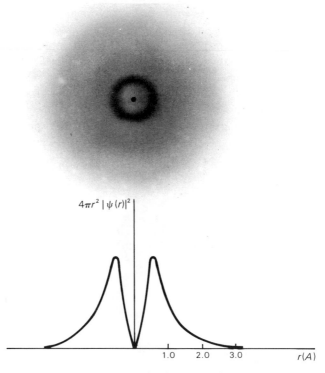

$4\pi r^2 \, |\psi(r)|^2$

1.0   2.0   3.0 $r(\text{A})$

Fig. 1.1 The electron density for the normal state of the hydrogen atom reaches a sharp maximum at a radial distance of 0.529 Å from the nucleus.

another is considerably smaller than the thermal, or kinetic, energy which tends to keep the atoms apart. Likewise, the high intensity of interionic attraction of sodium ions for chloride ions causes sodium chloride to be a solid at normal temperature. Also, electrical conductivity of a solid can be related to the energy and mobility of the electrons in a structure. Illustrations of the relation between physical properties and atomic nature are endless.

The important point is that if we are to understand why a material behaves as it does, we must often take an atomic or molecular view of the structure. Fortunately, as we shall discover, there are many extremely simple models which adequately predict behavior and at the same time promote an understanding of the fundamental nature of the material. Without going into the specific details of structure, let us first summarize the kinds of forces that are responsible for aggregates of particles coming together to form a cohesive mass of material.

1.2
Types of interatomic forces [1,2,3,6]

It is a fundamental fact of nature that all particles of matter tend to interact. An energy of interaction exists whether we are dealing with a group of helium atoms, where the interatomic forces are relatively weak, or an aggregate of carbon atoms (e.g., diamond), where the interatomic forces are very intense.

Suppose we have a crystal in which the atoms can be represented by an array of close-packed spheres. (This is actually a good representation for many kinds of real materials.) Figure 1.2 shows this kind of arrangement. Figure 1.2a can perhaps be more clearly visualized by putting down a layer of marbles on a flat surface, placing another layer on top of that, and so forth. Each

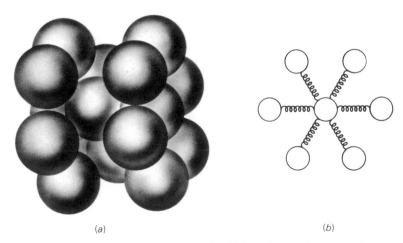

(a)   (b)

Fig. 1.2   A close-packed crystal is one in which each atom is surrounded by 12 adjacent atoms.

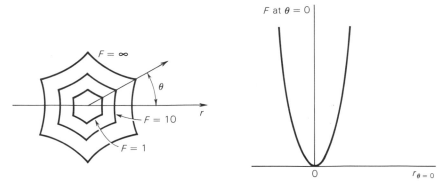

Fig. 1.3 The restoring force for an atom is a complex function of position in the crystal lattice and is zero at the equilibrium position.

sphere (atom) is thus in direct contact with 12 others. Real atoms must always have a certain amount of thermal energy which tends to keep them in random motion. Each atom in the crystal also interacts with all of its neighbors. This interaction might be visualized in the following way. Consider only one plane in the crystal so as to reduce the problem to two dimensions. Figure 1.2b shows an atom surrounded by six nearest neighbors, each of which is joined to the central one by imaginary springs. Let us fix the positions of the six surrounding atoms and permit the central one to move in a random fashion. When it is right in the center of the circle, the net force on the system is zero, so that this is the "equilibrium" position. When the atom moves off center in any direction, the springs have a tendency to force the atom back to the center. This is analogous to the behavior in a real solid.

Thermal, or Brownian, motion tends to scatter the particles in a random fashion, while the interactions between particles tend to keep the system in a fixed geometry. The net result is a restrained vibrational motion within the caged volume created by all the neighboring atoms. (Think again in three dimensions.) If we can write down an equation for the force on our springs as a function of displacement, we should then be able to predict the restoring force as a function of the displacement of the central particle. Figure 1.3 shows what the solution might look like for the hypothetical problem of Fig. 1.2b. In a real crystal, the intermolecular forces are equivalent to restoring forces on the springs and the net intermolecular force (or intermolecular potential) is a very complicated function of the position and orientation of all the particles involved. In this section we are interested in characterizing the nature of these intermolecular forces so that we may better understand the approximations that are required to solve real problems.

Actually, the net force on any one particle is the resultant of interactions with *all* the surrounding particles, whether they are nearest neighbors or not. One cannot say that the nature of the attraction between one atom and another a few atomic layers away is exactly the same as the attraction between nearest neighbors, because whereas the atom in question "sees" the whole elec-

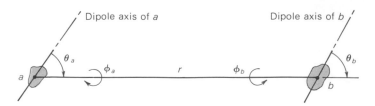

Fig. 1.4   The coordinate system for two molecules a and b.

trostatic field and shielded nucleus of a nearest neighbor, it sees something different in an atom several layers away. The shielding created by intervening layers of atoms will thus change the nature of the interaction. Thus in an almost infinite array of atoms (any size crystal you can see) it is impossible to obtain an exact and still useful characterization of the force felt by a specific atom. Herein lies our first assumption. *The force of interaction, F_{ab}, between two particles, a and b, is a function of only the interparticle separation and mutual orientation of the interacting pair, and a single expression can be used to represent this interaction.*

Thus for two stationary particles a and b separated by a distance r and whose orientations are characterized by angles θ_a, ϕ_a, θ_b, and ϕ_b (Fig. 1.4):

$$F_{ab} = f(r, \theta_a, \theta_b, \phi_a - \phi_b) \tag{1.1}$$

For most purposes it is more convenient to use a potential energy of interaction, ψ_{ab}, rather than the force. These quantities are related by the expression

$$F_{ab} = -\frac{\partial \psi_{ab}}{\partial r} \tag{1.2}$$

In addition to this force, there is a torque on particle a because of its interaction with the electromagnetic field emanating from particle b, and vice versa. For particles with no orientation dependence (e.g., spherical atoms), this torque is zero and Eqs. (1.1) and (1.2) may be written as

$$F_{ab} = f(r) = -\frac{d\psi_{ab}}{dr} \tag{1.3}$$

The total potential energy of interaction of particle a with its surroundings, ψ_{aT}, is assumed to be the sum of all two-body interactions. In an aggregate of N atoms, the potential energy of atom a is

$$\psi_{aT} = \sum_{j=1}^{N-1} \psi_{aj} \tag{1.4}$$

It is convenient to consider the net interaction between two particles as the resultant of repulsive forces (which are dominant when the atoms are forced together) and attractive forces (which are dominant when they are separated by more than three or four atomic diameters). In Fig. 1.5, the net force F_{ab} is shown as the sum of a repulsive and an attractive force. When particle b is very far from particle a, there is a net attraction between the two which increases as b comes closer to a. The net attraction reaches a maximum value at position r_y and then begins to decrease because of the increasing importance of the repulsive (positive) forces. At position r_0 the net force is zero, and at closer distances the particles repel one another. The potential energy of interaction also varies with the separation r and reaches a minimum value ψ_0 when the net force between the particles is zero. These curves have been approximated theoretically for pairs of simple atoms (e.g., two neon atoms) and empirically for a great number of "two-body" interactions.

The minimum potential energy of interaction for a pair of neon atoms is approximately -5×10^{-22} joules per pair [Ref. 1, p. 1072]. At ordinary temperature, the average thermal energy per degree of freedom for a neon atom is approximately $\frac{1}{2}kT$ or 2×10^{-21} joules per atom. Since the translational energy

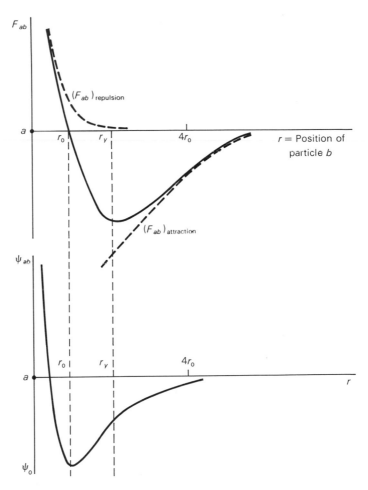

Fig. 1.5 The net potential energy of interaction between two molecules is at a minimum when the interaction force is zero.

at room temperature is an order of magnitude greater than the net potential energy of interaction, neon stays in a dispersed (or gaseous) state at room temperature. Near the boiling point of neon, 27°K, the quantity $\frac{1}{2}kT$ is approximately 2×10^{-22} joules per molecule. Although this is no longer an accurate measure of the average thermal energy, because of quantum-mechanical effects, one can see qualitatively, at least, that the thermal energy is becoming smaller than the interaction potential. When the atoms come together, they cannot often attain sufficient kinetic energy to separate again. Then an equilibrium separation of about r_0 is maintained where the potential energy of the pair is at a minimum. This gives us a two-body analogue for the process of solidification. Sublimation occurs when an atom in a solid body attains a high enough kinetic energy to overcome the attraction to its surroundings. The total energy required for the sublimation of a pair of atoms at 0°K is given by Eq. (1.5):

$$\text{Sublimation energy at 0°K per pair} = -\int_{r_0}^{\infty} F_{ab} \, dr \tag{1.5}$$

This gives the maximum bonding energy between the two particles.

1.3
Long-range forces [1,6]

Consider an atom as a slow-moving (stationary relative to the electronic motion), positively charged nucleus surrounded by fast-moving electrons which appear to form a cloud of electrostatic charge about the centrally located nucleus. The density of the cloud at any point measures the probability of finding an electron at that point. It is assumed that this cloud is completely contained within a sphere of radius r which will always be less than a few angstroms. This is a reasonable description of simple atoms in their ground states. When two such atoms interact without an overlapping of these equivalent electrostatic fields, they will interact with one another because of electrostatic, inductive, and dispersive interactions.

Electrostatic interactions For two discrete point charges of charge e_i and e_j, the potential energy of interaction in a vacuum, according to Coulomb's law of electrostatics, is

$$\psi_{ij} = \frac{e_i e_j}{r_{ij}} \tag{1.6}$$

where r_{ij} is the distance between them (Fig. 1.6a). The total potential energy of interaction between two complex distributions (Fig. 1.6b), such as two molecules a and b, consists of three parts: the self-energies of the two molecules, ψ_{aa} and ψ_{bb}, and the interaction between molecules, ψ_{ab}. For an arbitrary distribution,

$$\psi_{aa} = \frac{1}{2} \sum_i \sum_{i'} \frac{e_i e_{i'}}{r_{ii'}} \tag{1.7}$$

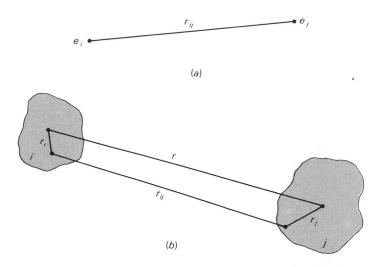

Fig. 1.6 The interaction between two charge distributions is represented by a set of r_{ij} vectors. (a) Two discrete point charges; (b) two groups of point charges (a model for two atoms).

$$\psi_{bb} = \frac{1}{2} \sum_j \sum_{j'} \frac{e_{jj'}}{r_{jj'}}$$ (1.8)

$$\psi_{ab} = \sum_i \sum_j \frac{e_i e_j}{r_{ij}}$$ (1.9)

The potentials ψ_{aa} and ψ_{bb} are of interest when studying the chemical bonding within a given molecule, while ψ_{ab} is of interest when studying the states of matter. Let us consider the interaction potential ψ_{ab}. In order to evaluate it, *the quantities* $1/r_{ij}$ *must be determined.* By a mathematical technique known as the *two-center expansion* [Ref. 1, p. 843], $1/r_{ij}$ may be rewritten as an infinite series of terms involving $r_i, r_j,$ and r, where r is the distance between two convenient points in the molecules (say, the center of gravity of each). This very complicated expression may be reduced to Eq. (1.10) when $r > r_i + r_j$:

$$\psi_{ab} = \frac{q_a q_b}{r} - \frac{q_a \mu_b \cos \theta_b}{r^2} - \frac{q_b \mu_a \cos \theta_a}{r^2}$$

$$+ \frac{q_a Q_b (3 \cos^2 \theta_b - 1)}{2r^3} + \frac{q_b Q_a (3 \cos^2 \theta_a - 1)}{2r^3}$$

$$- \frac{\mu_a \mu_b}{r^3} [(2 \cos \theta_a \cos \theta_b - \sin \theta_a \sin \theta_b \cos (\phi_a - \phi_b)]$$

$$+ \cdots +$$ (1.10)

Actually, Eq. (1.10) is an infinite series, but higher-order terms are usually negligible. The angles θ_a, θ_b, ϕ_a, and ϕ_b are defined in Fig. 1.4. The quantities q_a, μ_a, and Q_a are called the net charge, the dipole moment, and the quadrupole moment of the molecule a. For most reasonably accurate work, moments higher than a dipole can be neglected, so that the quadrupole and higher moment terms of Eq. (1.10) are usually negligible. The origins of the coordinate systems in Fig. 1.4 may be taken at either the center of gravity or the center of charge of the particle (whichever is most convenient). The net charge q is determined by adding up all of the unit charges in the particle. The first term in Eq. (1.10) is thus the coulombic interaction between the net charges of particles a and b. A pair of hydrogen molecules, for example, have net charges of zero, causing the first term to be zero. A sodium ion, on the other hand, contains 11 protons and 10 electrons for a net charge of one proton, or $q_{Na} = 1.60186 \times 10^{-19}$ coul. The net coulombic attraction of a sodium ion with a chloride ion of equal but opposite charge is then -10^{-18} joules per NaCl molecule or -6×10^8 joules/kg mole of NaCl (if $r \doteq 2.3$ Å).

When the centers of gravity of positive and negative charge do not coincide, a dipole moment is formed. For a neutral molecule with total charges $+e$ and $-e$ separated by a distance l, the total dipole moment μ is

$$\mu = el \tag{1.11}$$

The second term in Eq. (1.10) represents the electrostatic attraction between a net charge q_A and the dipole μ_B. Another way to arrive at this term is to represent it as an interaction between three points, as shown in Fig. 1.7. The net coulombic potential is

$$\psi_{AB} = \frac{q_A e_B}{r_1} - \frac{q_A e_B}{r_2} \tag{1.12}$$

where

$$r_1 = r \left(1 - \frac{l}{r} \cos \theta + \frac{l^2}{4r^2} \right)^{1/2} \tag{1.13}$$

$$r_2 = r \left(1 + \frac{l}{r} \cos \theta + \frac{l^2}{4r^2} \right)^{1/2} \tag{1.14}$$

Then

$$\psi_{AB} = -\frac{q_A e_B \cdot l}{r^2} \cos \theta \left[1 - \frac{3}{8} \left(\frac{l}{r} \right)^2 + \cdots \right]$$

$$= -\frac{q_A \mu_B}{r^2} \cos \theta \left[1 - \frac{3}{8} \left(\frac{l}{r} \right)^2 + \cdots \right] \tag{1.15}$$

For small values of l/r, the potential becomes independent of l/r and depends only on r. The second and third terms of Eq. (1.10) represent this type of ideal or *point dipole* interaction. The dipole moments of a number of simple molecules are listed in Table 1.1. The magnitude of the dipole moment is a measure of the *polarity* of the molecule; a molecule with a zero moment is said to be *nonpolar*. The magnitude depends on the geometry of the molecule and the nature of the chemical bonding. These topics will be covered in greater detail in Chap. 3.

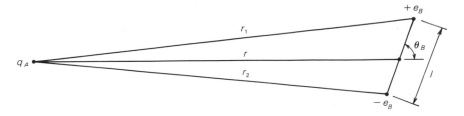

Fig. 1.7 A charge will interact with both ends of a dipole. The net interaction potential depends on the relative position and angular orientation of the dipole.

Inductive attractions When a molecule or an atom is in an electric field, the charge distribution will be distorted to a certain extent (Fig. 1.8). The distortion of the electronic field relative to the nucleus induces a temporary dipole in the particle. The difference between the dipole moment of the distorted distribution and that of the undistorted distribution is called the induced dipole moment. For weak fields, the magnitude of the induced dipole moment is proportional to the electric field; the proportionality constant is known as the *polarizability* α of the molecule

$$\mu^{\text{ind}} = \alpha \mathscr{E} \qquad\qquad (1.16)$$

Table 1.1

Dipole moments of molecules

Substance	Symbol or formula	Dipole moment debyes *
Argon	A	0.00
Hydrogen	H_2	0.00
Carbon tetrachloride	CCl_4	0.00
Ethane	C_2H_6	0.00
Acetylene	$CH{\equiv}CH$	0.00
Carbon monoxide	CO	0.12
Nitrous oxide	N_2O	0.25
α-Butylene	$CH_2{=}C_3H_6$	0.37
Hydrobromic acid	HBr	0.78
Hydrochloric acid	HCl	1.03
Ethyl alcohol	C_2H_5OH	1.10
Ammonia	NH_3	1.47
Sulfur dioxide	SO_2	1.65
Water	H_2O	1.84

* Approximate values based on a variety of literature sources;
1 debye $= 10^{-18}$ esu-cm $= \frac{1}{3} \times 10^{-29}$ coul-m.

Since molecules are generally *anisotropic* (i.e., have different properties along different axes), the polarizability is actually a tensor. For most practical calculations, *isotropy* is assumed and a single scalar value is used. This means a single average value is used for all axes. Table 1.2 shows both the "average" polarizability and the polarizabilities along different principal axes. Only single atoms and spherically symmetric molecules are truly isotropic.

The net charge and dipole of a molecule a emit electromagnetic fields which can induce a dipole in a neighboring molecule b. The induced dipole of b then interacts with the charge and dipole in a to give an energy of interaction. In general, the total inductive potential energy of interaction between two isotropic particles a and b is

Table 1.2

Polarizability of molecules *

Molecule	Symbol or formula	Average $\alpha \times 10^{31}$ m³	Principal axes		
			$\alpha_1 \times 10^{31}$ m³	$\alpha_2 \times 10^{31}$ m³	$\alpha_3 \times 10^{31}$ m³
Helium	He	2.06			
Neon	Ne	3.60			
Argon	Ar	16.50			
Krypton	Kr	20.60			
Xenon	Xe	33.30			
Hydrogen	H_2	7.9	9.3	7.1	7.1
Nitrogen	N_2	17.6	23.8	14.5	14.5
Chlorine	Cl_2	46.1	66.0	36.2	36.2
Hydrogen fluoride	HF	24.6	(9.6)	(7.2)	(7.2)
Hydrogen chloride	HCl	26.3	31.3	23.9	23.9
Carbon dioxide	CO_2	26.5	40.1	19.7	19.7
Sulfur dioxide	SO_2	37.2	54.9	27.2	24.9
Hydrogen sulfide	H_2S	37.8	40.4	34.4	40.1
Ammonia	NH_3	22.6	24.2	21.8	21.8
Hydrogen cyanide	HCN	25.9	39.2	19.2	19.2
Methane	CH_4	26.0	26.0	26.0	26.0
Ethane	C_2H_6	44.7	54.8	39.7	39.7
Ethylene	$CH_2{=}CH_2$	42.6	(56.1)	(35.9)	(35.9)
Benzene	C_6H_6	103.2	123.1	63.5	123.1
Methylchloride	CH_3Cl	45.6	54.2	41.4	41.4
Dichloromethane	CH_2Cl_2	64.8	50.2	84.7	59.6
Chloroform	$CHCl_3$	82.3	66.8	90.1	90.1
Carbon tetrachloride	CCl_4	105	105	105	105
Methyl alcohol	CH_3OH	32.3	40	25.6	31.4

* Mostly from Ref. 1, p. 950.

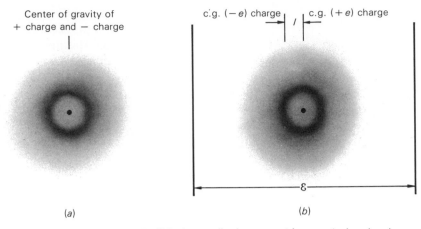

Center of gravity of
+ charge and − charge

c.g. (−e) charge   c.g. (+e) charge

l

ε

(a)   (b)

Fig. 1.8 An electric field will induce a dipole moment in a neutral molecule. (a) Neutral, spherically symmetric atom, $q = \mu = 0$; (b) polarized, neutral molecule, $q = 0$, $\mu = el$.

$$\psi_{ab}{}^{\text{ind}} = -\frac{q_a{}^2\alpha_b + q_b{}^2\alpha_a}{2r^4} - \frac{2q_a\mu_a\alpha_b \cos \theta_a + 2q_b\mu_b\alpha_a \cos \theta}{r^5}$$

$$- \frac{\mu_a{}^2\alpha_b(3 \cos^2 \theta_a + 1) + \mu_b{}^2\alpha_a(3 \cos^2 \theta_b + 1)}{2r^6} - \cdots \qquad (1.17)$$

The various terms represent different kinds of induction effects. The inverse fourth-power term, for example, represents the potential energy created by a charge q inducing a dipole moment in an adjacent molecule. This can be shown by calculating the work done in inducing the dipole and adding the electrostatic potential between the charge and the induced moment. The work done in inducing a dipole moment in molecule B is

$$W_B = \int_0^l q_B\mathscr{E}_A \, dl$$

$$= \int_0^l q_B \frac{\mu_B{}^{\text{ind}}}{\alpha_B} \, dl$$

$$= \int_0^l \frac{q_B{}^2}{\alpha_B} l \, dl$$

$$= \frac{1}{2} \frac{q_B{}^2 l^2}{\alpha_B} = \frac{1}{2} \alpha_B\mathscr{E}_A{}^2 \qquad (1.18)$$

The quantity $q_B\mathscr{E}_A$ is the force on charge q_B, and dl is the distance through which the charge is drawn. From Coulomb's law, the electric field is given by

$$\mathscr{E}_A = \frac{F}{q_A} = \frac{q_A}{r^2} \qquad (1.19)$$

so that

$$W_B = \frac{1}{2} \frac{\alpha_B q_A^2}{r^4} \tag{1.20}$$

The electrostatic potential between the induced moment and charge q_A is

$$\psi^{\text{electrostatic}} = - \frac{q_A \mu_B^{\text{ind}} \cos \theta_B}{r^2}$$

$$= - \frac{q_A \mu_B^{\text{ind}}}{r^2}$$

$$= - \frac{q_A \alpha_B \mathscr{E}_A}{r^2}$$

$$= - \frac{\alpha_B q_A^2}{r^4} \tag{1.21}$$

since $\cos \theta_B = 1$. The net induction potential due to a charge q_A inducing a dipole μ_B^{ind} is then the sum of Eqs. (1.20) and (1.21), which is the first term of Eq. (1.17). In a similar manner one may evaluate induced dipole-dipole interactions, etc. Induction potentials are almost always very much smaller than other types of attractions and can usually be neglected.

Dispersive attractions   The attraction of two spherical, neutral atoms for one another (e.g., inert-gas atoms) cannot be explained in terms of electrostatic or inductive attractions. A neutral, spherically symmetric system has no average charge or dipole or higher moment, which means the electrostatic attractions are zero. A theorem of electrostatics states that a spherical charge distribution has a field equal to that which an equivalent point charge at the center of the sphere would have. A spherically symmetric, neutral atom thus has no external field and, therefore, cannot induce moments in neighboring molecules (at least in the classical sense that was considered in the preceding section). Dispersive attractions can be visualized only by considering the electronic motion about a nucleus.

A neutral, spherically symmetric atom consists of a relatively slow moving, positively charged nucleus surrounded by shells of enough negatively charged electrons to balance the positive charge. The electrons orbit the nucleus at very high velocities. At any instant it is not likely that the electronic charge will be exactly symmetric relative to the nucleus. Thus, at any instant, a small dipole will exist in the atom. Since the electronic motion is very rapid, the orientation of this dipole will fluctuate rapidly. It is possible to show, wave-mechanically, that the time-averaged moment, based on a time very much greater than the period for the orbit, is zero. On the other hand, the fluctuating dipole moment can create a fluctuating field around the atom which in turn can induce fluctuating charge displacements in surrounding atoms. The interaction between these instantaneous, induced dipoles (and higher multipoles) results in an energy of interaction. It can be shown [Ref. 1, p. 960] that the averaged interaction energy is a net attraction. For two molecules at large separations relative to the atomic dimensions:

$$\psi_{ab}{}^{dis} = -\frac{c}{r^6} - \text{small higher-order terms} \tag{1.22}$$

The inverse sixth-power term is a result of an induced dipole-induced dipole interaction, while higher-order terms involve interactions with higher multipole moments. For spherically symmetric molecules the quantity c is a constant, while for asymmetric molecules c is a function of the angular orientation of both molecules. The evaluation of this constant is beyond the scope of this text, but we can quote the results of Slater and Kirkwood [7] for the dispersive attraction between two spherical nonpolar atoms, separated by relatively large distances:

$$c_{ab} = 362 \; \frac{\alpha_a \alpha_B}{\sqrt{\alpha_a/n_a} + \sqrt{\alpha_B/n_B}} \qquad \frac{\text{kcal-Å}^6}{\text{mole of bonds}} \tag{1.23}$$

where the polarizability α is in units of Å^3 and n_a is the number of electrons in the outer shell of atom a.

Although we have referred to neutral atoms in describing the nature of this force, one should recognize that dispersion attractions occur between all kinds of atoms and molecules. It is almost always a relatively important contribution to the total intermolecular attraction. Specific numerical examples will be given in Chap. 3.

1.4
Short-range repulsive forces

When the dense regions of the electronic clouds of two atoms begin to overlap, the charge distribution becomes very distorted and a repulsive force becomes dominant. A quantitative analysis of this potential energy of interaction is very difficult. Usually, empirical equations of the form of (1.24) and (1.25) are suitable for calculations.

$$\psi_{ab}{}^{rep} = ar^{-b} \tag{1.24}$$

or

$$\psi_{ab}{}^{rep} = ce^{-dr} \tag{1.25}$$

The quantities a, b, c, and d are empirically determined constants. For simple spherical molecules the constant b often has a value of between 9 and 15 and sometimes is as high as 28. The interpretation of the intermolecular spacing r for asymmetric molecules is not always clear, but empirical equations of this nature are often applied in those cases too.

Repulsion between atoms is caused by two factors. The first of these is easy to explain in terms of electrostatic forces. For simplicity, consider a pair

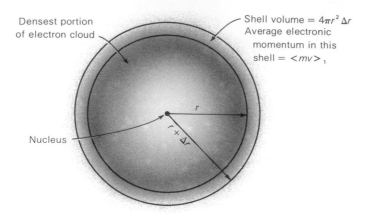

Nucleus

Densest portion of electron cloud

Shell volume = $4\pi r^2 \Delta r$
Average electronic momentum in this shell = $<mv>_1$

r

$r + \Delta r$

Fig. 1.9 The electronic cloud is spherically symmetric in a spherical atom. The density of the cloud is a function of the radius.

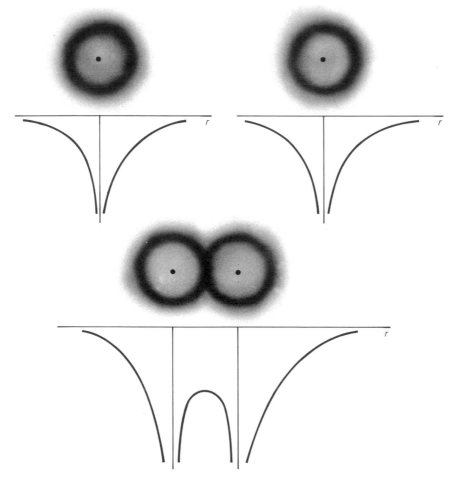

Fig. 1.10 The superposition of fields from overlapping atoms can reduce the potential along the internuclear axis.

of neutral, spherical atoms. Beyond the equivalent radius of the electronic field around the nucleus, the net field is zero because the positive nuclear charge is completely shielded. Within the electronic field, however, the nuclear charge is not completely shielded, so that a sphere with a radius less than that enclosing the whole charge will have a net positive charge (which is balanced by the negative charge outside this sphere). When the atoms interact, the electrons of one atom are attracted to the nucleus of the other, all electrons repel one another, and the positive nuclei repel one another ($\psi_{12} = q_1 q_2/r$). When the overlapping is appreciable, the nuclear repulsion predominates, resulting in a sharply increasing repulsive force. The other factor can only be explained through an understanding of the Pauli exclusion principle and the quantum-mechanical concept of filling electronic shells (see Chap. 3). For the time being, let us base our arguments on the following accepted fact: In ordinary three-dimensional space, there is a maximum allowable density of electrons with a certain value of kinetic energy.

With reference to Fig. 1.9, this means that if there is this maximum allowable density of electrons with a certain momentum $\langle mv \rangle_1$, in the volume $4\pi r^2\,\Delta r$, other electrons moving into this region must possess a momentum different from $\langle mv \rangle_1$. If the system is in its most stable state, the electrons already present have the lowest possible kinetic energy, which means that the additional electrons must obtain a higher kinetic energy. Figure 1.10 shows the potential energy of a single electron in the field of an isolated atom and also in the field of a pair of overlapping atoms. The superposition of the fields results in a lowering of the potential energy in the region between the atoms.

Let us suppose we have two isolated atoms in which the densities in the electronic shells are at a maximum. This condition will exist in the inert gases, for example, where all electrons are in "closed" shells (no more electrons below a certain energy level can be added to the shell). When the two electronic shells begin to overlap, there must be a redistribution of charge away from the region between the atoms because the electronic density is already at its maximum. Further increase in density can occur only if some electrons increase their kinetic energy considerably. It turns out to be more likely that the charge will redistribute to the opposite sides of the nuclei. This still involves some increase in kinetic energy, since the electrons are moving from the region of low potential between the nuclei, but the net effect is a strong repulsion between the atoms. Figure 1.11 shows the electronic charge densities around two attracting and repelling atoms.

1.5
Chemical bonding

General expressions for the various types of molecular interaction have been presented. The interaction potential between any given pair of particles may be obtained from these expressions.

Consider, for example, the interaction potential between two neon atoms.

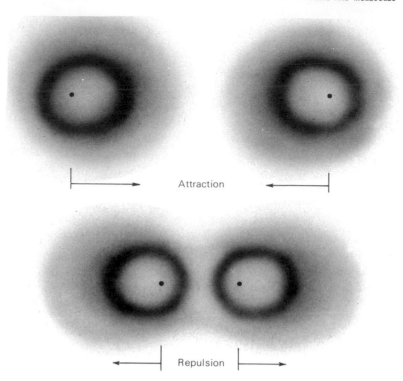

Fig. 1.11 The electronic charge is concentrated between the atoms when attraction occurs but is concentrated on the outer edges of the internuclear axis when repulsion occurs.

Since they are neutral ($q = 0$) and have spherically symmetric charge distributions ($\mu = 0$), the electrostatic and inductive potentials are zero. Assuming a dispersion attraction between point centers and an inverse twelfth-power repulsion, the interaction potential between two neon atoms is then

$$\psi = -\frac{c}{r^6} + \frac{a}{r^{12}} \tag{1.26}$$

This "two-parameter" function, called the Lennard-Jones 12-6 potential, is often adequate for describing the long-range attraction between nonpolar, spherical molecules. Consider, next, two HCl molecules in a fixed configuration. In this case, a positive dipole moment causes a dipole-dipole electrostatic attraction in addition to dispersion and repulsion forces:

$$\psi = -\frac{\mu^2 g(\theta\phi)}{r^3} - \frac{\mu^2 \alpha h(\theta)}{r^6} - \frac{c(\theta)}{r^6} + \frac{a}{r^{12}} \doteq -\frac{\mu^2 g(\theta\phi)}{r^3} - \frac{A}{r^6} + \frac{a}{r^{12}} \tag{1.27}$$

This latter form, called the Stockmayer potential, is adequate for describing the long-range attraction between polar molecules.

The important effect of molecular interaction is the formation of a chemical bond. When the interaction has an energy of 0.01 to 10 kcal/g mole (0.04 × 10⁶ to 40×10^6 joules/kg mole) and the average interparticle separation in a given state is more than 3 to 6 Å, the bond is called a Van der Waals bond or a secondary bond.

Some primary, or high-intensity, bonds are also describable by using the general equations. A lithium cation, for example, interacts with a fluoride anion to form an ionic bond Li^+F^- with a potential energy

$$\psi = -\frac{Be^2}{r} + \frac{a}{r^{10}} \qquad (1.28)$$

where the first term is coulombic attraction and the second term is repulsion and all inductive and dispersive effects are neglected.

Other primary bonds such as a covalent bond or a metallic bond cannot be described by the general equations discussed above and must be considered separately in other chapters. In general, a primary bond has a strength of 50 to 200 kcal/g mole (200×10^6 to 800×10^6 joules/kg mole) and a length of about 1 to 2 Å.

In the next chapter, we shall summarize the equations that interrelate the thermodynamic properties of matter with the potential energy of interaction. We shall then return to specific atomic systems in order to describe the nature of chemical bonds. The bonding characteristics will then be related to the vibrational and rotational freedom in molecules. The purpose of the next few chapters is thus to show how one may deduce the physical properties of relatively simple molecular systems from information on intermolecular forces.

References

1 Hirschfelder, J. O., C. F. Curtiss, and R. B. Bird: "Molecular Theory of Gases and Liquids," John Wiley & Sons, Inc., New York, 1964. *The standard reference text on intermolecular forces. Part 3 covers all aspects of the subject. Necessary reading for research students.*

2 Moelwyn-Hughes, E. A.: "States of Matter," chap. 1, Interscience Publishers, Inc., New York, 1961. *A very easily read introduction to the subject.*

3 Moelwyn-Hughes, E. A.: "Physical Chemistry," 2d ed., Pergamon Press, New York, 1961. *Chapter VII gives a concise but complete survey of the nature of intermolecular energy. A good supplement to this chapter.*

4 Pauling, L.: "The Nature of the Chemical Bond," Cornell University Press, Ithaca, N.Y., 1960. *A standard treatise on chemical bonding. Supplementary reading for advanced students.*

5 Richtmyer, F. K., E. H. Kennard, and T. Lauritsen: "Introduction to Modern Physics," McGraw-Hill Book Company, New York, 1955.

6 Slater, J. C.: "Introduction to Chemical Physics," McGraw-Hill Book Company, New York, 1939.

7 Slater, J. C., and J. G. Kirkwood: *Phys. Rev.,* **37**: 682 (1931).

8 Sproull, R. L.: "Modern Physics: A Textbook for Engineers," John Wiley & Sons, Inc., New York, 1956.

Questions

1.1 It is usually assumed that the mutual force of interaction between two particles is a function of only the interparticle separation and mutual orientation. Explain why this cannot be exactly true in any real solid.

1.2 The equation $F_{ab} = -\partial \psi_{ab}/\partial r$ may be considered as the definition of potential energy. *Suppose* the quantity $F_{ab}\, dr$ is *not* an exact differential. What would be the physical significance of such a situation?

1.3 Use the general formula for electrostatic attraction to write down the electrostatic potential energy of attraction between (*a*) a sodium ion and a chloride ion, (*b*) two water molecules, (*c*) two helium molecules. Physically describe the nature of the charge distributions for these particles.

1.4 Distinguish between inductive and dispersive attractions.

1.5 The electrostatic interaction of two point dipoles depends on the orientation of the dipole axes. If the dipoles are freely orienting, an average potential energy (for a fixed r_{ab}) may be obtained by integrating over all possible orientations

$$\langle \psi_{ab} \rangle = \frac{\int \int \int \int \psi_{ab} \exp{-(\psi_{ab}/kT)} \sin \theta_a \sin \theta_b \, d\theta_a \, d\theta_b \, d\phi_a \, d\phi_b}{\int \int \int \int \exp{(-\psi_{ab}/kT)} \sin \theta_a \sin \theta_b \, d\theta_a \, d\theta_b \, d\theta_a \, d\phi_b}$$

Explain why the weighting factor $\exp{(-\psi_{ab}/kT)}$ is physically realistic. Calculate the average potential for electrostatic dipole-dipole interaction. Show that the angle-averaged dipole-dipole interaction varies inversely with the sixth power of r.

1.6 Write down complete expressions for the potential energy of interaction between (*a*) two helium atoms and (*b*) two water molecules. Discuss the nature of each of the terms.

2
Statistical mechanics

2.1
Introduction

The purpose of statistical mechanics is to formulate relationships between the bulk properties of matter and the molecular properties of the particles in the system. In using statistical concepts, we can express the properties of a given material in terms of "most probable" behavior, without having to consider the dynamics of each individual particle. The subject matter may be divided into two branches: statistical thermodynamics, which deals with internal energy, specific heat, equations of state, and other "equilibrium" thermodynamic properties; and kinetic theory, which deals with diffusion, viscous flow, conductivity, and other "nonequilibrium" transport properties. The basic equations and some simple applications are presented in this chapter. It is not a rigorous development, but merely a survey of the ideas and equations that are needed in later chapters. Several statistical mechanics texts are listed in the bibliography for further study.

2.2
Distribution laws

Consider a system of N similar but distinguishable particles which do not interact. Suppose n_1 of these particles have an energy ϵ_1, n_2 have an energy ϵ_2, and, in general, n_i have an energy ϵ_i. The total energy of the system, E, is then

$$E = \sum_i n_i \epsilon_i \tag{2.1}$$

The total number of particles is

$$N = \sum_i n_i \tag{2.2}$$

There are obviously a large number of ways of

organizing these N particles to produce a system with a total energy E. If we assume that the "average" state is that which has the maximum probability of occurring and that the probability is proportional to the number of different ways of organizing the particles, we can then calculate the observable properties of the system.

Let us calculate the number of ways in which the N particles can be divided among the available energy levels. We start by placing n_1 of these particles into the first energy level ϵ_1. The number of distinguishable ways of choosing the n_1 particles, w_1, is

$$w_1 = \frac{N!}{n_1!(N - n_1)!} \qquad (2.3)$$

This leaves $N - n_1$ particles for the remaining energy levels. The number of distinguishable ways of next placing n_2 particles into the second level is then

$$w_2 = \frac{(N - n_1)!}{n_2!(N - n_1 - n_2)!} \qquad (2.4)$$

This can be continued until a level has been chosen for every particle. The total number of distinguishable arrangements is then given by Eq. (2.5).

$$\mathfrak{W} = w_1 \cdot w_2 \cdot w_3 \cdots = \frac{N!}{n_1! n_2! n_3! \cdots n_i!} \qquad (2.5)$$

If the probability of finding a system in a given state is proportional to $\mathfrak{W}$, then we can find the most probable state by maximizing $\mathfrak{W}$ with respect to all possible variations of the n_i terms, consistent with the constraints of Eqs. (2.1) and (2.2). We can do this by letting a small variation of $\ln \mathfrak{W}$ be equal to zero (that is, $\delta \ln \mathfrak{W} = 0$). From Eq. (2.5),

$$\delta \ln \mathfrak{W} = \delta \ln N! - \delta \sum_i \ln n_i! = 0 \qquad (2.6)$$

If the n_i are sufficiently large (i.e., if we are dealing with a large enough number of particles) to permit use of Stirling's approximation, $\ln X! = X \ln X - X$, and if we are dealing with a system of constant mass, $\delta N = 0$, Eq. (2.6) will reduce to

$$\delta \ln \mathfrak{W} = -\sum_i (\ln n_i) \, \delta n_i = 0 \qquad (2.7)$$

Since $\sum_i \delta n_i = 0$ and $\sum_i \epsilon_i \delta n_i = 0$ (i.e., the system is at constant mass and energy), there are $n - 2$ independent values of δn_i. Using the technique of Lagrangian multipliers [12], one can add $\alpha \sum \delta n_i + \beta \sum_i \epsilon_i \delta n_i$ to Eq. (2.7), where α and β are arbitrary constants whose values are chosen so that $\ln n_1 + \alpha + \beta \epsilon_1 = 0$ and $\ln n_2 + \alpha + \beta \epsilon_2 = 0$. This eliminates the two dependent variables, giving

$$\sum_{i=3} (\ln n_i + \alpha + \beta \epsilon_i) \, \delta n_i = 0 \qquad (2.8)$$

Since the variations $\delta n_3, \delta n_4, \ldots, \delta n_i$ are then independent of each other, it can be shown that the coefficient of each term must be zero:

$$n_i = [\exp(-\alpha)][\exp(-\beta\epsilon_i)] \tag{2.9}$$

The quantities α and β are arbitrary constants. If $\beta = 1/kT$, Eq. (2.9) may be rewritten as

$$\sum_i n_i = N = C \sum_i \exp\left(-\frac{\epsilon_i}{kT}\right) \tag{2.10}$$

$$\frac{n_j}{N} = \frac{\exp(-\epsilon_j/kT)}{\sum_i \exp(-\epsilon_i/kT)} \tag{2.11}$$

The number of particles, n_i, in states with energy ϵ_i is just directly proportional to the exponent of $(-\epsilon_i/kT)$. This is called the Maxwell-Boltzmann distribution law. In a slightly more general form, if there are s_j states with an energy ϵ_j,

$$\frac{n_j}{N} = \frac{s_j \exp(-\epsilon_j/kT)}{\sum_i s_i \exp(-\epsilon_i/kT)} \tag{2.12}$$

The total energy of the system can be written in terms of the distribution law by combining Eqs. (2.1) and (2.12):

$$E = \frac{N \sum_i \epsilon_i s_i \exp(-\epsilon_i/kT)}{\sum_i s_i \exp(-\epsilon_i/kT)} \tag{2.13}$$

In general, if we have some property P which is a function of the state of the system, then the observed (or average) value of that property is given by

$$\langle P \rangle = \frac{N \sum_i P_i s_i \exp(-\epsilon_i/kT)}{\sum_i s_i \exp(-\epsilon_i/kT)} \tag{2.14}$$

Thus, if the Maxwell-Boltzmann distribution applies and if we know all the possible energy states of a system, either from theory or from experimental data, we can calculate the average or observed value for any equilibrium property. If the energy states form a continuous range of energy or are very close together, Eq. (2.14) may be approximated by

$$\langle P \rangle = \frac{\int \cdots \int P(x_1, x_2, \ldots) \exp[-E(x_1, x_2, \ldots)/kT]\, dx_1\, dx_2 \cdots}{\int \cdots \int \exp-[E(x_1, x_2, \ldots)/kT]\, dx_1\, dx_2 \cdots} \tag{2.15}$$

where the quantities $x_1, x_2, \ldots$ are variables of the system.

The derivation of the Maxwell-Boltzmann distribution law is not quite correct from a quantum-mechanical point of view, since particles in a system are not always distinguishable and since there is not always complete freedom in choosing the number of particles that can go into a given energy state. It is possible, however, to derive distribution laws for indistinguishable particles with certain restrictions on the number of particles in a given energy state.

Two results of particular importance are the Bose-Einstein distribution law and the Fermi-Dirac distribution law:

$$n_i = \frac{s_i}{\left[C \exp\left(-\frac{\epsilon_i}{kT}\right)\right] \pm 1}$$

(2.16)

The minus sign represents Bose-Einstein statistics, and the plus sign represents Fermi-Dirac statistics. When the quantity $C \exp(-\epsilon_i/kT)$ is much greater than 1, Eq. (2.16) reduces to the Maxwell-Boltzmann distribution. For almost all situations encountered in this text, the Maxwell-Boltzmann distribution is correct to a fraction of a percent. The only important exception is the electron motion in metals, for which Fermi-Dirac statistics must be applied.

2.3
Partition functions

A useful quantity for calculating thermodynamic properties is the partition function Z. This quantity is defined by Eq. (2.17):

$$Z = \sum_i s_i \exp\left(-\frac{E_i}{kT}\right)$$

(2.17)

where E_i is the total energy of a system of N interacting particles in an energy level i. The probability of the total system being at level i, $\mathfrak{W}_i$, is

$$\mathfrak{W}_i = \frac{s_i \exp(-E_i/kT)}{Z}$$

(2.18)

The average energy of the system of N particles is then

$$U = \langle E \rangle = \frac{\sum_i s_i E_i \exp(-E_i/kT)}{Z}$$

$$= kT^2 \left(\frac{\partial \ln Z}{\partial T}\right)_V$$

(2.19)

Thus, a measurable thermodynamic property has been related to the partition function, which, in turn, is related to the energy levels of the individual particles.

The entropy of a system is defined as being related to the probability of a given state by

$$S = k \ln \mathfrak{W}$$

(2.20)

It can be shown that the entropy is related to the internal energy and the partition function by

$$S = \frac{U}{T} + k \ln Z$$

(2.21)

All other thermodynamic relations may be derived from Eqs. (2.19) and (2.21). Some of these are listed below:

Helmholtz free energy $= A = -kT \ln Z$ $\hspace{4cm}$ (2.22)

Gibbs free energy $= G = -kT \ln Z + kTV \left(\dfrac{\partial \ln Z}{\partial V} \right)_T$ $\hspace{2cm}$ (2.23)

Pressure $= p = kT \left(\dfrac{\partial \ln Z}{\partial V} \right)_T$ $\hspace{4cm}$ (2.24)

Measurable thermodynamic properties have thus been related to the energy levels of the individual molecules in the system. An objective of statistical thermodynamics is to evaluate the partition function from information on molecular interactions and from this to obtain values for thermodynamic properties.

One may also define a partition function for a single molecule:

$$z = \Sigma s_i \exp \left(-\frac{\epsilon_i}{kT} \right) \qquad \text{cf. (2.17)} \hspace{3cm} (2.25)$$

In this case, the ϵ_i are the energy levels for the individual molecules. For a gas containing N particles, behaving in the limit of Maxwell-Boltzmann statistics, it can be shown that

$$Z = \frac{z^N}{N!} \hspace{6cm} (2.26)$$

Frequently, the partition function can be written as the product of factors related to the different "degrees of freedom" of molecules. The motion of a polyatomic molecule, for example, has six parts: the overall translation of the molecule, the rotation of the whole molecule, various rotations of atoms within the molecule, various stretching and bending vibrations, electronic motion, and nuclear spin. Neglecting the coupling between degrees of freedom, the partition function is then

$$Z = Z_{tr} Z_{rot} Z_{\text{int rot}} Z_{vib} Z_{elec} Z_{nuc}$$

$$= \frac{z_{tr}^N}{N!} z_{rot}^N z_{\text{int rot}}^N z_{vib}^N z_{elec}^N z_{nuc}^N \hspace{3cm} (2.27)$$

The most important separation is that of the translational motions, which are a function of the positions and velocities of the centers of mass of the molecules, from all the other degrees of freedom. The translational partition function for a system of N particles may be approximated as

$$Z_{tr} = \frac{1}{N!} \frac{1}{h^{3N}} \int \cdots \int \left[\exp \left(-\frac{\mathscr{H}}{kT} \right) \right] d\mathbf{p}_1 \, d\mathbf{p}_2 \cdots d\mathbf{p}_N \, d\mathbf{r}_1 \, d\mathbf{r}_2 \cdots d\mathbf{r}_N \hspace{1cm} (2.28)$$

The constant h is the universal Planck's constant, and the quantity $\mathscr{H}$ is called the "classical Hamiltonian" of the system and is defined by Eq. (2.29). The symbol $\int d\mathbf{p}_i$ is shorthand for the quantity $\int dp_{xi} \, dp_{yi} \, dp_{zi}$ and signifies integration over the three components of momentum for particle i. The symbol $\int d\mathbf{r}_i$ is shorthand for the quantity $\int dr_{xi} \, dr_{yi} \, dr_{zi}$ and signifies integration over the volume available to particle i. The integrations on momenta generally extend from $-\infty$ to $+\infty$, and the integration on the position coordinates extends over the total volume available to the particle. The classical Hamiltonian for the system is

$$\mathscr{H} = \sum_{k=1}^{N} \frac{p_k^2}{2m_k} + \frac{1}{2} \sum_{i=1}^{N} \sum_{j=1}^{N} \psi_{ij}(r_{ij}) \tag{2.29}$$

The quantity m_k is the mass of one particle. The first term is the total kinetic energy of the N particles, and the second is the total potential energy of interaction. Substituting Eq. (2.29) into (2.28), one finds that the translational partition function factors into a kinetic and an intermolecular potential term.

$$Z_{tr} = \left[\frac{1}{h} (2\pi m k T)^{1/2} \right]^{3N} \mathscr{Q} \tag{2.30}$$

$$\mathscr{Q} = \frac{1}{N!} \int \cdots \int \left[\exp\left(-\frac{\Sigma_i \Sigma_j \psi_{ij}(r_{ij})}{2kT} \right) \right] d\mathbf{r}_1 \, d\mathbf{r}_2 \cdots d\mathbf{r}_N \tag{2.31}$$

The factor $\mathscr{Q}$ is called the configurational partition function because it depends only on the position coordinates of the N particles.

We shall next show how these equations are used to calculate the properties of low-density gases.

2.4
Thermodynamic properties of ideal gases

Consider first an ideal monoatomic gas made up of N identical atoms at a very low density. An ideal gas is defined as one in which the particles take up no volume (i.e., the atoms are point centers of mass) and one in which there is no interaction energy between particles. Since we are dealing with independent point centers of mass, there are no rotational, vibrational, or internal rotational energy states. This is equivalent to $z_{\text{rot}} = z_{\text{vib}} = z_{\text{int rot}} = 1$. We can evaluate the electronic and nuclear partition functions relative to the ground state chosen as zero energy. This means that $\epsilon_0 = 0$ and

$$z = \sum_{0}^{\infty} \exp\left(-\frac{\epsilon_i}{kT} \right) = 1 + \sum_{1}^{\infty} \exp\left(-\frac{\epsilon_i}{kT} \right) \tag{2.32}$$

If the energies of the excited states are greater than kT, as is usually the case for electronic and nuclear states, the contribution of the excited states to the partition function may be neglected and thus $z_{\text{elec}} = z_{\text{nuc}} \doteq 1$. The total partition function is thus

$$Z = Z_{tr}$$

$$= \left[\frac{1}{h} (2\pi m k T)^{1/2} \right]^{3N} \mathscr{Q} \tag{2.33}$$

Since the potential energy of interaction is zero,

$$\mathscr{Q} = \frac{1}{N!} \int \cdots \int d\mathbf{r}_1 \, d\mathbf{r}_2 \cdots d\mathbf{r}_N$$

$$= \frac{V^N}{N!} \tag{2.34}$$

and

$$Z = \frac{(2\pi mkT)^{3N/2} V^N}{N! h^{3N}} \tag{2.35}$$

From Eq. (2.19),

$$U = kT^2 \left(\frac{\partial \ln Z}{\partial T} \right)_V$$

$$= \tfrac{3}{2} NkT = \tfrac{3}{2} RT \tag{2.36}$$

and from Eq. (2.24)

$$pV = VkT \left(\frac{\partial \ln Z}{\partial V} \right)$$

$$= RT \tag{2.37}$$

These are both familiar results for an ideal monoatomic gas.

Next, consider a gas made up of N identical diatomic molecules at a very low density. Let us assume that there are no electronic, nuclear, or internal rotational states that have to be considered (that is, $Z_{\text{elec}} = Z_{\text{nuc}} = Z_{\text{int rot}} = 1$). The partition function for the gas is then

$$Z = Z_{tr} Z_{\text{rot}} Z_{\text{vib}} \tag{2.38}$$

The translational partition function is given by Eq. (2.30). The ideal gas is, by definition, one in which the potential energy of interaction is zero, so that the translational partition function reduces to

$$Z_{tr} = \frac{1}{h^{3N}} (2\pi mkT)^{3N/2} \frac{1}{N!} (\textstyle\int\int\int dx \, dy \, dz)^N$$

$$= \frac{V^N (2\pi mkT)^{3N/2}}{N! h^{3N}} \tag{2.39}$$

The quantity V is just the total volume of the mole (N molecules) of gas.

The rotational partition function is obtained from Eq. (2.25). One must therefore have values for the i different energy levels of a rigid, rotating diatomic molecule. Since we have not yet discussed the techniques for calculating the energy levels in molecules, we shall merely state that it can be shown quantum-mechanically that the energy of the Jth energy level is

$$\epsilon_J = J(J + 1) \frac{h^2}{8\pi^2 I} \tag{2.40}$$

where J is an integer (that is, 0, 1, 2, 3, etc.). The quantity I is the moment of inertia of the molecule, which can be calculated from scale models or determined from spectroscopic data. It can also be shown that the Jth energy level contains $2J + 1$ states, so that the partition function for *one* of the molecules, z_{rot}, is

$$z_{rot} = Z_{rot}^{1/N} = \sum_{J=0}^{\infty} (2J + 1) \exp \left[- \frac{J(J + 1)h^2}{8\pi^2 IkT} \right] \tag{2.41}$$

By using an Euler-Maclaurin summation formula, one can convert Eq. (2.41) to the following series:

$$z_{rot} = Z_{rot}^{1/N} = \frac{8\pi^2 IkT}{\delta h^2} + \frac{1}{3\delta} + \frac{1}{15\delta} \left(\frac{h^2}{8\pi^2 IkT} \right) + \cdots \tag{2.42}$$

where δ is unity for heteropolar molecules (for example, NO, CO, HCl, etc.) and 2 for homopolar molecules (H_2, N_2, O_2, etc.). For diatomic molecules at normal temperatures, the first term is much greater than one, so that

$$Z_{rot} \doteq \left(\frac{8\pi^2 IkT}{\delta h^2} \right)^N \tag{2.43}$$

It can also be shown quantum-mechanically that the energy of the nth vibrational state of a harmonically vibrating diatomic molecule is given as

$$\epsilon_n = h\nu(n + \tfrac{1}{2}) \tag{2.44}$$

where n is an integer (0, 1, 2, 3, . . .) and ν is the natural vibration frequency of the molecule, which is obtained from spectroscopic data. Since there is only one energy state per level, the vibrational partition function for *one* of the molecules is

$$z_{vib} = Z_{vib}^{1/N} = \exp \left(- \frac{h\nu}{2kT} \right) \sum_{n=0}^{\infty} \exp \left(- \frac{nh\nu}{kT} \right)$$

$$= \frac{\exp (-h\nu/2kT)}{1 - \exp (-h\nu/kT)} \tag{2.45}$$

$$Z_{vib} = \left(2 \sinh \frac{h\nu}{2kT} \right)^{-N} \tag{2.46}$$

Thus, the partition function for an ideal gas made up of rigid, harmonically oscillating, diatomic molecules, is

$$\ln Z = N \ln \frac{(2\pi mkT)^{3/2}}{[N!]^{1/N} h^3} + N \ln V + N \ln \frac{8\pi^2 IkT}{\delta h^2} - N \ln 2 \sinh \frac{h\nu}{2kT} \tag{2.47}$$

The internal energy is obtained by differentiating Eq. (2.47) as required by Eq. (2.19):

$$U = \frac{3}{2} RT + RT + \frac{Nh\nu}{2} \operatorname{ctnh} \frac{h\nu}{2kT} \tag{2.48}$$

An equation of state is obtained from Eq. (2.24):

$$pV = RT \tag{2.49}$$

This is the well-known ideal-gas law. Similar expressions for other thermo-dynamic properties may be calculated in the same way. These equations are only approximations to real behavior, since potential energies of interaction, anharmonicity of vibration, nonrigidity, electronic behavior, and nuclear spin effects have all been neglected. The value of approaching the subject in this way is that it becomes clear what the reasons are for nonideal behavior. We shall next show how deviations from ideality in the equation of state may be studied by including intermolecular potential-energy terms in the translational partition function.

2.5
The equation of state for real gases

The equation of state is obtained by differentiating the partition function with respect to volume at constant temperature. One may therefore assume that only the configurational portion need be considered:

$$p = kT \left(\frac{\partial \ln \mathscr{Q}}{\partial V} \right)_T \tag{2.50}$$

When there are intermolecular forces, the configurational partition function $\mathscr{Q}$ is a very complicated $3N$-fold integral [Eq. (2.31)]. Fortunately, one may rewrite the integrand as a series of terms called "cluster-integrals" [8]. The details of the procedure are not considered here, but the end result is a series expansion of the equation of state, called the virial equation of state:

$$\frac{pV}{RT} = 1 + B_2 \left(\frac{1}{V} \right) + B_3 \left(\frac{1}{V} \right)^2 + B_4 \left(\frac{1}{V} \right)^3 + \cdots$$

$$= 1 + \sum_{n \geq 2} B_n \left(\frac{1}{V} \right)^{n-1} \tag{2.51}$$

where

$$B_n = -\frac{N^{n-1}}{n(n-2)!V} \int \cdots \int S_{1,2,3\ldots,n} \, d\mathbf{r}_1 \cdots d\mathbf{r}_n \tag{2.52}$$

The integrand $S_{1,2,3\ldots,n}$, called the irreducible cluster integral for a cluster of n particles, is a function of the interaction potentials of all the particles involved. Equation (2.52) contains all the possible interactions that can arise in Eq. (2.31), but they are rearranged in a form that is convenient for calcula-tion. Thus, the *second virial coefficient,* B_2, can be calculated by considering interactions between clusters of two particles; the third virial coefficient, B_3, can be calculated by considering interactions between clusters of three particles; and so forth. It turns out that for low- and moderate-density gases, the series converges rapidly enough to neglect all but the first few terms. It can be shown [8] that the second and third virial coefficients are

$$B_2 = 2\pi N \int_0^\infty \left\{ 1 - \exp\left[-\frac{\psi(r)}{kT} \right] \right\} r^2 \, dr \tag{2.53}$$

$$B_3 = -\frac{8\pi^2}{3} N^2 \int_0^\infty \int_0^\infty \int_0^\infty f_{12} f_{13} f_{23} r_{12} r_{13} r_{23} \, dr_{12} \, dr_{13} \, dr_{23} \tag{2.54}$$

where

$$f_{ij} = -\left\{ 1 - \exp\left[-\frac{\psi_{ij}(r_{ij})}{kT} \right] \right\} \tag{2.55}$$

The second virial coefficient can be calculated for a given gas by substituting the proper pair potential-energy function. Its magnitude is not too sensitive to the form of the function, so very good approximations may be obtained from estimates. The third virial coefficient, on the other hand, is very sensitive to the form of the potential-energy function and is thus much more difficult to predict accurately. Fortunately, many data can be correlated with just the second virial coefficient.

These equations illustrate the interrelationship between thermodynamic and molecular properties. If one were able to a priori calculate the potential function for a pair of molecules, the thermodynamic properties of the gas could be predicted. Conversely, by curve-fitting thermodynamic data, one can get information about molecular constants. Since very little is known about the nature of intermolecular forces, the latter approach is more common.

The Lennard-Jones 12-6 potential [Eq. (2.56)] has been a widely used function for calculations of this type.

$$\psi(r) = 4\epsilon^* \left[\left(\frac{\sigma}{r} \right)^{12} - \left(\frac{\sigma}{r} \right)^6 \right] \tag{2.56}$$

The general shape of the curve is the same as shown in Fig. 1.5. The parameter ϵ^* gives the maximum depth of the potential well, and the parameter σ is the point at which the potential is zero (an effective collision diameter for the particle). The twelfth-power term is a repulsion, and the sixth-power term is a dispersive attraction. This two-constant function should only be good for nonpolar, spherically symmetric particles because electrostatic effects, orientation effects, and shape factors are all omitted. Substitution of the 12–6 potential into the equation for the second virial coefficient gives

$$B_2^*(T^*) = \sum_{j=0}^\infty b^{(j)} T^{*-(2j+1)/4} \tag{2.57}$$

$$b^{(j)} = -\frac{2^{j+1/2}}{4j!} \Gamma\left(\frac{2j-1}{4} \right) \tag{2.58}$$

$$B_2^* = \frac{B_2}{\tfrac{2}{3}\pi N\sigma^3} \tag{2.59}$$

$$T^* = \frac{kT}{\epsilon} \tag{2.60}$$

The starred quantities B_2^* and T^* are "reduced" (dimensionless) virial coefficients and reduced temperatures, respectively. The coefficients b^j are proportional to gamma functions Γ, which are tabulated in many handbooks. Figure 2.1 is a plot of reduced second virial coefficient as a function of temperature, and Table 2.1 gives the molecular parameters for a number of gases. A number of polar and nonspherical molecules are included in the list in spite of the fact that they are not really described by a Lennard-Jones potential. Since the molecular constants are evaluated by curve-fitting data, however, the "apparent" constants do describe thermodynamic behavior fairly well. There have been many other potential functions used which attempt to account for dipoles, quadrupoles, and the shapes of complex molecules [3,4], but their analysis is beyond the scope of this chapter. The major improvements over the Lennard-Jones potential have been better curve-fitting to a theoretical expression for the second virial coefficient, more specific information on intermolecular forces, and better correlation with expressions for the third virial coefficient.

An expression for the third virial coefficient can be obtained by substituting the Lennard-Jones potential into Eq. (2.54). The results are given by Eqs. (2.61) and (2.62) and are plotted in Fig. 2.2. The experimental points shown in the figure are based on the constants obtained from second virial coefficients, and the agreement is relatively poor, as would be expected.

$$B_3^*(T^*) = \Sigma c_j T^{*-(j+1)/2} \qquad (2.61)$$

$$B_3^* = \frac{B_3}{4/9\pi^2 N^2 \sigma^6} \qquad (2.62)$$

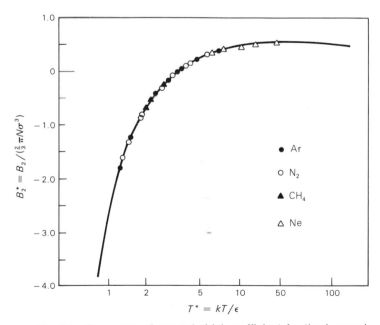

Fig. 2.1 The reduced second virial coefficient for the Lennard-Jones potential. The classical curve of $B_2^*(T)$ is shown along with the experimental points for several gases.

The coefficients c^j are complicated integrals which have been evaluated by Kihara [11] and others [4].

The objective of this section has been to show a direct interrelation between the molecular and thermodynamic properties of matter. For a simple material, such as a dilute gas, one can evaluate the partition function and develop theoretical expressions linking the two. In later chapters, we shall show how the properties of complex solid materials can also be related to molecular nature. The more complicated the material gets, however, the cruder are our approximations and the less quantitative are our results.

2.6
Transport properties of gases

Average velocities and mean free path Another objective of statistical mechanics is to interrelate the transport properties, such as diffusivity, viscosity, and conductivity, with the molecular properties of the materials. By doing

Table 2.1 *

Molecular constants for the Lennard-Jones 12-6 potential *

Gas	Symbol or formula	ϵ/k, °K		σ, Å	
		From second virial coefficients	From viscosity data	From second virial coefficients	From viscosity data
Helium	He	6.03	10.22	2.63	2.58
Hydrogen	H_2	29.2	33.3	2.87	2.97
Neon	Ne	34.9	35.7	2.78	2.79
Argon	Ar	122	124	3.40	3.42
Krypton	Kr	158	190	3.60	3.61
Xenon	Xe	217	229	3.96	4.06
Nitrogen	N_2	95.9	91.5	3.71	3.68
Oxygen	O_2	118	113	3.46	3.43
Carbon monoxide	CO	100	110	3.76	3.59
Carbon dioxide	CO_2	205	213	4.07	3.90
Nitric oxide	NO	131	119	3.17	3.47
Methane	CH_4	148.2	144	3.82	3.80
Ethylene	C_2H_4	199.2	205	4.52	4.23
Ethane	C_2H_6	243	230	3.95	4.42
Propane	C_3H_8	242	254	5.64	5.06
n-Butane	C_4H_{10}	297	410	4.97	5.00
Hydrogen chloride	HCl		360		3.31
Hydrogen iodide	HI		324		4.12

* Selected values from Ref. 9, pp. 1110–1112.

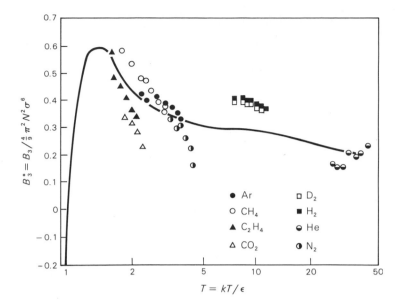

Fig. 2.2 The reduced third virial coefficient for the Lennard-Jones potential. Experimental points are obtained from second virial coefficients. [By permission from R. B. Bird, E. L. Spotz, and J. O. Hirschfelder, *J. Chem. Phys.*, **18**: 1395 (1950).]

this, one can then interrelate the "nonequilibrium" properties with the thermodynamic properties through the common ground of intermolecular forces. In this section we shall show how this is done for the relatively simple case of dilute gases.

In deriving the Maxwell-Boltzmann law [Eq. (2.12)] we considered the general case of a system that could exist in specific energy states $\epsilon_1, \epsilon_2, \epsilon_3, \ldots$, etc. Nothing was specified about these states, but the implication was that they were discrete and that energies in between these values were forbidden. This, as we will see in Chap. 3, is consistent with the quantum-mechanical ideas that must often be used with atomic-sized particles. In the case of an ideal gas, however, it may be assumed that the atoms are in a state of chaotic or random motion and that the velocities of the particles can be any value between plus and minus infinity. If the potential energy of interaction is neglected, the energy of a single particle is equal to its kinetic energy:

$$\epsilon_i = \frac{(mv_i)^2}{2m} = \frac{p_i^2}{2m} \tag{2.63}$$

The allowable energy states thus form a continuous, rather than a discrete, variation of energy. The distribution laws may then be rewritten in terms of the number of particles, dN, with momentums lying between p_1 and $p_1 + dp_1$, p_2 and $p_2 + dp_2$, etc., and having positions between x_1 and $x_1 + dx_1$, x_2 and $x_2 + dx_2$, etc.:

$$\frac{dN}{N} = \frac{[\exp{(-\epsilon/kT)}]\, dx_1\, dx_2 \cdots dp_1\, dp_2 \cdots}{\displaystyle\int_{-\infty}^{\infty} \cdots \int_{-\infty}^{\infty} [\exp{(-\epsilon/kT)}]\, dx_1\, dx_2 \cdots dp_1\, dp_2 \cdots} \qquad (2.64)$$

In a monoatomic ideal gas, where the energy of a single particle is a function of only its own three components of momentum:

$$\frac{dN}{N} = \frac{[\exp{(-\epsilon/kT)}]\, dp_x\, dp_y\, dp_z}{\displaystyle\iiint_{\infty} [\exp{(-\epsilon/kT)}]\, dp_x\, dp_y\, dp_z} \qquad (2.65)$$

Since the momentum is related to the energy by

$$2m\epsilon = p_x{}^2 + p_y{}^2 + p_z{}^2 = R^2 \qquad (2.66)$$

one can replace the differential element $dp_x\, dp_y\, dp_z$ (cartesian coordinates) by the equivalent element in polar coordinates, $4\pi R^2\, dR$, and rewrite Eq. (2.65) in terms of the energy ϵ:

$$\frac{dN}{N} = \frac{\epsilon^{1/2}\, [\exp{(-\epsilon/kT)}]\, d\epsilon}{\displaystyle\int_0^{\infty} \epsilon^{1/2}\, [\exp{(-\epsilon/kT)}]\, d\epsilon}$$

$$= \frac{2\pi\epsilon^{1/2}\, [\exp{(-\epsilon/kT)}]\, d\epsilon}{(\pi kT)^{3/2}} \qquad (2.67)$$

The average internal energy $\langle U\ \text{cal/mole}\rangle$ of a monoatomic gas is then

$$\langle U \rangle = N \int_0^{\infty} \epsilon\, \frac{dN}{N} = \frac{2}{\pi^{1/2}(kT)^{3/2}} \int_0^{\infty} \epsilon^{3/2}\, [\exp{(-\epsilon/kT)}]\, d\epsilon \qquad (2.68)$$

$$= \sqrt[3]{2}RT$$

This is consistent with the result obtained from the translational partition function as shown in Sec. 2.4.

In determining the transport properties, it is important to know how many times a molecule will collide with another in the gas. In order to calculate this, one must know the average spatial velocity and also the average velocity in a given direction. The average velocity is obtained by rewriting Eq. (2.67) in terms of the spatial velocity v, where $\epsilon = \frac{1}{2}mv^2$:

$$\frac{dN}{N} = \frac{\pi}{2} \left(\frac{2m}{\pi kT}\right)^{3/2} v^2 \left[\exp\left(-\frac{mv^2}{2kT}\right)\right] dv \qquad (2.69)$$

The average velocity $\langle v \rangle$ is then

$$\langle v \rangle = \int_0^{\infty} v\, \frac{dN}{N}$$

$$= \left(\frac{8kT}{\pi m}\right)^{1/2} \qquad (2.70)$$

The average velocity in a given direction is found by rewriting Eq. (2.65) in terms of the velocity components:

$$\frac{dN}{N} = \left(\frac{m}{2\pi kT}\right)^{3/2} \exp\left(-\frac{m}{2kT}\left(v_x{}^2 + v_y{}^2 + v_z{}^2\right)\right) dv_x \, dv_y \, dv_z \tag{2.71}$$

The fraction of particles with an x velocity component between v_x and $v_x + dv_x$, irrespective of what the other two components are, is then

$$\frac{dN_{v_x}}{N}$$

$$= \left(\frac{m}{2\pi kT}\right)^{3/2} \left[\exp\left(-\frac{mv_x{}^2}{2kT}\right)\right] dv_x \int_{-\infty}^{\infty} \left[\exp\left(-\frac{mv_y{}^2}{2kT}\right)\right] dv_y \int_{-\infty}^{\infty} \left[\exp\left(-\frac{mv_z{}^2}{2kT}\right)\right] dv_z$$

$$= \left(\frac{m}{2\pi kT}\right)^{1/2} \left[\exp\left(-\frac{mv_x{}^2}{2kT}\right)\right] dv_x \tag{2.72}$$

The average velocity in the positive x direction is then

$$\langle v_{+x}\rangle = \int_0^{\infty} v_x \frac{dN_{v_x}}{N}$$

$$= \left(\frac{kT}{2\pi m}\right)^{1/2} \tag{2.73}$$

If the integration of Eq. (2.72) is carried out over the whole range of values for v_x, $-\infty$ to $+\infty$, the result is an average of zero. This is what would be expected, since as long as there are no external forces present, the gas molecules will just as likely move in the positive x direction as in the negative x direction. Thus the positive values of v_x will just balance the negative values, to give an average of zero. The value given by Eq. (2.73) is the average velocity in the *positive* x direction. The same result can, of course, be derived for any other direction.

All treatments of ideal gases assume that the gas molecules are noninteracting, perfectly elastic spheres that have a negligible volume relative to the total volume of the system. In the random motion of these particles there are going to be collisions; the most frequent type will be between two particles (a binary collision), but there is also a finite probability of ternary and higher-order collisions. The frequency of binary collisions, f_{12} collisions per second per unit volume, between a particle 1 (diameter $= d_1$, mass $= m_1$, concentration $= n_1$) and a particle 2 can be shown to be equal to

$$f_{12} = n_1[\pi(d_1 + d_2)^2 n_2] \left(\frac{kT}{2\pi m_R}\right)^{1/2} \tag{2.74}$$

where m_R is a reduced mass and is equal to $m_R = m_1 m_2/(m_1 + m_2)$. If we visualize the type 1 particles as moving relative to stationary type 2 particles, then the first term is the concentration of impinging particles, the second term in brackets is the total target area for impingement, and the third term is a relative velocity of approach normal to the target surface (Fig. 2.3). If we have a pure gas, all the particles are identical and Eq. (2.74) reduces to

$$f_{12} = 4\pi d^2 n^2 \left(\frac{kT}{\pi m}\right)^{1/2} \tag{2.75}$$

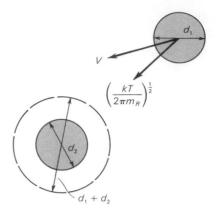

Fig. 2.3 The frequency of collision for two spherical particles with a relative velocity normal to the spherical surface is proportional to the surface area of a sphere with a radius equal to the sum of the radii of the colliding particles.

The average distance traveled by a particle between two consecutive collisions is called the mean free path l_p. The number of collisions per particle per second is f/n, and the average spatial velocity is $\langle v \rangle$, so the average mean free path in a pure gas is

$$l_p = \frac{\langle v \rangle}{f/n}$$

$$= \frac{(8kT/\pi m)^{1/2}}{4\pi d^2 n (kT/\pi m)^{1/2}}$$

$$= \frac{1}{2^{1/2} \pi d^2 n} \tag{2.76}$$

Thus, the mean free path is inversely proportional to the square of the particle diameter times the concentration of the particles. The ideal-gas laws are valid when the mean free path is large relative to the diameter of the particles but small relative to the total volume of the system. It can also be shown that, in a binary mixture, the mean free path for type 1 particles is

$$(l_p)_1 = \frac{1}{2^{1/2} \pi n_1 d_1{}^2 + (\pi/4) n_2 (d_1 + d_2)^2 (1 + m_1/m_2)^{1/2}} \tag{2.77}$$

The same expression holds for the mean free path of type 2 particles by reversing the subscripts.

Transport properties   In the preceding section we described the "equilibrium" properties of a uniform gas. In order to discuss transport phenomena, we must consider a gas that has variations in certain properties. Thus, at thermal equilibrium, the temperature of the gas is the same at all points and there is no net exchange of thermal energy. When there is a temperature gradient, however, there is a net flow of energy from the high-temperature to the low-temperature region. The resistance to this flow is measured by a property called the thermal conductivity. The Maxwell-Boltzmann distribution law holds strictly for systems at equilibrium and thus is not exact for perturbed systems. The subject of "nonequilibrium" distributions is complicated and will not be discussed here. It will suffice to say that as long as the disturbance is not too extreme, the equilibrium distribution will describe the system very well.

Let us next consider three parallel planes in a pure, ideal gas (Fig. 2.4). Suppose the planes have a unit area, are separated by a distance equal to the mean free path of the particles, and are perpendicular to the x axis. The average flux in the positive x direction is $n\langle v_{+x}\rangle$ molecules/m^2-sec. Now let us suppose there is a certain property, P units per molecule, that is not distributed in a uniform manner but rather varies in the x direction. Let us imagine that this property can be transmitted from one molecule to the next through molecular collision and that the change occurring upon collision can be represented by $l_p \, dP/dx$. Thus, the amount of property P leaving plane 1 (in Fig. 2.4) and approaching plane 2 is $n\langle v_{+x}\rangle(P - l_p \, dP/dx)$, while the amount leaving plane 3 and approaching plane 2 is $n\langle v_{+x}\rangle(P - l_p \, dP/dx)$. The net rate of transport, j_P units/m^2-sec, is thus the difference

$$j_P = -2n\langle v_{+x}\rangle l_p \frac{dP}{dx} \qquad (2.78)$$

Substitution of Eqs. (2.73) and (2.76) into (2.78) gives

$$j_P = -\frac{1}{\pi d^2}\left(\frac{kT}{\pi m}\right)^{1/2}\frac{dP}{dx} \qquad (2.79)$$

This general equation may now be used to define viscosity, thermal conductivity, and diffusivity for an ideal gas.

Consider the flow of an ideal gas in the z direction with a velocity gradient in the x direction.

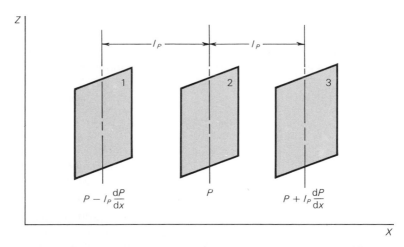

Fig. 2.4 Schematic representation of a property P which varies in the x direction. The planes are separated by one average mean free path for molecular collision.

$$P = m\langle v_z \rangle \tag{2.80}$$

$$\frac{dP}{dx} = m\,\frac{d\langle v_z \rangle}{dx} \tag{2.81}$$

The net rate of momentum flux in the x direction is, according to Newton's second law, the force per unit area (i.e., shear stress), τ_{xz}, in the x direction and normal to the yz plane

$$j_p = \tau_{xz} = -\frac{1}{\pi d^2}\left(\frac{mkT}{\pi}\right)^{1/2}\frac{d\langle v \rangle_z}{dx} \tag{2.82}$$

This is Newton's law of viscosity. The proportionality factor between the stress and the velocity gradient (i.e., rate of strain) is called the coefficient of viscosity, η_v, or simply, viscosity.

$$\eta_v = \frac{1}{\pi d^2}\left(\frac{mkT}{\pi}\right)^{1/2} \tag{2.83}$$

Thus, the viscosity of a dilute gas of rigid spheres is inversely proportional to the square of the diameter and directly proportional to the square root of the mass times the absolute temperature.

Consider the transfer of energy, q_x, in the x direction because of a temperature gradient in the x direction. The energy per molecule, u, is equal to $c_v T/N$, where c_v/N is the specific heat per molecule.

$$P = u = \frac{c_v T}{N} \tag{2.84}$$

$$\frac{dP}{dx} = \frac{c_v}{N}\frac{dT}{dx} \tag{2.85}$$

$$j_P = q_x = -\frac{1}{\pi d^2}\left(\frac{kT}{\pi m}\right)^{1/2}\frac{c_v}{N}\frac{dT}{dx} \tag{2.86}$$

This is the Fourier law of heat conduction. The proportionality between heat flux and temperature gradient is called the thermal conductivity κ.

$$\kappa = \frac{c_v}{m\pi d^2 N}\left(\frac{mkT}{\pi}\right)^{1/2} \tag{2.87}$$

Combining Eqs. (2.87) and (2.83), one gets

$$\frac{m\kappa N}{\eta_v c_v} = 1.0 \tag{2.88}$$

Equations (2.83), (2.87), and (2.88) give a qualitatively correct picture of the behavior of many gases. They predict that both viscosity and thermal conductivity are independent of pressure, which is generally true below ten or so atmospheres. The predicted temperature dependence is less satisfactory; experimental data usually show a more rapid variation than $T^{1/2}$. The ratio of thermal conductivity to viscosity is actually constant over wide ranges of variables, but the quantity shown in Eq. (2.88) is never unity but is 2.5 for monoatomic gases and 1.9 for diatomic gases.

With somewhat greater effort, one may derive an analogous expression for the interdiffusion of two gases 1 and 2:

$$j_1 = -(n_1 + n_2)D_{12}\frac{dN_1}{dx} \tag{2.89}$$

$$D_{12} = \frac{4}{\pi(d_1 + d_2)^2(n_1 + n_2)}\left(\frac{2kT}{\pi m_R}\right)^{1/2} \tag{2.90}$$

where j_1 is the net flux of species 1, n_1 is the number of molecules of gas 1 per cubic centimeter, dN_1/dx is the gradient of the mole fraction of component 1, and D_{12} is the binary diffusion coefficient in units of square meters per second. If the equation of state for an ideal gas is valid, then

$$p = (n_1 + n_2)kT \tag{2.91}$$

$$D_{12} = \frac{4}{\pi^{3/2}}\left(\frac{2}{m_R}\right)^{1/2}\frac{1}{(d_1 + d_2)^2}\frac{(kT)^{3/2}}{p} \tag{2.92}$$

Equation (2.92) predicts that a binary diffusion coefficient varies inversely with pressure and directly with the three-halves power of temperature. This agrees moderately well with data on gas mixtures over wide ranges of temperature and pressure. In the limit of type 2 particles being the same as type 1 particles, we get a "self-diffusion" coefficient for the pure gas:

$$\mathscr{D}_{11} = \frac{m_1}{d_1^2}\left(\frac{kT}{\pi m_1}\right)^{3/2}\frac{1}{p} \tag{2.93}$$

Combining Eq. (2.93) with Eq. (2.83), one gets

$$\frac{\mathscr{D}_{11}}{\eta_v}m_1 n_1 = \frac{\mathscr{D}_{11}\rho_1}{\eta_v} = 1.0 \tag{2.94}$$

The quantity ρ_1 is the density of the pure gas. Experimentally, one finds that this ratio is constant at about $2^{1/2}$ for most pure gases. Thus we again have a qualitative, but not a quantitative, agreement with theory.

There are a number of inadequacies in the approach just presented. First of all, real-gas molecules, even monoatomic particles, cannot be represented as rigid, noninteracting spheres. Rather, a realistic potential energy of interaction must be incorporated. Second, when the system is not in a true state of equilibrium, one should not use a Maxwell-Boltzmann distribution function. The true distribution is really a function of time, space, and momentum, and the dependence upon the variables of the system is different in nonequilibrium situations.

A rigorous kinetic theory for monoatomic gases at low density has been developed independently by Chapman and Enskog [5]. The Chapman-Enskog equations give the transport coefficients as functions of the molecular parameters of the Lennard-Jones 12-6 potential [i.e., the parameters σ and ϵ in Eq. (2.56)]. The details of the theory are beyond the scope of this text, but the results may be presented in a very simple form.

To a first approximation, the coefficient of viscosity for a monoatomic gas is

$$\eta_v = 2.6693 \times 10^{-5} \frac{(MT)^{1/2}}{\sigma^2 \Omega_v} \tag{2.95}$$

The viscosity is in units of kilograms per meter per second, the temperature is $T°K$, the atomic weight is M kg/kg atom, the parameter σ is in angstroms, and Ω_v is a dimensionless function of the reduced temperature $T^* = kT/\epsilon$ and is tabulated in Table 2.2. The molecular parameters for a variety of gases are given in Table 2.1. Although the theory was developed for nonpolar monoatomic gases, it holds very well for polyatomic gases as well.

The analogous expression for thermal conductivity is

$$\kappa = 8.3174 \times 10^{-2} \frac{(T/M)^{1/2}}{\sigma^2 \Omega_v} \tag{2.96}$$

The units of thermal conductivity κ are joules/m-sec.°K, and the others are the same as in Eq. (2.95).

The Chapman-Enskog equation for the binary diffusion coefficient is

$$D_{12} = 1.9200 \times 10^{-3} \frac{[T^3(1/M_1 + 1/M_2)]^{1/2}}{p\sigma_{12}^2 \Omega_D} \tag{2.97}$$

The units for the diffusion coefficient are square meters per second and for the pressure are kilograms weight per square meter. The function Ω_D is a dimensionless function of the reduced temperature $T^* = kT/\epsilon_{AB}$ and is tabulated in Table 2.2. The parameter σ_{12} is the collision diameter in the Lennard-Jones 12-6 potential for the interacting pair:

$$\psi_{12} = 4\epsilon_{12} \left[\left(\frac{\sigma_{12}}{r}\right)^{12} - \left(\frac{\sigma_{12}}{r}\right)^6 \right] \tag{2.98}$$

Estimates of the molecular parameters can be obtained from Table 2.1 by assuming the following mixing laws:

$$\sigma_{12} = \tfrac{1}{2}(\sigma_{11} + \sigma_{12}) \tag{2.99}$$

$$\epsilon_{12} = (\epsilon_{11}\epsilon_{22})^{1/2} \tag{2.100}$$

Equations (2.95) to (2.97) show that the transport properties of gases at low density may be predicted from information on intermolecular forces. Similarly, thermodynamic properties may also be related to these same forces. Thus, in principle at least, one should be able to interrelate thermodynamic and transport properties. The mathematical problems are usually immense, even for the simplest of gases, but this becomes a less important restriction as electronic computing techniques develop. The biggest bottleneck is an a priori knowledge of intermolecular forces. Very little is now known about them, but it is reasonable to say that a precise knowledge of the forces in solids and liquids is in the future. At present, the most fruitful approach is to develop thermodynamic and transport equations in terms of empirical functions and then curve-fit experimental data in order to evaluate the parameters. Initially, two-parameter models, such as the Lennard-Jones equation, were the

Table 2.2

Functions for prediction of transport properties of gases at low densities †

$T* = kT/\epsilon$	Ω_v	Ω_D	$T* = kT/\epsilon$	Ω_v	Ω_D
			2.50	1.093	0.9996
0.30	2.785	2.662	2.60	1.081	0.9878
0.35	2.628	2.476	2.70	1.069	0.9770
0.40	2.492	2.318	2.80	1.058	0.9672
0.45	2.368	2.184	2.90	1.048	0.9576
0.50	2.257	2.066	3.00	1.039	0.9490
0.55	2.156	1.966	3.10	1.030	0.9406
0.60	2.065	1.877	3.20	1.022	0.9328
0.65	1.982	1.798	3.30	1.014	0.9256
0.70	1.908	1.729	3.40	1.007	0.9186
0.75	1.841	1.667	3.50	0.9999	0.9120
0.80	1.780	1.612	3.60	0.9932	0.9058
0.85	1.725	1.562	3.70	0.9870	0.8998
0.90	1.675	1.517	3.80	0.9811	0.8942
0.95	1.629	1.476	3.90	0.9755	0.8888
1.00	1.587	1.439	4.00	0.9700	0.8836
1.05	1.549	1.406	4.10	0.9649	0.8788
1.10	1.514	1.375	4.20	0.9600	0.8740
1.15	1.482	1.346	4.30	0.9553	0.8694
1.20	1.452	1.320	4.40	0.9507	0.8652
1.25	1.424	1.296	4.50	0.9464	0.8610
1.30	1.399	1.273	4.60	0.9422	0.8568
1.35	1.375	1.253	4.70	0.9382	0.8530
1.40	1.353	1.233	4.80	0.9343	0.8492
1.45	1.333	1.215	4.90	0.9305	0.8456
1.50	1.314	1.198	5.0	0.9269	0.8422
1.55	1.296	1.182	6.0	0.8963	0.8124
1.60	1.279	1.167	7.0	0.8727	0.7896
1.65	1.264	1.153	8.0	0.8538	0.7712
1.70	1.248	1.140	9.0	0.8379	0.7556
1.75	1.234	1.128	10.0	0.8242	0.7424
1.80	1.221	1.116	20.0	0.7432	0.6640
1.85	1.209	1.105	30.0	0.7005	0.6232
1.90	1.197	1.094	40.0	0.6718	0.5960
1.95	1.186	1.084	50.0	0.6504	0.5756
2.00	1.175	1.075	60.0	0.6335	0.5596
2.10	1.156	1.057	70.0	0.6194	0.5464
2.20	1.138	1.041	80.0	0.6076	0.5352
2.30	1.122	1.026	90.0	0.5973	0.5256
2.40	1.107	1.012	100.0	0.5882	0.5170

† By permission from R. B. Bird, W. E. Stewart, and E. N. Lightfoot, "Transport Phenomena," p. 746, John Wiley & Sons, Inc., New York, 1960, and taken from J. O. Hirschfelder, R. B. Bird, and E. L. Spotz, *Chem. Revs.*, **44**: 205 (1949), and *J. Chem. Phys.*, **16**: 968 (1948).

rage, but lately these have been supplanted by three- or four-parameter potential-energy functions, which often give better predictions of third virial coefficients and other derivative properties. The main trouble with this approach is
that experimental data on different properties will give different values for the
molecular parameters, thus limiting their predicting capacity. This, of course,
is to be expected unless one puts an exact potential-energy function into a
rigorous theoretical development. The fact that we are not able to do this even
for simple gases need not discourage us from trying to obtain qualitative information on more complex systems.

2.7
Thermally activated rate processes

In preceding sections we have considered the relation between the transport
properties of gases and the intermolecular forces between gas molecules. In
this way we have a relationship between transport properties and partition functions. Transport phenomena in liquids and solids cannot be formally handled
in this manner because of the relative immobility and close packing of molecules in condensed states and because the transfer of energy from one molecule to the next is not always described by a simple collision process.

Transport processes in condensed systems are generally described as
"thermally activated" processes. This means that in order to overcome the resistance to change, a molecule must first acquire a certain amount of thermal
energy, called *activation energy.* As a specific example, consider the diffusion
of a small molecule in a crystalline solid. We have already said that a simple
crystal can be visualized as a lattice of close-packed spheres. Suppose we have
a small molecule trapped in the interstices of a lattice, as shown in Fig. 2.5.
The molecule is capable of diffusing through the lattice to position 3 if it can obtain enough thermal energy to force its way between the close-packed molecules
A and B. The reaction rate theory for a thermally activated process visualizes
this process by assuming that the diffusing molecule passes from state 1 to
state 3 by first going through an *activated state* 2. This is schematically shown
in Fig. 2.6. The rate of molecular transport is then proportional to the number

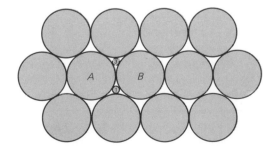

Fig. 2.5 A small molecule can
diffuse in a crystal lattice by moving from one interstitial space to
another.

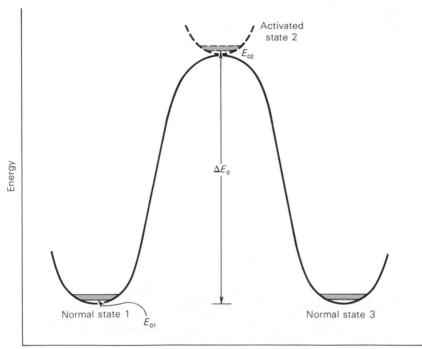

Fig. 2.6   In order for a particle to transform from state 1 to state 3, it must first pass through an activated state 2 by attaining the activation energy ΔE_0.

of molecules that can attain the energy of the activated state and cross the barrier to state 3.

Although we have used the diffusion of a small molecule in a crystal lattice as an illustration, Fig. 2.6 can be imagined to represent any three states for any activated process.   States 1 and 3 are the stable states for the process, while state 2 is a *metastable* state.   The simple physical model shown in Fig. 2.7 may help to visualize the nature of the changes.   The box is in a stable energy state when at position 1.   It can be moved to stable position 3 by adding enough potential energy to raise the box to position 2.   Any further change causes a spontaneous change to position 3.   Thus, the change from state 1 to state 3 is not spontaneous but first requires the input of an activation energy.

The rate of a thermally activated change can be related to the partition functions representing the states.   Since the probability that any molecule will have an energy E_i is proportional to the quantity $\exp(-E_i/kT)$, the total probability that a molecule will be in a state j is proportional to the sum of all the $\exp(-E_i/kT)$ appropriate to that state, or in other words, is proportional to the partition function for the state, Z_j.   The ratio of the number of molecules in an activated state 2 to the number of molecules in a normal state 1 is then proportional to the ratio of the partition functions for the two states:

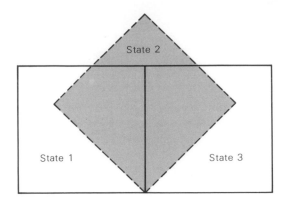

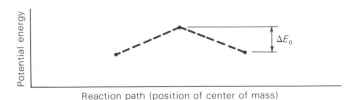

Reaction path (position of center of mass)

Fig. 2.7   A mechanical analog to thermally activated processes.

$$\frac{n_2}{n_1} = \frac{Z_2}{Z_1} = \frac{\sum\limits_{i=0}^{\infty} \exp\left(-E_i/kT\right)}{\sum\limits_{j=0}^{\infty} \exp\left(-E_j/kT\right)}$$

$$= \frac{\exp\left(-E_{02}/kT\right)}{\exp\left(-E_{01}/kT\right)} \frac{\sum\limits_{i=0}^{\infty} \exp\left[-(E_i - E_{02})/kT\right]}{\sum\limits_{j=0}^{\infty} \exp\left[-(E_j - E_{01})/kT\right]}$$

$$= \frac{Z_2{}^1}{Z_1{}^1} \exp\left(-\frac{E_{02} - E_{01}}{kT}\right) \qquad\qquad (2.101)$$

The quantities $Z_2{}^1$ and $Z_1{}^1$ are the partition functions of the two states relative to the ground-state energies E_{02} and E_{01}. The quantity $E_{02} - E_{01}$ is the difference between the zero-level energies of the activated state and the normal state. This is the amount of energy that a molecule in state 1 must acquire, at 0°K, before it can become activated. Thus, it is the activation energy at 0°K. If the rate of change from state 1 to state 3 is proportional to the fraction of molecules that can be activated, then

$$j_{1\to3} = j_0 \frac{Z_2{}^1}{Z_1{}^1} \exp\left(-\frac{E_{02} - E_{01}}{kT}\right)$$

$$= j_0 \frac{Z_2{}^1}{Z_1{}^1} \exp\left(-\frac{\Delta E_0}{kT}\right) \qquad\qquad (2.102)$$

It can be shown that the "frequency factor" j_0 is about equal to kT/h, so that

$$j = \left(\frac{kT}{h}\right) \left(\frac{Z_2{}^1}{Z_1{}^1}\right) \exp\left(-\frac{\Delta E_0}{kT}\right) \qquad (2.103)$$

In many rate processes the partition functions in the preexponential factor cannot be evaluated, but rather are lumped together as a single frequency factor A_f.

$$j = A_f \exp\left(-\Delta E_0/kT\right) \qquad (2.104)$$

This latter form of the equation is identical with the well-known Arrhenius equation, which has been found to describe a large number of chemical and nonchemical rate processes.

We can see that the thermally activated transport processes are also related to the energy states of the molecules through both the preexponential frequency factor and the thermal activation energy. We shall use these concepts several times in considering the properties of solid materials.

References

1 Andrews, F. C.: "Equilibrium Statistical Mechanics," John Wiley & Sons, Inc., New York, 1963. *An elementary development of equilibrium statistical thermodynamics. An excellent first exposure.*

2 Aston, J. G., and J. J. Fritz: "Thermodynamics and Statistical Thermodynamics," John Wiley & Sons, Inc., New York, 1959. *An undergraduate text in thermodynamics and statistical thermodynamics. A good summary of simple calculations.*

3 Bird, R. B., J. O. Hirschfelder, and C. F. Curtiss: Theoretical Calculations of the Equation of State and Transport Properties of Gases and Liquids, *Trans. ASMF*, pp. 1011–1038, October, 1954. *A summary of the standard calculation techniques for dilute gases and other materials.*

4 Bird, R. B., E. L. Spotz, and J. O. Hirschfelder: *J. Chem. Phys.*, **18:** 1395 (1950).

5 Chapman, S., and T. G. Cowling: "Mathematical Theory of Nonuniform Gases," Cambridge University Press, New York, 1951. *A detailed mathematical treatise on the kinetic theory of monoatomic gases. For advanced study.*

6 Daniels, F., and R. A. Alberty: "Physical Chemistry," 2d ed., John Wiley & Sons, Inc., New York, 1961. *An elementary text for sophomores and juniors. There are introductory chapters on spectroscopy, statistical mechanics, and thermodynamics.*

7 Hammett, L. P.: "Introduction to the Study of Physical Chemistry," McGraw-Hill Book Company, New York, 1952. *A general introduction to physical chemistry with good discussions of kinetic concepts, intermolecular forces, and the Boltzmann equation.*

8 Hill, T. L.: "Statistical Mechanics," McGraw-Hill Book Company, New York, 1956. *An advanced text on the principles and applications of statistical mechanics. The discussions of virial coefficients are especially pertinent to this chapter.*

9 Hirschfelder, J. O., C. F. Curtiss, and R. B. Bird: "Molecular Theory of Gases and Liquids," 2d ed., John Wiley & Sons, Inc., New York, 1964. *An advanced treatise on all aspects of the subjects covered in this chapter. Essential reading for all interested in research in this area.*

10 Hougen, O. A., and K. M. Watson: "Chemical Process Principles," part 2, "Thermo-dynamics," chap. XVII, John Wiley & Sons, Inc., New York, 1947. *This edition of the text contains a very readable summary of methods for evaluating thermodynamic properties from molecular structure.*

11 Kihara, T.: *J. Phys. Soc. Japan,* **6:** 184 (1951).

12 Margenau, H., and G. M. Murphy: "The Mathematics of Physics and Chemistry," 2d ed., p. 209, D. Van Nostrand Company, Inc., Princeton, N.J., 1956.

13 Mayer, J., and M. Mayer: "Statistical Thermodynamics," John Wiley & Sons, Inc., New York, 1940.

14 Moelwyn-Hughes, E. A.: "Physical Chemistry," 2d ed., The Macmillan Company, New York, 1961. *Highly recommended intermediate-level discussions of kinetic theory, inter-molecular forces, and partition functions. There are discussions of both the experimental and mathematical foundations for physical chemistry.*

15 Tolman, R. C.: "Principles of Statistical Mechanics," Oxford University Press, New York, 1938. *A classic work on statistical mechanical theory. An advanced-level book.*

Questions

2.1 Calculate the density of the earth's atmosphere at heights of 1, 5, and 10 miles. Use the Maxwell-Boltzmann distribution law and assume that the gravitational energy is the only variable. Thus, $\epsilon = \epsilon_0 + mgh$, where ϵ_0 is the energy of a gas molecule at the earth's surface, m is average mass per particle, g is the acceleration due to gravity, and h is the height above the earth's surface.

2.2 The internal energy in an ideal monoatomic gas is due entirely to the kinetic energy of the atoms, $\epsilon = \frac{1}{2}mv^2$. Calculate the internal energy by using Eq. (2.15). Show that this is equivalent to the result one gets by using Eq. (2.19).

2.3 Starting with the equations $A = -kT \ln Z$ and $p = kT \, (\partial \ln Z/\partial V)_T$, derive expressions for the Gibbs free energy G, the specific heat at constant volume $c_v = (\partial U/\partial T)_V$, and the specific heat at constant pressure $c_p = (\partial H/\partial T)_p$.

2.4 A linear harmonic oscillator of mass m is acted on by a force of $-kx$, where k is a force constant and x is the displacement from an equilibrium position. Use the partition function of Eq. (2.15) to prove that the average internal energy of a classical system of N linear harmonic oscillators is $\langle U \rangle = RT$.

2.5 Derive the equation of state for an ideal gas by using the definitions of the partition functions given in Sec. 2.3. Explain why one gets the same equation for monoatomic, diatomic, and polyatomic particles.

2.6 Rewrite the virial equation of state in terms of the following reduced variables:

$$V^* = \frac{V}{\frac{2}{3}\pi\sigma^3} \qquad p^* = \frac{(\frac{2}{3}\pi\sigma^3)p}{\epsilon} \qquad T^* = \frac{kT}{\epsilon}$$

and the reduced virial coefficients defined by Eqs. (2.59) and (2.61):

$$\frac{p^*V^*}{T^*} = 1 + \frac{B_2^*}{V^*} + \frac{B_3^*}{V^{*2}} + \cdots$$

Plot p^*V^*/T^* as a function of V^* for the isotherms $T^* = 1, 2, 5, 10, 50, 100$. The second virial coefficient (from a Lennard-Jones 12-6 potential) is to be estimated from Eq. (2.57) and the third virial coefficient from Fig. 2.2. Also show the curve for ideal gases. Under what conditions do the virial coefficients become very important?

2.7 Use the molecular constants from Table 2.1 and the results of Question 2.6 to plot isotherms (that is, p versus V at constant T) for neon, carbon dioxide, and n-butane at 300°K, 500°K, and 1000°K. Compare the predicted behavior with experimental data from the International Critical Tables or any other reliable source. Explain any deviations that arise.

2.8 The collision diameter for most simple molecules is of the order of 3 to 5 Å. At what molar volume (cubic centimeters per mole) does the mean free path between collisions come within a factor of 10 of the collision diameter of 4.0 Å (that is, 40 Å)? If the gas is confined to a 1-mm tube, at what molar volume does the mean free path reach one-tenth of the diameter of the tube (0.1 mm)? Discuss how the mean free path affects the validity of the gas laws.

2.9 Estimate the viscosity and thermal conductivity of neon, carbon dioxide, and n-butane at low pressure and 300°K, 500°K, and 1000°K. Compare the results of the Chapman-Enskog equations with the results from ideal-gas laws. (Use the parameter σ as an estimate of the diameter d of the rigid sphere.) Compare your results with experimental data from any reliable source.

2.10 Estimate the binary diffusion coefficient for the following gas pairs at 1 atm and 273.2°K: CO_2-CO, CO_2-N_2, and A-O_2. Use both the Chapman-Enskog equation and the ideal-gas equation. Compare your answers with the experimental values of 0.137, 0.144, and 0.193×10^{-4} m²/sec.

2.11 Calculate the coefficient of self-diffusion for neon at 273.2°K. Compare results of the ideal-gas equation, the Chapman-Enskog equation, and the experimental value of 0.452×10^{-4} m²/sec.

3
Bonding in atoms and molecules

3.1
Introduction

In the preceding two chapters we have looked at the interrelationships that exist between bulk properties and molecular properties. The ideal situation is to a priori determine the fundamental particle interactions and the molecular interactions and then predict the physical properties. This requires specific information about the dynamics and the distribution of fundamental particles in the atoms or molecules.

The first successful attempt to describe an atom was made in 1913 by Niels Bohr. He visualized a hydrogen atom as consisting of a relatively fast moving electron in a circular orbit about a relatively slow moving proton (Fig. 3.1). Assuming a planetary motion described by Newton's laws, he postulated that a stable orbit developed when the centrifugal force exerted by the electron was balanced by the electrostatic attraction between the proton and the electron (gravitational forces are negligible):

$$\frac{m_e v^2}{r} = \frac{e^2}{r^2} \tag{3.1}$$

The total energy of the electron moving in an orbit is the sum of the kinetic energy and the potential energy:

$$E_e = \frac{1}{2} m_e v^2 + \left(-\frac{e^2}{r}\right)$$

$$= -\frac{1}{2} \frac{e^2}{r} \tag{3.2}$$

The electronic energy may be calculated once the orbital radius r is specified.

At this point Bohr had to depart from the usual Newtonian concepts of particle dynamics in order to explain the experimental behavior of hydrogen atoms. It had been known for a long time that when energy in the form of electromagnetic radiation is supplied, the atoms absorb only certain characteristic frequencies and these frequencies can be observed as a series of lines on a photographic plate, referred to as an *absorption spectrum*. Similarly, when this energy is released, a discrete *emission spectrum* is obtained. Experimentally, the change from one energy level to another is always a multiple of the frequency of the absorbed or emitted radiation:

$$E_A = E_n - E_m = h\nu_A$$

$$= 2.1795 \times 10^{-18} \left(\frac{1}{n^2} - \frac{1}{m^2}\right) \frac{\text{joules}}{\text{atom}} \qquad (3.3)$$

where ν_A is the frequency of the radiation (cycles per second), h is the universal Planck's constant (6.625×10^{-34} joule-sec), and n and m are integers. Whereas Newton's laws permit any value of the orbital radius r and thus any value of the energy E, experimental data show that electrons existed only in certain discrete energy states.

Bohr's hypothesis was that only discrete *quantum units* of angular momentum are allowed:

$$rm_e v = \frac{nh}{2\pi} \qquad (3.4)$$

where n is an integer with values 1, 2, 3, . . . , ∞. Substitution of Eq. (3.4) into (3.2) leads to

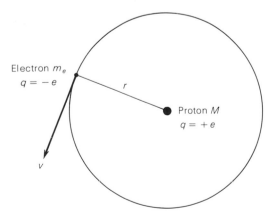

Fig. 3.1 In the Bohr model for a hydrogen atom, the electron moves in a fixed orbit about the proton.

$$E_n = -\frac{2\pi^2 m_e e^4}{h^2 n^2} = -\frac{2.1795 \times 10^{-18}}{n^2} \quad \frac{\text{joules}}{\text{atom}} \tag{3.5}$$

$$r = \frac{h^2}{4\pi^2 m_e e^2} n^2 = 0.529 n^2 \quad \text{Å} \tag{3.6}$$

Equation (3.5) expresses the energy level in terms of the quantum number n. The ground state of the atom is $E_1 = -2.1795 \times 10^{-18}$ joules $= -13.60$ ev. This is the maximum binding energy of the electron to the proton. The *ionization potential* is the energy required to remove the electron from the atom in its ground state (i.e., to go from $n = 1$ to $n = \infty$):

$$\Im = E_\infty - E_1 = 2.1795 \times 10^{-18} \frac{\text{joules}}{\text{atom}} = 13.60 \frac{\text{ev}}{\text{atom}} \tag{3.7}$$

Agreement of the theory with experiment showed the value of these ideas. Equation (3.6) indicates that only certain orbitals are permitted; the orbital radius is 0.529 Å in the ground state, 2.116 Å in the first excited state $n = 2$, etc. An absorption of a discrete amount of electromagnetic radiation is thus seen to cause the electron to "jump" from one orbit to the next. As we shall see later, this concept is essential to the idea of electronic shells surrounding a nucleus.

Although the Bohr theory explained the behavior of the hydrogen atom, it did not account for the details in the absorption spectra of more complicated atoms. It was soon evident that a more drastic modification of Newtonian mechanics was necessary. The proper direction was suggested by Louis de Broglie in 1924, when he postulated that electron beams travel in the same manner as light waves, that is, with a specific frequency or wavelength. Combining the Einstein equation for the equivalence of mass and energy with Eq. (3.3), one obtains the wavelength λ of an *electron wave:*

$$E = m_e v^2 = h\nu \tag{3.8}$$

$$\lambda = \frac{v}{\nu} = \frac{h}{m_e v} \tag{3.9}$$

If an electron wave is traveling in a circular orbit, a standing wave is produced when the path length is an integral number of wavelengths:

$$n\lambda = 2\pi r \tag{3.10}$$

Combination of Eqs. (3.9) and (3.10) gives

$$2\pi r m_e v = nh \tag{3.11}$$

which is identical with the Bohr hypothesis [Eq. (3.4)]. Thus, the "things" that we call electrons appear to have a fixed mass and charge, while at the same time beams of these "things" have a wavelength and a frequency and can be diffracted. An easy answer to this apparent contradiction is to say that electrons have a dual particle-wave nature, and since we have a strong intuitive sense for the properties of both particles and waves, this approach has definite advantages. On the other hand, it is more logical to say that electrons are entities which simply do not conform to classical laws of physics and that the description of their behavior requires a whole new set of rules. In other words, we recognize that Newton's laws describing the exact position and velocity of a moving particle are simply not correct for describing electronic behavior and chemical bonding. It is in this light that wave-mechanical principles and the Schrödinger wave equation have replaced the classical laws. It is interesting to note, however, that we may retain our classical notions of particles and waves and still use the new rules. In fact, it turns out that Newton's laws are just one of the limiting cases of wave-mechanical laws. Thus, wave mechanics is a more general description of the behavior of matter.

In order to rationalize experimental observation, the Heisenberg uncertainty principle has been enunciated. One statement of this principle is that if one tries to describe the behavior of matter in terms of the classical concepts of position and momentum, one can do it only in a statistical sense. If one tries to measure the position and momentum simultaneously, there will always be an uncertainty of

$$4\pi\,\Delta x\,\Delta mv \doteq h = 6.625 \times 10^{-34} \text{ joule-sec} \qquad (3.12)$$

The measuring errors are of no consequence when dealing with large masses moving at low velocities (relative to the speed of light), but they become very significant when considering the motion of electrons.

If, for example, we were measuring the position of a 1,800-kg automobile traveling at a speed of 100 km/hr with a precision of 10^{-4} m, the minimum uncertainty in the simultaneous measurement of velocity would be about 10^{-34} m/sec. Obviously, this restriction is of no importance in this case. On the other hand, if we were measuring the position of a slow-moving electron with a precision of 10^{-10} m, the minimum uncertainty in the simultaneous measurement of velocity would be about 10^6 m/sec.

Newton's laws of motion are exact relationships between position, momentum, and energy (for example, $F = mg$) and thus make it possible to calculate the exact energy and velocity of a particle at a specific point in space. This is all right for large enough masses where the minimum uncertainties are negligible, but it is not at all consistent with the uncertainty principle for very small masses. It is thus necessary to replace Newton's laws with more general laws of mechanics. This is the subject matter of wave mechanics.

The basic axiom of wave mechanics is that the state of a system can be represented by a continuous, single-valued function Ψ of certain variables:

$$\Psi = \Psi(x_1, x_2, \ldots, x_n, t) \qquad (3.13)$$

The variables can be chosen as the position coordinates, at time t, of the *classical analogue* of the system. All the problems that we shall consider will involve "steady-state" behavior, so that time will not be a variable. Thus, the wave function for the hydrogen atom is a function of six coordinates, three for the electron and three for the proton. The function may be positive, negative, real, or complex, and it is chosen in such a way that the product of the function and its complex conjugate is proportional to the probability of finding mass at a specific point in space. Integration of this product over the whole of space in which the system can exist gives a value of 1.

$$\int_{\substack{\text{all}\\ \text{variables}}} \Psi^*\Psi \; dx_1 \, dx_2 \cdots dx_n = 1 \tag{3.14}$$

The basic equation in wave mechanics (akin to Newton's laws) is the Schrödinger wave equation:

$$\mathcal{H}\Psi_n = E_n\Psi_n \tag{3.15}$$

The quantity Ψ_n is the wave function for the system when it has an energy E_n. The quantity $\mathcal{H}$ is the *Hamiltonian operator* for the wave function:

$$\mathcal{H} = \sum_j -\frac{h^2}{8m_j\pi^2} \nabla_j^2 + \frac{1}{2}\sum_k\sum_l \psi_{kl} \tag{3.16}$$

The last term of Eq. (3.16) is just the classical potential energy of interaction for the whole system, and ∇_j^2 is the operator $d^2/dx_j^2 + d^2/dy_j^2 + d^2/dz_j^2$ (rectilinear coordinates) for the jth particle. Note the similarity between Eqs. (3.16) and (2.29). Here again we have a tie-up between the dynamic properties of a system and the intermolecular forces.

We obviously have not even begun to describe all of the properties of wave functions, nor have we attempted to develop wave mechanics mathematically. Our present purpose is only to understand enough about the nature of the wave function to utilize solutions of the Schrödinger equation intelligently. Since this is a very complicated second-order differential equation, the mathematics of even the simplest systems is difficult. We shall not go through the mathematics in this chapter, but rather shall merely present the results for some important systems and interpret them in terms of chemical bonding.

3.2
The hydrogen atom and the periodic table

The purpose of looking at the hydrogen atom is to show how the wave function may be used to determine the electron distribution. This will lead to the concept of orbitals that participate in chemical bonding. Molecular-orbital theory will later be used to describe qualitatively the strength and shape of the bonds that hold solid materials together.

In the hydrogen atom, a single electron moves in the field created by a single proton. The wave function is going to depend on the six spatial coordinates of the two particles. Since we are interested in the electron distribution around the nucleus, let us forget about the translational motion of the proton and write the wave function for the moving electron relative to a stationary proton. It can then be shown that the electron wave function depends only on the relative position of the electron. The "steady-state" Schrödinger equation reduces to

$$\nabla^2 \Psi_n + \frac{8\pi^2 m_e M}{h^2(m_e + M)} \left(E_n - \frac{e^2}{r}\right) \Psi_n = 0 \tag{3.17}$$

The wave function Ψ_n describes the motion of an electron of energy E_n. The mass of the electron is m_e and the charge is $-e$. The mass of the proton is M and the charge is $+e$. The distance between the proton and the electron is represented by r, and the operator ∇^2, in spherical coordinates, is

$$\nabla^2 = \frac{1}{r^2} \frac{\partial}{\partial r}\left(r^2 \frac{\partial}{\partial r}\right) + \frac{1}{r^2 \sin \theta} \frac{\partial}{\partial \theta}\left(\sin \theta \frac{\partial}{\partial \theta}\right) + \frac{1}{r^2 \sin^2 \theta} \frac{\partial^2}{\partial \phi^2} \tag{3.18}$$

The wave function is, therefore, a complicated function of r, θ, and ϕ. The solution to (3.17) is given by the following equations [7]:

$$E_n = - \frac{2\pi^2 e^4}{h^2 n^2} \frac{m_e M}{m_e + M} \tag{3.19}$$

$$\Psi_{nlm} = A \left[\exp\left(-\frac{r}{na_0}\right)\right] \left(\frac{r}{a_0}\right)^l L_{n+l}^{2l+1}\left(\frac{2r}{na_0}\right) P_l^m (\cos \theta) \exp im\phi \tag{3.20}$$

$$a_0 = \frac{h^2}{4\pi^2 m_e e^2} \tag{3.21}$$

The functions $L(2r/na_0)$ and $P(\cos \theta)$ are the associated Laguerre and the associated Legendre polynomials (see Question 3.5) and have different values for each set of the quantum numbers. The constant A is the normalizing factor and may be evaluated using Eq. (3.14). The *quantum numbers* n, l, and m can only be integers; for a given value of n, l may have values from 0 to $n - 1$ and m may have values from $-l$ to $+l$.

The product of the wave function and its complex conjugate is a measure of the probability of finding the electron at a specific place. The quantity $4\pi r^2 \Psi \Psi^*$ gives the density of the "electron cloud" at a distance r from the proton.

The principal quantum number n roughly measures the radius at which this electron density is a maximum. It can be shown that the maximum densities occur at approximately $0.529n^2$ Å, which is identical with the orbit radii of the Bohr theory. Although we cannot use the concept of fixed orbits, we see that the Bohr radius gives the most probable radius for the electron in its wave-mechanical "orbital."

The azimuthal quantum number l gives an indication of the shape of the electron cloud. When $l = 0$, a spherically symmetric cloud (an s orbital) is obtained; when $l = 1$ (p orbitals) or $l = 2$ (d orbitals), spheroidal clouds result. The magnetic quantum number m specifies the orientation of these electron clouds in space.

A function with a given set of quantum numbers, Ψ_{nlm}, is called an *orbital*. The first few orbitals for the hydrogen atom are listed in Table 3.1 and sketched in Fig. 3.2. Notice that s orbitals are spherically symmetric, p orbitals have high concentrations of electrons along specific axes, and higher orbitals (for example, d orbitals) have more complicated shapes. It is rather difficult to show three-dimensional density gradients by shading a two-dimensional drawing, so the radial functions are plotted in Fig. 3.3 in order to give an idea of the electron distribution as one moves away from the nucleus in a specific direction.

The quantum numbers n, l, and m describe the behavior of an atom in terms of only the space coordinates of the electrons. It has been found from spectroscopic data, however, that two energy levels, with slightly different energies, are present where the wave equation predicts one. This doubling effect is explained by postulating that the electron spins on its own axis and its wave function must depend on a fourth *spin coordinate* x_s as well as its spatial position:

$$\Psi = \Psi(x_1,x_2,x_3,x_s) \qquad \text{cf. Eq. (3.13)} \tag{3.22}$$

Table 3.1

Orbitals for the hydrogen atom

n	l	m	Orbital	$-E_n$, ev	$-\Psi_{nlm}/A$
1	0	0	$1s$	13.6	$\exp\left(-\dfrac{r}{a_0}\right)$
2	0	0	$2s$	3.4	$2\left(2 - \dfrac{r}{a_0}\right)\exp\left(-\dfrac{r}{2a_0}\right)$
2	1	1	$2p_x$	3.4	$6\dfrac{r}{a_0}\left[\exp\left(-\dfrac{r}{2a_0}\right)\right]\sin\theta\,\exp i\phi$
2	1	0	$2p_z$	3.4	$6\dfrac{r}{a_0}\left[\exp\left(-\dfrac{r}{2a_0}\right)\right]\cos\theta$
2	1	−1	$2p_y$	3.4	$6\dfrac{r}{a_0}\left[\exp\left(-\dfrac{r}{2a_0}\right)\right]\sin\theta\,\exp(-i\phi)$
3	0	0	$3s$	1.5	$3\left(6 - 4\dfrac{r}{a_0} + \dfrac{4r^2}{9a_0{}^2}\right)\exp\left(-\dfrac{r}{3a_0}\right)$
3	1	1	$3p_x$	1.5	$16\left(6\dfrac{r}{a_0} - \dfrac{r^2}{a_0{}^2}\right)\left[\exp\left(-\dfrac{r}{3a_0}\right)\right]\sin\theta\,\exp i\phi$
3	1	0	$3p_z$	1.5	$16\left(6\dfrac{r}{a_0} - \dfrac{r^2}{a_0{}^2}\right)\left[\exp\left(-\dfrac{r}{3a_0}\right)\right]\cos\theta$
3	1	−1	$3p_y$	1.5	$16\left(6\dfrac{r}{a_0} - \dfrac{r^2}{a_0{}^2}\right)\left[\exp\left(-\dfrac{r}{3a_0}\right)\right]\sin\theta\,\exp(-i\phi)$
3	2	2	$3d_{x^2-y^2}$	1.5	$360\left(\dfrac{r}{a_0}\right)^2\left[\exp\left(-\dfrac{r}{3a_0}\right)\right]\sin^2\theta\,\exp 2i\phi$
3	2	1	$3d_{xz}$	1.5	$360\left(\dfrac{r}{a_0}\right)^2\left[\exp\left(-\dfrac{r}{3a_0}\right)\right]\sin\theta\cos\theta\,\exp i\phi$
3	2	0	$3d_{z^2}$	1.5	$60\left(\dfrac{r}{a_0}\right)^2\left[\exp\left(-\dfrac{r}{3a_0}\right)\right](3\cos^2\theta - 1)$

Quantum number header applies to columns n, l, m.

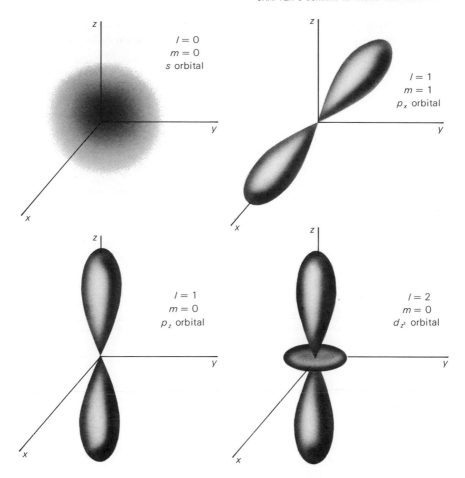

Fig. 3.2 Electron-cloud distributions for a hydrogen atom are schematically represented by drawings of orbitals in order to show the general shapes of the electron cloud.

It can be shown that this fourth coordinate merely introduces a fourth quantum number m_s which can take on values of either $+\frac{1}{2}$ or $-\frac{1}{2}$.

A solution of the wave equation for more complicated atoms is many times more difficult. An atom of sodium, for example, contains a nuclear charge of $+11$, plus 11 electrons "orbiting" the nucleus. From Eqs. (3.15) and (3.16) we can see that the wave function depends on all 36 space coordinates. This makes for an immensely complicated second-order differential equation. The results for the hydrogen atom may be applied to other atoms, however, if it is assumed that the real potential energy of interaction between one of the electrons and all of the other particles can be replaced by an "equivalent" central electrostatic field (i.e., a self-consistent field). The predicted energy states for such a model are

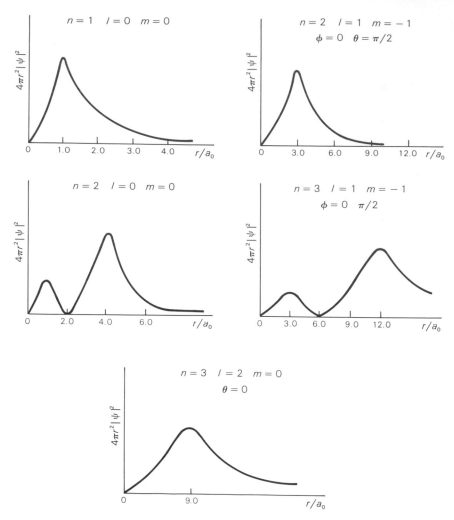

Fig. 3.3 The radial distribution densities for a hydrogen atom show sharp maxima, meaning that the electrons reside primarily in narrow shells surrounding the proton.

$$E_{n,l} = -\frac{2\pi^2 e^4 m}{h^2 n^2}(q - q_0)^2 \tag{3.23}$$

where q is the total nuclear charge and q_0 is a shielding constant which is a measure of how much a given electron is shielded from the nuclear charge by other electrons in the atom and is a function of both the principal and azimuthal quantum numbers (n and l). This does not change the general picture in any way, but it does make it possible for an electron in, say, a $4s$ orbital to have a lower energy than one in a $3d$ orbital. Experimental evidence shows that the energy levels in multielectron, neutral atoms increase in the following order:

$$1s < 2s < 2p < 3s < 3p < 4s < 3d < 4p < 5s < 4d < 5p < 6s$$

$$< 5d \doteq 4f < 6p < 7s < 5f \doteq 6d$$

The electron orbitals of multielectron atoms are thus described in terms of the hydrogen atom orbitals. The electron configurations are determined by assigning each electron a set of four quantum numbers, n, l, m, and m_s, and filling successive energy levels in such a way that the total energy of the atom is minimized. An additional hypothesis, the Pauli exclusion principle, which states that no two electrons in a given atom can have the same set of four quantum numbers, must also be utilized.

Each principal quantum number is designated as a shell, and each shell can hold a certain number of electrons. The first, designated as the K shell, holds two electrons (with quantum numbers $1,0,0,\frac{1}{2}$ and $1,0,0,-\frac{1}{2}$). The second, the L shell, holds eight electrons ($2,0,0,\pm\frac{1}{2}$; $2,1,\pm1,\pm\frac{1}{2}$; $2,1,0,\pm\frac{1}{2}$). The first five shells are listed in Table 3.2. The s, p, d, etc., orbitals within a shell are called subshells. The electron configurations and the first ionization potentials (energy required to strip the outermost electron) for the atoms are listed in Table 3.3. The superscripts refer to the number of electrons in a given orbital; thus $1s^2$ means an atom with two $1s$ electrons. The atoms may also be arranged in a periodic table, Table 3.4, and in general the ionization potentials increase in groups from left to right and in periods from bottom to top. Thus, it is easy to form cations with the alkali-metal atoms but very difficult to do so with the halogens and the inert-gas atoms. The variations in ionization potentials are an indication of the stability of atoms with filled shells or subshells.

The electron affinities $\mathfrak{E}$ of a few atoms are also listed in Table 3.3; $\mathfrak{E}$ is the energy released when an atom takes on an electron to form a negative ion. The halogen atoms have high electron affinities and thus form stable anions, while metallic elements have small or even negative electron affinities, which means they do not form very stable anions.

We shall next see how a knowledge of atomic orbitals can help explain the chemical bonding characteristics of molecules.

Table 3.2

Electron shells for atoms

Shell designation	Principal quantum number	Max number of electrons in shell
K	1	2
L	2	8
M	3	18
N	4	32
O	5	50

Table 3.3

The electronic characteristics of atoms *

Z	Atom	Orbital electronic configuration	$\mathfrak{I}$, ev	$\mathfrak{E}$, ev
1	H	$1s$	13.595	+0.747
2	He	$1s^2$	24.580	
3	Li	[He]$2s$	5.390	0.54
4	Be	[He]$2s^2$	9.320	−0.6
5	B	[He]$2s^22p$	8.296	0.2
6	C	[He]$2s^22p^2$	11.264	1.25
7	N	[He]$2s^22p^3$	14.54	−0.1
8	O	[He]$2s^22p^4$	13.614	1.47
9	F	[He]$2s^22p^5$	17.42	3.45
10	Ne	[He]$2s^22p^6$	21.559	
11	Na	[Ne]$3s$	5.138	0.74
12	Mg	[Ne]$3s^2$	7.644	−0.3
13	Al	[Ne]$3s^23p$	5.984	0.6
14	Si	[Ne]$3s^23p^2$	8.149	1.63
15	P	[Ne]$3s^23p^3$	11.0	0.7
16	S	[Ne]$3s^23p^4$	10.357	2.07
17	Cl	[Ne]$3s^23p^5$	13.01	3.61
18	Ar	[Ne]$3s^23p^6$	15.755	
19	K	[Ar]$4s$	4.339	
20	Ca	[Ar]$4s^2$	6.111	
21	Sc	[Ar]$4s^23d$	6.56	
22	Ti	[Ar]$4s^23d^2$	6.83	
23	V	[Ar]$4s^23d^3$	6.74	
24	Cr	[Ar]$4s3d^5$	6.763	
25	Mn	[Ar]$4s^23d^5$	7.432	
26	Fe	[Ar]$4s^23d^6$	7.90	
27	Co	[Ar]$4s^23d^7$	7.86	
28	Ni	[Ar]$4s^23d^8$	7.633	
29	Cu	[Ar]$4s3d^{10}$	7.724	
30	An	[Ar]$4s^23d^{10}$	9.391	−0.9
31	Ga	[Ar]$4s^23d^{10}4p$	6.00	0.18
32	Ge	[Ar]$4s^23d^{10}4p^2$	7.88	1.2
33	As	[Ar]$4s^23d^{10}4p^3$	9.81	0.6
34	Se	[Ar]$4s^23d^{10}4p^4$	9.75	1.7
35	Br	[Ar]$4s^23d^{10}4p^5$	11.84	3.36
36	Kr	[Ar]$4s^23d^{10}4p^6$	13.996	
37	Rb	[Kr]$5s$	4.176	
38	Sr	[Kr]$5s^2$	5.692	
39	Y	[Kr]$5s^24d$	6.5	
40	Zr	[Kr]$5s^24d^2$	6.95	
41	Nb	[Kr]$5s4d^4$	6.77	
42	Mo	[Kr]$5s4d^5$	7.10	

* From H. B. Gray, "Electrons and Chemical Bonding," pp. 24–34, W. A. Benjamin, Inc., New York, 1964.

Table 3.3 (*Continued*)

Z	Atom	Orbital electronic configuration	$\mathfrak{J}$, ev	$\mathfrak{E}$, ev
43	Tc	$[Kr]5s^24d^5$	7.28	
44	Ru	$[Kr]5s4d^7$	7.364	
45	Rh	$[Kr]5s4d^8$	7.46	
46	Pd	$[Kr]4d^{10}$	8.33	
47	Ag	$[Kr]5s4d^{10}$	7.574	
48	Cd	$[Kr]5s^24d^{10}$	8.991	−0.6
49	In	$[Kr]5s^24d^{10}5p$	5.785	0.2
50	Sn	$[Kr]5s^24d^{10}5p^2$	7.342	
51	Sb	$[Kr]5s^24d^{10}5p^3$	8.639	
52	Te	$[Kr]5s^24d^{10}5p^4$	9.01	2.2
53	I	$[Kr]5s^24d^{10}5p^5$	10.454	3.06
54	Xe	$[Kr]5s^24d^{10}5p^6$	12.127	
55	Cs	$[Xe]6s$	3.893	
56	Ba	$[Xe]6s^2$	5.210	
57	La	$[Xe]6s^25d$	5.61	
58	Ce	$[Xe]6s^24f5d$	6.91	
59	Pr	$[Xe]6s^24f^3$	5.76	
60	Nd	$[Xe]6s^24f^4$	6.31	
61	Pm	$[Xe]6s^24f^5$		
62	Sm	$[Xe]6s^24f^6$	5.6	
63	Eu	$[Xe]6s^24f^7$	5.67	
64	Gd	$[Xe]6s^24f^75d$	6.16	
65	Tb	$[Xe]6s^24f^9$	6.74	
66	Dy	$[Xe]6s^24f^{10}$	6.82	
67	Ho	$[Xe]6s^24f^{11}$		
68	Er	$[Xe]6s^24f^{12}$	6.08	
69	Tm	$[Xe]6s^24f^{13}$	5.81	
70	Yb	$[Xe]6s^24f^{14}$	6.2	
71	Lu	$[Xe]6s^24f^{14}5d$	5.0	
72	Hf	$[Xe]6s^24f^{14}5d^2$		
73	Ta	$[Xe]6s^24f^{14}5d^3$	7.88	
74	W	$[Xe]6s^24f^{14}5d^4$	7.98	
75	Re	$[Xe]6s^24f^{14}5d^5$	7.87	
76	Os	$[Xe]6s^24f^{14}5d^6$	8.7	
77	Ir	$[Xe]6s^24f^{14}5d^7$	9.	
78	Pt	$[Xe]6s^24f^{14}5d^9$	9.0	
79	Au	$[Xe]6s4f^{14}5d^{10}$	9.22	
80	Hg	$[Xe]6s^24f^{14}5d^{10}$	10.43	
81	Tl	$[Xe]6s^24f^{14}5d^{10}6p$	6.106	
82	Pb	$[Xe]6s^24f^{14}5d^{10}6p^2$	7.415	
83	Bi	$[Xe]6s^24f^{14}5d^{10}6p^3$	7.287	
84	Po	$[Xe]6s^24f^{14}5d^{10}6p^4$	8.43	
85	At	$[Xe]6s^24f^{14}5d^{10}6p^5$		
86	Rn	$[Xe]6s^24f^{14}5d^{10}6p^6$	10.746	
87	Fr	$[Rn]7s$		

Table 3.3 (*Continued*)

Z	Atom	Orbital electronic configuration	$\mathfrak{I}$, ev	$\mathfrak{E}$, ev
88	Ra	$[Rn]7s^2$	5.277	
89	Ac	$[Rn]7s^26d$		
90	Th	$[Rn]7s^26d^2$	6.95	
91	Pa	$[Rn]7s^25f^26d$		
92	U	$[Rn]7s^25f^36d$	6.1	
93	Np	$[Rn]7s^25f^46d$		
94	Pu	$[Rn]7s^25f^6$	5.1	
95	Am	$[Rn]7s^25f^7$	6.0	
96	Cm	$[Rn]7s^25f^76d$		
97	Bk	$[Rn]7s^25f^9$		
98	Cf	$[Rn]7s^25f^{10}$		
99	Es	$[Rn]7s^25f^{11}$		
100	Fm	$[Rn]7s^25f^{12}$		
101	Md	$[Rn]7s^25f^{13}$		
102	No	$[Rn]7s^25f^{14}$		
103	Lw	$[Rn]7s^25f^{14}6d$		

3.3
Covalent bonding in homonuclear diatomic molecules

In this section we shall see how atomic-orbital concepts can be extended to simple molecules and how the chemical bonding characteristics can then be predicted.

Consider the formation of a hydrogen molecule. When two hydrogen atoms are very far apart, they do not interact and are present in their normal $1s$ ground-state configurations. As they approach one another, there will be a superposition of the electrostatic fields resulting in a lowering of the potential energy in the region between the two protons (i.e., along the internuclear axis). Since the K shell can accommodate two $1s$ orbitals, it is possible for the electron density to increase in this region of lower potential. The net result is the formation of a stable diatomic molecule with a high electron density between the two protons. The new "molecular orbitals" for the electrons are much different than the original ones. If we were able to determine these new wave functions, they could be used to calculate the electron distribution (schematically shown in Fig. 3.4) and the bond energy. The approximate solutions for molecules come from either *molecular-orbital theory* [2] or *valence-bond theory* [2,6]. We shall not go into the details of these theories in this text, but rather we shall look at a simplified development of molecular-orbital concepts in order to see the relationship between orbitals and chemical bonding.

The general idea is that a molecular orbital is a linear combination of the available atomic orbitals. Consider a single electron in the field of two protons.

Table 3.4

Periodic table of the elements

Group

	IA	IIA	IIIA	IVA	VA	VIA	VIIA	VIII			IB	IIB	IIIB	IVB	VB	VIB	VIIB	0
1	1 H	→											→	→	→	→	→	2 He
2	3 Li	4 Be	←	←	←	←	←						5 B	6 C	7 N	8 O	9 F	10 Ne
3	11 Na	12 Mg	←	←	←	←	←						13 Al	14 Si	15 P	16 S	17 Cl	18 Ar
4	19 K	20 Ca	21 Sc	22 Ti	23 V	24 Cr	25 Mn	26 Fe	27 Co	28 Ni	29 Cu	30 Zn	31 Ga	32 Ge	33 As	34 Se	35 Br	36 Kr
5	37 Rb	38 Sr	39 Y	40 Zr	41 Nb	42 Mo	43 Tc	44 Ru	45 Rh	46 Pd	47 Ag	48 Cd	49 In	50 Sn	51 Sb	52 Te	53 I	54 Xe
6	55 Cs	56 Ba	57* La	72 Hf	73 Ta	74 W	75 Re	76 Os	77 Ir	78 Pt	79 Au	80 Hg	81 Tl	82 Pb	83 Bi	84 Po	85 At	86 Rn
7	87 Fr	88 Ra	89** Ac															

Lanthanum Series *

58 Ce	59 Pr	60 Nd	61 Pm	62 Sm	63 Eu	64 Gd	65 Tb	66 Dy	67 Ho	68 Er	69 Tm	70 Yb	71 Lu

Actinium Series **

90 Th	91 Pa	92 U	93 Np	94 Pu	95 Am	96 Cm	97 Bk	98 Cf	99 Es	100 Fm	101 Md	102 No	103 Lw

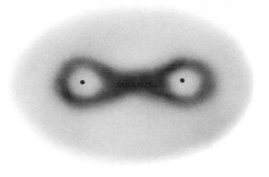

Fig. 3.4 The stable ground state for the hydrogen molecule has a high electron density between the protons, along the internuclear axis.

The electron is able to form a stable $1s$ atomic orbital with either of the two protons; thus, the molecular orbital is some linear combination of the two:

$$\Psi(\sigma_s) = a_1(1s)_a + a_2(1s)_b \tag{3.24}$$

In this case the two atomic orbitals are identical, so it is probable that they contribute equally to the molecular orbital (that is, $|a_1| = |a_2|$). The two possible combinations of the atomic orbitals are thus

$$\Psi(\sigma_s) = A[(1s)_a + (1s)_b] \tag{3.25}$$

$$\Psi(\sigma_s^*) = A^*[(1s)_a - (1s)_b] \tag{3.26}$$

When the atomic orbitals are overlapping, the sum [Eq. (3.25)] is equivalent to an increase in electron density in the overlap region, and the difference [Eq. (3.26)] is equivalent to a decrease in electron density in the overlap region. This is shown schematically in Fig. 3.5. The function $\Psi(\sigma_s)$ is called a *bonding orbital*, and $\Psi(\sigma_s^*)$ is called an *antibonding orbital*. The relative stability of the two is obtained from the steady-state Schrödinger equation. Multiplying both sides of Eq. (3.15) by Ψ and integrating, one gets

$$\int \Psi \mathcal{H} \Psi \, dx_1 \, dx_2 \cdots dx_n = E \int \Psi^2 \, dx_1 \, dx_2 \cdots dx_n \tag{3.27}$$

From Eq. (3.14), $\int \Psi^2 \, dx_1 \, dx_2 \cdots dx_n = 1$,

$$E = \int \Psi \mathcal{H} \Psi \, dx_1 \, dx_2 \cdots dx_n \tag{3.28}$$

The energy for each molecular orbital is obtained by substituting Eqs. (3.25) and (3.26) into (3.28):

$$E(\sigma_s) = 2\Re_{AA} + 2\mathfrak{Q}_{AB} \tag{3.29}$$

$$E(\sigma_s^*) = 2\Re_{AA} - 2\mathfrak{Q}_{AB} \tag{3.30}$$

The quantity $\Re$, called the *Coulomb integral,* is an ionization potential for the electron in the field of the protons:

$$\Re_{AA} = \Re_{BB} = A^2 \int (1s)_a \mathcal{H} (1s)_a \, dx_1 \cdots dx_n \tag{3.31}$$

and $\mathfrak{Q}$, called the *exchange integral,* represents a resonance stabilization energy for the molecule:

$$\mathfrak{Q}_{AB} = \mathfrak{Q}_{BA} = A^2 \int (1s)_a \mathscr{H} (1s)_b \, dx_1 \, dx_2 \cdots dx_n \qquad (3.32)$$

Without having to evaluate the integrals, we can see from Eqs. (3.29) and (3.30) that the bonding orbital σ_s is more stable by an amount of energy equal to $4\mathfrak{Q}_{AB}$. Since these terms are negative [cf. Eq. (3.19)], the energy in the bonding orbital is more negative by an amount $4\mathfrak{Q}_{AB}$. The relative energies of the orbitals are shown schematically in Fig. 3.6. The significance of bonding orbitals and antibonding orbitals is clear, in this case, since the bonding orbital gives a more stable arrangement than the separated atoms, while the antibonding orbital gives a less stable arrangement.

The electronic configuration for the hydrogen molecule is built up by placing the electrons consecutively into the most stable molecular orbitals (states); each state can accommodate two electrons with opposite spin. The ground state of the hydrogen molecule is thus σ_s^2, with two electrons in bonding orbitals. This "sharing" of two bonding orbitals is called a *single covalent bond.*

The same procedure is followed for other molecules. Helium, for example, has the stable configuration of $1s^2$. The diatomic molecule He_2 would have the molecular configuration $\sigma_s^2 \sigma_s^{*2}$, or two electrons in bonding orbitals and two electrons in antibonding orbitals. If we define the total number of covalent bonds holding two atoms together as one-half the difference between the number of electrons in bonding and antibonding orbitals, the He_2 configuration has a net of zero covalent bonds [$\frac{1}{2}(2-2) = 0$], which is consistent with the fact that helium gas is monoatomic. [Notice that this definition also gives a net of one bond for hydrogen: $\frac{1}{2}(2-0) = 1$.] The technique is a little more complicated for other molecules because there are more atomic orbitals available. The atoms in the second row of the periodic table for example, Li to Ne, can form chemical

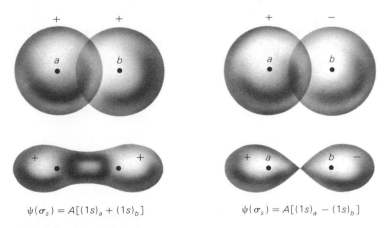

$$\psi(\sigma_s) = A[(1s)_a + (1s)_b] \qquad\qquad \psi(\sigma_s) = A[(1s)_a - (1s)_b]$$

Fig. 3.5 A molecular bonding orbital is formed by adding two overlapping atomic s orbitals, and a nonbonding orbital is formed by subtracting one from the other.

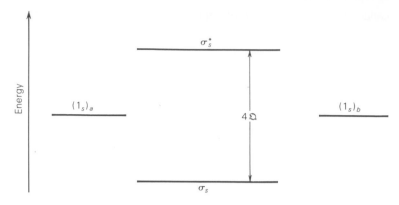

Fig. 3.6 The energy of the stable σ bonding orbital for hydrogen is lower than the energy of the component atomic orbitals, while the energy of the unstable antibonding orbital is greater than the component atomic orbitals.

bonds with $2s$, $2p_x$, $2p_y$, and $2p_z$ orbitals. The homonuclear diatomic molecules, type A_2, have eight atomic orbitals. Allowing the z axis to be the internuclear axis, we can get the following σ orbitals:

$$\Psi(\sigma_s) = A[(2s)_a + (2s)_b] \tag{3.33}$$

$$\Psi(\sigma_s^*) = A^*[(2s)_a - (2s)_b] \tag{3.34}$$

$$\Psi(\sigma_z) = A[(2p_z)_a + (2p_z)_b] \tag{3.35}$$

$$\Psi(\sigma_z^*) = A[(2p_z)_a - (2p_z)_b] \tag{3.36}$$

These orbitals, shown schematically in Fig. 3.7, involve the same kind of overlapping as in the hydrogen molecule. If the σ_s orbitals are rotated 180° about the internuclear axis (i.e., the z axis), they remain unchanged. The $2p_y$ and $2p_x$ orbitals can also overlap, but they are different from σ orbitals. Remember that the atomic orbitals have an angular dependence (see Table 3.1) and $2p_x$ and $2p_y$ are not symmetric with respect to the z axis. Thus, the molecular orbitals that form by the overlapping of $2p_x$ or $2p_y$ will change sign when they are rotated 180° about the z axis. Molecular orbitals of this type are called π *orbitals:*

$$\Psi(\pi_x) = A[(2p_x)_a + (2p_x)_b] \tag{3.37}$$

$$\Psi(\pi_x^*) = A^*[(2p_x)_a - (2p_x)_b] \tag{3.38}$$

$$\Psi(\pi_y) = A[(2p_y)_a + (2p_y)_b] \tag{3.39}$$

$$\Psi(\pi_y^*) = A^*[(2p_y)_a - (2p_y)_b] \tag{3.40}$$

The π_x and π_x^* orbitals are shown in Fig. 3.7. Notice that a 180° rotation about the internuclear axis changes the sign of the orbital at every point in space.

It is important to recognize that we have been completely arbitrary in picking the linear combinations for forming the molecular orbitals. It is conceivable, for example, that one could form a σ_s orbital from a linear combination of $2s$ and $2p_z$ states:

$$\Psi(\sigma'_s) = a_1(2s)_a + a_2(2s)_b + a_3(2p_z)_a + a_4(2p_z)_b \qquad (3.41)$$

This "hybridization" is indeed an important feature of molecular theory. In a complete story, all of these possibilities must be considered and the proper choice made on the basis of what combination gives the most stable molecular states and also on the basis of experimental data.

The important thing to recognize is that when diatomic molecules are formed from atoms with s and p atomic orbitals, the σ and π molecular orbitals are developed. Experimental data on homonuclear diatomic molecules show that the relative stability of the molecular states are in the following order: σ_s, σ_s^*, $\pi_x = \pi_y$, σ_z, $\pi_x^* = \pi_y^*$, σ_z^*. This is shown schematically in the energy-level diagram of Fig. 3.8.

Now let us examine the bonding characteristics of some familiar substances. Neon has the atomic configuration $[\text{He}]2s^2 2p^6$. The hypothetical diatomic molecule Ne_2 has the bonding configuration $\sigma_s^2 \sigma_s^{*2} \pi_x^2 \pi_y^2 \sigma_z^2 \pi_x^{*2} \pi_y^{*2} \sigma_z^{*2}$. Thus, there are eight electrons in bonding orbitals, eight in antibonding orbitals for a net of zero covalent bonds. Neon gas is monoatomic. Fluorine has the atomic configuration $[\text{He}]2s^2 2p^5$. The bonding configuration of F_2 is $\sigma_s^2 \sigma_s^{*2} \pi_x^2 \pi_y^2 \pi_x^{*2} \pi_y^{*2} \sigma_z^2$, giving a net of one σ-type covalent bond. Experimentally, fluorine forms a diatomic molecule with a bond energy of 36 kcal/g mole

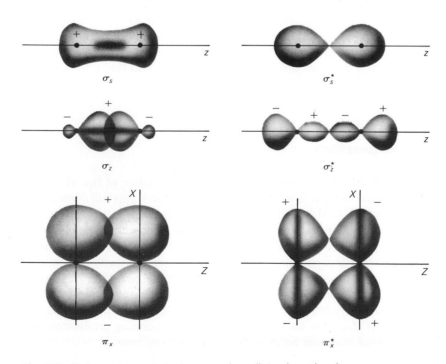

Fig. 3.7 Molecular orbitals for homonuclear diatomic molecules.

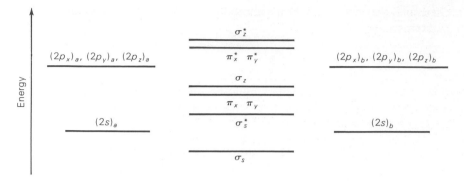

Fig. 3.8 The relative energies of the molecular orbitals determine the order in which the orbitals are filled by the electrons.

(151×10^6 joules/kg mole) and an internuclear distance of 1.42 Å. The smaller dissociation energy and the greater separation compared with the hydrogen molecule are due to the presence of the filled K shells surrounding the nuclei.

The bonding configuration of O_2 is $\sigma_s^2\sigma_s^{*2}\pi_x^2\pi_y^2\sigma_z^2\pi_x^*\pi_y^*$, for a net of two covalent bonds, one σ type and one π type. This combination is called a *double bond*. Experimentally the bond energy is 118 kcal/g mole (494×10^6 joules/kg mole) and the internuclear separation is 1.21 Å.

The bonding configuration of N_2 is $\sigma_s^2\sigma_s^{*2}\pi_x^2\pi_y^2\sigma_z^2$, for a net of three covalent bonds, one σ type and two π type. This combination is called a *triple bond*. Experimentally, the bond energy is 225 kcal/g mole (943×10^6 joules/kg mole) and the internuclear separation is 1.10 Å. In general, the addition of bonds increases the dissociation energy (bond energy) and tends to pull the nuclei closer together.

3.4
Polarity and electronegativity

When a molecular orbital is formed from a linear combination of two identical atomic orbitals, it is reasonable to expect that the atomic states will contribute equally to the molecular state. In other words, an electron will be "shared" equally between two identical nuclei. Under these conditions, the electron distribution is symmetric about the center of gravity of the molecule, the center of gravity of negative charge coincides with the center of gravity of positive charge, and there is no permanent dipole moment. When two different atoms bond to form a heteronuclear molecule, type AB, the molecular orbitals are developed by the overlapping of atomic orbitals with different degrees of stability. Consider the case shown in Fig. 3.9. A σ_s bonding orbital can be formed by the linear combination of an $(ns)_A$ and an $(ns)_B$ orbital:

$$\Psi(\sigma_s) = a_1(ns)_A + a_2(ns)_B \tag{3.42}$$

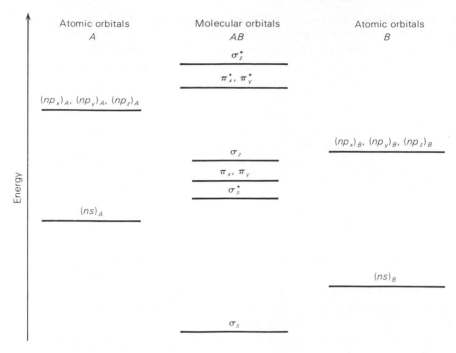

Fig. 3.9 Energy levels for heteronuclear (AB) molecular orbitals.

Since the $(ns)_B$ state is more stable than the $(ns)_A$, an electron in a σ_s state will be more like an $(ns)_B$ electron. In terms of the wave function, $(ns)_B$ would contribute more to the molecular orbital than $(ns)_A$ (that is, $a_2 > a_1$). Conversely, the antibonding orbital σ_s^* would show more $(ns)_A$ character:

$$\Psi(\sigma_s^*) = a_3(ns)_A - a_4(ns)_B \qquad a_3 > a_4 \qquad (3.43)$$

The electron distributions are shown in Fig. 3.10. The electron density is greater near the B nucleus in the σ_s bonding orbital, but it is greater near the A nucleus in the σ_s^* antibonding orbital. Atom B is said to be more "electronegative" than atom A because it has a greater tendency to attract electrons in bonding orbitals.

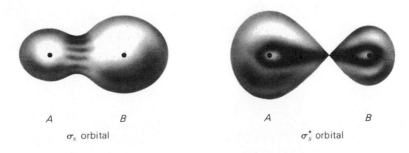

Fig. 3.10 Molecular orbitals for heteronuclear (AB) molecules.

Since the center of gravity of the electronic charge does not coincide with the center of gravity of the positive charge, an electric dipole moment is present. In order to calculate a value for the dipole moment, $\mu = el$, one must be able to solve the wave equation. There have been techniques developed that enable one to approximate values for the constants a_1 and a_2 in Eq. (3.42); these are beyond the scope of this text. In general, the greater the difference in electronegativity of A and B, the larger is the ratio a_2/a_1.

The electron configuration in heteronuclear molecules is determined by placing the valence electrons into the molecular orbitals. When the two nuclear charges are about the same and the bonding atomic states have similar stability, the approach is about the same as for the homonuclear molecules. Carbon monoxide, CO, for example, uses the two $2s$ orbitals and two $2p$ orbitals of carbon and the two $2s$ orbitals and four $2p$ orbitals of oxygen, to give a ground state of $\sigma_s^2 \sigma_s^{*2} \pi_x^2 \pi_y^2 \sigma_z^2$. This gives a net of one σ-type and two π-type bonds. This is basically the same configuration as in nitrogen, N_2, except for the electronegativity difference creating a dipole of 0.12 debye. The bond energy for CO is 255.8 kcal/g mole (1070×10^6 joules/kg mole) compared to 225 kcal/g mole (943×10^6 joules/kg mole) for N_2. The polarity thus has a tendency to further stabilize the bond.

Molecular-orbital concepts can also be used to describe the bonding between atoms of considerably different nuclear charge, such as bonding in the diatomic hydrides (for example, LiH or HCl). In these cases, however, the concept of bonding and antibonding orbitals is not as clear-cut. In HCl, for example, the available atomic orbitals are the $1s$ orbitals of hydrogen and the $3s$ and $3p$ orbitals of chlorine. The $3p_x$ and $3p_y$ states of chlorine, however, cannot interact with the lone ($1s$) state of hydrogen to give a molecular orbital. One way of looking at this is that the overlapping of $1s$ with the positive lobe of $3p_x$ is canceled by the overlapping with the negative lobe (Fig. 3.11). The π_x

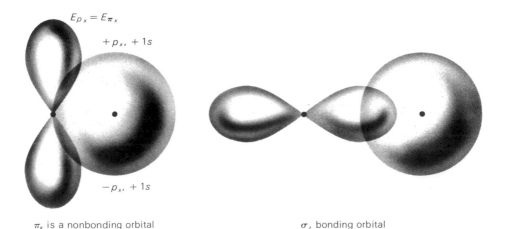

$$E_{p\,x} = E_{\pi\,x}$$

$+p_x, +1s$

$-p_x, +1s$

π_x is a nonbonding orbital σ_z bonding orbital

Fig. 3.11 Certain combinations of atomic orbitals lead to nonbonding molecular orbitals, while other combinations lead to stable bonding orbitals.

and π_y states are therefore called "nonbonding" orbitals; naturally, they have the same energy as the p states. Since there are big differences in energy between the H($1s$), Cl($3s$), and Cl($3p$) states, the formation of the σ orbitals is not easy to characterize. The idea of a bonding orbital that is more stable than a corresponding atomic orbital and an antibonding orbital that is less stable is no longer as clear cut. The ground state of HCl is $\sigma_s^2\sigma_z^2\pi_x^2\pi_y^2$, but we shall not try to distinguish between bonding and antibonding electrons. The net result, however, is known to be a single covalent bond. The same results are obtained with HF, HBr, and HI.

One of the goals of materials science is to predict bond strengths from information on the individual atoms. The difficulty in handling the mathematics has limited the ability to accomplish this. Pauling [6], however, has developed an empirical technique, based on thermodynamic data, for evaluating *single-bond* energies.

A *single covalent bond* joining two atoms A and B is "normal" if the bond energy is the geometric mean of the energies of the single homonuclear bonds:

$$(\psi_{A-B})_{normal} = \sqrt{\psi_{A-A}\psi_{B-B}} \tag{3.44}$$

When the two atoms have different electronegativities, the actual bond strength is greater than this. The "excess bond energy" per covalent bond, Δ, is characterized by assigning an electronegativity L to each of the elements:

$$\Delta_{A-B} = 30(L_A - L_B)^2 \frac{\text{kcal}}{\text{g mole}} = 126 \times 10^6(L_A - L_B) \frac{\text{joules}}{\text{kg mole}} \tag{3.45}$$

The energy per mole of single covalent bonds is then

$$\psi_{A-B} = \sqrt{\psi_{A-A}\psi_{B-B}} + \Delta_{AB} \tag{3.46}$$

Table 3.5 gives the energies for a variety of single bonds, and Table 3.6 gives the atomic electronegativities. Since only the electronegativity difference is important, one arbitrarily assigns a value to one element and then defines the others relative to that. Table 3.7 lists some values of electric dipole moments, total bond strengths, and excess bond strengths for a few simple halogen compounds. One cannot expect perfect agreement between experiment and the empirical equations, since a single constant is really not sufficient to define the electronegativity of an element. Actually, each atomic orbital has a different stability and the net electronegativity depends upon how each orbital is participating in the bond. This can certainly vary from one situation to the next. Pauling has shown that there is about a ±0.1 unit average deviation in $L_A - L_B$ when comparing experimental data on 42 heteronuclear bonds.

The total bond energy of a given molecule is then just the sum of its single bond strengths. To a first, rough approximation, a double bond has the same strength as two single bonds between the same two atoms and a triple bond is the same as three single bonds. This is *not* a satisfactory assumption for multiple bonds which involve either nitrogen or oxygen; in both cases the multiple bonds are considerably more stable than the equivalent single bonds.

Table 3.5

Energies of single bonds, * **kcal/g mole** †

Bond	Bond energy	Bond	Bond energy
As—As	32.1	N—N	38.4
As—H	58.6	N—H	93.4
As—F	111.3	N—F	64.5
As—Cl	68.9	N—Cl	47.7
As—Br	56.5	O—O	33.2
As—I	41.6	O—H	110.6
Bi—Bi	25.	O—F	44.2
Br—Br	46.1	O—Cl	48.5
Br—Cl	52.3	P—P	51.3
C—C	83.1	P—H	76.4
C—H	98.8	P—Cl	79.1
C—Si	72.0	P—Br	65.4
C—N	69.7	P—I	51.4
C—O	84.0	Rb—Rb	12.4
C—S	62.0	S—S	50.9
C—F	105.4	S—H	81.1
C—Cl	81.0	S—Cl	59.7
C—Br	68.0	S—Br	50.7
C—I	51.0	Sb—Sb	30.2
Cl—Cl	58.0	Se—Se	44.0
Cs—Cs	10.7	Se—H	66.1
F—F	36.6	Si—Si	42.2
F—Cl	60.6	Si—H	70.4
Ge—Ge	37.6	Si—S	54.2
H—H	104.2	Si—F	129.3
H—F	134.6	Si—Cl	85.7
H—Cl	103.2	Si—Br	69.1
H—Br	87.5	Si—I	50.9
H—I	71.4	Si—O	88.2
I—I	36.1	Sn—Sn	34.2
I—Cl	50.3	Te—Te	33.
I—Br	42.5	Te—H	57.5
K—K	13.2		
Li—Li	26.5		
Na—Na	18.0		

* From Ref. 6, p. 85.

† Multiply by 4.186×10^6 to get joules/kg mole.

Table 3.6

The complete electronegativity scale [*a]

Li	Be	B					H								C	N	O	F
1.0	1.5	2.0					2.1								2.5	3.0	3.5	4.0
Na	Mg	Al													Si	P	S	Cl
0.9	1.2	1.5													1.8	2.1	2.5	3.0

K	Ca	Sc	Ti	V	Cr	Mn	Fe	Co	Ni	Cu	Zn	Ga	Ge	As	Se	Br
0.8	1.0	1.3	1.5	1.6	1.6	1.5	1.8	1.8	1.8	1.9	1.6	1.6	1.8	2.0	2.4	2.8

Rb	Sr	Y	Zr	Nb	Mo	Te	Ru	Rh	Pd	Ag	Cd	In	Sn	Sb	Te	I
0.8	1.0	1.2	1.4	1.6	1.8	1.9	2.2	2.2	2.2	1.9	1.7	1.7	1.8	1.9	2.1	2.5

Cs	Ba	La-Lu	Hf	Ta	W	Re	Os	Ir	Pt	Au	Hg	Tl	Pb	Bi	Po	At
0.7	0.9	1.1–1.2	1.3	1.5	1.7	1.9	2.2	2.2	2.2	2.4	1.9	1.8	1.8	1.9	2.0	2.2

Fr	Ra	Ac	Th	Pa	U	Np-No
0.7	0.9	1.1	1.3	1.5	1.7	1.3

* By permission from L. Pauling, "The Nature of the Chemical Bond," p. 93, 3d ed., Cornell University Press, Ithaca, New York, 1960.

[a] The values given in the table refer to the common oxidation states of the elements. For some elements variation of the electronegativity with oxidation number is observed; for example, Fe^{II} 1.8, Fe^{III} 1.9; Cu^I 1.9, Cu^{II} 2.0; Sn^{II} 1.8, Sn^{IV} 1.9. For other elements see W. Gordy and W. J. O. Thomas, *J. Chem. Phys.*, **24:** 439 (1956).

Table 3.7

Properties of halogen compounds

A—B	μ, debyes	ψ_{AB}, kcal/g mole,* exptl.	Δ_{AB}, kcal/g mole,* exptl., Eq. (3.46)	Δ_{AB}, kcal/g mole,* Eq. (3.45)
H—F	1.98	134.6	72.8	95.0
H—Cl	1.03	103.2	25.4	27.7
H—Br	0.79	87.5	18.3	17.3
H—I	0.38	71.4	10.0	6.4
H—H	0.00	104.2	0.0	0.0

* Multiply by 4.186×10^6 to get joules/kg mole.

3.5
Van der Waals bonding between simple molecules

The nature of the intermolecular forces can be predicted from the electronic distributions. Neon, for example, is a neutral, monoatomic substance whose electron distribution is spherically symmetric; there are no net charges, dipoles, or higher moments. The intermolecular potential consists of a dispersive and a repulsive potential [cf. Eqs. (1.22) to (1.24)]:

$$\psi_{Ne-Ne} = -\frac{181\alpha_{Ne}^{3/2}n_{Ne}^{1/2}}{r^6} + \frac{b}{r^m}\frac{kcal}{g\ mole} \tag{3.47}$$

where α is the polarizability of a neon atom in Å^3, n_{Ne} is the number of valence (outer shell) electrons (eight), m and b are empirical constants, and r is the distance between neon atoms in Å. As you will recall, the polarizability is a measure of the ability of an electric field to induce a dipole in the atom. This, in turn, should be a function of the number of valence electrons, how tightly bound to the nucleus they are, and how far they are from the nucleus. This is precisely the kind of information we have obtained in this chapter. It has been shown [1] that the polarizability of simple molecules is approximately:

$$\ln \alpha = \frac{13 \ln \sigma - 14.8}{\ln n} - 0.16 \tag{3.48}$$

where n is the number of valence electrons, σ is the parameter in the Lennard-Jones 12-6 potential (Table 2.1) in Å, which is proportional to the radius of the electron distribution, and α is in units of Å^3. This gives a value of $\alpha = 0.40\ \text{Å}^3$ for neon, compared to an experimental value of $0.398\ \text{Å}^3$. The intermolecular potential reduces to

$$\psi_{Ne-Ne} = -\frac{120}{r^6} + \frac{b}{r^m} \tag{3.49}$$

The repulsion term cannot be easily predicted, but using the constants from Table 2.1 based on second virial coefficient data:

$$\psi_{Ne-Ne} = -\frac{128}{r^6} + \frac{59,100}{r^{12}}\frac{kcal}{g\ mole} \tag{3.50}$$

The agreement between the calculated and experimental dispersion energy is as good as can be expected. The maximum bond energy is obtained from Eq. (3.50) and is 0.0693 kcal/g mole (0.298×10^6 joules/kg mole) at a separation of 3.13 Å. This is many orders of magnitude weaker than the covalent bonds between atoms of diatomic molecules. This kind of a chemical bond is called a *Van der Waals bond,* and it represents the interaction between particles that have no orbitals available for further bonding. The normal translational (kinetic) energy for neon atoms at room temperature is about $3/2RT \doteq 0.9$ kcal/g mole (3.77×10^6 joules/kg mole), which is an order of magnitude greater than the strength of the Van der Waals bonds. This explains why neon remains in a dispersed (gaseous) state at room temperature.

The oxygen molecule is diatomic with an electron distribution that is symmetric about the internuclear axis. Since the two nuclei are identical, there will be no dipole moment for the molecule. The absence of spherical symmetry indicates an anisotropic polarizability, and the theoretical potential-energy function reduces to

$$\psi_{O_2-O_2} = -\frac{181\alpha_{O_2}^{3/2}n_{O_2}^{1/2}}{r^6} + \frac{b}{r^m} \quad \frac{\text{kcal}}{\text{g mole}} \tag{3.51}$$

Since the molecule is spheroidal and the polarizability is anisotropic, the coefficient on the dispersion term is somewhat angle-dependent. The usual approach is to take an average polarizability and utilize a simple Lennard-Jones b-6 type of function. Since $n_{O_2} = 12$ and $\sigma_{O_2} \doteq 3.46$ Å, the average polarizability is calculated to be approximately 1.5 Å³ and the potential energy is

$$\psi_{O_2-O_2} = -\frac{1,150}{r^6} + \frac{b}{r^m} \tag{3.52}$$

The experimental data of Table 2.1 give

$$\psi_{O_2-O_2} = -\frac{1,590}{r^6} + \frac{2.7 \times 10^6}{r^{12}} \quad \frac{\text{kcal}}{\text{g mole}} \tag{3.53}$$

The experimental data show a larger dispersion energy than is obtained theoretically. Since the theoretical equation for the dispersion energy [Eq. (1.23)] is only an approximation for spherical nonpolar atoms, and since the repulsion term is not exact, the deviations should not be surprising. (Note the better agreement for neon.) The maximum Van der Waals bond strength between oxygen molecules is about 0.23 kcal/g mole (0.963×10^6 joules/kg mole) at an intermolecular separation of 3.89 Å. This compares with 118 kcal/g mole (494×10^6 joules/kg mole) at an internuclear separation of 1.21 Å for the covalent bonds between oxygen atoms.

These examples illustrate the differences between covalent bonds and Van der Waals bonds. A covalent bond involves the overlapping of atomic orbitals, is relatively short-range (1 to 2 Å in length), and is relatively strong (50 to 200 kcal/g mole or 200×10^6–800×10^6 joules/kg mole). A Van der Waals bond does not involve the overlapping of atomic orbitals, is a long-range bond (greater than 3 to 4 Å in length), and is relatively weak (0.01 to 10 kcal/g mole or 0.04×10^6–40×10^6 joules/kg mole). It will be important to remember these differences when we discuss the properties of solid materials.

The Van der Waals bonding energy between polar molecules is approximately

$$\psi_{AB-AB} = \frac{b}{r^{12}} - \frac{C_{AB-AB}}{r^6} - \frac{N\mu_{AB}^2}{r^3} g(\theta,\phi) - \frac{\mu_{AB}^2\alpha_{AB}h(\theta)}{2r^6} \tag{3.54}$$

where

$$g(\theta,\phi) = 2 \cos \theta_{AB1} \cos \theta_{AB2} - \sin \theta_{AB1} \sin \theta_{AB2} (\cos \phi_{AB1} - \phi_{AB2}) \qquad \text{cf. Eq. (1.10)}$$

$$\text{(3.55)}$$

and

$$h(\theta) = 3 \cos^2 \theta_{AB1} + 3 \cos^2 \theta_{AB2} + 2 \qquad \text{cf. Eq. (1.17)} \qquad \text{(3.56)}$$

The first term on the right side of Eq. (3.54) is a repulsion, the second is a dispersion attraction, the third is an electrostatic dipole-dipole interaction, and the fourth is a dipole-dipole induction effect. Averaging over all possible orientations of the two dipoles (see Question 1.5), gives

$$\langle \psi_{AB-AB} \rangle = \frac{b}{r^{12}} - \frac{C_{AB-AB} + 2N\mu_{AB}^2/3kT + 2N\mu_{AB}^2\alpha_{AB}}{r^6} \qquad \text{(3.57)}$$

Thus, a 12-6-type potential-energy function may be used to describe the gas-phase behavior of polar molecules. The coefficient on the attraction term, however, is temperature-dependent. The various contributions to the attraction may be estimated by using the data of Tables 1.1 and 1.2 and also Eq. (1.23). The values for HCl at 300°K, for example, are $C_{AB-AB} = 4,300$ ($n_{AB} = 8$), $2N\mu_{AB}^2/3kT = 260$ and $2N\mu_{AB}^2\alpha_{AB} = 80$ kcal-Å^6/g mole. This means that dispersion accounts for about 92.7 percent of the intermolecular attraction, dipole-dipole attraction about 5.5 percent, and induction effects about 1.8 percent. These are typical numbers; induction effects are always relatively small and dispersion usually dominates unless the dipole moments are very large. The experimental 12-6 potential for HCl is given in Table 2.1 as

$$\psi_{HCl-HCl} = \frac{4.81 \times 10^6}{r^{12}} - \frac{3,710}{r^6} \frac{\text{kcal}}{\text{g mole}} \qquad \text{(3.58)}$$

The experimentally determined attraction thus differs from the calculated one by about 25 percent at room temperature. Again, the use of Eq. (1.23) for calculating the dispersion energy is only a rough approximation for an anisotropic, polar molecule.

3.6
Ionic bonding

When a very electronegative element interacts with a very electropositive one, there is a tendency for an electron transfer to the electronegative element. Thus, in the molecule NaF, sodium tends to lose its $3s$ electron and form a positive ion and fluorine tends to attract the electron and form a negative ion. This is obviously the limiting case of polar bonding. The greater the difference in electronegativity, the more chance there is of forming two ions. A cesium fluoride molecule, CsF, is almost purely ionic in character, while LiI is partially ionic. The bond energies for the alkali halide gases can be calculated by visualizing them as being purely *ionic* bonds.

Consider the sodium fluoride molecule, NaF. Sodium loses a $3s$ electron and becomes a positive ion with a net charge of $+e$. The electron configuration is identical with that of a neon atom (that is, K and L shells are filled). The fluorine atom attracts the electron and becomes a negative ion with a net charge of $-e$. The electron configuration is also identical with that of a neon atom. These stable ions will then electrostatically attract one another to form a high-energy, *ionic bond*. The potential energy of interaction is

$$\psi_{AB} = \frac{a}{r^b} - \frac{c}{r^6} - \frac{e^2}{r} - \cdots \qquad (3.59)$$

The first term on the right-hand side of Eq. (3.59) is a repulsion term, the second is a dispersive attraction, and the third is an electrostatic attraction. The induction terms associated with the distortion of the ion charge distributions are usually negligible. Since both electron distributions are identical with the distribution of neon, one can assume that the constants a, b, and c are roughly the same as for a Ne—Ne interaction. The constant e^2 is equal to 333 kcal-Å g mole. Equation (3.59) is then

$$\psi_{NaF} = \frac{59{,}100}{r^{12}} - \frac{128}{r^6} - \frac{333}{\cdot \ r} \quad \frac{kcal}{g \ mole \ NaF} \qquad (3.60)$$

This gives a maximum bond energy of 154 kcal/g mole (650×10^6 joules/kg mole) at 1.98 Å compared to a maximum of 0.0693 kcal/g mole at 3.13 Å for neon-neon interaction. The ionic bond, like the covalent bond, is orders of magnitude stronger than a Van der Waals bond. Remember this when we compare the properties of ionic and molecular crystals.

The maximum bond energy is equal to the energy required to separate a sodium ion from a fluoride ion. The experimental dissociation energy of the molecule is usually the energy required to form sodium and fluorine *atoms* from

---

Table 3.8

Bond characteristics of alkali halides *

Molecule	Dissoc. energy, kcal/g mole †	Bond length, Å	Molecule	Dissoc. energy, kcal/g mole †	Bond length, Å
CsF	121	2.35	NaF	107	1.85
CsCl	101	2.91	NaCl	98	2.36
KCl	101	2.67	NaBr	88	2.50
KBr	91	2.82	RbCl	102	2.79
KI	77	3.05	RbBr	90	2.95
LiBr	101	2.17			
LiI	81	2.39			

---

* T. L. Cottrell, "The Strengths of Chemical Bonds," Butterworth & Co. (Publishers), Ltd., London, 1958.

---

† Multiply by 4 186 × 10⁶ to get joules/kg mole.

NaF.   The difference between the bond energy and the dissociation energy is thus the energy required to transfer an electron from the fluoride ion to the sodium ion.   This can be obtained by subtracting the ionization potential of sodium from the electron affinity of fluorine.   From Table 3.3, the difference is $3.45 - 5.138 = -1.688$ ev $= 39$ kcal/g mole (163×10^6 joules/kg mole), so that the calculated dissociation energy of NaF is 115 kcal/g mole (482×10^6 joules/kg mole).   The experimental value is 107 kcal/g mole (449×10^6 joules/kg mole). One cannot expect perfect agreement, since the Lennard-Jones 12-6 potential is only an approximation for the alkali halide gases.   Some experimental dissociation energies for other alkali halides are given in Table 3.8.

References

1 Brandt, W.: Calculation of Intermolecular Force Constants from Polarizabilities, *J. Chem. Phys.*, **24:** 501–506 (1956).

2 Coulson, C. A.: "Valence," 2d ed., Oxford University Press, London, 1961. *A detailed, but nonmathematical, treatment of molecular-orbital and valence-bond theory. For advanced study.*

3 Gray, H. B.: "Electrons and Chemical Bonding," W. A. Benjamin, Inc., New York, 1964. *An elementary treatment of molecular-orbital concepts in chemical bonding. Very highly recommended for the beginner.*

4 Heitler, W.: "Elementary Wave Mechanics," Oxford University Press, London, 1956.

5 Linnett, J. W.: "Wave Mechanics and Valency," John Wiley & Sons, Inc., New York, 1960. *Excellent discussions on the behavior of diatomic molecules.*

6 Pauling, L.: "The Nature of the Chemical Bond," Cornell University Press, Ithaca, N.Y., 1960. *The major reference on valence-bond theory. A necessity for all advanced students.*

7 Pauling, L., and E. B. Wilson, Jr.: "Introduction to Quantum Mechanics," McGraw-Hill Book Company, New York, 1935. *An advanced text on quantum-mechanical methods. Very readable and highly recommended for further study.*

8 Rice, F. O., and E. Teller: "The Structure of Matter," John Wiley & Sons, Inc., New York, 1949. *An introductory text on the behavior of atoms and molecules.*

9 Richtmyer, F. K., E. H. Kennard, and T. Lauritsen: "Introduction to Modern Physics," McGraw-Hill Book Company, New York, 1955. *An introductory treatment of the behavior of particles.*

Questions

3.1   The mass of an electron is 9.1091×10^{-31} kg and its charge is 1.601864×10^{-19} coul. Compare the electrostatic and gravitational forces on an electron that is 0.529 Å from a proton.

3.2   What is the minimum uncertainty in determining the velocity of an electron if the uncertainty in simultaneously determining its position is one angstrom unit? What is the uncertainty in simultaneous measurement of the position of a 0.14-kg (5-oz) baseball traveling at 130 km/hr if the uncertainty in its velocity is 0.03 m/sec?

3.3 Write down the time-independent form of the Schrödinger equation and explain the significance of each term. Show how to write the wave equation for a hydrogen molecule.

3.4 Derive the wave equation for a hydrogen atom [Eq. (3.17)]. Use the solution, given by Eq. (3.20), to obtain an expression for the allowable energy states. Show that the ground state of the atom has a maximum electron density at 0.529 Å. (See Pauling and Wilson, Ref. 7, chap. 5, for the solution.)

3.5 The associated Legendre polynomials are defined by

$$P_l{}^m (\cos \theta) = \frac{1}{2^l l!} \sin^m \theta \, \frac{d^{m+l}}{d (\cos \theta)^{m+l}} (\cos^2 \theta - 1)^l$$

The associated Laguerre polynomials are defined by

$$L_n{}^m(z) = (-1)^m \frac{n!}{(n-m)!} e^z z^{-m} \frac{d^{n-m}}{dz^{n-m}} e^{-z} z^n$$

Write out the wave functions for the $1s$, $2s$, $2p_x$, $2p_y$, and $2p_z$ states of the hydrogen atom. Plot the electron density in each state as a function of the distance from the proton for $\phi = 0$, $\theta = 0$, for $\phi = 0$, $\theta = \pi/4$, and also for $\phi = \pi/4$, $\theta = \pi/4$. (Remember that the density is proportional to the wave function times its complex conjugate.)

3.6 What is the Pauli exclusion principle and why must it be enunciated?

3.7 Give a physical interpretation of the Coulomb integrals $\Re$ and the exchange integrals Ω that show up in molecular-orbital theory.

3.8 Determine the bonding characteristics of Li_2, Be_2, B_2, C_2, N_2, O_2, F_2, Ne_2, Na_2, Cl_2, and I_2 in terms of molecular orbitals.

3.9 Determine the bonding characteristics of CO, NO, and the ion CN^- in terms of molecular orbitals.

3.10 Estimate the dispersion attraction between methane molecules, using Eq. (3.48) to approximate the polarizability. Compare the result with that obtained from the Lennard-Jones 12-6 potential (Table 2.1).

3.11 Use the 12-6 potential (Table 2.1) to find the maximum potential energy of interaction between N_2 molecules. Also calculate the kinetic energy at room temperature and explain why N_2 is a gas at room temperature.

3.12 The dissociation energies of hydrogen (H_2) and bromine (Br_2) are 104.2 kcal/g mole and 46.1 kcal/g mole, respectively. Calculate the dissociation energy of hydrogen bromide (HBr).

3.13 Show that Eq. (3.57) describes the behavior of freely rotating polar molecules.

3.14 Estimate the magnitude of dispersive, electrostatic, and inductive attractions between H_2O molecules in the gas phase. Whenever you do not have sufficient data, use the best approximation that you can.

3.15 Calculate the dissociation energies of $CsCl$, KCl, and $NaCl$ by using the data in Tables 2.1 and 3.3. Compare your answers with the experimental values in Table 3.8.

4
Complex molecules

4.1
Introduction

In the preceding chapter, we examined the properties of monoatomic and diatomic molecules. This will serve as the basis for studying the properties of metallic, ionic, and simple molecular crystals. There are also many organic and inorganic solids that are aggregates of much more complex molecules. A crystal of polymethylene, for example, is a condensed aggregate of linear hydrocarbon molecules, each with a structural formula $R(-CH_2-)_xR$, where the *degree of polymerization, x,* may be any number up to about 10^6 and the R's are the "end groups" which could be catalyst residues or other organic groups. In this chapter, we shall discuss chemical bonding and intermolecular forces in organic and silicate molecules.

4.2
Building blocks for complex molecules

All complex molecules are built up from simple structural units. The saturated hydrocarbons, for example, consist of repeating units of carbon. Each carbon atom is bonded to four other atoms with the internuclear axes directed toward the corners of a tetrahedron. The simplest example is that of methane, CH_4. This structure is shown in Fig. 4.1. With the carbon atom at the center of the cube, the hydrogen atoms are positioned at the opposite corners, defining a regular tetrahedron.

Chemical bonding occurs between the $1s$ orbitals of the hydrogen atoms and the $2s$, $2p_x$, $2p_y$, and $2p_z$ orbitals of the carbon atom. Four identical σ bonds are formed with bond energies of 99.3 kcal/g mole (416×10^6 joules/kg mole) and a C—H bond length of 1.093 Å. The H—C—H bond angles are 109°28′. Following the molecular-orbital treatment given in Chap. 3, we may express the molecular states as linear combinations of atomic orbitals. Referring to Fig. 4.1, we see that the hydrogen atoms overlap with all of the available 2s and 2p orbitals. (Remember that the choice of axes is arbitrary and that we can just as logically choose one of the major axes as directed along a C—H bond. This would merely require a slightly different set of wave functions than those given below.) A possible set of bonding molecular orbitals is

$$\Psi_s = a_1(2s) + a_2(1s_A + 1s_B + 1s_C + 1s_D) \tag{4.1}$$

$$\Psi_z = a_3(2p_z) + a_4(1s_A + 1s_B - 1s_C - 1s_D) \tag{4.2}$$

$$\Psi_x = a_5(2p_x) + a_6(1s_A - 1s_B + 1s_C - 1s_D) \tag{4.3}$$

$$\Psi_y = a_7(2p_y) + a_8(1s_A - 1s_B - 1s_C + 1s_D) \tag{4.4}$$

The minus signs are needed to account for the positive 1s wave functions overlapping with the negative lobes of the 2p functions. The ground state for

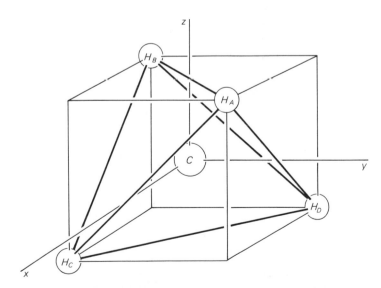

Fig. 4.1 The methane molecule is composed of four hydrogen-atom nuclei positioned at the four corners of a tetrahedron with the carbon nucleus in the center.

CH_4 is thus $\sigma_s^2\sigma_z^2\sigma_y^2\sigma_x^2$. This gives a total of four σ-type, single covalent bonds, as expected. The σ_x, σ_y, and σ_z orbitals are identical, since the hydrogen atoms overlap equally with all $2p$ orbitals, but the σ_s state is considerably different than the others. Experimentally, however, it is evident that all four bonds are identical. More suitable orbitals can be developed by "hybridizing" the wave functions. For methane, we can easily write down a more adequate set by considering combinations of Eqs. (4.1) to (4.4). For simplicity, let $a_1 = a_3 = a_5 = a_7$ and also let $a_2 = a_4 = a_6 = a_8$. Then add Eq. (4.1) to (4.4) to get

$$\Psi(sp^3)_A = a_1(2s + 2p_z + 2p_x + 2p_y) + 4a_2(1s)_A \tag{4.5}$$

The other linear combinations are

$$\Psi(sp^3)_B = a_1(2s + 2p_z - 2p_x - 2p_y) + 4a_2(1s)_B \tag{4.6}$$

$$\Psi(sp^3)_C = a_1(2s - 2p_z + 2p_x - 2p_y) + 4a_2(1s)_C \tag{4.7}$$

$$\Psi(sp^3)_D = a_1(2s - 2p_z - 2p_x + 2p_y) + 4a_2(1s)_D \tag{4.8}$$

The latter four orbitals are identical, except for orientation in space, and each overlaps with only one hydrogen atom. These functions are called the sp^3 hybrid orbitals. The tetrahedral carbon bonding unit is thus a carbon nucleus surrounded by four sp^3 hybrid bonds directed toward the corners of a tetrahedron. This is the basic building block for many organic compounds.

Carbon atoms are also capable of forming other kinds of bonding units. In terms of molecular orbitals, it means different linear combinations of the $2s$ and $2p$ states. Some of these bonding forms are shown in Fig. 4.2. The "carbonyl" bonding unit has two single bonds and one double bond. The angles between the double bond and the others are about 121 to 124°, and the angle between the single bonds is 118 to 112°. (The experimental values vary from one compound to the next.) This may be approximately described by forming three sp^2 hybrid orbitals with a $2s$ and two $2p$ orbitals, leaving a third $2p$ orbital available for π bonding. This model gives two σ-type single bonds at 120° apart and a coplanar σ-π-type double bond. The *allene* bonding unit has two double bonds at 180° to each other with each double bond containing an sp hybrid orbital and a π orbital. The *acetylene* bonding unit is a triple bond and a single bond at 180° to each other. The single bond is a σ-type sp hybrid, and the triple bond contains an sp hybrid and two mutually perpendicular π orbitals.

Besides the single-, double-, and triple-bond characteristics of carbon, there is also the possibility of forming "partial" double bonds. In the *graphite* form of carbon, for example, three partial double bonds are formed by hybridizing a $2s$ and two $2p$ orbitals into three identical sp^2 hybrids, with the third $2p$ orbital sharing itself equally with the other three. This gives three coplanar bonds at 120° to one another and each with about $1\frac{1}{3}$ covalent character.

We shall next see how various complex molecules are formed from these basic building blocks.

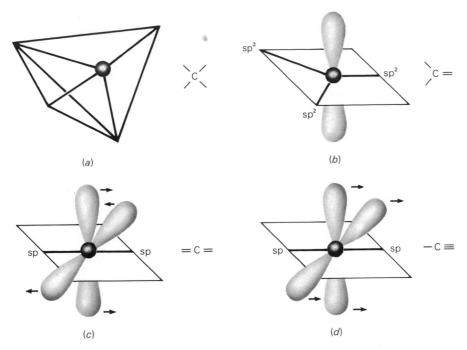

Fig. 4.2 The atomic orbitals of carbon can be combined in a number of different ways to give a variety of hybrid bonding orbitals. (a) Tetrahedral carbon atom; (b) carbonyl atom; (c) allene atom: (d) acetylene atom.

4.3
Linear molecules

Organic molecules are formed when carbon atoms bond to other units. In methane, we saw that each sp^3 hybrid of the tetrahedral unit overlapped with the $1s$ orbitals of hydrogen atoms to form four identical σ bonds. More complex molecules may be formed by replacing the hydrogens with other groups. Thus, if one of the hydrogens is replaced by a CH_3— group, an ethane molecule, CH_3—CH_3, is formed. This molecule has one C—C bond and six C—H bonds. The C—C bond is formed by the overlapping of sp^3 hybrids. The bond strength is 83.1 kcal/g mole (348×10^6 joules/kg mole), and the bond length is 1.54 Å. Each C—H bond is formed by the overlapping of an sp^3 hybrid and a $1s$ orbital. The bond strength is 98.8 kcal/g mole (414×10^6 joules/kg mole), and the bond length is 1.08 Å. The total bond energy is approximately the sum of the single bond strengths, that is, 675.9 kcal/g mole (2830×10^6 joules/kg mole).

In a similar manner other organic molecules are formed. When only single bonds are involved, the molecule is said to be *saturated*. *Unsaturated* molecules are formed when the carbonyl, allene, or acetylene bonding units are used. Among the most important unsaturated molecules are the vinyl compounds, $X_2C{=}CX_2$, and the dienes, $CX_2{=}CX{-}CH{=}CX_2$, where the X's represent any elements or organic groups capable of bonding with carbon. These molecules are the basic raw materials (i.e., monomers) for many commercial polymers.

The bonding energy can be estimated as the sum of the energies of all bonds in the molecule. The properties of single bonds are given in Table 3.5, and the properties of some important carbon bonds are also shown in Table 4.1.

Dipole moments may be roughly approximated from information on bond angles and electronegativities. Since dipoles arise because of the difference in electronegativity between two bonded atoms, a dipole moment can be assigned to each bond. The actual moment for a given bond probably varies from one compound to the next, since the surrounding orbitals also have some effect on it, but if one neglects these differences, a specific value can be assigned. The net dipole moment of a molecule is then the *vector* sum of the bond moments. Approximate bond dipole moments are given in Table 4.2.

Since methane, CH_4, and other linear saturated hydrocarbons are perfectly symmetric, their net dipole moments will be zero. Methyl chloride, CH_3Cl, on the other hand, is tetrahedral and has a net dipole moment of 2.0 debyes. This can be calculated using Table 4.2 and Fig. 4.3. Representing the dipoles as vectors along the bond axes, one can add the vectors to get a net dipole moment of 1.99 debyes, which agrees with the experimental value.

Average polarizability can also be approximated by assigning a *bond polarizability* to each bond and adding the group contributions. Some bond polarizabilities are given in Table 4.3. Using these numbers, one calculates $\alpha = 4 \times 0.65 = 2.6$ Å^3 (2.6×10^{-30} m^3) for methane and $\alpha = 3 \times 0.65 + 2.61 = 4.56$ Å^3 (4.56×10^{-30} m^3) for methylchloride. Calculation of the dispersion energy of interaction between complex molecules, from polarizability data, is too difficult to be considered here.

Tetrahedral carbon atoms can string together to form a backbone chain for

---

Table 4.1

Properties of some carbon bonds

Bond	Bond length, Å	Bond energy, kcal/g mole*	Bond	Bond length, Å	Bond energy, kcal/g mole*
C—H	1.08	98.8	C=O	1.22	170–180
C—C	1.54	83.1	C—F	1.36	116
C=C	1.35	145.8	C—Cl	1.76	81
C≡C	1.21	199.6	C—Br	1.94	68
C—N	1.47	69.7	C—I	2.14	51
C≡N	1.14	212	C—Si	1.93	72
C—O	1.43	84			

* Multiply by 4.186×10^6 to get joules/kg mole.

Table 4.2

Dipole moments for bonds

Bond $+--$	Avg dipole moment, debyes *	Bond $+--$	Avg dipole moment, debyes *
$\leftarrow$		$\leftarrow$	
H—C	0.4	C—F	1.5
C—O	0.8	C—Cl	1.6
H—N	1.3	H—O	1.6
C—I	1.3	C=O	2.4
C—Br	1.5	C≡N	3.6

* 1 debye $= \frac{1}{3} \times 10^{-29}$ coul-m.

a polymer molecule. When the chain grows in only two directions, a "linear" polymer molecule is formed. This is shown in Fig. 4.4a. Each carbon atom is joined to two others by σ-type covalent bonds that are formed by the over-lapping of sp^3 hybrid orbitals. In the homologous series of linear hydrocarbons, C_xH_{2x+2}, all of the other bonds are σ-type C—H bonds. Pure compounds have been isolated with x as high as 94. The polymeric material polymethylene is a mixture of molecules with x varying from very low values to values as high as 10^5 or 10^6.

In a similar manner, other hydrogen atoms can be replaced to form an in-finite variety of organic compounds. Nonsymmetric, or branched, hydrocarbons form by further addition of carbon to the linear chain (Fig. 4.4b). Covalent bonds may also be formed between carbon and other elements. Table 4.4

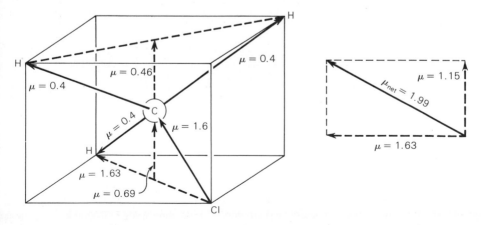

Fig. 4.3 The net dipole moment of methylchloride is obtained by taking the vector sum of the four bond moments.

lists a variety of organic polymer molecules that are commercially important. The size of the molecule, the amount of branching, and the nature of the substituted units all influence the properties of the molecules.

The intermolecular potential between two complex molecules is usually represented by three-parameter empirical functions. A methane molecule, for example, is not a point center of interaction, and the Lennard-Jones 12-6 potential cannot be very accurate when two such particles are close together. (This statement is also true for very simple molecules, but the deviations are less important.) A molecular model must take into account the shape of the molecule if one is to expect a reasonable curve-fitting of experimental data. A three-parameter model used by Kihara [10,13] is an impenetrable central core whose shape is determined by the configuration of the molecule. For

spherical molecules, such as argon, methane, and neopentane, $CH_3\!-\!\overset{\displaystyle CH_3}{\underset{\displaystyle CH_3}{\overset{|}{\underset{|}{C}}}}\!-\!CH_3$,

the core is a solid sphere of diameter d_c and the potential may be written as

$$\psi(r) = 4\epsilon \left[\left(\frac{\sigma - d_c}{r - d_c} \right)^{12} - \left(\frac{\sigma - d_c}{r - d_c} \right)^{6} \right] \tag{4.9}$$

The equation has about the same form as the Lennard-Jones equation, but now there is one additional adjustable parameter, d_c. This extra parameter is generally sufficient for getting reasonable curve-fitting of second and third virial coefficients. For polar and/or nonspherical molecules, the models must become much more complex and writing the potential-energy function becomes a much more difficult job. (Some typical models are shown in Fig. 4.5.)

A convenient model for linear molecules is a line of point centers with the total interaction as the sum of all possible combinations [2,3]. This is illus-

Table 4.3

Bond polarizabilities *

Bond	α, Å^3, or $\alpha \times 10^{30}$, m^3	Bond	α, Å^3, or $\alpha \times 10^{30}$, m^3
C—C (aliphatic)	0.64	C—Br	3.60
C—C (aromatic)	1.07	C=O (carbonyl)	1.16
C=C	1.66	C=O (CO_2)	1.32
C≡C	2.03	C≡N	1.97
C—H (aliphatic)	0.65	N—H	0.75
C—Cl	2.61		

* Adapted from "Molecular Theory of Gases and Liquids," p. 949, John Wiley & Sons, Inc., New York, 1964.

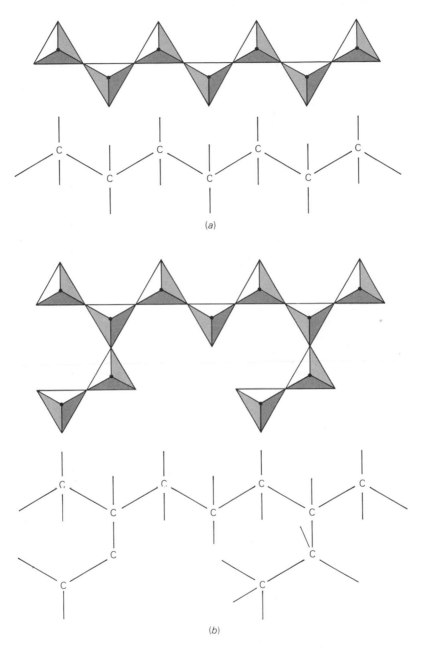

Fig. 4.4 Carbon atoms can be joined through covalent bonding to form the backbone for polymer molecules. (a) Backbone for a linear polymer; (b) branching in linear carbon chains.

trated in Fig. 4.6 for butane. The potential energy is given by Eqs. (4.10) and (4.11)

$$\psi(r) = \frac{1}{2} \sum_{i=1}^{4} \sum_{j=1}^{4} 4\epsilon \left[\left(\frac{\sigma}{r_{ij}}\right)^{12} - \left(\frac{\sigma}{r_{ij}}\right)^{6} \right] \tag{4.10}$$

$$\psi(r,\theta,\phi) = 4\epsilon(r,\theta,\phi) \left[\left(\frac{\sigma(r,\theta,\phi)}{r}\right)^{12} - \left(\frac{\sigma(r,\theta,\phi)}{r}\right)^{6} \right] \tag{4.11}$$

The parameters ϵ and σ are now complex functions of the orientation and the length l of the molecules.

Studies on the behavior of complex organic molecules are still in an early stage of development. Group-contribution techniques are very useful for predicting properties. That is, one can assign a certain property to a chemical bonding unit (for example, a CH_3— or a Cl— bonding unit) and assume additivity for any molecule. This approach will be pursued further when we discuss the physical properties of solid materials.

Table 4.4

Some commercially important organic polymer molecules

Name	Structure
Polyamide (nylon)	$(-(-CH_2-)_n NH\overset{\overset{O}{\|\|}}{C}(-CH_2-)_m \overset{\overset{O}{\|\|}}{C}-NH-)_x$
Polybutadiene	$(-CH_2-CH=CH-CH_2-)_x$
Cellulose nitrate	
Polychloroprene (Neoprene)	$(-CH_2-CH=CCl-CH_2-)_x$
Polyethylene	$(-CH_2-CH_2-)_x$
Polyformaldehyde (acetal resin)	$(-CH_2-O-)_x$
Polypropylene	$(-CH_2-CH-)_x$ with CH_3 branch
Polystyrene	$(-CH_2-CH-)_x$ with C_6H_5 branch
Polytetrafluoroethylene (Teflon)	$(-CF_2-CF_2-)_x$
Polyvinylchloride	$(-CH_2-CH-)_x$ with Cl branch

Cellulose nitrate structure:

$$
\begin{array}{c}
\quad NO_3 \quad\quad NO_3 \\
\quad | \quad\quad\quad | \\
\quad CH{-\!-\!-}CH \\
\diagup \quad\quad\quad\quad \diagdown \\
(-CH \quad\quad\quad\quad\quad CH-)_x \\
\diagdown \quad\quad\quad\quad \diagup \\
\quad CH{-\!-\!-}O \\
\quad | \\
\quad CH_2 \\
\quad | \\
\quad NO_3
\end{array}
$$

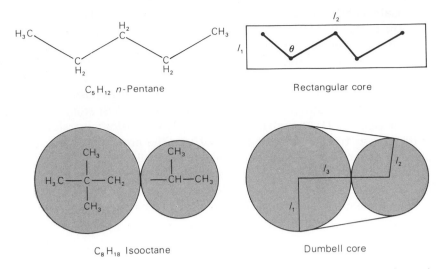

C_5H_{12} *n*-Pentane

Rectangular core

C_8H_{18} Isooctane

Dumbell core

Fig. 4.5 Kihara models for complex molecules take into account the size and shape in an idealized fashion.

Silicon may also develop four sp^3 hybrid orbitals. The basic building block for the silicate compounds (which constitute about 25 percent of the earth's crust) is the SiO_4 bonding unit with the silicon nucleus in the center of a tetrahedron formed by four oxygen atoms (Fig. 4.7a). The Si—O bonds are formed by the overlapping of the sp^3 hybrids with an appropriate bonding orbital from the oxygen. The bond energy is 88.2 kcal/g mole (372×10^6 joules/kg mole), and the bond length is about 1.6 Å. Since the electronegativity difference between oxygen and silicon is large, $3.5 - 1.8 = 1.6$, the bond is highly polar. An approximate model can be visualized for the tetrahedral unit by assuming a central core with an electrostatic charge of $+0.96e$, ionically bonded to the surrounding negative charge of $-0.96e$ [12]. Since each oxygen has formed a single bond with the silicon unit, only one more electron per oxygen atom is needed to fill the L shells. The SiO_4 unit thus has a very high electron affinity and easily forms the tetrahedral anion, SiO_4^{4-}.

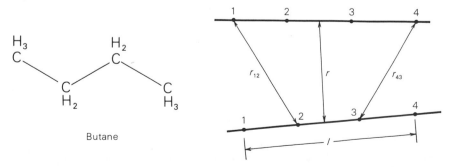

Butane

Fig. 4.6 The interaction potential of linear molecules such as butane can be expressed in terms of the interaction between lines of point centers of interaction.

Linear silicate molecules are formed when one oxygen is bonded to two silicon atoms. The backbone for the chain is shown in Fig. 4.7b; the analogy with linear carbohydrate molecules is clear. An infinitely long chain has two negatively charged oxygen ions per silicon atom. The ionic bonding may be with hydrogen (metasilicic acid which forms silica gel in water solution), alkali ions (Na_2SiO_3 to Na_4SiO_3 form water glasses in solution), or other electropositive elements. Long, double silicate chains of 12-membered rings (6 Si atoms, 6 O atoms) form the anion $(Si_4O_{11})^{6-}$ as shown in Fig. 4.8. The asbestos minerals are typical of these [e.g., tremolite, $Ca_2Mg_5Si_8O_{22}(OH)_2$]. The properties of these chain molecules depend on the number of ionic bonds available, chain length, chain stiffness, and the type of positive ions in the structure. Other atoms, such as sulfur, tellurium, and selenium, which need two electrons to form a stable electronic shell, also form chainlike molecules. The organics and the

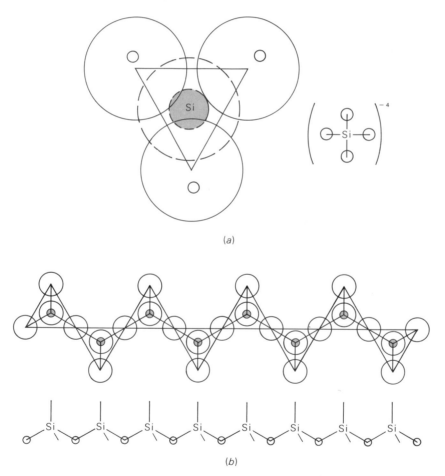

(a)

(b)

Fig. 4.7 The silicate tetrahedron is the basic repeating unit for silicate structures. Linear silicate chains can form in a manner similar to carbon chains. (a) The silicate tetrahedron; (b) backbone for linear silicate chain.

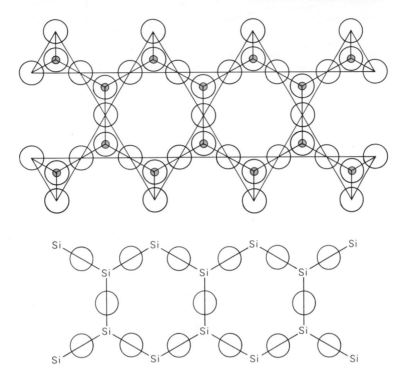

Fig. 4.8 A double silicate chain forms by the sharing of a single oxygen nucleus by adjacent silicon nuclei.

silicates, however, form the most important materials of construction. When linear molecules aggregate to form a solid, they may arrange in a rather random manner, thus forming an *amorphous* solid, or they may line up parallel to one another, thus forming an ordered or *crystalline* solid. The nature and geometry of these crystals will be elaborated in Chap. 8.

4.4
Sheetlike molecules

The hybridizing of a $2s$ and two $2p$ orbitals in carbon can result in three coplanar bonds at angles of 120°. When every carbon is covalently bonded to three other carbon atoms, a sheetlike molecule of graphite results. A graphite crystal consists of parallel layers of these sheetlike molecules, about 3.41 Å apart (Fig. 4.9). The bonding forces within each sheet molecule are strong covalent bonds, while adjacent molecules are held together by much weaker Van der Waals bonding.

Some silicates are two-dimensional or sheetlike ions. Each silicate tetrahedron is joined to three others in the same plane by sharing oxygen atoms (Fig. 4.10). The two-dimensional anion has the composition $(—Si_2O_5^{--}—)_x$. The

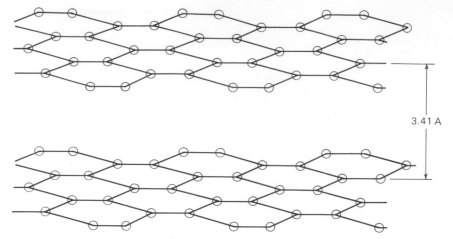

Fig. 4.9 Graphite is composed of layers of sheetlike molecules.

3.41 A

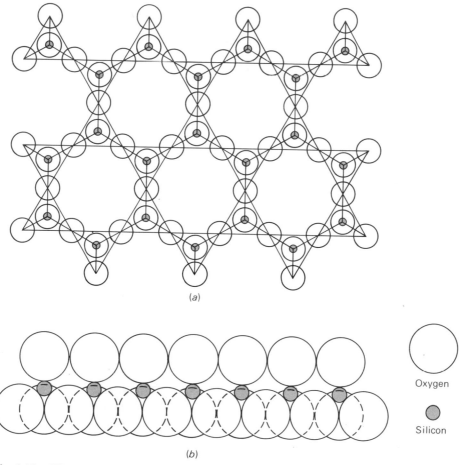

(a)

Oxygen

Silicon

(b)

Fig. 4.10 Silicates can also form sheetlike molecules in a manner similar to graphite molecules. (a) Top view of sheet; (b) edge view of sheet. (Based on drawings in L. Van Vlack, "Elements of Materials Science," chap. 5, Addison-Wesley Publishing Company, Inc., Reading, Mass., 1959.

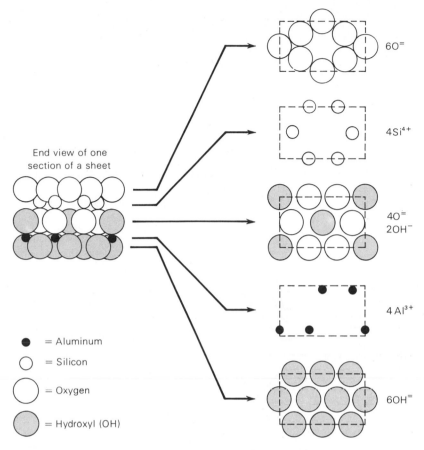

Fig. 4.11 Kaolinite is a double-layered structure in which an $(Si_2O_5)_x{}^{--}$ sheet is ionically bonded to an $(Al_2(OH)_4)^{++}$ sheet. (Based on drawings in F. H. Norton, "Elements of Ceramics," Addison-Wesley Publishing Company, Inc., Reading, Mass., 1954.)

upper face of the sheet contains one negatively charged oxygen atom per silicon atom, while the lower face contains its full complement of electrons. The upper face can ionically bond to a cationic sheet, forming a neutral molecule. A single sheetlike molecule of clay or kaolinite (Fig. 4.11) is a double-layered structure in which an $(—Si_2O_5{}^{--}—)_x$ sheet ionically bonds to a $[—Al_2(OH)_4{}^{++}—]_x$ sheet. The sheet has a dipole moment and therefore bonds to other molecules through both electrostatic and dispersive attractions. A talc molecule (Fig. 4.12) is a three-layered sheet in which a layer of $[—Mg_3(OH)_2{}^{4+}—]_x$ is sandwiched between two layers of $(—Si_2O_5{}^{--}—)_x$. Since the molecule is symmetric about its central plane, it does not have a net dipole moment and interacts with other sheets primarily through dispersive attraction.

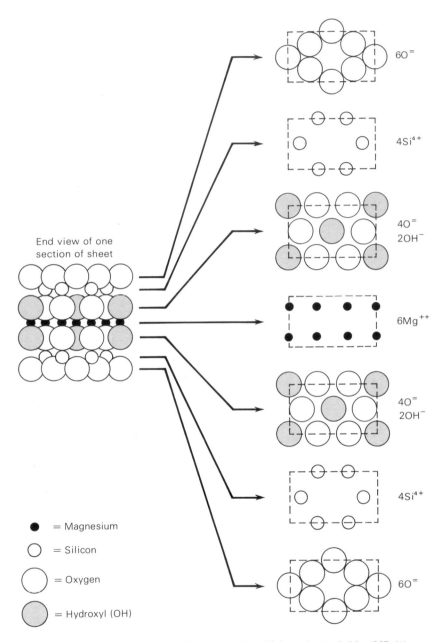

Fig. 4.12 Talc is a three-layered structure in which a sheet of $(\mathrm{Mg_3(OH)_2^{4+}})_x$ is sandwiched between two layers of $(\mathrm{Si_2O_5})_x{}^{--}$. (Based on drawings in Ref. 18, chap. 5.)

4.5
Three-dimensional molecules

Diamond is a hard, rigid material in which every carbon atom is joined to four other carbon atoms by covalent bonding. The bonds are directed toward the corners of a tetrahedron and are 1.54 Å in length. Thus a molecule of diamond is an infinite array of carbon atoms joined in a "diamond cubic" lattice with each atom having four nearest neighbors (Fig. 4.13). The hardness, insolubility, high strength, high temperature stability, and all other physical properties are related to the fact that all bonding within the structure is strongly covalent.

There are many other natural and synthetic "three-dimensional" molecules in which practically all of the main chains are interlinked by primary bonding. Theoretically, a single molecule can have an infinite molecular weight, and thus a finite mass of material (for example, 1 cm^3 of matter) can be a single molecule. Single crystals are, in this sense, also single molecules. The physical properties of these materials depend upon the character of the main chains, the character of the cross-links, and the number of cross-links. Table 4.5 lists a few important organic-based "space" polymers.

In each molecule, every atom is bonded to every other atom through an unbroken chain of covalent or ionic bonds. Since the bond angles are not necessarily coplanar, the molecules have a three-dimensional character. These kinds of molecules form the basic structures for a large number of very important materials of construction. The properties of such materials are considered in later chapters.

Two types of three-dimensional silicate molecules are frequently encountered. In the orthosilicates, the SiO_4^{4-} tetrahedra are ionically bonded to one another by metallic cations. The mineral forsterite, for example, is composed of magnesium ions, Mg^{++} and silicate tetrahedra, SiO_4^{4-}. The structural formula is $(Mg_2SiO_4)_x$. The silicon atoms are coordinated to four nearest-neighboring oxygen atoms, while each magnesium ion is ionically

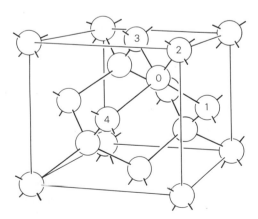

Fig. 4.13 The diamond cubic structure forms a complex unit cell in which each carbon atom is surrounded by four nearest neighbors.

bonded to six surrounding oxygens. This type of lattice network permits valence requirements to be satisfied with a minimum of distortion in the crystal lattice. (Crystal lattices will be discussed in much greater detail in the next section of the text.) Minerals of this type are formed with many different cations including Fe^{++}, Fe^{3+}, Cr^{3+}, Al^{3+}. Minerals may also contain varying proportions of one cation in place of another. Thus, a molecule may contain both Fe^{++} and Mg^{++} ions in varying proportions. A wide range of molecular types exists only when the cations involved have similar electronic and physical properties. Thus Ca^{++} ions do not readily substitute for Mg^{++} ions because of a 30 percent difference in ionic radii. Likewise, an Li^+ ion would not substitute for an Mg^{++} ion, in spite of the fact that their ionic radii are almost identical, because of the difference in net charge. Here again, an infinite variety of molecules containing silicon, oxygen, and cations is possible.

Table 4.5

Some organic space-polymer molecules

Polymer   *Schematic representation of structure*

(one possible representation)

(one possible structure)

When each silicate tetrahedron shares corners with four other silicate tetrahedra, a three-dimensional network of primary Si—O—Si bonds is formed in which every oxygen atom is bonded to two silicon atoms. This three-dimensional molecule is called silica, $(SiO_2)_x$. Different spatial arrangements of the tetrahedra give different materials. Thus, quartz, which is stable at room temperature, has a complicated screwlike symmetry with the tetrahedra spiraling about a hexagonal lattice, while crystabolite, stable above 1470°C, has the same tetrahedral lattice as diamond.

The discussion of three-dimensional molecules must ultimately lead to a study of the possible ways in which the atoms can arrange themselves in space. Silica, for example, has six different spatial arrangements of the SiO_4 tetrahedra that are stable under certain conditions, plus many metastable arrangements that appear stable for long periods of time.

By virtue of the high-energy bonds between the atoms, all three-dimensional molecules are solids or form polycrystalline solid materials at normal conditions. Under the proper conditions, any system of particles can condense to form a solid or liquid aggregate. Thus if neon gas is cooled to 27.2°K, the atoms will agglomerate to form a stable liquid because the interatomic forces are large enough to counterbalance the thermal energy tending to keep the atoms moving in a random fashion. Further cooling, to 24.4°K, will cause the atoms in liquid neon to rearrange into a very specific spatial geometry which is called a crystalline solid. In this case, the Van der Waals bonds holding the atoms together are analogous to (though much weaker than) the ionic bonds holding an $(Mg_2SiO_4)_x$ molecule together and are similar to the polar bonds holding the three-dimensional $(SiO_2)_x$ molecule together. In this sense, a crystal of neon is a three-dimensional molecule.

The point is that all solids are either aggregates of smaller molecules or large three-dimensional molecules. The intensity of the bonding between particles and the spatial geometry of the material determine many of the physical properties.

4.6
Spectroscopic analysis

In the preceding few sections we have discussed the properties of complex molecules without regard for the molecular motion of the structural units. As we have emphasized in preceding chapters, no structure is really a mass of fixed, immobile atoms, but rather each individual particle is in a constant state of motion that is determined by the nature of the chemical bonding. A knowledge of the molecular motion is just as important as a knowledge of the spatial geometry, because by studying these motions we can deduce the nature of the bonding forces.

When a molecule absorbs or emits electromagnetic radiation, it will "jump" to a new quantum state. The quantum of energy absorbed in a jump is always proportional to the frequency of the absorbed radiation (that is, $\Delta E = h\nu$). This characteristic is utilized in identifying the various chemical groups on the molecule. As we know, molecules exist in specific energy states. These are shown schematically in Fig. 4.14. The energy in any given state may be partitioned among the various degrees of freedom of the molecule. Thus, a molecule in its ground state has a certain amount of energy associated with the electronic distribution, plus a certain amount associated with molecular vibrations, plus an amount associated with molecular rotations, etc. When electromagnetic radiation impinges on a molecule it can be absorbed; the frequency ν of the absorbed radiation is related to the energy change in going from one state to another, $E_i - E_j$, by the Einstein equation

$$\nu = \frac{E_i - E_j}{h} \qquad\qquad (4.12)$$

When a molecule goes from one *electronic* state to the next, it usually involves energy changes of 10^{-18} to 10^{-19} joule and corresponds to wavelengths of 10^3

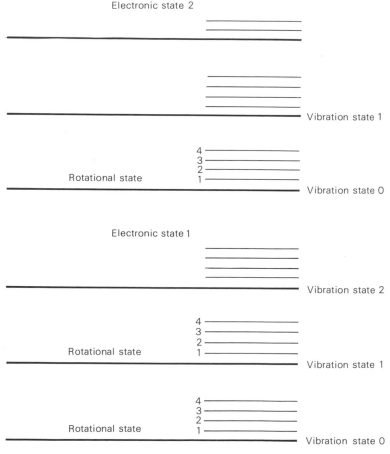

Fig. 4.14 A molecule has many different energy states associated with its various modes of motion and its different electronic structures.

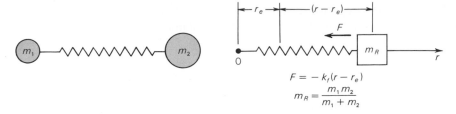

Fig. 4.15 The vibrational motion of a diatomic molecule can be analyzed in terms of a one-dimensional harmonic oscillator.

to 10^4 Å. Electronic transitions are thus studied with radiation in the ultraviolet and visible range. *Vibrational* transitions normally involve 10^{-19} to 10^{-21} joule, corresponding to wavelengths of 10^4 to 10^6 Å, or the infrared range. *Rotational* transitions normally involve 10^{-21} to 10^{-22} joule, corresponding to wavelengths of 10^6 to 10^7 Å, or the far-infrared region. Molecular structure is normally studied with the molecules in their electronic ground states, and usually the rotational spectra of polyatomic molecules is so complex that it is very difficult to interpret. This leaves the vibrational spectra as the most important for structure elucidation and *infrared spectroscopy* as one of the more important experimental techniques.

It can be assumed that the vibrations in a diatomic molecule, or for that matter the vibrations of any two particles joined by a chemical bond, are simple harmonic motions. Such a motion of two particles can be reduced to the harmonic vibration of a single mass point about an equilibrium position. Referring to Fig. 4.15, one may write

$$F = -k_f(r - r_e) \tag{4.13}$$

where the proportionality constant k_f is called the force constant. From Newton's second law,

$$F = m_R \frac{d^2r}{dt^2} = -k_f(r - r_e) \tag{4.14}$$

where m_R is the reduced mass of the two-particle system and is given by

$$m_R = \frac{m_a m_b}{m_a + m_b} \tag{4.15}$$

The solution to Eq. (4.14) is

$$r - r_e = A \sin (2\pi\nu t + \phi) \tag{4.16}$$

where A is the amplitude of the vibration, ϕ is a phase angle which is dependent on the initial boundary condition, and ν is the frequency of the vibration which is related to the force constant by the equation

$$\nu = \frac{1}{2\pi} \sqrt{\frac{k_f}{m_R}} \tag{4.17}$$

Since the force is the negative of the first derivative of the potential energy, $F = -d\psi/dr$, the potential energy of a harmonic oscillator is

$$\psi = \tfrac{1}{2} k_f (r - r_e)^2 = 2\pi^2 m_R \nu^2 (r - r_e)^2 \qquad (4.18)$$

Since we are considering a molecule in harmonic motion, we must use the Schrödinger wave equation to determine the allowable energy states. Equation (3.17), for a one-dimensional harmonic oscillator, reduces to

$$\frac{h^2}{8 m_R \pi^2} \frac{d^2 \psi_n}{d(r - r_e)^2} + \left(E_n - \frac{1}{2} k_f (r - r_e)^2 \right) \psi_n = 0 \qquad (4.19)$$

It can be shown [9] that wave functions exist only for the energy values

$$E_n = \left(n + \frac{1}{2} \right) \frac{h}{2\pi} \sqrt{\frac{k_f}{m_R}}$$

$$= (n + \tfrac{1}{2}) h\nu$$

where n is an integer (that is, $n = 0, 1, 2, 3, \ldots$). Thus, if electromagnetic radiation is used to excite the vibrational mode of a molecule from $n = 0$ to $n = 1$, the energy change is $E_1 - E_0 = h\nu$, which is the same as in Eq. (4.12). Thus, by measuring the frequency of the absorbed or emitted radiation in an infrared spectrometer, one can determine the fundamental vibration frequency for a given chemical bond and thus calculate the force constant and the potential energy.

4.7
Infrared absorption spectra

An infrared prism spectrometer is schematically shown in Fig. 4.16. The radiation source is usually an electrically heated silicon carbide or rare-earth-oxide rod emitting radiation with wavelengths in the range of 10^4 to 10^6 Å (or 1 to 100 μ). The radiated sample can be a gas, a liquid, or a thin film of solid. The radiation is dispersed by either a diffraction grating or one of various types of salt crystals. The incident radiation is measured by a heat detector such as a multiple-junction thermocouple. The output is amplified and suitably recorded. One obtains the percent absorption as a function of the wavelength of the radiation.

According to classical electrodynamics, a transition from one vibrational level to another can occur when the dipole moment of the oscillator changes with a frequency equal to that of the oscillation. When the dipole moment is zero, no change can occur and thus no absorption of radiation can occur. Thus, homonuclear chemical bonds (that is, N_2, O_2, etc.) do not absorb infrared radiation. On the other hand, all other bonds, or chemical groups, will absorb radiation, and the absorption spectra can be used to identify the type of chemical bond involved. A simple diatomic molecule will have only one mode of

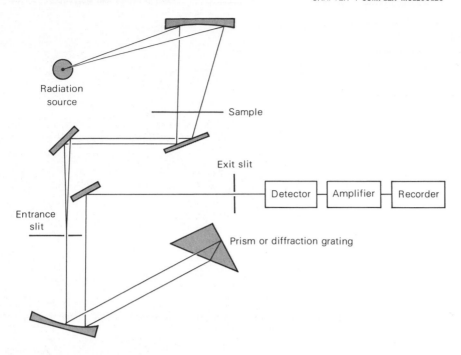

Fig. 4.16 An infrared spectrometer.

vibration and a relatively simple infrared absorption spectra. By measuring the wavelength of the absorbed radiation, one can then calculate the force constant by using Eq. (4.17). The force constant is a measure of the resistance of the bond to elastic deformation. Some typical force constants and vibration frequencies for carbon bonds are given in Table 4.6.

Polyatomic molecules have multiple modes of vibration and thus produce absorption spectra which are both complex and difficult to interpret. One of the simplest polyatomic molecules is CO_2. It contains an allene carbon bonding unit and is thus linear. Since there are three atoms, there is a total of nine degrees of freedom. The molecule has translational freedom in three dimensions and rotational freedom in two dimensions, which leaves four vibrational degrees of freedom. These are sketched in Fig. 4.17. The first two are called stretching vibrations and have the frequencies $\nu_1 = 3.963 \times 10^{13}$ sec^{-1} and $\nu_2 = 7.084 \times 10^{13}$ sec^{-1}. The third and the fourth are identical bending vibrations and have the frequency $\nu_3 = \nu_4 = 2.002 \times 10^{13}$ sec^{-1}. The bending of the chemical bond thus requires less force than that required for stretching.

The more complex the molecule, the more complicated will be its vibration spectrum. Consider the linear hydrocarbon, polymethylene $R(—CH_2—)_xR$, for example. Each $—CH_2—$ group, if mounted on a rigid backbone of carbon atoms, could vibrate in the six modes shown in Fig. 4.18. When in a real chain, each mode of vibration of a given $—CH_2—$ unit couples with appropriate modes

Table 4.6

Force constants and vibration frequencies for carbon bonds *

Bond	$\nu \times 10^{-13}$, sec^{-1}	$k_f \times 10^{-5}$ dynes/cm or $k_f \times 10^{-2}$ newtons/m
C—C	2.978	4.6
C—O	3.085	5.0
C—N	3.095	4.9
C=C	4.856	10.6
C=O	5.096	11.6
C=N	4.946	10.4
C≡C	6.355	15.8
C≡O	6.433	18.5
C≡N	6.445	17.5

* Data from J. H. Hibben, "The Raman Effect and Its Chemical Applications," Reinhold Publishing Corporation, New York, 1939.

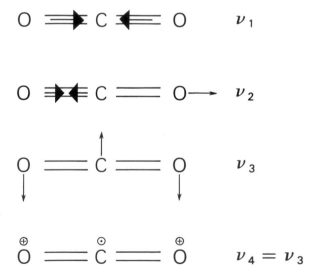

Fig. 4.17 A carbon dioxide molecule can vibrate in four fundamental vibrational modes.

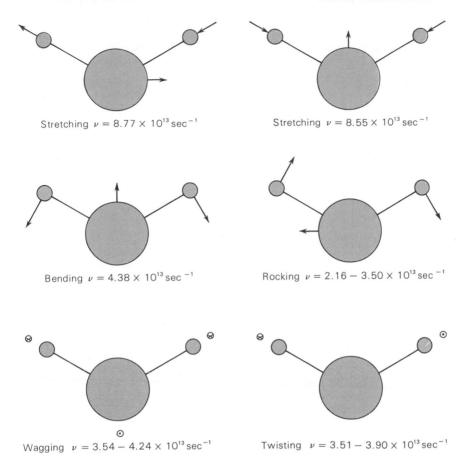

Stretching $\nu = 8.77 \times 10^{13} \, sec^{-1}$ Stretching $\nu = 8.55 \times 10^{13} \, sec^{-1}$

Bending $\nu = 4.38 \times 10^{13} \, sec^{-1}$ Rocking $\nu = 2.16 - 3.50 \times 10^{13} \, sec^{-1}$

Wagging $\nu = 3.54 - 4.24 \times 10^{13} \, sec^{-1}$ Twisting $\nu = 3.51 - 3.90 \times 10^{13} \, sec^{-1}$

Fig. 4.18   There are six fundamental modes of vibration for a —CH_2— group attached to a rigid frame. [By permission from American Chemical Society, from B. Wunderlich, *Ind. Eng. Chem.,* **56** (2): 23 (1964).]

of other units. Also, there will be new modes of vibration associated with the stretching, bending, and twisting of the carbon-to-carbon bonds along the chain. This complex interaction will cause the spectrum to look more like a frequency distribution than a discrete spectrum. This is illustrated by the qualitative sketches of some infrared spectra in Fig. 4.19. Each material will have a different spectrum which is a function of both its molecular and physical state. It takes a considerable amount of experience to either rationalize the spectrum of a known material or identify an unknown. Figure 4.20 shows the infrared absorption bands for a variety of chemical groups.

In summary, the purpose of this chapter has been to describe the structure of complex molecules. The nature of the chemical bonding units determines the geometry of a molecule and can be qualitatively described in terms of molecular orbitals. Since we have relatively little a priori knowledge of inter-

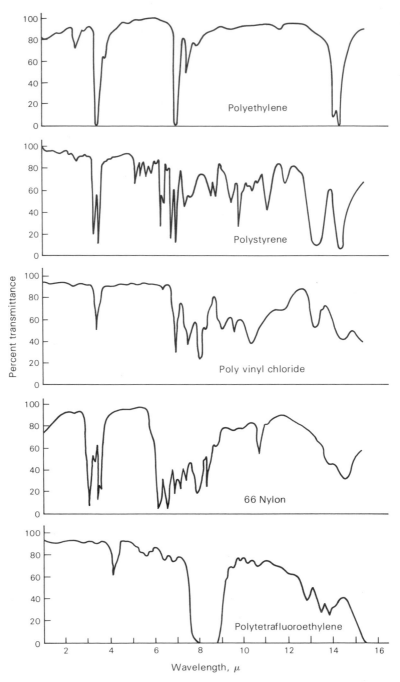

Fig. 4.19 These qualitative sketches of infrared absorption spectra for some polymeric materials indicate the difficulties in interpreting experimental data on complex materials.

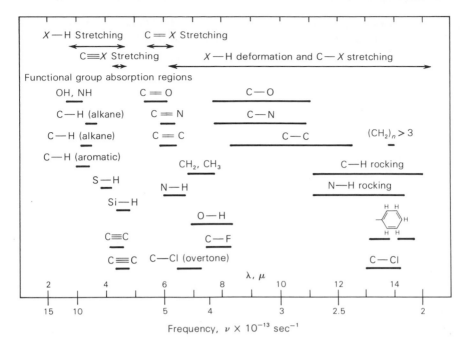

Fig. 4.20 Infrared absorption bands for various chemical bonds. (By permission from John Wiley & Sons, Inc., from F. W. Billmeyer, "Textbook of Polymer Science," p. 91, Interscience Publishers, Inc., New York, 1962.)

molecular forces and chemical bonding, we must rely very heavily on experimental studies, usually using electromagnetic radiation, for structure elucidation.   In this chapter we have discussed infrared spectroscopy as a tool for identifying chemical groups; in other chapters we shall discuss the use of x-ray diffraction and microscopy for investigating other aspects of structure elucidation.

References

1 Billmeyer, F.: "Textbook of Polymer Science," chap. 4, Interscience Publishers, Inc., New York, 1962. *A brief summary (with bibliography) of the important techniques for the analysis and testing of polymeric materials. There is also considerable information in other chapters on molecular structure.*

2 Corner, J.: *Proc. Roy. Soc. (London),* Ser. A, **192:** 275 (1948).

3 DiBenedetto, A. T.: *J. Polymer Sci.,* Ser. A, **1:** 3459 (1963).

4 Eitel, W.: "The Physical Chemistry of Silicates," The University of Chicago Press, Chicago, 1954. *A detailed reference book on the chemistry of silicate compounds. It is reading for the advanced student.*

5 Fieser, L., and M. Fieser: "Organic Chemistry," 3d ed., Reinhold Publishing Corporation, New York, 1956. *An introductory text for organic chemistry.*

6   Fieser, L., and M. Fieser: "Advanced Organic Chemistry," Reinhold Publishing Corporation, New York, 1961. *A more advanced follow-up of the preceding text.*

7   Gray, H. B.: "Electrons and Chemical Bonding," W. A. Benjamin, Inc., New York, 1964. *Chapters V and VIII are excellent introductions to the use of molecular-orbital concepts with organic molecules.*

8   Herz, W.: "The Shape of Carbon Compounds," W. A. Benjamin, Inc., New York, 1963. *A very readable introduction to the behavior of simple organic molecules.*

9   Herzberg, G.: "Molecular Spectra and Molecular Structure," I. "Spectra of Diatomic Molecules," D. Van Nostrand Company, Inc., Princeton, N.J., 1950. *A complete discussion of the interpretation of molecular spectra for diatomic molecules.*

10   Kihara, T.: *Rev. Mod. Phys.,* **25:** 831 (1953).

11   Kline, G. M. (ed.): "Analytical Chemistry of Polymers," part II, "Molecular Structure and Chemical Groups," John Wiley & Sons, Inc., New York, 1962. *Several chapters on x-ray diffraction, optical techniques, mass spectrometry, ultraviolet spectrophotometry, and other techniques with application to polymers.*

12   Pauling, L.: "The Nature of the Chemical Bond," 3d ed., Cornell University Press, Ithaca, N.Y., 1960. *Several chapters on the properties of complex molecules. Advanced-level reading.*

13   Prausnitz, J. M., and R. N. Keeler: *AIChE J.,* **7:** 399 (1961).

14   Price, C. C.: The Geometry of Giant Molecules, *J. Chem. Educ.,* **36:** 160 (1959). *A readable introduction to polymer molecules.*

15   Schmidt, A. X., and C. A. Marlies: "Principles of High-polymer Theory and Practice," McGraw-Hill Book Company, New York, 1948. *The first few chapters give an excellent picture of the molecular character of polymers.*

16   *Scientific American,* Giant Molecules, p. 197, September, 1957. *An issue devoted to the properties of polymeric materials. Interesting supplementary reading.*

17   Sherwood, A. E., and J. M. Prausnitz: *J. Chem. Phys.,* **41:** 429 (1964).

18   Van Vlack, L. H.: "Elements of Materials Science," Addison-Wesley Publishing Company, Inc., Reading, Mass., 1959. *Chapters 3, 5, and 6 are highly recommended as supplementary reading for this chapter at a more elementary level.*

19   Weissberger, A. (ed.): "Physical Methods of Organic Chemistry," parts II to IV, Interscience Publishers, Inc., New York, 1960. *Numerous articles on microscopy, crystallography, x-ray diffraction, electron diffraction, neutron diffraction, infrared spectroscopy, and other analytical techniques.*

20   Wilson, E. B., Jr., J. C. Decius, and P. C. Cross: "Molecular Vibrations: The Theory of Infrared and Raman Vibrational Spectra," McGraw-Hill Book Company, New York, 1955.

Questions

4.1   Qualitatively describe the tetrahedral bonds of the carbon atom in terms of "hybrid" wave functions. Assume that the four orbitals describing the bonds are linear combinations of $2s$, $2p_x$, $2p_y$, and $2p_z$ orbitals for the isolated atoms.

$$\Psi_j = a_j\Psi_{2s} + b_j\Psi_{2p_x} + c_j\Psi_{2p_y} + d_j\Psi_{2p_z} \qquad j = 1, 2, 3, 4$$

Procedure

(a)   In Chap. 3 the wave functions for the hydrogen atom were determined.   Neglect the radial portion of the wave function and write down the angular portions as:

$$\Psi_{2s} = A$$

$$\Psi_{2p_z} = B \cos \theta$$

$$\Psi_{2p_y} = C \sin \theta \sin \phi$$

$$\Psi_{2p_x} = D \sin \theta \cos \phi$$

(b)   Evaluate the constants by utilizing:

$$\int_0^\pi \int_0^\pi \Psi^2 \sin \theta \, d\theta \, d\phi = 4\pi$$

Solution:

$$\Psi_{2s} = 1$$

$$\Psi_{2p_z} = \sqrt{3} \cos \theta$$

$$\Psi_{2p_y} = \sqrt{3} \sin \theta \sin \phi$$

$$\Psi_{2p_x} = \sqrt{3} \sin \theta \cos \phi$$

(c)   Determine what values of the constants a_1, b_1, c_1, and d_1 will give a maximum electronic density in a given direction.   Since the direction is immaterial, let us choose the first bond as directed along the z axis (that is, $\cos \theta = 1$).

(d)   Show that $\Psi_1 = \frac{1}{2} + \frac{3}{2} \cos \theta$ by utilizing the fact that the wave function can be normalized to

$$\int_0^{2\pi} \int_0^\pi \Psi^2 \sin \theta \, d\theta \, d\phi = 4\pi \qquad \text{or} \qquad a^2 + d^2 = 1$$

and that $a = \frac{1}{2}$ will give a maximum bond strength at $\theta = 0$.

(e)   Plot the product $|\Psi_1|^2$.

(f)   Evaluate the electronic density for a second bond, $|\Psi_2|^2$, if the maximum density lies in the xz plane (that is, $\cos \theta = 1$).   Utilize the orthogonality condition for the wave functions

$$\int_0^{2\pi} \int_0^\pi \Psi_1\Psi_2 \sin \theta \, d\theta \, d\phi = 0$$

and the normalizing equation

$$\int_0^{2\pi} \int_0^\pi \Psi_2{}^2 \sin \theta \, d\theta \, d\phi = 4\pi$$

(g)   Compare Ψ_2 with Ψ_1 and describe the difference between the two.

(h)   Construct two other orbitals in a similar manner and show that the four wave functions Ψ_1, Ψ_2, Ψ_3, and Ψ_4 describe the tetrahedral bonds in a carbon atom.

4.2   Describe the bonding in carbon tetrachloride in terms of molecular orbitals.   What are the polarizability and dipole moment for a CCl_4 molecule?   Is the C—Cl bond polar? Why?

4.3 Ethylene, $CH_2\!=\!CH_2$, is approximately a trigonal planar molecule. The observed H—C—H bond angle is 117°, and the observed H—C=C bond angle is 121.5°. Use the concepts of hybrid orbitals to describe the bonding in ethylene.

4.4 Acrylonitrile,

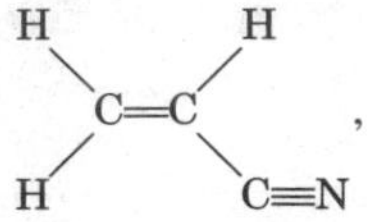

, is an important raw material for many commercial polymers. Describe the bonding in terms of molecular orbitals.

4.5 Ethylene, $CH_2\!=\!CH_2$, is a nonpolar molecule, while α-butylene, $CH_2\!=\!CHCH_2CH_3$, has a dipole moment of 0.37 debye. Explain the difference in terms of molecular structure.

4.6 Dichloroethylene exists in three isomeric forms:

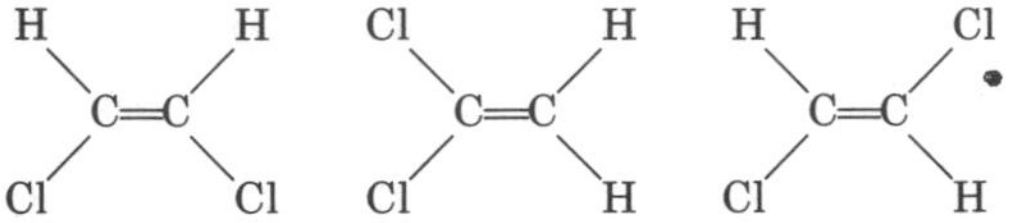

The first has a dipole moment of 1.89 debyes and the second of 1.18 debyes, the third is nonpolar. Explain in terms of molecular structure.

4.7 The diunivalent oxygen bonding unit forms triangular molecules with a bond angle of about 105°. Thus the bond angle for water,

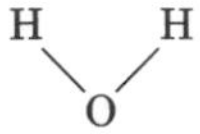

is 105° and the same is true in ether compounds,

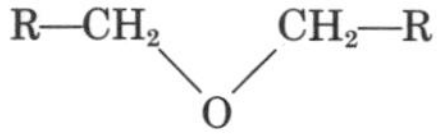

where R is any organic group. Water, H_2O, has a dipole moment of 1.87 debyes and ethyl ether, $C_2H_5OC_2H_5$, has a dipole moment of 1.1 debyes. Explain why they are polar in terms of molecular structure. Explain the differences in terms of electronegativity.

4.8 Assume that the net dipole moment of a molecule is the vector sum of the bond dipole moments and calculate the moments for the following molecules using Table 4.2: methane, ethylene, α-butylene, acrylonitrile, the three isomers of dichloroethylene (see

Question 4.6), water, ethyl ether, acetone,

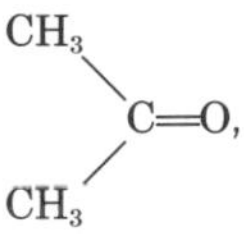

$C\!=\!O$, and ethyl alcohol, $CH_3\!-\!CH_2OH$.

4.9 Use Table 4.1 to estimate the polarizability of methane, ethylene, and n-butane. Estimate the total dispersion attraction between pairs and compare the results with those obtained from a 12-6 potential (Table 2.1).

4.10 Use group-contribution techniques to estimate the polarity and polarizability per 5 Å of chain length (about four carbon atoms along the chain) of polybutadiene, polychloroprene, polyformaldehyde, polyamide, and polyvinylchloride. List these molecules in order of increasing polarity and also increasing polarizability.

4.11 Use the Kihara technique and sketch molecular models for benzene and ethyl-benzene. Write down the potential-energy expression for the interaction of two like molecules at a fixed orientation. Define all terms in the expression. Qualitatively describe how one goes about evaluating an "average" potential for a given value of r if the molecules are freely orienting.

4.12 Use a "four-center" technique to write down the intermolecular potential-energy function for butadiene molecules, $CH_2{=}CH{-}CH{=}CH_2$. Assume a 12-6 potential. How many molecular constants are needed to characterize this function?

4.13 How do the Van der Waals bonds between sheetlike molecules of clay differ from those between sheetlike molecules of talc? Explain in terms of molecular structure.

4.14 Qualitatively explain, in terms of interatomic bonding, why diamond is an extremely hard substance.

4.15 It is often said that "space polymers" are infusible and insoluble materials. In terms of molecular bonding, why would you expect this?

4.16 Calculate the wavelength of the electromagnetic radiation that is absorbed when the electron of a hydrogen atom is excited from the $1s$ to the $2s$ state. What kind of spectrograph must be used to investigate the electronic states of the hydrogen atom? What is the range of wavelength required to study all the electronic states of hydrogen?

4.17 The infrared spectrum of HCl vapor shows an intense absorption line at a wave number of $2,885.9$ cm^{-1} and several other low-intensity lines. (The wave number is frequency divided by the speed of light, v/c.) The absorption spectrum can be described as a series of lines with wave numbers given by the equation $v/c = 2,937.30n - 51.60n^2$ cm^{-1}, where n is an integer. How does this compare with what one would expect from a harmonic oscillator? Can you attribute a physical significance to the quadratic term? Calculate the force constant for the HCl bond and also the energy required to increase the nuclear separation by 1 Å.

4.18 Close examination of the first absorption band of HCl ($n = 1$ in Question 4.17), shows that it is really a set of closely spaced absorption bands that can be represented by $v/c = 2,885.90 + 20.577m - 0.3034m^2 - 0.00222m^3$, where $m = \pm 1, \pm 2, \pm 3, \ldots$. Discuss the causes of this spectrum.

4.19 Compare the force constant for the bending of a C—H bond with that for the stretching of a C—C bond. Which possesses a larger restoring force, a deformed valence angle or a stretched chain?

Part B
Structure of
engineering materials

5
Simple crystals

5.1
Introduction

Many solid materials are aggregates of atoms or simple molecules. A crystal of neon, for example, can be represented by an array of close-packed spheres, with each sphere in direct contact with 12 others. The diameter of the sphere is equivalent to the collision diameter of the neon atom. The aggregate is held together by the Van der Waals bonding between atoms, and each atom harmonically vibrates about a fixed point in space. In an "ideal" crystal, all of the atoms are arranged in a regular and definite geometry. There are many properties, such as density, thermal expansion coefficient, heat of sublimation, and modulus of elasticity, which are primarily a function of this arrangement and are insensitive to the small number of defects that are normally present in real crystals. These are called *structure-insensitive* properties.

Salt crystals are also relatively simple structures. Sodium chloride, for example, can be represented by a regular and definite arrangement of two different-size spheres representing the spherical sodium cations and the spherical chloride anions. The arrangement is cubic, and each ion is "in contact" with six ions of opposite charge. The structure-insensitive properties of salt crystals can be predicted from information on the geometry of the structure and the interionic potential-energy function.

Metallic crystals also have a specific geometric structure. The simplest physical model is that of an array of positive cores, containing a nucleus and all inner-shell electrons, arranged in a regular and definite geometric lattice. These "cores" vibrate about fixed points in the lattice, while the outermost shell of electrons (i.e., the valence electrons) move with relative freedom through the whole lattice. The geometry of the lattice and the nature of the vibrating cores determine the *structure-insensitive* properties of the solid, while the nature of the valence electrons controls the *structure-sensitive* conductivity of the solid.

The purpose of this chapter is to describe the geometry of simple crystals and to show how the structure is related to the properties of the solid. It should be emphasized that in this and the following chapter we shall limit ourselves to properties that are associated with either single crystals or submicroscopic aggregates of atoms. This eliminates the effects of polycrystallinity, grain boundaries, and all other *microscopic* aspects of real engineering materials. These latter factors will be considered in other chapters of the text.

5.2
Space lattices

One can learn much about the geometric properties of crystals by forgetting about the structure and motion of the atomic units and considering the crystal lattice as an infinite array of points in space. By doing this, it is possible to catalogue the overall symmetry properties of crystals and to interpret x-ray diffraction data logically. This abstraction should be viewed with care, since the harmonically vibrating atoms are not always found at these centralized points and, furthermore, there are always defects in real crystals which locally distort the symmetry of the structure.

It can be proved that there are 14 different ways in which points can be arranged in three dimensions so that each point has identical surroundings. Thus, the space lattice for any crystal must be catalogued as one of the 14 types listed in Table 5.1. The *unit cell* of a space lattice is defined as the smallest repeating volume which has a lattice point in each of its corners. The simple cubic unit cell, shown in Fig. 5.1, is completely described by specifying the reference axes and the lattice parameters. The lattice parameters are the lengths of the edges of the unit cell along the reference axes. The space lattice for a crystal is an infinite array of these unit cells.

Directions in a space lattice are represented by vectors. The *indices of direction* are the vector components resolved along each of the coordinate axes and reduced to the smallest set of integers. This is illustrated for cubic lattices in Fig. 5.2. Point 0 on the vector is chosen as the origin, and the point *P* has the coordinates $\frac{1}{2}$, $\frac{1}{3}$, $\frac{1}{2}$ or $\frac{3}{6}$, $\frac{2}{6}$, $\frac{3}{6}$. The smallest set of integers, placed in brackets, gives the direction indices [323]. In the same manner the

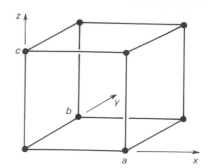

Fig. 5.1 The geometry of a simple crystal is described by specifying its unit cell and its reference axes.

three diagonals on the cube faces have the indices [110], [101], and [011], as shown in Fig. 5.2. An important property of direction indices *in cubic lattices* is that equivalent directions are represented by the same combination of three numbers. Thus, the properties of the lattice in the [110] direction are the same as those in the [101] direction.

Because of the regular spacing of points, it is possible to pass sets of equidistant parallel planes upon which the points will have the same orientation. A widely used labeling system for these *crystallographic planes* is the *Miller indexing method.* The Miller indices are particularly useful because in

Table 5.1

The fourteen space lattices

Lattice type	Reference axes
1. Simple cubic	
2. Face-centered cubic	Three axes at right angles, $a = b = c$
3. Body-centered cubic	
4. Simple tetragonal	
5. Body-centered tetragonal	Three axes at right angles, $a = b \neq c$
6. Simple orthorhombic	
7. Base-centered orthorhombic	
8. Face-centered orthorhombic	Three axes at right angles, $a \neq b \neq c$
9. Body-centered orthorhombic	
10. Simple rhombohedral	Three axes equally inclined but not at right angles, $a = b = c$
11. Simple monoclinic	One axis at right angles to the other two, which are
12. Base-centered monoclinic	not at right angles to each other, $a \neq b \neq c$
13. Simple triclinic	Three axes not at right angles, $a \neq b \neq c$
14. Simple hexagonal	Three coplanar axes at 120° and a fourth at 90° to these, $a_1 = a_2 = a_3 \neq c$

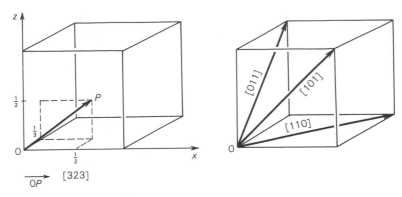

Fig. 5.2 Directions in cubic lattices are specified by means of direction indices.

cubic systems all the planes of a given set (those with equivalent properties) will have the same set of numbers defining them. A modified version of the Miller indices, the Miller-Bravais indices, may be used to the same advantage with hexagonal systems. To determine the Miller indices of a plane in a cubic lattice, one must first select an origin for the reference axes that is outside the plane of interest. The intercepts of the plane with the reference axes, in terms of multiples or fractions of the lattice parameters, are then recorded. The reciprocals of these numbers are reduced to the smallest set of integers and placed in parentheses. The resulting numbers represent the Miller indices for that plane or any other plane in the set.

This is illustrated for cubic lattices in Fig. 5.3. The origin of the reference axes is chosen at point 0. The x, y, z intercepts are ½, ¾, ½. The reciprocals of the intercepts are 2, ⁴⁄₃, 2, and, finally, 3,2,3 are obtained by reducing to the smallest set of integers. The Miller indices are thus (323). All planes parallel to the above and on the same side of the origin (e.g., the plane cutting the axes

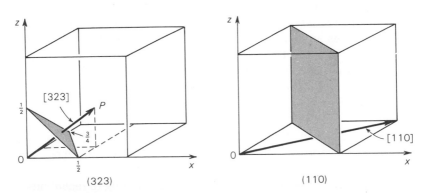

Fig. 5.3 Crystallographic planes in cubic lattices are specified by means of Miller indices.

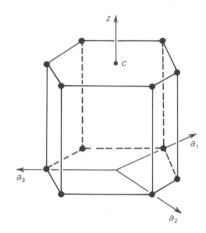

Fig. 5.4 A simple hexagonal cell.

at 1, ³/₂, 1), will have exactly the same indices, while those on the other side of the origin will differ only in minus signs (e.g., at −¹/₂, −³/₄, −¹/₂ the Miller indices are written as ($\bar{3}\bar{2}\bar{3}$)). The important feature is that all planes with the absolute numbers 3, 2, and 3 for indices have identical arrangements of points. The corresponding planes in a real crystal would therefore have identical physical properties. Notice also that the Miller indices for a plane are the same as the direction indices for the vector normal to that plane. This is true only for cubic systems.

There are also many planes in a space lattice that have identical arrangements of points but are not parallel to one another. Thus the diagonal plane (110), shown in Fig. 5.3, has the same character as the (011) plane, which is parallel to the x axis. All planes having the same *combination* of numbers for Miller indices are said to belong to the same *family*. In cubic crystals, all atomic planes of the same family have identical character.

Miller indices are generally used in hexagonal systems also. In this case one of the coplanar axes is merely neglected. Thus the base plane of a simple hexagonal cell has the coordinates ∞, ∞, ∞, 1 relative to an origin outside the base plane, or taking reciprocals, 0, 0, 0, 1. If one neglects one of the coplanar axes, the Miller indices are (001). A simple hexagonal cell is shown in Fig. 5.4. One can determine that the three front prism faces are, from left to right, ($\bar{1}$00), ($\bar{1}$10), and (010). Although identical, the three prism faces are not characterized by the same combination of indices. For this reason, the Miller-Bravais indices, which are based on using all four coordinates, were devised. They have the same set-family characteristics that the Miller indices have for cubic systems. Since Miller-Bravais indices of direction are difficult to obtain, the method is not universally used and Miller indices are probably more convenient.

There are a number of very important reasons for wanting to record directions and planes in crystals. Many real solids have relatively simple crystal lattices. Since the arrangement of the atoms is different in different directions, the physical and chemical properties of the crystal are different in different directions. Thus, the conductivity of a crystal might vary with direction, certain planes might be stronger than others, the chemical activity might be different in different planes, and so forth. Another reason is that in order to relate the properties of a material to its molecular structure, one has to determine the geometry and the lattice parameters experimentally. This is generally accomplished by using x-ray diffraction techniques, and concepts of planar notation are very useful in the analysis of diffraction data. Before discussing real crystals, let us first consider the technique of x-ray diffraction.

5.3
x-ray emission

The x-rays used in x-ray diffraction techniques usually have wavelengths of the order of 0.5 to 3.0 Å. They are generally produced in a high-vacuum tube called an x-ray tube (Fig. 5.5). Electrons from a heated filament are accelerated in a direct-current electric field and impinge on a metallic electrode. The absorption of energy by the metallic target results in the exciting of the target electrons to higher energy states. The return of these excited electrons to the ground state (i.e., normal state) of the target results in the emission of radiation. Most of the energy appears as heat, but a small fraction results in the emission of white x-radiation and, if the voltage is high enough, a characteristic

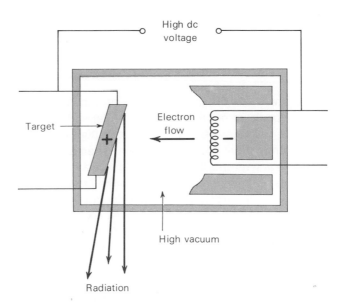

Fig. 5.5 Schematic drawing of an x-ray tube.

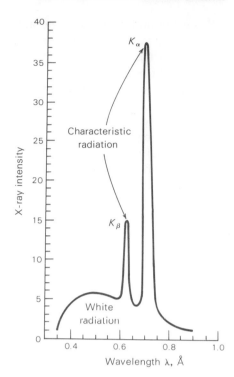

Fig. 5.6 The radiation from a molybdenum x-ray tube operating at 35,000
volts shows two high-intensity characteristic radiation peaks. [C. T. Ulrey, *Phys.
Rev.,* **11:** 405 (1918).]

x-radiation.   The maximum energy imparted by an accelerating electron is
eV, where e is the electronic charge and V is the accelerating voltage.   The
shortest wavelength of radiation is thus, from the Einstein equation,

$$\lambda = \frac{hc}{eV} = \frac{12.4}{V} \tag{5.1}$$

where c is the speed of light, λ is the wavelength in Å, and V is the voltage in
kilovolts.   The spectrum of white x-radiation depends on the target material
and the exciting voltage.   When the voltage is high enough, it is possible to
dislodge $1s$ electrons from the target nuclei.   When a $1s$ electron is excited to
the L shell ($n=2$) and returns to the K shell ($n=1$), a high-intensity $K\alpha$ radiation
is given off.   When a $1s$ electron is excited to the M shell ($n=3$) and returns to
the K shell, a lower-intensity, shorter wavelength $K\beta$ radiation is given off.
These emitted x-rays are called the characteristic x-rays for the target material.
Figure 5.6 shows the spectrum for a molybdenum target with a 35,000-volt
applied voltage.   Figure 5.7 shows the variation in frequency and wavelength
for the characteristic radiation as a function of the atomic number of the
target.   In x-ray diffraction work, one may use a beam of white x-radiation, but
very often the beam is filtered to produce a *monochromatic* (i.e., single-wave-
length) beam.

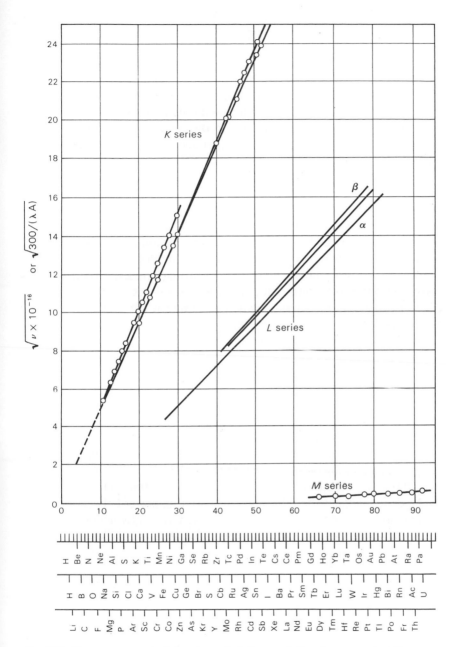

Fig. 5.7 The square root of the characteristic x-radiation frequency is a linear function of the atomic number of the target. (By permission from F. Daniels, "Outlines of Physical Chemistry," p. 622, John Wiley & Sons, Inc., New York, 1948.)

5.4
x-ray scattering

When monochromatic x-rays encounter an electron, the electron tends to vibrate at the same frequency as the radiation. These vibrations then generate secondary waves of the same frequency as the incident radiation. Since electromagnetic waves are propagated at right angles to the electrical vibrations, the intensity of the scattered radiation is angle-dependent, with a minimum occurring normal to the incident beam (Fig. 5.8):

$$\mathbf{I}(\theta) = \mathbf{I}(0) \, \frac{1 + \cos^2 \theta}{2} \tag{5.2}$$

where $\mathbf{I}(\theta)$ is the intensity of the scattered wave at the scattering angle θ.

When an incident beam strikes two electrons in close proximity, the intensity of the scattered radiation will be even more angle-dependent because of mutual interference of the two points. From Fig. 5.9 we see that the path length to the two electrons can be different. If the waves are not exactly in phase, there will be a destructive interference which will lower the net scattered radiation. When the path difference Δx is an exact multiple of the wavelength of the radiation, however, the two beams will reinforce each other. From Fig. 5.9 we see that

$$\Delta x = 2d \sin \theta \tag{5.3}$$

The intensity will be a maximum when $\Delta x = n\lambda$, where n is an integer; and the two beams cancel, giving zero intensity, when $\Delta x = (n + \frac{1}{2})\lambda$.

In an atom, one cannot consider the electrons as point scattering centers, but rather they must be considered as a charge distribution surrounding a nucleus. The scattering effect will be similar to that of a series of point centers, but the nature of the charge distribution and the structure of the atom will influence the angle dependence. The difference in scattering power between a charge distribution and a set of point centers is expressed by an *atomic-form factor*. In a polyatomic molecule, each atom in the molecule is at a different

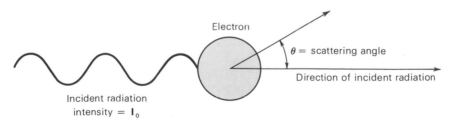

Fig. 5.8 Incident monochromatic x-radiation is scattered when it interacts with an electron.

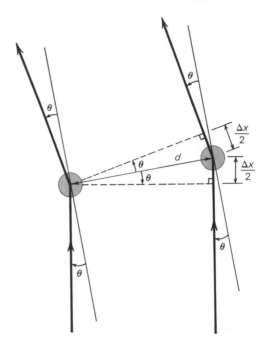

Fig. 5.9 When an x-ray interacts with two adjacent electrons, the intensity of the scattered radiation will depend on mutual interference or reinforcement of the scattered beams.

position and therefore the scattered waves from each atomic unit also interfere with one another, causing further change in the angle dependence of the scattered radiation. This is accounted for by a *molecular-form factor.* In principle, at least, it is possible to sort out these various factors and obtain information about the structure of the molecule from a measurement of the intensity as a function of scattering angle.

5.5
x-ray diffraction techniques

Figure 5.10 shows a strip of film curved into a circle, with the material being studied at the center of the circle. An incident x-ray beam enters from one end, interacts with the sample, and is scattered. If we are dealing with a dilute gas, the spacing of the molecules is large and each molecule can be considered as an independent scattering center. The scattered radiation impinges on the photographic film and darkens it wherever it passes through. The intensity of the exposure is a measure of the intensity of the radiation. Simple monoatomic gases and some diatomic molecules produce photographs in which the intensity falls off with no very sharp maxima or minima. A more complex molecule, such as CCl_4, produces a diffuse film with sharper concentric rings superimposed. These rings form at the proper angles for mutual reinforcement of the radiations from the adjacent scattering centers. The angles at which the maxima appear are related to the tetrahedral structure of the gas molecule.

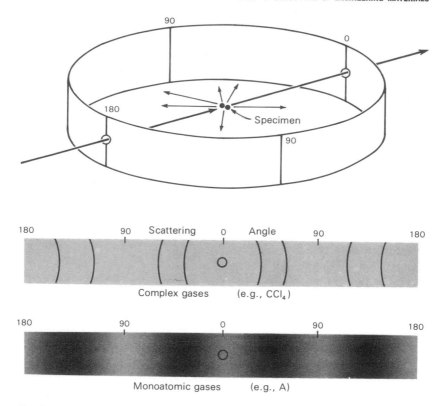

Fig. 5.10 Diffraction patterns for gases always have a diffuse background and sometimes show more intense regions associated with the molecular geometry.

Similar patterns are obtained when the sample is a liquid. The molecules of a liquid are so closely packed, however, that they cannot be independent scattering centers. Rather, there is a further intermolecular interference of the scattered radiation, giving a different x-ray diffraction photograph than that for the same material in the gaseous state. Figure 5.11 shows this schematically for carbon tetrachloride in the vapor and liquid states. The analysis of x-ray diffraction photographs has been extensively studied [1–4], but it is beyond the scope of this text.

The most important application of x-ray diffraction has been in the elucidation of simple crystalline solids. Analysis has proved that simple metallic, molecular, and salt crystals can be represented by a lattice of points, each of which has identical surroundings. A line of these points will scatter radiation in the same manner as two points, but the more points there are in a line, the sharper will be the change from intensity maxima to intensity minima. The diffraction photograph for an infinite row of points is thus a set of concentric cones with the maxima occurring at the angles that give path lengths in multiples of the radiation frequency. Reinforcement occurs when

$$n\lambda = 2d \sin \theta \tag{5.4}$$

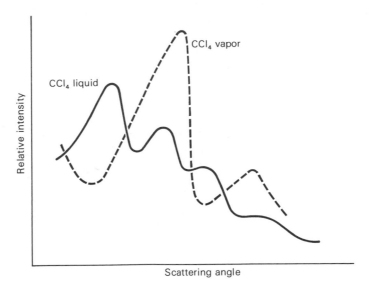

Fig. 5.11   The x-ray diffraction patterns for CCl_4 are different for the liquid and vapor states.

where n is any integer and the angle θ is as shown in Fig. 5.12.   Equation (5.4) is the Bragg equation.   A crystal lattice, however, is a three-dimensional network, so that each scattering center belongs to at least three different rows of points. The scattered radiation from each of these rows can be represented as a set of concentric cones, and reinforcement will occur only at the points of intersection of the three sets, as is shown in Fig. 5.13.   Thus, if a crystal structure has a

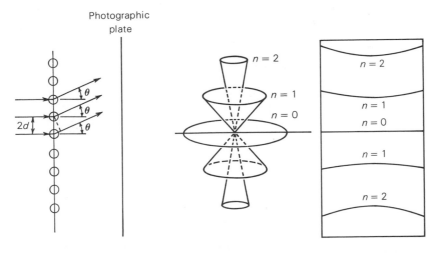

Fig. 5.12   Diffraction from a row of lattice points causes reinforcement at cone angles that give path lengths in multiples of the radiation frequency.

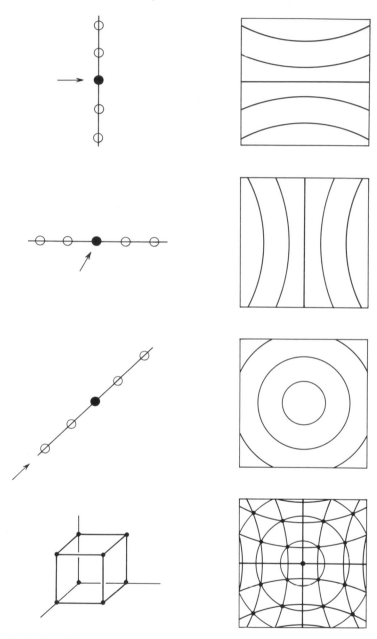

Fig. 5.13   The diffraction from a three-dimensional lattice of points results in a set of high-intensity spots on the photographic film.

cubic geometry, one would expect an x-ray diffraction photograph for a single crystal to appear as an orderly set of spots of different intensities, with the sharpness and position of the spots being controlled by the geometry of the crystal and the structure of the atoms. This, in fact, is precisely what one does get. Figure 5.14 is a diffraction photograph for an NaCl crystal. It is usually not too difficult to predict the x-ray diffraction pattern for a known structure, but the reverse task of determining an unknown structure from a diffraction photograph is extremely difficult.

There are three standard experimental techniques for determining the lattice dimensions by x-ray diffraction. In the *Laue Method,* a single crystal is held stationary and incident white radiation is reflected at a fixed angle θ (Fig. 5.15). The Bragg equation (5.4), can be satisfied, since a range of wavelengths is available. Each plane in the crystal can select the proper wavelength for reinforcement and produce a spot on the photographic plate. Analysis of the film will give the geometry of the crystal and the relative distances between different sets of planes. The absolute dimensions cannot be determined, since only angles are actually measured. In the *rotating-crystal method,* a single crystal is rotated in the path of a monochromatic x-ray beam. When a plane is rotated to the proper θ for the wavelength of the x-ray, a diffraction spot is

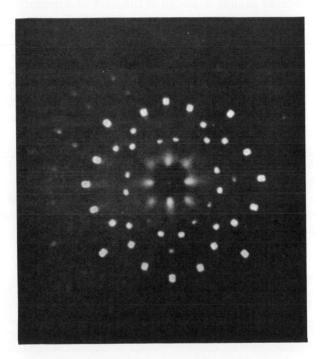

Fig. 5.14 The diffraction photograph of rock salt is typical of cubic, crystalline structures. (By permission from G. L. Clark, "Applied X-Rays," 4th ed., Fig. 194*b*, p. 361, McGraw-Hill Book Company, New York, 1955.)

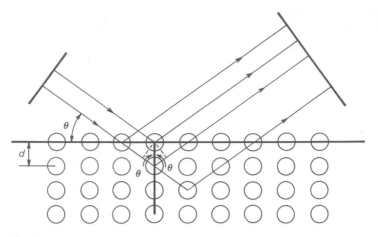

Fig. 5.15   Reflection of x-rays showing reinforcement at $n\lambda = 2d \sin\theta$.

produced.   Since the wavelength and the angle are known, the interatomic separation d can be calculated by using Eq. (5.4).   In the *powder method,* a finely powdered sample is placed in the path of a monochromatic x-ray.   The sample contains a multitude of very small, randomly oriented crystals, which is equivalent to having planes of atoms at all possible angles to the incident radiation.   A plane at the proper angle for satisfying Bragg's equation will thus produce a spot on the photographic film.   Since planes are at all possible angles, a cone of radiation rather than just a spot strikes the film.   A typical powder diagram is shown in Fig. 5.16.   Since the wavelength is known, the diameter of the concentric rings can be related to the interatomic distances between the various crystal planes.

Recalling our definition of lattice parameters as the lengths of the edges of the unit cell along the reference axes, one can easily show how these may be calculated for simple cubic crystals.   For the simple cubic cell shown in Fig. 5.1, the lattice parameters are $a = b = c$.   If the reflecting planes have the Miller indices (hkl), the relationship between the lattice parameter a and the interplanar spacing d is given by

Fig. 5.16   The powder diffraction pattern for metallic lead is typical for crystalline materials.   The structure is related to the spacing of the high-intensity rings.   (By permission, from G. L. Clark, "Applied X-Rays," 4th ed., fig. 209, p. 374, McGraw-Hill Book Company, New York, 1955.)

$$d^2 = \frac{a^2}{h^2 + k^2 + l^2} \tag{5.5}$$

The Bragg equation for a cubic crystal is

$$\sin^2 \theta_{hkl} = \frac{\lambda^2}{4a^2} (h^2 + k^2 + l^2) \tag{5.6}$$

One must therefore measure all the values of θ which produce reinforcement and then associate them with the proper reflecting planes. The quantity $(h^2 + k^2 + l^2)$ can have any integral value except 7, 15, 23, 28, 31, ... Simple cubic lattices can reflect from all values of $h^2 + k^2 + l^2$, while other cubic lattices have characteristic absences that serve to identify the lattices. Face-centered cells will reflect only from planes where $h^2 + k^2 + l^2 = 3, 4, 8, 11, 12, 16, \ldots$; body-centered cells will reflect only from planes where $h^2 + k^2 + l^2 = 2, 4, 6, 8, 10, \ldots$.

There are many other techniques for structure elucidation which use electromagnetic radiation, electron beams, or neutron beams. References that thoroughly discuss all of these are listed in the bibliography.

5.6
The structure of simple crystals

The long-range symmetry properties of many important engineering materials can be described in terms of simple crystal lattices. The ion cores of most metals, for example, can be represented by rigid, perfect spheres arranged in a hexagonal close-packed, face-centered cubic, or body-centered cubic space lattice. The first two types can be visualized by stacking rigid spheres on a flat surface.

Figure 5.17a shows a layer of rigid spheres stacked in such a way as to occupy the smallest possible volume. In such a "close-packed" arrangement, each sphere is in contact with six neighbors. In order to close-pack a second layer over the first, each sphere must be placed in the depression between three touching spheres of the first layer. Figure 5.17b shows it is possible to fill the depressions of every other row. If the spheres of the third layer are then placed directly over the spheres of the first layer, as shown in Fig. 5.17c, the result is a hexagonal close-packed structure. Crystals of beryllium, cadmium, magnesium, titanium, and zinc are all examples of hexagonal close-packed structures. The hexagonal-shaped cell shown in Fig. 5.16d and e has a density of six spheres per cell, while the unit cell, also shown, has a density of two spheres per cell.

An alternative way of stacking the third layer is to place the spheres in the depressions between three touching spheres of the second layer so that the third layer does not repeat the first. The fourth layer may then be stacked so as to repeat the first. The result is the close-packed, face-centered cubic structure shown in Fig. 5.18.

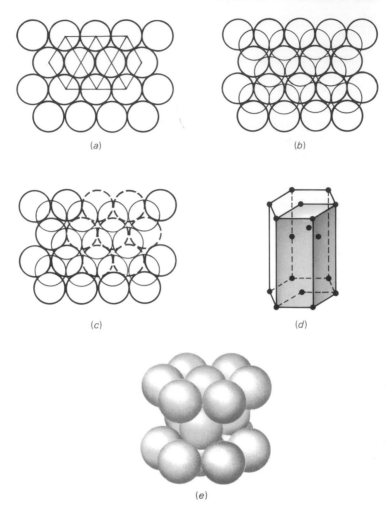

Fig. 5.17 Hexagonal close-packing of spheres gives a coordination number of 12. (a) First close-packed layer; (b) two close-packed layers; (c) three close-packed layers in a hexagonal arrangement; (d) unit cell for hexagonal close-packed array; (e) three-dimensional model.

The face-centered cubic unit cell contains 14 spheres each of which is surrounded by 12 nearest neighbors. Each corner is shared by 7 other unit cells, and each face-centered sphere is shared with another unit cell. The density is thus 4 spheres per unit cell. Silver, aluminum, copper, lead, and platinum are examples of metals that have face-centered cubic structures.

A third type of crystal structure is represented by the body-centered cubic space lattice shown in Fig. 5.19. The unit cell consists of 8 corner spheres plus one in the center of the cell. Each has 8 nearest neighbors, and the density is 2 spheres per unit cell. Sodium, tungsten, molybdenum, and alpha iron are examples of metals with body-centered cubic structures.

Not all metals can be classified into these three structural arrangements, but quite a few can be. Why one type of regular close-packed arrangement is preferred to another depends on the nature of the bonding. Since non-nearest neighbors also contribute to the potential energy of an atom, slight changes in the long-range order can change the average potential energy of the structure; the most stable state is the one of lowest free energy. It is only on this basis that a preference for a body-centered structure, with only eight nearest neighbors, can be explained. The low coordination number is compensated by the presence of six next-nearest neighbors. Some metals show a preference for one structure at one temperature and pressure and a different structure at another set of conditions. The transition from one crystal structure to another at a definite temperature is called a *polymorphic change.* The polymorphic forms of a few materials are indicated in Table 5.2.

The geometry of salt crystals is similar to that of metals. Ionic crystals are slightly more complicated because they usually have two ions of different size. Figures 5.20 and 5.21 illustrate two of the most common, and simplest, of the salt crystals. In each case the tendency is for each ion to be surrounded by a maximum number of ions of *opposite* charge. The maximum number of nearest

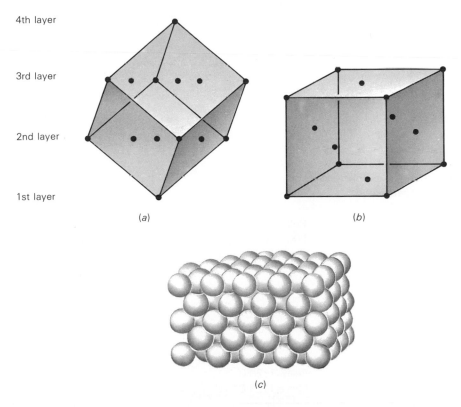

4th layer

3rd layer

2nd layer

1st layer

(a)

(b)

(c)

Fig. 5.18 Face-centered cubic close-packing of spheres gives a coordination number of 12. (a) Unit cell oriented relative to four adjacent close-packed layers; (b) unit cell reoriented; (c) a three-dimensional model.

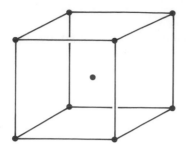 

Fig. 5.19 Body-centered cubic packing of spheres gives a coordination number of 8.

Table 5.2

The crystal structures of some metals

Metal	Structure	Temp. range
Zinc	Hcp	
Cadmium	Hcp	
Lanthanum	Hcp	Below 350°C
	Fcc	Above 350°C
Copper	Fcc	
Silver	Fcc	
Gold	Fcc	
Calcium	Fcc	Below 440°C
	Hcp 1.638 (axial ratio)	Above 440°C
Mercury	Simple rhombohedral	
Aluminum	Fcc	
Carbon	Diamond cube	
	Graphite	
Tin	Diamond cube (gray)	Below 13°C
	Tetragonal (axial ratio 0.546	Above 13°C
Lead	Fcc	
Iron	Bcc, α	Below 906°C
	Fcc, γ	906–1401°C
	Bcc, δ	Above 1401°C
Nickel	Fcc	
Thallium	Hcp	Below 234°C
	Bcc	Above 234°C
Titanium	Hcp	Below 882°C
	Bcc	Above 882°C
Zirconium	Hcp	Below 852°C
	Bcc	Above 852°C
Cobalt	Hcp	Below 1120°C
	Bcc	Above 1120°C

Bcc = body-centered cubic; Fcc = face-centered cubic; Hcp = hexagonal close-packed.

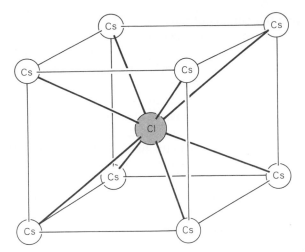

Fig. 5.20 Cesium chloride has a body-centered cubic structure in which each chloride ion is surrounded by eight cesium atoms, and vice versa.

neighbors will be a function of the difference in diameters of the two ions. The highest number of nearest neighbors in a cubic lattice of spherical particles was shown to be 12 for metals, where all atoms were the same size. As the difference in size between cation and anion increases, the maximum number of nearest neighbors decreases. Thus cesium chloride, with a radius ratio of $r+/r- = 0.91$, can have a body-centered cubic structure with eight cesium ions

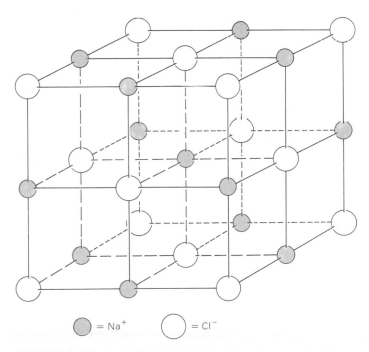

= Na$^+$ = Cl$^-$

Fig. 5.21 Sodium chloride is a simple cubic structure with alternate positions occupied by positive and negative ions and in which each ion is surrounded by six neighbors of opposite charge.

occupying the corners of the unit cell and a chloride ion occupying the center. In this way, both size and valency requirements (1 to 1) are met. Sodium chloride, with a radius ratio of $r+/r- = 0.54$, can have a simple cubic structure with alternate positions occupied by positive and negative ions. Thus, each sodium ion is surrounded by six nearest-neighbor chloride ions, and vice versa.

The diamond cubic structure, shown in Fig. 4.13, is also of very practical importance. The strong covalent bonds of the tetrahedral bonding unit prevent the close-packing of atoms and limit the number of nearest neighbors to four. The unit cell, shown in the figure, contains eight atoms per cell. Silicon, germanium, and gray tin, which are important semiconducting materials, also form crystals of this type.

It should be noted that a crystal is rarely a perfect array of spheres and that many stacking faults, point imperfections, and other defects can appear. Sometimes very small and subtle changes in the structure can have a large effect on the bulk properties of the solid. These imperfections will be discussed in later chapters.

5.7
Bonding in simple crystals

If each particle in a solid were at rest at a point in the space lattice, it would have a specific potential energy, $\frac{1}{2}\psi_{aT}$ energy per particle. It would require $(N/2)\psi_{aT}$ units of energy to separate a solid of N particles into its constituent particles. When the amount of this "lattice energy" is much greater than the energy associated with the thermal motions (i.e., Brownian motions) of the particles, the solid is stable. This potential energy, or lattice energy, is a function of the geometry of the structure and the nature of the intermolecular forces between pairs of particles. It can be calculated by adding up all the interactions of a given particle with its surroundings. Let us make these calculations for a few simple crystals.

Consider first a crystal consisting of spherical, nonpolar atoms. Suppose the potential energy of interaction between a pair of these atoms can be represented by the general equation

$$\psi_{ab} = -\frac{a}{r^n} + \frac{b}{r^m} \tag{5.7}$$

and that N such atoms form a crystal lattice with each particle having δ nearest neighbors. The total potential energy for atom a is the sum of the interactions with all of the other atoms in the lattice:

$$\psi_{aT} = \sum_{i=1}^{N-1} -\frac{a}{r_{ai}{}^n} + \frac{b}{r_{ai}{}^m} \tag{5.8}$$

This summation can be rewritten in terms of the nearest-neighbor distance r by merely rewriting the r_{ai} in terms of multiples of r. In the body-centered cubic structure, for example (Fig. 5.19), there are eight nearest neighbors at a distance r, six next-nearest neighbors at a distance $\sqrt{4/3}\,r$, twelve atoms in the next layer at $\sqrt{8/3}\,r$, and so forth.   Since the intensity of the forces varies inversely with high powers of r, one usually need not consider more than a few layers of atoms.   The total interaction potential can be expressed as

$$\psi_{aT} = -_{\delta}\left(\frac{s_a a}{r^n} - \frac{s_b b}{r^m}\right) \tag{5.9}$$

where $_{\delta}$ is the number of nearest neighbors and the constants s_a and s_b are characteristic of the lattice geometry and the types of forces.   Several values are tabulated in Table 5.3.   On applying the equilibrium conditions $d\psi_{aT}/dr = 0$ and $\psi_{aT} = (\psi_{aT})_{r=r_0}$ at $r = r_0$, one obtains:

$$\psi_{aT} = \frac{(\psi_{aT})_{r=r_0}}{m-n}\left[m\left(\frac{r_0}{r}\right)^n - n\left(\frac{r_0}{r}\right)^m\right] \tag{5.10}$$

The total lattice energy, in energy per mole, for a crystal of N identical atoms is thus

$$\psi_T = \frac{N(\psi_{aT})_{r=r_0}}{2(m-n)}\left[m\left(\frac{r_0}{r}\right)^n - n\left(\frac{r_0}{r}\right)^m\right] \tag{5.11}$$

where the factor of $1/2$ accounts for the fact that each particle is counted twice. Equation (5.11) gives the total bonding energy of a crystal when all the particles are at rest at their own lattice points.

For a face-centered cubic crystal of neon, $n = 6$, $m = 12$, $a = 128$, $b = 59{,}100$ [see Eq. (3.50)], and also $s_a = 1.2045$ and $s_b = 1.011$, to give $\psi_T = -0.600$ kcal/g mole (-2.55×10^6 joules/kg mole) and $r_0 = 3.03$ Å. The observed value of r_0 is 3.1 Å at the crystallization temperature of 24.5°K.   Since the thermal energy, $3/2 RT$, is about 0.900 kcal/g mole (3.77×10^6 joules/kg mole) at room temperature, neon is a gas at this temperature. This kind of calculation can be made with any simple molecular crystal if one has values for the molecular constants.

The total lattice energy for ionic crystals is calculated in a similar manner. The total potential energy for a single ion in a crystal lattice of $2N$ ions (that is, N molecules of salt) is

---

Table 5.3

Summation constants for different cubic lattices

n or m	No. of nearest neighbors		
	$_{\delta} = 6$	$_{\delta} = 8$	$_{\delta} = 12$
6	1.4003	1.5317	1.2045
9	1.1048	1.2368	1.0410
12	1.0337	1.1394	1.0110

$$\psi_{aT} = \sum_{i=1}^{2N-1} \frac{q_a q_i}{r_{ai}} + \frac{b}{r_{ai}{}^m} \qquad (5.12)$$

In terms of the nearest-neighbor distance r, Eq. (5.12), is

$$\psi_{aT} = \frac{3s_b b}{r^m} - \frac{\mathfrak{A}e^2}{r}$$

$$= \frac{(\psi_{aT})_{r=r_0}}{m-1} \left[m \frac{r_0}{r} - \left(\frac{r_0}{r} \right)^m \right] \qquad (5.13)$$

The total lattice energy per N molecules of salt ($2N$ ions) is then

$$\psi_T = \frac{N(\psi_{aT})_{r=r_0}}{m-1} \left[m \frac{r_0}{r} - \left(\frac{r_0}{r} \right)^m \right] \qquad (5.14)$$

The quantity $\mathfrak{A}$, known as the Madelung constant, is tabulated in Table 5.4 for various salt crystals. In Chap. 3 we estimated the potential-energy function for pairs of ions, and these estimates can be used to give reasonably good predictions of the total lattice energies for crystals. Actually, there has been extensive research done in this area and analysis has been carried out with potential-energy functions that include induction effects, dispersion attractions, and more accurate repulsion terms [7]. A comparison of some theoretical and experimental lattice energies is given in Table 5.5.

The lattice energies for metals are much more difficult to predict. The total lattice energy consists of electrostatic interactions between the geometrically arranged ion cores, electrostatic interactions between valence electrons, and the interaction energy between the electrons and the ion cores. The problem is that one cannot write down a simple potential-energy function to represent these interactions, but rather a detailed knowledge of the electron distribution is required.

The nature of the bonding forces in a metallic crystal may be visualized by considering the formation of metallic sodium. Each isolated atom has one $3s$ valence electron. As two atoms approach one another, the potential energy

---

Table 5.4

Madelung constants for ionic crystals

Structure	$\mathfrak{A}$
NaCl	1.7476
CsCl	1.7627
ZnS (diamond lattice)	1.6381
CaF₂	5.0388
Cu₂O	4.1155

Table 5.5

Theoretical and experimental lattice energies for ionic crystals at room temperature *

		Lattice energy, kcal/mole †	
Crystal	Lattice parameter, Å	Theoretical	Experimental
LiCl	5.13	199.2	198.1
LiBr	5.49	188.3	189.3
NaCl	5.63	183.1	182.8
NaBr	5.96	174.6	173.3
KCl	6.28	165.4	164.4
KBr	6.59	159.3	156.2
KI	7.05	150.8	151.5
CsCl	4.11	152.2	155.1
AgCl	5.55	203	205.7
CuCl	5.41	216	221.9

* Data are taken from C. Kittel, "Introduction to Solid State Physics," 2d ed., p. 80, John Wiley & Sons, Inc., New York, 1956.
† Multiply by 4.186×10^6 to get joules/kg mole.

between the atoms decreases and the electronic density increases. One may thus visualize a "covalent" bond forming through a "sharing" of $3s$ electrons with the molecular orbitals as combinations of the original atomic orbitals. Since the valence electrons are relatively far removed from the nuclei, a relatively weak covalent bond is formed. Since sodium packs into a body-centered cubic crystal, seven other sodium atoms, with unshared electrons, can approach the first pair. Since $3p$ states have approximately the same energy as $3s$ states, there are potentially a large number of available molecular orbitals which allow much the same kind of covalent bonding as with the first pair. The eight adjacent orbitals of nearest neighbors tend to overlap and "take turns" in forming weak covalent bonds with the single valence electron of the central atom.

The metallic bond is thus visualized as a covalent bond weak enough to be easily broken and reformed, thus allowing a large number of atoms to be held together by the mutual sharing of their valence electrons. The electronic density between the atoms is much lower than the maximum allowed by the Pauli exclusion principle, which permits the valence electrons to move freely from one atom to the next without an appreciable change in potential energy. The valence electrons spend only a fraction of their time between two specific atoms, bonding alternately with other neighbors the rest of the time. Although each fractional bond is relatively weak, the total cohesive energy of a crystal is the sum of the energies of all of these "fractional" covalent bonds.

The lattice energy can be calculated by the method of Wigner and Seitz [8]. The general technique may be outlined as follows. A body-centered or a face-centered cubic crystal is divided into a network of polyhedra with one polyhedron surrounding each atom in the crystal. To a good approximation, each polyhedron is a sphere with a radius r_0 fixed by the volume per atom of the crystal. Within each sphere is a positively charged ionic core, located at the center, plus a valence electron (for a univalent metal). The lattice energy then consists of the interaction energy of each electron with its own ionic core plus the interaction energy between spheres. Since each sphere is neutral, the latter term is a relatively small dispersion interaction. The idea is then to assume a spherically symmetric potential-energy function $\psi(r)$ for the electron in the field of its ionic core and calculate the total energy E_0 from the wave equation for the electron,

$$\frac{1}{r^2}\frac{d}{dr}\left(r^2\frac{d\Psi_0}{dr}\right) + \frac{8\pi^2 m}{h^2}[E_0 - \psi(r)]\Psi_0 = 0 \tag{5.15}$$

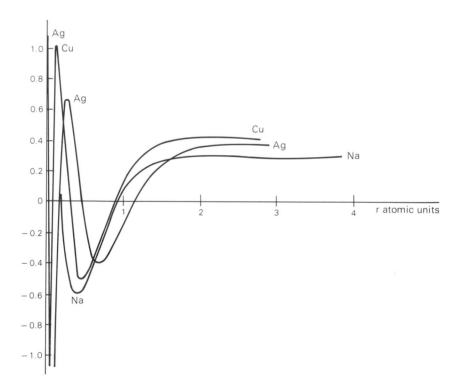

Fig. 5.22 Wave functions of electrons in lowest states of metals, the wave functions normalized so that $\int \Psi^2 r^2\,dr = 1$. The values of r_0 for which these are calculated Cu, 2.65; Ag, 2.9; Na, 3.88 (atomic units = 0.54 Å). (By permission from N. F. Mott, and H. Jones, "The Theory of the Properties of Metals and Alloys," p. 79, Dover Publications, Inc., New York, 1958.)

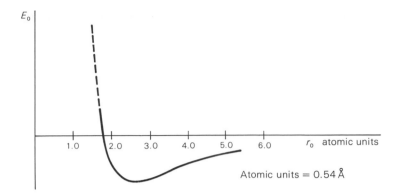

Fig. 5.23 The schematic of the ground-state energy of a valance electron as a function of the interatomic separation. The most stable state occurs at the separation corresponding to the minimum.

using the boundary condition that the first derivative of the wave function goes to zero at the surface of the sphere:

$$\left(\frac{d\Psi_0}{dr}\right)_{r=r_0} = 0 \qquad (5.16)$$

The solutions to these equations are beyond the scope of this text, but one can solve to obtain both the wave function Ψ_0, shown in Fig. 5.22 for a few metals, and the total binding energy E_0 as a function of r_0 (Fig. 5.23). This technique and other modifications have been successful in predicting the lattice energies of simple metals such as sodium and lithium, which are univalent and have a small ionic radius relative to the distance between atoms in the crystal. A discussion of how the lattice energy per electron is related to the measured binding energy of the crystal must be deferred to Chap. 13, on the electronic properties of metals.

References

1 Barrett, C. S.: "Structure of Metals," 2d ed., McGraw Hill Book Company, New York, 1952. *A reference text on crystallography and a summary of published literature on the structure of metals.*

2 Buerger, M. J.: "Crystal Structure Analysis," John Wiley & Sons, Inc., New York, 1960. *Supplies detailed methods for determining geometry of crystals and formulates the theory underlying the techniques.*

3 Bunn, C. W.: "Chemical Crystallography," 2d ed., Oxford University Press, London, 1961. *A standard reference on the techniques of x-ray diffraction.*

4 Clark, G. L.: "Applied X-Rays," McGraw-Hill Book Company, New York, 1955. *A thorough coverage of all aspects of x-ray technology.*

5 Cottrell, A. H.: "Theoretical Structural Metallurgy," St. Martin's Press, Inc., New York 1960. *Several chapters on structure of metals and cohesion in metals.*

6 Hume-Rothery, W., and G. V. Raynor: "Structure of Metals and Alloys," Institute of Metals, London, 1954. *A good reference on crystal structure.*

7 Kittel, C.: "Introduction to Solid State Physics," John Wiley & Sons, Inc., New York, 1956. *A very readable summary of space lattices, cohesion energy in crystals, and many other aspects of the analysis of crystal structures. A highly recommended text.*

8 Mott, N. F., and H. Jones: "The Theory of Metals and Alloys," Dover Publications, Inc., New York, 1958. *Reprint of a classic work in the field of metals. The fourth chapter, Cohesion, summarizes the Wigner-Seitz and other methods.*

9 Smith, M. C.: "Principles of Physical Metallurgy," Harper & Row, Publishers, Incorporated, New York, 1956. *A very readable text on crystal structure of metals. Discussions of space lattices are especially pertinent to this chapter.*

Questions

5.1 Copper has a face-centered cubic lattice with a lattice parameter of 3.6096 Å. The atomic weight is 63.54 g/g atom. Calculate the density at 25°C and compare it with a value from a handbook.

5.2 Sketch the body-centered cubic, face-centered cubic, and hexagonal close-packed unit cells. Find and label the planes with highest atomic density (i.e., the close-packed planes). Find and label the directions in the unit cell that have the greatest number of atoms per unit length (i.e., the close-packed directions).

5.3 What kind of a volume change would you expect in pure iron on cooling through the transformation temperature 1670°F?

$$\gamma\text{-Iron (face-centered cubic)} \xrightarrow[\text{heating}]{\text{cooling}} \alpha\text{-iron (body centered cubic)}$$

How is this related to the internal stresses developed on quenching iron or steel?

Atomic radius bcc structure $= 1.248$ Å
Atomic radius fcc structure $= 1.292$ Å

5.4 Describe all of the polymorphic transformations in pure iron. In what ways are polymorphic transformations analogous to fusion and boiling?

5.5 Why do most simple metals crystallize to a lattice in which each ionic core has 8 or 12 nearest neighbors?

5.6 The ionic radii of Na^+, Cs^+, and Cl^- are 0.980 Å, 1.650 Å, and 1.810 Å, respectively. Assume that the ions can be represented by spheres and that at an equilibrium spacing the spheres are just touching each other. Determine the maximum number of nearest-neighbor anions that each cation can have in the crystals NaCl and CsCl.

5.7 Derive Eq. (5.11) for the lattice energy of a molecular crystal.

5.8 Show that the summation constant s_a is 1.2045 for dispersion attraction ($n = 6$) in a close-packed structure ($\mathfrak{z} = 12$).

5.9   Derive Eq. (5.14) for the lattice energy of a simple salt. *Hints:* Let $r_{1j} = \lambda_{1j}r$, where $r =$ nearest-neighbor separation. Obtain:

$$\psi_1 = \frac{b\sum_j 1/\lambda_{1j}{}^m}{r^m} - \frac{\mathfrak{A}e^2}{r}$$

where $\mathfrak{A} = \sum_j \frac{(\mp)}{\lambda_{1j}}$. Use the condition $(\partial\psi/\partial r) = 0$ at $r = r_0$ to eliminate $b\sum_j 1/\lambda_{1j}{}^m$. Then calculate the total lattice energy for $2N$ ions at their equilibrium separation.

5.10   Evaluate the Madelung constant $\mathfrak{A}$ for sodium chloride. *Hints:*

$$\mathfrak{A} = \sum_j \frac{(\mp)}{\lambda_{1j}}$$

Take a negative ion as the reference ion and use the plus sign for interactions with positive ions and the minus sign for interactions with other negative ions. The sodium chloride structure is a simple cube with sodium and chloride in alternating positions. Start at a negative ion. At $\lambda = 1$ (the nearest neighbors) there are 6 positive ions giving a contribution of $+6$ to $\mathfrak{A}$. At $\lambda = \sqrt{2}$ there are 12 negative ions giving a contribution of $-12/\sqrt{2}$ to $\mathfrak{A}$. Continue this scheme to account for all other ions until the series appears to be converging to a constant value.

5.11   Show that $\lambda = hc/eV = 12.4/V$, where λ is in Å and V is in kilovolts. Remember that 1 volt $= 1$ joule/coul.

5.12   Calculate the wavelength of an electron beam that is accelerated by a 30,000-volt potential. Remember the De Broglie equation (3.9). What is the shortest wavelength of white x-radiation that can be produced by such a beam?

5.13   The characteristic $(K\alpha)$ radiation is usually emitted in a $2p \rightarrow 1s$ transition. Calculate the energy of the $2p$ state for **Mg, Cu, Mo,** and **W,** using Fig. 5.7. The energy values for the $1s$ states are **Mg,** 1,300 ev; **Mo,** 20,000 ev; **Cu,** 9,000 ev; **W,** 70,000 ev. 1 joule/molecule $= 6.2422 \times 10^{18}$ ev $= 1.5098 \times 10^{33}$ sec^{-1}.

5.14   Table 5.6 gives angles of diffraction in a tantalum powder-diffraction photograph using x-radiation with a wavelength of 1.5405 Å (Cu-K α radiation).

Table 5.6 *

Line	θ, deg	Line	θ, deg
1	19.611	6	54.119
2	28.136	7	60.876
3	35.156	8	68.912
4	41.564	9	81.520
5	47.769		

* From T. S. Hutchison and D. C. Baird, "The Physics of Engineering Solids," John Wiley & Sons, Inc., New York, 1963.

Use Eq. (5.6) to calculate the lattice parameter. Tantalum is a body-centered cubic structure. Prove that the best value of the lattice parameter will be obtained by extrapolating
the calculated results to $\theta = 90°$.

5.15 The potential energy of interaction between two neon atoms was estimated, in Chap.
3, as

$$\psi_{Ne-Ne} = -\frac{128}{r^6} + \frac{59,100}{r^{12}} \text{ kcal/g mole of bonds}$$

Use this to estimate the maximum lattice energy for a face-centered neon crystal.

5.16 Use the data of Table 2.1 and Table 3.3 to estimate the intermolecular potential between a cesium cation and a chloride anion. Estimate the lattice energy for a cesium chloride crystal with a lattice parameter of 4.11 Å. Compare your result with the experimental
value of 155.1 kcal/g mole and discuss the reasons for any differences.

6
Formation of metallic materials

6.1
Introduction

There are many important engineering materials that have simple crystal structures. Single crystals of silicon, germanium, cadmium sulfide, lead sulfide, and cuprous chloride, among others, are used in a very pure form as semiconductors for rectifiers, transistors, and the like. There are also a variety of oxides, carbides, borides, and nitrides that have simple crystal structures and are commercially important refractory materials. The most widely used engineering materials, however, are the metallic crystals.

The "engineering" metals are of great value for both economic reasons and uniqueness of properties. The economics is determined by the abundance of the element in the earth and the ease with which the element can be extracted from its ore. The unique properties are varied, but among the most important are the ability to conduct heat and electricity, the ability to become hardened and strengthened by deformation, the ability to be fabricated and the ability to combine with other materials to form *alloys*. The most important engineering materials are formed from iron, copper, aluminum, tin, zinc, lead, nickel, and magnesium. An almost endless variety of materials of construction can be formed in either the pure state or in combination with each other. In addition to these eight, there are a number of less frequently used metals that also have important applications. Among these are antimony, beryllium, cadmium, chromium, cobalt, colombium, gold, magnesium, mercury, molybdenum, platinum, palladium, rhodium, titanium, tungsten, vanadium, and zirconium.

Usually, engineering metals are "polycrystalline" or, in other words, are made up of large numbers of crystals held together by *grain boundaries*. The size and orientation of these crystals, or *grains,* and the nature of the grain boundaries all contribute to the physical properties of the material. The microscopic structure of the solid is a consequence of the way in which the metal is formed.

In this chapter, we shall consider the factors that influence the formation of a polycrystalline material. Although most of the discussion refers specifically to metals, the general concepts are applicable to other simple crystal structures as well.

6.2
Metallurgical methods

Metallurgy is the art and science of utilizing metallic elements. First of all, the metal must be *recovered* from its ore. This usually involves a preliminary concentrating step, followed by a reduction of metal oxides and a final refining step for removing unwanted impurities. Second, the refined metal is usually *cast* in the form of an ingot. This step involves the crystallization of a molten metal. Finally, the cast ingot is heat-treated and worked into a final consumer or industrial product.

Over 50 percent of the earth's crust (on the average) consists of seven elements: silicon (27.6 percent), aluminum (8.1 percent), iron (5.1 percent), calcium (3.6 percent), sodium (2.8 percent), potassium (2.6 percent), and magnesium (2.1 percent). All other metals are in much smaller percentages. Occasionally, one particular element will be found in an unusually high concentration. Such a deposit is called an *ore*. A metal will usually be present in an ore in a combined state. Hematite, for example, is an iron ore in which the iron is combined as an oxide, Fe_2O_3. A commercial ore of this type might contain 50 to 70 percent iron by weight. Magnesite is a magnesium ore in which the metal is present as $MgCO_3$ and, when pure, contains 28.8 percent magnesium. Ores generally contain smaller percentages of oxides of other metals as well. Since some of these "impurities" might be less active chemically than the major constituent, there is always the problem of removing these compounds in refining operations. Table 6.1 indicates a few of the mineral sources that are exploited as ores.

Very often, an ore must first be concentrated before the metal oxides can be economically reduced to the pure state. These concentration operations may involve *roasting* to change the chemical nature of the metal or impurities, *leaching* to separate the metal from the rest of the ore, or physical separation methods, such as a gravity separation technique.

An illustration of the need for a roasting operation is galena, PbS, which is not reduced readily by carbon or carbon monoxide. The galena is thus first oxidized in continuous sintering machines which reach temperatures of about 800°C. At these temperatures the ores become sticky and tend to agglomerate.

The final sintered product might contain roughly 52 percent lead, 2 percent sulfur, 8 percent silica, 15 percent iron oxide, 3 percent lime, and small percents of other oxides. The most common oxidation reactions on the lead are

$$2PbS + 3O_2 \rightleftharpoons 2PbO + 2SO_2$$

$$2PbO + 2SO_2 + O_2 \rightleftharpoons 2PbSO_4$$

$$2PbO + SiO_2 \rightleftharpoons 2PbO \cdot SiO_2 \text{ (slag)}$$

Oxidations of other impurities also occur. Generally, an objective of the sintering operation is to minimize the sulfides and sulfates, since the oxides are more easily reduced to metallic lead.

Leaching is an effective concentration step when ores can be roasted to a soluble form. Copper ores, for example, may be partially refined to soluble copper and copper sulfates, which can then be leached in sulfuric acid. A typical leached solution might contain 3 to 4 percent copper in 10 to 15 percent sulfuric acid. Very pure copper may then be deposited electrolytically on a cathode in an electrolytic cell.

Table 6.1

Some illustrations of metal ores

Metal	Ore – types
Aluminum	Bauxite: $Al_2O_3 \cdot 3H_2O$, $Al_2O_3 \cdot 4H_2O$, oxide impurities of Fe, Si, Ti
Copper	Types: Native ores, 1 to 2% Cu; oxide ores contain varying amounts of $CuCO_3 \cdot Cu(OH)_2$, $2CuCO_3 \cdot Cu(OH)_2$, Cu_2O, $CuO \cdot SiO_2 \cdot H_2O$, and other oxides; sulfide ores contain varying amounts of $CuFeS_2 \cdot Cu_2S$, $3Cu_2S \cdot Fe_2S_3$ and other complex sulfides
Iron	Hematite, Fe_2O_3 (ore might contain about 50% iron); hydrated iron oxides, $mFe_2O_3 \cdot nH_2O$ (e.g., limonite); magnetite, Fe_3O_4 (ores might contain about 63% iron); siderite, $FeCO_3$
Lead	Galena, PbS, sometimes occurs pure; anglesite, $PbSO_4$ (often 4 to 5% lead in ore); cerrussite, $PbCO_3$, a very common oxidized ore
Magnesium	Carnallite, $MgCl_2 \cdot KCl \cdot 6H_2O$; magnesite, $MgCO_3$; dolomite, $MgCO_3 \cdot CaCO_3$; brucite, $Mg(OH)_2$. These minerals are generally found in low concentrations
Nickel	Complex nickel-copper sulfide mixed with Fe_8S_9, $CuFeS_2$, $(FeNi)_{11}S_{10}$ (2 to 4% Ni)
Tin	Cassiterite, SnO_2 (ore usually less than 8% tin)
Zinc	Calamine, $ZnO \cdot Zn(OH)_2 \cdot SiO_2$; sphalerite, ZnS; zincite, ZnO; willemite, $2ZnO \cdot SiO_2$

The type of concentrating step used is highly specific, the treating of each ore being an art in itself. These two illustrations merely show the kinds of things that might be done. Once an ore had been suitably concentrated, the metal oxide may then be reduced to the pure state. The reduction of lead oxide to metallic lead, for example, occurs rapidly at 1000°C in the presence of carbon monoxide or carbon. Typical reduction reactions are

$$2PbO + C \rightleftharpoons 2Pb + CO_2$$

$$PbO + CO \rightleftharpoons Pb + CO_2$$

$$PbO + Fe \rightleftharpoons Pb + FeO$$

$$2PbO + PbS \rightleftharpoons 3Pb + SO_2$$

Any number of other reactions may also occur, depending on the composition of the charge. The optimum operation of a blast furnace depends on the furnace design, the charge, the fuel, the air, mixing, and other variables. Again, each operation is an art in itself and we can do no more than illustrate with a typical case.

The type of reduction method that can be used depends on the stability of the pure metal at the operating conditions of the furnace. The stability of the pure metal is determined by the *free energy of formation*, ΔG_f, in a combined state. For a simple oxide MO, for example,

$$M + \tfrac{1}{2}O \rightleftharpoons MO$$

the free energy of formation at constant temperature is

$$\Delta G_f = \Delta H - T \, \Delta S$$

where ΔH is the enthalpy (or heat) of reaction and ΔS is the entropy of reaction. When ΔG_f is negative, the reaction is spontaneous; when ΔG_f is positive, the reaction does not occur spontaneously. Table 6.2 lists the free energies of formation for a number of metal oxides at different temperatures. Negative free energy of formation means that the oxide is more stable than the pure metal at the given temperature. Positive free energy of formation means that the pure material is more stable. Only the *noble metals*, silver, gold, platinum, etc., exist as pure metals in the earth's crust because of this. Table 6.2 shows, however, that as temperature increases, the free energy of formation becomes less negative, thus increasing the relative stability of the pure metal. From data of this type, one can determine whether a given metal can be purified under a given set of blast furnace conditions.

Pure iron, for example, is formed in a blast furnace into which is charged the ore, coke, air, and a limestone carrier that can combine with the non-metallic portion of the ore to form a low-melting slag that separates from the metal. The potential reduction reactions (neglecting FeO formation) are

$$Fe_2O_3 + 3CO \rightarrow 2Fe + 3CO_2$$

$$Fe_2O_3 + 3C \rightarrow 2Fe + 3CO$$

The overall free-energy changes are the algebraic sums of the separate reactions listed below

	440°F	2240°F
$Fe_2O_3 \rightarrow 2Fe + \frac{3}{2}O_2$	$\Delta G_f = +164.4$	$+105.3$
$3C + 3O_2 \rightarrow 3CO_2$	-283.5	-283.5
$3CO \rightarrow 3C + \frac{3}{2}O_2$	$+111.3$	$+174.9$
$Fe_2O_3 + 3CO \rightarrow 2Fe + 3CO_2$	-7.8	-3.3

	440°F	2240°F
$Fe_2O_3 \rightarrow 2Fe + \frac{3}{2}O_2$	$\Delta G_f = +164.4$	$+105.3$
$3C + \frac{3}{2}O_2 \rightarrow 3CO$	-111.3	-174.9
$Fe_2O_3 + 3C \rightarrow 2Fe + 3CO$	$+53.1$	-69.6

This analysis shows that at 440°F iron oxide has some tendency to oxidize in the presence of CO but will not oxidize in the presence of C. At 2240°F,

---

Table 6.2

Free energy of formation of the oxides of several metals *

Reaction

$n\,M + \dfrac{m}{2}\,O_2 \rightarrow M_nO_m$	ΔG, kcal/g mole of O in oxide, *at*			
Metal	440°F	1340°F	2240°F	3140°F
Ag	+0.06			
Cu	−31.5	−23.3	−15.2	−10.7
C (to CO)	−37.1	−47.9	−58.3	−68.5
C (to CO$_2$)	−47.25	−47.25	47.25	−47.25
Pb	−40.4	−28.7	−18.7	
Ni	−46.1	−35.0	−24.2	−13.0
Fe (to Fe$_2$O$_3$)	−54.8	−44.8	−35.1	
Zn	−71.3	−61.4	−38.9	−15.0
Co	−47.9	−38.8	−29.5	−19.9
Cd	−50.4	−37.7	−14.4	
Cr	−81.6	−69.7	−59.5	−49.1
Mn	−83.1	−74.5	−65.6	−55.1
V	−89.0	−79.0	−69.5	−60.5
Si (quartz)	−94.0	−83.4	−73.1	−61.9
Ti (rutile)	−101.2	−91.1	−80.5	−70.1
Al	−120.7	−108.2	−95.1	−82.0
Mg	−130.8	−117.7	−101.3	−76.1

* Data from J. P. Coughlin, *U.S. Bur. Mines Bull.* 542, 1954.

on the other hand, oxidation in the presence of C is very rapid. These calculations help determine the operating temperature and charge composition in a blast furnace.

Table 6.2 also shows that Al_2O_3 is a very stable compound up to 3140°F and is not easily reduced by carbon

$$Al_2O_3 + \frac{3}{2}C \rightarrow 2Al + \frac{3}{2}CO_2$$

$$\Delta G_f = +104.25$$

In this case it is necessary either to go to much higher temperatures (e.g., in an electric-arc furnace) or to use other techniques (e.g., reduction by electrolysis).

When impurities are carried along with the extracted metal, a final refining step may be necessary. This also can be carried out in a number of ways. In some cases oxygen may be used to separate the impurities; the efficiency of an oxidizing process depends, of course, on the relative chemical activities of the various constituents. If the metal can be ionized in a solution and redeposited on an electrode, an electrolysis technique can be employed. When ultra-high purity is required, physical techniques such as zone melting can be used.

The molten metal from an ore-reducing operation is then poured into an open mold and allowed to solidify. There are a variety of sizes and shapes for industrial castings; some of them are shown schematically in Fig. 6.1. A metal in this form is rarely suitable for a final product and must be treated further. Some of the metal-fabricating techniques are casting, forging, rolling, extrusion, and sintering.

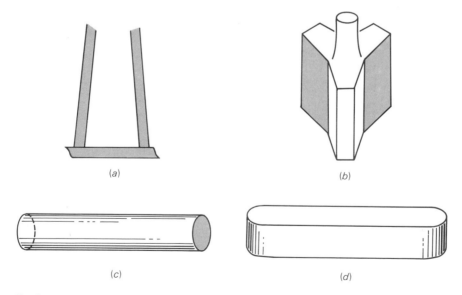

(a)

(b)

(c)

(d)

Fig. 6.1 Some typical refinery casting shapes. (a) Big-end-down ingot; (b) winged ingot; (c) billet; (d) wire bar.

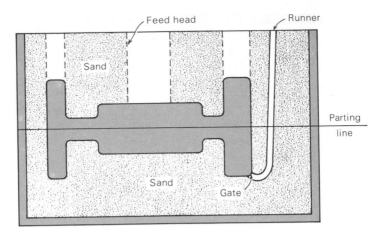

Fig. 6.2 Schematic of a sand mold.

Let us consider casting as an example of forming a shaped metal. Several methods are commonly used in industry. Among the more important is gravity casting into open molds. Castings are made by pouring a liquid metal, at a controlled temperature, into a mold and allowing it to solidify in a controlled environment. Generally, a permanent mold pattern is made out of wood or metal, depending on the number of castings desired. A mold (schematically shown in Fig. 6.2) is made from the pattern. If the mold is to be used only once, it is made out of sand. If it is to be more permanent, it may also be made out of plaster of paris, cement, or metal, depending on the required life.

The molten metal is fed at a controlled speed through one or more gates. As the metal fills the cavity, it begins to nucleate and freeze. The rate of solidification will depend on the mold cross section, thinner sections cooling more rapidly than heavier ones. The metal will normally shrink as it freezes, and this is compensated for by proper use of feed heads through which the molten metal may rise as the mold is filled. The feed heads have a large volume and thus act as reservoirs from which molten metal can flow to fill up the casting as it shrinks. The feed heads and gates are removed from the finished casting, and the piece may often go to a few machining operations for final finishing. A multitude of other fabricating techniques are used, and many of these are discussed in detail in the references listed at the end of the chapter.

The structure of a cast polycrystalline metal must be considered at two levels. The molecular structure is determined by the nature of the metallic atoms and the geometry of the space lattice. The microscopic structure is determined by the way in which the molten metal freezes in the mold. Both aspects of the structure influence the measured physical properties of the material.

The procedure for studying the microstructure of metals has been developed to a fine art. A specimen with dimensions of the order of one inch is cut from the metal being investigated. One face of the specimen is first ground

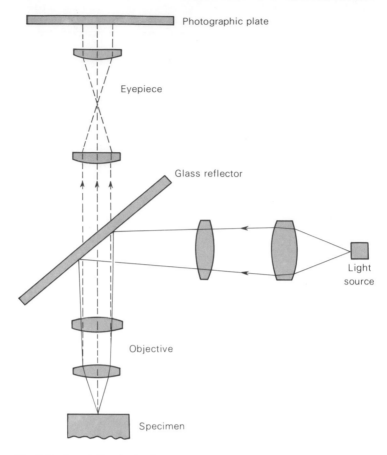

Fig. 6.3 A metallurgical microscope.

on an abrasive wheel and then polished to a mirror finish in a series of polishing steps on successively finer emery papers followed by lapping on revolving cloth-covered wheels, the cloths being saturated with suspensions of fine abrasives. This polished surface is then *etched* with a chemical solution. The etchant attacks various parts of the surface at different rates, thereby making it possible to distinguish grain boundaries, different phases, nonmetallic inclusions, or any other structural characteristic. Some characteristics can be seen with the naked eye, but usually a metallurgical microscope, schematically shown in Fig. 6.3, is used. A permanent image is produced by placing a photographic plate in the lens system and taking a *photomicrograph* of the structure. The usual range of magnification is 100 to 2,000 times. Several photomicrographs are shown in this chapter.

6.3
The freezing process

The freezing of a molten metal takes place in three stages. The first stage is the nucleation of a solid phase. The number of nuclei depends on the mechanism of formation, the amount and nature of the impurities (if present), and the rate of cooling. Generally, a larger number of impurity surfaces and a rapid cooling rate result in a larger number of nuclei. The second stage is the growth of these nuclei. The initial growth is uneven or *dendritic,* while the later stages promote a more equiaxed structure. This second stage continues until the total volume of the material is divided among the growing grains. When only a few atomic layers of liquid are left between adjacent grains, the remaining atoms cannot move into the space lattice of either one. The final stage of crystallization is then the formation of an irregular or a disordered transition region between the grains. This grain boundary is most likely two to five atomic layers thick. Figure 6.4 is a photomicrograph of the surface of a piece of cast copper after polishing and etching. The grain boundaries are clearly visible. The irregular black areas are small bits of nonmetallic impurities, while the more spherical black areas are caused by voids and trapped gas in the structure.

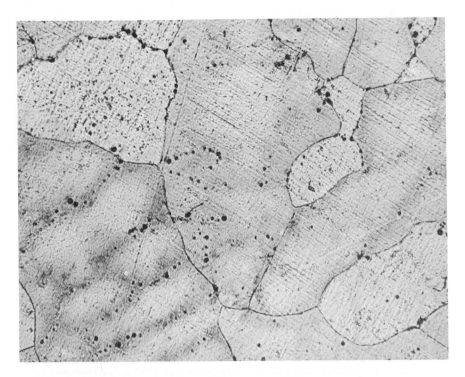

Fig. 6.4   A photomicrograph of the surface of cast copper showing grain boundaries, impurities, and voids.

The rate of *homogeneous* nucleation of impurity-free metals has been extensively studied. Turnbull [3] has directly measured rates of nucleation by dispersing very pure metals into a large number of very small drops. A small number of these drops contain impurities and crystallize rapidly, but they are kept separate from the others by protective coatings. The remaining drops homogeneously nucleate upon supercooling and form grains. By assuming one nucleus per drop and a very rapid growth rate, one may equate the volume change of the dispersed metal to the rate of nucleation. Typical results are illustrated in Figs. 6.5 and 6.6 for mercury at various temperatures. A linear plot of the log of nucleation rate versus the reciprocal of $(T_m - T)^2 T$ is typical for most homogeneous nucleations. (T_m is the melting point of the metal, and T is the temperature at which the process is carried out.) These results can be explained in terms of simple nucleation theory.

In the solid state, the atoms of a metal are arranged in the fixed geometry of the crystal lattice. In the molten state there is no long-range order, but rather a more random array of atoms (even amorphous structures may have a short-range, localized order, however). Below the melting point of the material, the crystal array has the lower average free energy, while above the melting point the amorphous array has the lower free energy (Fig. 6.7).

Since there is an enormous number of atoms in even the smallest easily observable mass of metal, one may use the laws of probability to describe arrangements of the atoms within the mass. Above the melting point the molten material is stable, but at any instant of time it can be assumed that there is a finite

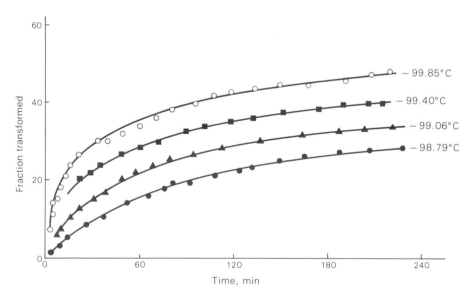

Fig. 6.5 The rate of solidification of aggregates of mercury droplets increases with decreasing temperature (i.e., greater supercooling). (By permission from J. H. Hollomon and D. Turnbull. The Nucleation of the Solid, in "The Solidification of Metals and Alloys," AIME, New York, 1951; also *J. Metals,* p. 803, AIME, September, 1951.)

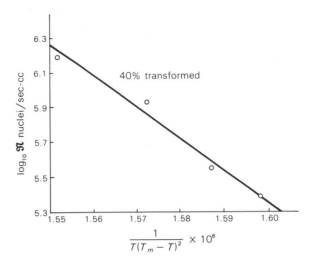

Fig. 6.6 Nucleation frequency of mercury droplets as a function of temperature. (By permission from J. H. Hollomon and D. Turnbull. The Nucleation of the Solid, in "The Solidification of Metals and Alloys," AIME, New York, 1951; also *J. Metals,* p. 803, AIME, September, 1951.)

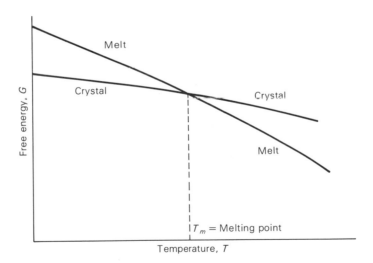

Fig. 6.7 Relative free energies for the molten and crystalline states of a metal. The stable state has the lower free energy.

probability that some of the atoms, in their random motions, might arrange into the same geometry that they would have in the crystalline state. These chance "aggregates," being at a higher free energy than the surrounding molten material, would be unstable and tend to disband to a more random arrangement through molecular motion. The life of a given aggregate will depend on the mobility of the atoms and the size of the aggregate; the lower the mobility and the larger the size, the longer it will take to disband. Thus, intuitively one can see that lowering the temperature of a melt increases the life of any aggregates that might form in the system and thereby increases the possibility of permanent crystal formation. When an ordered aggregate develops from a random array, a certain latent heat of formation is given off. If a solid particle is to develop from such an aggregate, a certain amount of surface energy must be supplied in order to create an interface between the crystalline and amorphous phases. When the energy given off during the aggregate formation is greater than the energy required to form a free surface, it is possible for a solid nucleus to form. Since the energy released is proportional to the volume of the aggregate and the surface energy required is proportional to the surface area, large aggregates (lower temperatures) favor nucleation.

The requirements for nucleation may be obtained analytically. Consider the homogeneous nucleation of an impurity-free metal. Assume that spherical aggregates are formed, the average free energy of fusion is ΔG_f, and γ is the surface energy required to form one square centimeter of free interface. The overall free-energy change that results from the formation of spherical nuclei of radius r is then:

$$\Delta G_{\text{overall}} = 4\pi r^2 \gamma + \tfrac{4}{3}\pi r^3 \, \Delta G_f \tag{6.1}$$

Equation (6.1) is plotted in Fig. 6.8 for a typical case.

When the aggregates first begin to grow, the free energy increases because of the predominance of the surface-energy term. Thus the process is not, at first, spontaneous and the aggregates are not stable. After a critical radius r^* is reached, a further increase in size is accompanied by a decrease in free en-

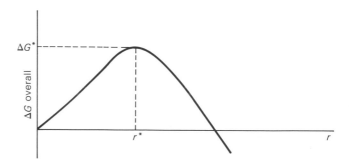

Fig. 6.8 The free-energy change accompanying nucleation is a function of the size of the nucleus that forms. Nuclei with radii greater than r^* are stable.

ergy because of the predominance of the negative latent-energy term (below the melting point). Any aggregate with a radius greater than r^* will grow spontaneously and thus be stable. The critical radius can be obtained by differentiating Eq. (6.1). Since a maximum in free energy exists at that point:

$$\left(\frac{d \, \Delta G_{overall}}{dr}\right)_{r=r^*} = 0 = 8\pi r^* \gamma + 4\pi r^{*2} \, \Delta G_f \tag{6.2}$$

From Eqs. (6.1) and (6.2):

$$r^* = -\frac{2\gamma}{\Delta G_f} \tag{6.3}$$

$$\Delta G^* = \frac{16\pi\gamma^3}{3 \, (\Delta G_f)^2} \tag{6.4}$$

Equation (6.3) expresses the minimum aggregate radius for stable nucleation, while Eq. (6.4) expresses the *activation energy* for the nucleation process. Referring to Fig. 6.7, one can see that ΔG_f is positive above the melting point. This leads to a negative critical radius which may be interpreted to mean that the liquid phase is always stable above T_m. The energy of fusion is zero at the melting point, which leads to an infinite critical radius and an infinite activation energy. It is thus apparent that stable nucleation is possible only *below* the melting point of the solid. One must therefore *supercool* an absolutely pure metal in order to induce homogeneous nucleation. To a first approximation, the free energy of fusion is proportional to the degrees of supercool:

$$(\Delta G_f)_T \approx \Delta H_f \frac{T_m - T}{T_m} \tag{6.5}$$

The quantity ΔH_f is the heat (enthalpy) of fusion at the melting point T_m.

The rate of nucleation may be approximated by assuming that all aggregates with the critical radius are capable of "solidifying." The number of "critical" aggregates in the liquid phase is assumed to be an exponential function of the activation energy. (That is, a Maxwell-Boltzmann distribution of aggregates exists.)

$$n_{r^*} = n_T \exp\left(-\frac{\Delta G^*}{kT}\right) \tag{6.6}$$

The quantity n_T is the total number of zero-size aggregates per cubic centimeter in the liquid phase, or approximately the atomic density of the liquid. In order for a stable nucleus to form, atoms must be added to the critical aggregate. The specific rate of movement of atoms from the liquid phase into the solid may be represented by Eq. (6.7).

$$j_L = A_f \exp\left(-\frac{\Delta E_{DL}}{kT}\right) \tag{6.7}$$

The quantity A_f is a constant, and ΔE_{DL} is the "activation energy" for the diffusion process. If the spontaneous solidification of larger aggregates and the decomposition of critical (or larger) aggregates back to the liquid state are neglected, the rate of nucleus formation in terms of nuclei per second per cubic centimeter is proportional to the product $n_{r*}j_L$

$$\mathcal{N} = Kn_{r*}j_L$$

$$= KA_f n_T \exp\left\{-\frac{1}{kT}\left[\frac{16\pi\gamma^3 T_m^2}{3(\Delta H_f)^2(T_m - T)^2} + \Delta E_{DL}\right]\right\} \qquad (6.8)$$

Thus, the log of the rate is proportional to $(1/T)(1/T_m - T)^2$ as shown in Fig. 6.6. The quantities γ, T_m, and ΔH_f are all measurable properties of the metal, while A_f and ΔE_{DL} may be estimated from the rate of self-diffusion in the molten metal. Because of the high probability of zero-size aggregates ($r = 0$, $\Delta G = 0$), n_T is probably not much different than the atomic density of the liquid in atoms per cubic centimeter. Equation (6.8) shows that a maximum rate of nucleation is attained at a finite number of degrees of supercooling.

Homogeneous nucleation can occur *only in an impurity-free phase.* If foreign particles are present, they will induce a *heterogeneous* nucleation on their surfaces. Energetically, heterogeneous nucleation is favored because part of the surface of the nucleus is already present.

Since metals are cubic close-packed crystals, a nucleus is likely to take on a truncated cubic shape (Fig. 6.9). If the cooling rate is very slow, one may visualize the initial growth process as follows: The critical nucleus grows by the addition of layers of atoms to the faces. If any one face starts to develop much faster than others, the excess latent heat given off warms the surrounding liquid, thereby slowing the growth. Thus the crystal grows with reasonable regularity in all directions, forming an equiaxed grain. If the cooling rate is very rapid, the surrounding liquid will be colder than the growing nucleus. If one portion of a crystal face grows rapidly, for some reason, it will move into colder surroundings and its growth rate will be accelerated. Thus rapid cooling can lead to the development of a dendritic grain structure. Figures 6.10 and 6.11 show a dendritic growth, while Fig. 6.4 shows a more equiaxed grain structure.

The overall growth rate during freezing has rarely been determined accurately because of the extreme difficulty in making direct observations in an opaque material and because of the very rapid growth rate. Undoubtedly, it

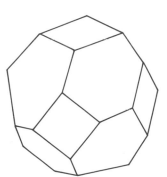

Fig. 6.9 Nuclei formed during the homogeneous nucleation of cubic crystals have truncated cubic shapes rather than simple spherical shapes.

Fig. 6.10 The dendritic growth of a cast 1023 steel. The irregular crystal structure is typical of growth under rapid cooling conditions.

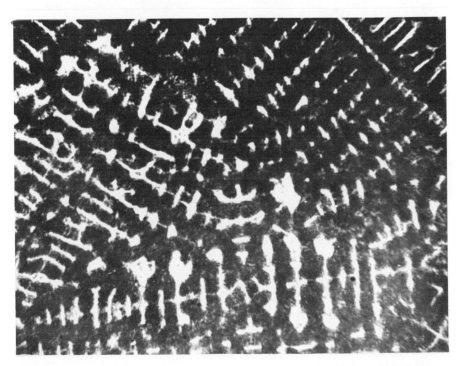

Fig. 6.11 The dendritic growth in this cast Monel metal is caused by rapid solidification.

depends strongly on the nature of the heat transfer from the system.   For this reason, one can never neglect the vessel in which the freezing is occurring or the environmental conditions.   The surfaces of the mold also act as catalysts for "heterogeneous" nucleation, since they are usually the coldest surfaces in the system (maximum supercooling).   Thus, the shape of the mold strongly influences the nature of the final grain structure.   Figure 6.12 shows the columnar structure formed by rapid cooling in a square-column mold.   The nucleation starts at the walls of the container, and the dendrites grow rapidly, normal to the walls.   The last material to freeze is at the main diagonals of the square. These diagonals form *planes of weakness* owing to a concentration of impurities in the resulting boundaries.   This wall effect illustrates the influence of free surfaces, in general, on the nucleation rate.   A fully developed crystal, a non-metallic impurity, the wall of a container, or any other fully developed surface can act as a catalyst for nucleation, provided that the molten metal can wet the surface.   Thus, at any given temperature, impurities can increase the nucleation rate many times over.   It is well known that, under the proper conditions,

Fig. 6.12   The macrostructure of a typical ingot shows that crystallization proceeded from the walls of the mold inward, causing two planes of weakness along the main diagonals. (Schematic)

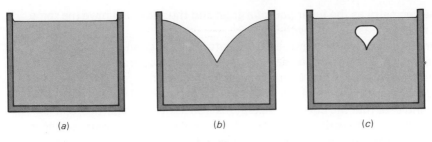

Fig. 6.13   The formation of pipe by shrinkage. (a) Molten metal; (b) pipe formation when surface freezes last; (c) pipe formation when surface layer freezes.

an ultrapure metal may be supercooled hundreds of degrees without crystallizing, whereas the same metal with small amounts of impurities present cannot be supercooled more than a few degrees. It is also well known that "seeding" a supercooled liquid with crystals induces crystallization.

Crystals often have gas bubbles and voids trapped within. These are undesirable defects which usually have a detrimental effect on physical properties. The gas bubbles result from a decrease in the solubility of gases within the solid (relative to the molten state). Voids may develop whenever a volume of molten liquid is trapped within a solid ring of crystal. Further cooling results in a solidification of the remaining liquid accompanied by the usual shrinkage. Since the solid ring may not be able to adjust to the contraction, an internal void may result. In a square-column mold, uneven cooling in the vertical and horizontal directions causes the formation of a gross void called "pipe" (Fig. 6.13). The shape and severity of the defect depends on the cooling process. In general, it is desirable to minimize gross voids in ingots and castings, since they are nearly impossible to remove during subsequent treatments.

The crystallization of alloys is still *more* complex because of the effects of composition. In situations where more than one phase precipitates, the nucleation and growth rates of the two phases are most likely not the same. It is also very common for one type of growing particle to nucleate crystals of the other phase. In the next chapter, the multiphase precipitations in steel will be discussed.

6.4
Grain boundaries

In the last stages of the freezing process, the individual grains are separated by only a few atomic layers of liquid. Since the orientations of the growing grains are normally random and since the remaining atoms "feel" interactions with more than one growing grain, it is easy to see that the formation of a continuous single crystal is not likely. Rather, the last few atomic layers to "freeze" form a less-ordered transition zone between grains. This transition zone does not have the same geometry as the inner part of a grain and thus does not have the same amount of energy associated with it.

There are two possible views as to the nature of the grain boundary; one is that it is completely amorphous and has the same lack of long-range order as the liquid state, and the other is that it is a very imperfect crystal lattice whose nature depends on the orientation of the adjacent grains. There is much evidence to indicate that the boundary energy, as well as other properties, of a low-angle boundary (<20°) varies markedly with the angle between grains, and so it must be concluded that the latter view is closer to reality. The more common "large-angle" boundaries (>20°) do not exhibit these varying properties, but there is very little information available about their nature. It can be assumed that almost all boundaries in a polycrystalline metal are large-angle boundaries with equal free energies per unit area. Since these zones of mismatched crystals must have higher free energies than the surroundings, the system tends to restore an equilibrium structure by minimizing the surfaces. The attempt to minimize the grain boundary area creates a surface tension parallel to the interface. If the boundaries were sufficiently mobile (as, say, a liquid interface would be), the geometry of the boundary would be determined by the three interfacial tensions pictured in Fig. 6.14. Since all the boundaries have the same surface tension, 120° angles should be attained. An ideal two-dimensional model of an array of regular hexagons produces the minimum energy requirements for a metastable equilibrium of grain boundaries (Fig. 6.15). The actual three-dimensional, random network of grains is much more complicated than this. Real grain boundaries do not always meet at exactly the same angle; the surfaces are usually slightly curved; and the crystals are not always the same size and shape, as is shown in Fig. 6.4. A real polycrystalline material is in neither an equilibrium state nor a metastable equilibrium state and may change rapidly if given a sufficient driving force.

The presence of grain boundaries greatly modifies the properties of metals. Tensile strength and fatigue strength are increased by orders of magnitude; ductility is markedly decreased; chemical activity is higher in the grain boundaries; and overall thermal, electrical, and elastic properties are also modified.

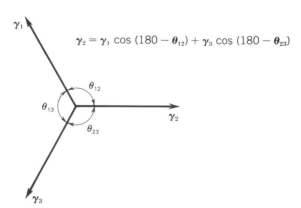

$$\gamma_2 = \gamma_1 \cos (180 - \theta_{12}) + \gamma_3 \cos (180 - \theta_{23})$$

Fig. 6.14 The dynamic equilibrium of surface tensions at a fluid interface.

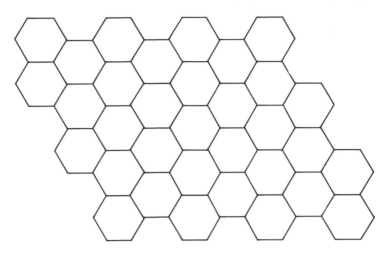

Fig. 6.15 A two-dimensional sketch of an ideal grain boundary arrangement for metastable equilibrium.

Since all of these changes are dependent on the amount of grain boundary present, a knowledge of grain size is important.

A standard ASTM procedure for determining grain size is to count the number of grains per unit area in a magnified photomicrograph. A grain-size number may then be assigned to a given sample by using Eq. (6.9):

$$\text{Actual no. of grains per square millimeter} = 16 \times 2^{N-1} \qquad (6.9)$$

Table 6.3 shows the variation of number of grains per unit area and per unit volume with the ASTM grain size number N.

6.5
Structural imperfections

In Chap. 5, a crystal structure was described as a perfect array of particles in which every particle had identical surroundings. It is obvious that these ideal geometries cannot even be approached in the grain boundaries of a polycrystalline material. Likewise, even the internal portions of real crystals are rarely perfect. Deviations from a perfect array are generally classified as structural imperfections. There are a number of properties, such as conductivity, diffusivity, yield stress, hardness and, in fact, most mechanical and rheological properties, that are extremely sensitive to their presence. In many cases, the presence of a minute number of structural faults can change a property by many orders of magnitude.

Structural imperfections may be classified geometrically. If the disturbance is localized about a specific lattice point and involves only a rela-

Table 6.3

ASTM grain size *

N	Grains/mm²	Grains/mm³
−3	1	0.7
−2	2	2.0
−1	4	5.6
0	8	16.0
1	16	45
2	32	128
3	64	360
4	128	1,020
5	256	2,900
6	512	8,200
7	1,024	23,000
8	2,048	65,000
9	4,096	185,000
10	8,200	520,000
11	16,400	1,500,000
12	32,800	4,200,000

* From "Metals Handbook," p. 405, ASM, Cleveland, 1948.

tively few atoms, it is called a *point defect;* if it extends along a line of microscopic dimensions and involves a row of many atoms, it is called a *line defect;* and if it involves whole planes of atoms, it is called a *planar defect.*

6.6
Point defects

Point defects are caused by either the absence of an atom from a lattice point in the crystal structure or the presence of a foreign atom. The local distortion produces a strain in the lattice in the immediate vicinity of the point but has no effect on more distant parts of the crystal. Substitutional and interstitial alloying elements and impurities cause distortions of this type. (Actually, whether a substance is an alloying element or an impurity depends only on whether it was intentionally added or not; the effect on the structure is the same.) Figure 6.16*a* and *b* illustrates the two types of *impurity defects.* A *vacancy* is illustrated in Fig. 6.16*c.* Such a defect occurs when an atom is absent from a normally occupied lattice position. Vacancy defects may also cluster together in a given region, thereby producing larger voids in the struc-

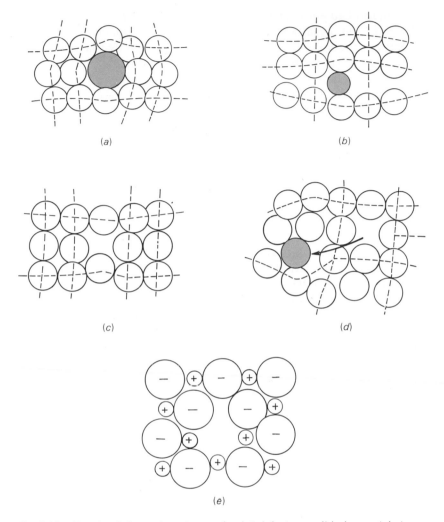

Fig. 6.16 Sketch of the various types of point defects possible in crystal structures. (a) Substitutional impurity; (b) interstitial impurity; (c) vacancy; (d) Frenkel
defect; (e) Schottky defect.

ture. The combination of an interstitial defect and a vacancy defect comes
about when an atom is displaced from a normally occupied lattice position
and dissolves into the interstices of the structure. This is called a *Frenkel
defect;* it is pictured in Fig. 6.16d. A *Schottky defect* occurs in an ionic solid
when a cation vacancy is balanced by an anion vacancy (Fig. 6.16e).

It is easy to see how the presence of vacancies can affect the diffusivity
of an atom in a crystalline solid. If the lattice were absolutely perfect, one
way that an atom could change its position in the lattice is by a direct interchange of two atoms on adjacent lattice sites (Fig. 6.17a). This is not a very
likely occurrence, especially in close-packed structures. On the other hand,

if an atom is adjacent to a vacancy, it merely has to break its existing bonds and "jump" into the empty lattice site (Fig. 6.17b). This is a much more likely occurrence and will occur orders of magnitude more frequently than a direct interchange. It is not surprising, then, that diffusion will occur much more rapidly in the grain boundary of a metal than in the grains themselves. The approximate ratio of the grain boundary self-diffusion coefficient to the volume self-diffusion coefficient for silver is given by Eq. (6.10) [4]. (Self-diffusion is measured by the rate of diffusion of radioactive traces of an element in the pure material.)

$$\frac{D_{gbd}, \, m^2/sec}{D_{vd}, \, m^2/sec} = \frac{1.4 \times 10^{-5} \exp \, (-10,830/T^\circ K)}{7.2 \times 10^{-5} \exp \, (-22,650/T^\circ K)}$$

$$= 0.19 \, \exp \frac{11,820}{T^\circ K} \tag{6.10}$$

Although the grain-boundary diffusion coefficient is 1 million times larger at 800°C, the total grain-boundary diffusion is not too important because of the small number of atoms in the grain boundaries relative to the total volume.

Intuitively, one would feel that the possibility of point defects is large in a material that is formed by normal freezing methods. Actually, the presence of vacancies makes a structure thermodynamically more stable, regardless of the mode of formation. If the energy required to form a vacancy in a perfect lattice were known, one could calculate the equilibrium number of vacancies at any given temperature. Suppose that a certain amount of energy, $\Delta H/N$, is required to remove an atom from a perfect array of atoms and place it on the surface of a crystal. Next consider a crystal with a mole fraction of N_1 such vacancies and N_2 filled lattice sites. At constant temperature and pressure, vacancies will form spontaneously as long as the rate of change of free energy is negative, $dG/dN_1 < 0$. When a minimum free energy is established, the crystal will be in thermodynamic equilibrium. Thus, the criterion for equilibrium is $dG/dN_1 = 0$. From the definition of free energy, $dG = dH - d(TS)$, one can get, at constant temperature:

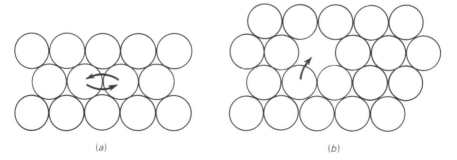

(a)   (b)

Fig. 6.17 Diffusion into a vacancy is energetically more favorable than diffusion by direct interchange. (a) Diffusion by direct interchange; (b) diffusion into a vacancy.

$$\frac{dG}{dN_1} = \frac{dH}{dN_1} - T\frac{dS}{dN_1} \tag{6.11}$$

The first term on the right side of the equation is just the enthalpy change ΔH kcal/g mole associated with the formation of a mole of vacancies, and the second term is the change in configurational entropy associated with the random mixing of n_1 vacancies with n_2 atoms.

$$-\frac{dS}{dN_1} = R\frac{d}{dN_1}(N_1 \ln N_1 + N_2 \ln N_2) \tag{6.12}$$

$$N_1 + N_2 = 1 \tag{6.13}$$

At equilibrium,

$$\frac{dG}{dN_1} = 0 = \Delta H + RT \ln \frac{N_1}{1 - N_1} \tag{6.14}$$

$$\frac{N_1}{1 - N_1} = \exp\left(-\frac{\Delta H}{RT}\right) \tag{6.15}$$

Since ΔH is the energy change associated with the removal of atoms from the crystal structure, it should be closely related to the heat of vaporization. For copper, ΔH has been estimated as 20 to 40 kcal/g mole, while the heat of vaporization is 81.7 kcal/g mole. It has been found that the activation energy for diffusion of metals in metals is also on the order of one-third to one-half of the sublimation energy of the solute. This could mean that vacancies might form by the stepwise diffusion of an atom from a given internal site to the surface of the crystal. If ΔH is 20 kcal/g mole, N_1 will be about 10^{-15} at 300°K. Thus, the number of vacancies is always a small fraction of the number of atoms in the crystal.

6.7
Line defects

Electron microscope studies of crystals have shown the presence of lines of atoms that do not conform to the normal coordination of the structure. These *dislocations*, as they are called, may be classified as either edge or screw. An edge dislocation is a row of atoms, each of which has a coordination number of one less than a normal atom in the structure. Figure 6.18 is a schematic drawing of an edge dislocation. The dislocation runs normal to the page, and its position is marked by the symbol ⊥. Above the dislocation, the crystal has to be in compression because an extra row of atoms has been squeezed in, while below the dislocation the structure is in tension. The size of the dislocation can be characterized by its Burger's vector as shown in Fig. 6.18(b). The Burger's vector is obtained by closing a circuit around the dislocation line. Start at the left and above the defect and move x atomic units down (below the defect), y atomic units to the right (to right of defect), x atomic units

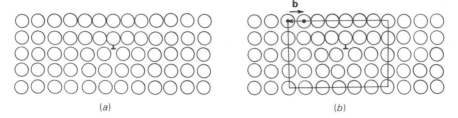

(a)   (b)

Fig. 6.18 A schematic of an edge dislocation showing that the Burger's vector is normal to the direction of the defect. (a) The edge dislocation runs normal to the plane of the paper; (b) the Burger's vector is normal to the defect.

up, and y atomic units to the left. This circuit will remain open by a distance equal to the dimension of the defect. A vector between the end of the circuit and the origin of the circuit is the Burger's vector **b**. The Burger's vector of an edge dislocation is always perpendicular to the line of the defect.

A screw dislocation is a defect in which a row of atoms has the proper number of nearest neighbors but the orientation is somewhat distorted. Figure 6.19 is a three-dimensional schematic drawing which shows the type of distortion and the Burger's vector for the defect. In this case, the Burger's vector is parallel to the dislocation line and its length is a measure of the amount of distortion. If the circuit is continued for repeated loops, it traces a screwlike displacement with a pitch equal to **b**.

Figure 6.20 shows photomicrographs of etch pits in a GaAs (gallium arsenide) crystal. Each etch pit reveals the position of a single dislocation line piercing the surface. The surfaces are prepared by fine polishing, followed by a

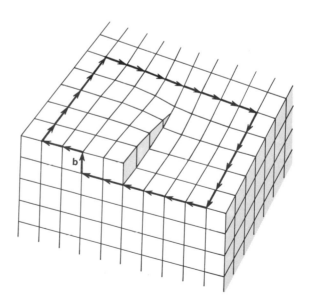

Fig. 6.19 In a screw dislocation the Burger's vector is parallel to the direction of the defect.

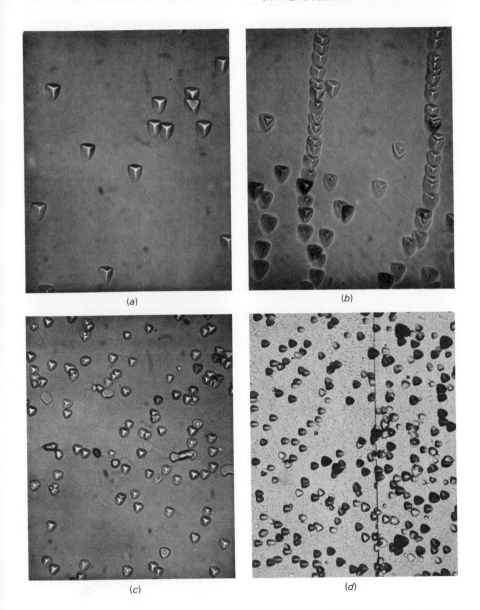

(a)

(b)

(c)

(d)

Fig. 6.20 The positions of individual dislocations are revealed by means of etch pits. (a) Etch pits within a single crystal of gallium arsenide, GaAs. Dislocation density about 10^3 cm^{-2}. (b) A subboundary in a crystal of GaAs is formed by rows of dislocations. (c) The dislocation density in this polycrystalline GaAs is about 10^4 to 10^5 cm^{-2}. (d) Expitaxial GaAs growth on a GaAs substrate. A view of the (111)B orientation. Dislocation density about 10^4 cm^{-2}. (Samples a, b, and c courtesy of J. B. McNeely, Monsanto Company, St. Louis; photograph d courtesy of F. V. Williams, Monsanto Company, St. Louis.)

treatment with dilute nitric acid. The acid preferentially attacks the areas around the dislocations, clearly marking their positions. The photographs also show that the density and distribution may vary quite markedly, depending on the mode of formation of the crystal.

Now let us visualize these defects inside a crystal. First consider a solid cube of material in which a planar cut is made down to line RS, as shown in Fig. 6.21a. Next, shear the plane $ABQP$ relative to $PQCD$ and parallel to line RS so that the displacement of line AP is one Burger's vector **b**. This will give a screw dislocation with RS as the dislocation line (Fig. 6.21b). The atoms on one side of plane $PQSR$ are thus mismatched relative to the atoms on the other side. Next, imagine that the cut is on only two surfaces of the crystal, as shown in Fig. 6.21c, and that the atoms behind plane BQS cannot be displaced. Now, shear plane $ABQP$ parallel to RS so that every atom in the plane is shifted one Burger's vector **b**. If the atoms along line BQ are not free to move, however,

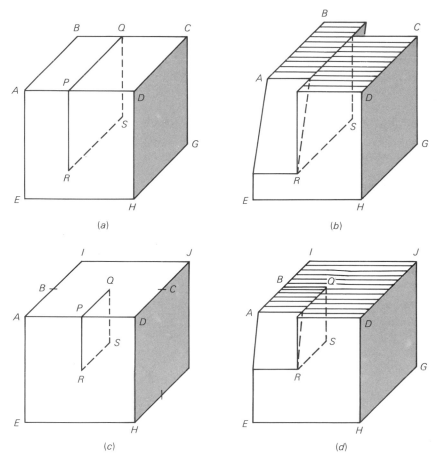

Fig. 6.21 The presence of dislocations in crystals causes distortions of the normal geometry.

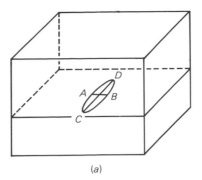

(a)

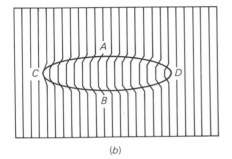

(b)

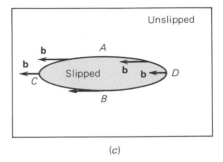

(c)

Fig. 6.22 The dislocation loop within a crystal separates the slipped portion of the crystal from the unslipped portion. The distortion is concentrated along the loop.

there will be a pileup of atoms at this boundary causing a distortion at plane BQS. Looking along line BQ, one would see an extra row of atoms squeezed into this area, or in other words, BQ will be an edge dislocation (Fig. 6.21d). Looking along RS, one would still see a screw dislocation.

Finally, suppose that the cut is entirely within the crystal and that plane $ABCD$ of Fig. 6.22a represents the area that may be moved relative to the rest of the crystal lattice. Now let us suppose that all of the atoms on one side of this plane can be moved a distance **b** relative to the atoms on the other side, as is shown in two dimensions in Fig. 6.22b. The lattice is perfect both within plane $ABCD$, where the atoms have been displaced from their original positions, and outside this plane, where there has been no relative motion. All of the distortion is concentrated at the boundary of the two regions. This is called the "dislocation loop" for the distortion. The Burger's vector **b** which measures the amount of displacement is the same at all points of the loop (Fig. 6.22c). At points C and D, where the Burger's vector is perpendicular to the tangent to the loop, the line is an edge dislocation. At point C there is an extra half-plane of atoms above plane $ABCD$, so the dislocation is symbolized as $\perp$ (looking from bottom to top along the plane of the page). At point D there is an extra half-plane of atoms below $ABCD$, so the dislocation is symbolized as $\top$. At points A and B, where the Burger's vector is parallel to the tangent, the line is a screw dislocation. At point A, looking along the plane of the page from right to left, one moves along the screw dislocation line in a counterclockwise helical path, symbolized by $\circlearrowleft$. At point B the helical path is in a clockwise direction $\circlearrowright$.

At all other points along the dislocation loop the Burger's vector is at an angle between 0 and 90° with the tangent, producing what is called a *mixed dislocation*. Although these are more difficult to visualize, they may be broken down into screw and edge components.

6.8
Planar defects

A change in coordination of a whole plane of atoms can come about by a change in the stacking of planes during crystallization. For example, a close-packed, face-centered cubic structure is formed when every fourth plane of close-packed spheres repeats the stacking sequence (i.e., the stacking sequence is $\cdots ABC\ ABC\ ABC \cdots$). If the sequence that forms is actually $\cdots ABC\ AB\ ABC\ ABC \cdots$, a disruption in the normal face-centered structure (which may be described as a layer of hexagonal close-packed cells $\cdots ABAB \cdots$) has developed. A certain amount of excess energy is associated with the defect. A value of 0.02 joule/m^2 for such an imperfection in copper, for example, means that an energy of the order of 10^{-21} joule/atom is present. During crystallization, if a new layer starts off incorrectly and if the crystallization is too rapid to permit readjustment of positions, it is likely that the fault will persist, since a larger aggregate of atoms will not be able to readjust by virtue of thermal energy alone. Plastic deformation can also lead to the formation of stacking faults (Chap. 11).

When the orientation of growing crystals is random, it is natural for large-angle grain boundaries to form between grains. If by chance, however, the orientation is such that two adjacent grains can match perfectly to form a single coherent grain, a special type of planar defect can result. Figure 6.23 schematically illustrates a twin boundary within a grain. A mirror-image relationship exists between the two parts of the crystal relative to their common plane. Figure 6.24 is a photomicrograph of Monel metal which has been annealed to show a homogeneous solid solution with twinning.

The most obvious planar defects are the grain boundaries themselves. Most grain boundaries that form during crystallization are large-angle grain boundaries. To a first approximation, their properties are fairly uniform and independent of boundary angle. They are probably 4 to 6 Å thick and have a surface tension (or energy) that is higher than solid-liquid interfacial tension but lower than a solid-vapor interfacial tension. Annealed copper, for example, has a solid-vapor interfacial tension of 1.65 joules/m^2, a grain boundary tension of 0.600 joule/m^2, and a solid-liquid interfacial tension of 0.150 joule/m^2. The nature of the molecular order (or lack of order) in a large-angle boundary is not completely understood, and no satisfactory model has yet been devised. Low-

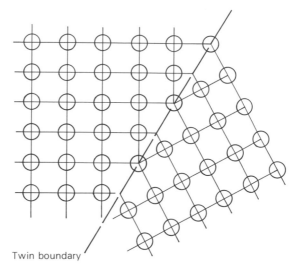

Fig. 6.23 The atomic structure on one side of a twin boundary is the mirror image of the structure on the other side.

Twin boundary

Fig. 6.24 The microstructure of a hot-rolled and annealed Monel metal shows a homogeneous solid solution with twinning.

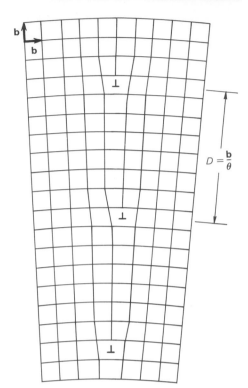

Fig. 6.25 The structure of a low-energy grain boundary can be idealized by using an edge-dislocation model. (By permission from W. T. Read, Jr., "Dislocations in Crystals," McGraw-Hill Book Company, New York, 1953.)

angle boundaries, where the angle between grains is less than 20°, have been described in terms of an array of edge dislocations. The "tilted" grains are matched by inserting extra planes of atoms at intervals of b/θ, where b is the unit Burger's vector and θ is the angle between planes (Fig. 6.25). The grain-boundary energy is then a function of the tilt angle. It can be shown that

$$\Gamma = \Gamma_0 \frac{\theta}{\theta_0} \left(1 - \ln \frac{\theta}{\theta_0} \right) \quad \frac{\text{joules}}{\text{m}^2} \tag{6.16}$$

There is much experimental evidence that this model is satisfactory up to angles of about $\theta \approx 20°$.

References

1 Azároff, L. V.: "Introduction to Solids," McGraw-Hill Book Company, New York, 1960. *Chapter 5 considers imperfections in atomic packing; chap. 7 considers mechanisms of crystal growth.*

2 Chalmers, B.: "Physical Metallurgy," John Wiley & Sons, Inc., New York, 1959. *The fourth chapter discusses imperfections in great detail; the sixth chapter is a detailed treatment of the principles of freezing.*

3 Doremus, R. H., B. W. Roberts, and D. Turnbull: "Growth and Perfection of Crystals," John Wiley & Sons, Inc., New York, 1958.

4 Guy, A. G.: "Elements of Physical Metallurgy," Addison-Wesley Publishing Company, Inc., Reading, Mass., 1959. *Chapters 1 and 2 are a brief summary of metallurgical techniques.*

5 Hollomon, J. H., and D. Turnbull: The Nucleation of the Solid, pp. 1–23 in "The Solidification of Metals and Alloys," AIME, New York, 1951.

6 Koehler, J. S., F. Seitz, W. Read, W. Shockley, and E. Orowan: "Dislocations in Metals," AIME, New York, 1954.

7 Mehl, R. F.: The Growth of Metal Crystals, pp. 24–51 in "The Solidification of Metals and Alloys," AIME, New York, 1951.

8 Pound, G. M.: Nucleation in the Solidification of Metals, pp. 87–105 in "Liquid Metals and Solidification," ASM, Cleveland, 1958.

9 Read, W. T., Jr.: "Dislocations in Crystals," McGraw-Hill Book Company, New York, 1953. *A classic text on the nature of imperfections in crystals.*

10 Samans, C. H.: "Engineering Metals and Their Alloys," The Macmillan Company, New York, 1953. *A general, descriptive text on many aspects of metallurgy.*

Questions

6.1 Use the "Metals Handbook," ASM, 1960, or any metallurgy text and look up the metallurgical techniques used in the production of steel. Describe how iron is removed from its ore, how it is transformed to a steel, and how it is cast into an ingot. Also describe some of the fabricating techniques that are used to make industrial products.

6.2 A process is spontaneous when the free-energy change accompanying the process is negative. When a crystal nucleates, two energy changes occur; a free surface is formed with a surface energy, γ joules/m², and a latent energy of fusion, ΔG_f joules/m³, is given off. If a spherical nucleus of radius r is formed:
(a) Calculate the overall free-energy change accompanying the nucleus formation in homogeneous nucleation (i.e., no impurity surfaces present).
(b) Show that all nuclei with a radius less than $-2\gamma/\Delta G_f$ will be unstable, while all those with a larger radius will be stable.
(c) From the definition of free energy

$$\Delta G_f = \Delta H_f - T\,\Delta S_f$$

at constant temperature and also from the fact that ΔG_f at the melting point T_m is zero, explain why nucleation is impossible either at or above the melting point, in terms of the size of stable nuclei.

(d) $\quad (\Delta G_f)_T \doteq \Delta H_f \dfrac{T_m - T}{T_m}$

where ΔH_f is the latent heat of fusion, T_m is the melting point, and $T_m - T$ is the degrees of supercooling under which the process is being carried out. If the surface energy of a copper crystal is 0.180 joule/m², its latent heat of fusion is 13.05×10^6 joules/kg mole, its melting point is 1083°C, and its density is 8.96 gms/cm³, calculate the smallest size for a stable nucleus at 1082°C and at 983°C.

6.3 Schottky defects are formed in ionic crystals. Calculate the mole fraction of defects, N_1, at 25 and 800°C (0.4° below the melting point) if the energy of formation, ΔH, is 1.01 ev per defect.

6.4 Equation (6.10) gives the ratio of the grain boundary self-diffusion coefficient to the volume self-diffusion coefficient for silver. Assume that a grain boundary is approximately two atomic layers thick (about 5 Å) and that the ASTM grain size is $N = 5$. Estimate what fraction of the total molecular diffusion is actually grain-boundary diffusion at 900°C.

6.5 Derive Eq. (6.16) for the grain-boundary energy of a low-angle boundary. Use the edge-dislocation model shown in Fig. 6.25 and assume that the total strain energy in a cylindrical shell of unit length, with an inner radius r and an outer radius $r + dr$, surrounding an edge dislocation, is proportional to dr/r.

$$d\Gamma = K\frac{dr}{r} \text{ joules/m of dislocation}$$

Hints: Divide the boundary into cylindrical rods surrounding each dislocation and then calculate the effect of changing the angle on the elastic strain energy. The diameter of each rod will be proportional to distance between dislocations

$$r_1 = aD = \frac{ab}{\theta}$$

$$\frac{dr_1}{r_1} = -\frac{d\theta}{\theta} = a\frac{dD}{D}$$

6.6 In your own words, describe the spatial geometry within a crystal in the vicinity of (a) an edge dislocation, (b) a screw dislocation, and (c) a mixed dislocation. Try to make large sketches of the region surrounding the dislocation.

7
Formation of alloys

7.1
Introduction

Alloys are formed by the combination of two or more metals or nonmetals. The resulting structures very often have greater strength and hardness than the pure materials from which they are made. An almost unlimited variety of combinations leads to an unlimited variety of materials with different physical properties. Since the prediction of the effects of combining elements is virtually impossible, except for a few simple cases, experimental data form the basis for studying the nature of alloy systems. In this chapter, we shall first discuss the most important types of alloys and then illustrate the use of thermodynamic principles to characterize their behavior.

It is sometimes difficult to visualize the behavior of solid solutions because of their inherent "rigidity." This problem is minimized if one recognizes that solid solutions behave much the same as liquid solutions except that the rate at which things happen is many orders of magnitude slower. For example, the diffusivity of sodium chloride in water is of the order of 10^{-9} m²/sec at 20°C, while the diffusivity of aluminum in copper is of the order of 10^{-34} m²/sec at 20°C. Just as one may mix salt and water to form a solution, aluminum and copper may also be "mixed" to form a solution, but the "mixing," of course, must be carried out at much higher temperatures and pressures to obtain a measurable rate (e.g., sintering and powder metallurgy). Just as salt has a maximum solubility in water, so aluminum has a maximum solubility in copper; just as salts can be made to dissolve below their melting points, so aluminum can be made to dissolve below its melting point. When two dissimilar liquids such as benzene and water are mixed, two immiscible phases of pure components result. In the same way, when two dissimilar metals such as lead and copper are mixed, two phases of almost pure components result. When two liquids with a slight degree of similarity, such as phenol and water, are mixed, two phases each containing both components can result. Likewise, when two metals with some similarity, such as copper and silver, are mixed, two phases each containing both components can result.

If one keeps in mind the many analogies between liquid solutions and the more complicated solid solutions, the many solid-state phenomena we shall be discussing later will be more easily visualized.

There are a number of ways by which alloys may be formed:

1. All components can be melted and mixed in the liquid (i.e., molten) state.

2. The major component can be melted and the minor alloying elements can be dissolved.

3. All components can be finely powdered, intimately mixed, heated, and compressed. At high temperature and pressure and with sufficient interfacial contact, the total mass diffusion can be sufficient to form a homogeneous, dense alloy without melting the components. This is known as the powder metallurgy process.

Let us next consider the important types of homogeneous solid solutions.

7.2
Substitutional solid solutions

When two metals have similar atomic sizes and electronic structures, atoms of the "solute" will replace atoms of the "solvent" at lattice points. The resulting crystal will have the same type of space lattice as the original components but with different unit cell dimensions. Among the relatively few binary alloys that show complete solubility over the whole composition range and over a wide range of temperature are Ag-Au, Pt-Rh, and Cu-Ni, and among those showing complete solubility at elevated temperature are Fe-Ni, Fe-Mn, and Cr-Fe. There are also many other binary systems with limited ranges of substitutional solid-solution formation.

It has been observed that two metals can form a substitutional solid solution only when certain size and valency requirements are met. These conditions are summarized in the four "Hume-Rothery Rules" listed below:

1. Atomic size requirement. Other factors being equal, the smaller the distortion of the solvent lattice, the greater the range of solubility of the solute atom. Solubility data on various elements in copper, silver, and gold show that a wide range of solid solution is possible when the atomic diameters of the alloying elements are within 15 percent of each other.

2. Crystal structure requirement.   Two elements will form a wide range of solid solutions only if their crystal structures are identical.   For example, copper and nickel form a continuous range of substitutional solid solutions because their atomic diameters are within 3 percent of each other and they are both face-centered cubic crystals.   On the other hand, tin, a tetragonal crystal, has a maximum solubility of about 12 percent in antimony, a rhombic crystal, in spite of the fact that the atomic diameters of tin and antimony are within 4 percent of each other.

3. Electrochemical requirement.   If two elements have very different electro-negativities, they will probably not form a wide range of solid solutions.   When an electropositive element is mixed with an electronegative element, a more stable material can often be formed through ionic and/or covalent bonding.

4. Relative valency requirement.   A wide range of substitutional solid solutions will be obtained between elements with the same valency.   Thus copper and gold are mutually soluble, since their atomic diameters are within 12 percent of each other, they are both face-centered cubic structures, their electro-negativities are similar, and both are univalent.   (Copper has one valence elec-tron in the N shell and gold has one valence electron in the P shell.)   It is also true that metals of lower valency are more likely to dissolve metals of high valency than vice versa.   Thus, up to 38 percent zinc, valency $+2$, will dis-solve in copper, valency $+1$, but a maximum of only 2.5 percent copper will dissolve in zinc.   This may be interpreted in terms of the availability of free valence electrons for metallic bonding.   Pure zinc has two $4s$ electrons per atom available for metallic bonding.   When a copper atom is substituted in the zinc lattice, only one available $4s$ electron is replaced.   This shortage of free electrons for metallic bonding thus restricts the ability to form a substitutional solution through metallic bonding.   Just the reverse is true when zinc is added to copper, since there is an excess of free electrons for bonding.

When substitutional solid solutions form at elevated temperature, the atomic array is normally random (i.e., the probability of finding atom A at a certain lattice position is equal to the mole fraction of A in the alloy).   The reason for this behavior is that substitutional solid solutions are normally formed between similar elements, and at high temperatures the slight differ-ences are masked by the thermal motion.   Thus, each atom in the system is more or less indifferent to its surroundings and the mixing process is not de-pendent on the interatomic bonding.   In many alloys, however, dissimilar atoms may be attracted to one another more strongly than similar ones.   The overall free energy of the system may therefore by lowered by the tendency for atom A to be surrounded by a maximum number of B atoms, thus resulting in a stable ordered arrangement.   An alloy of 50 percent copper and 50 percent gold is an example of an ordered solid solution.   Above 500°C the atoms are randomly distributed in a face-centered cubic lattice.   Below 500°C this alloy becomes ordered into a lattice in which the eight corners and the upper and lower faces of the unit cell are gold atoms while the remaining four faces are copper atoms. The "order-disorder" transition temperature marks enough of a change in the alloy that some people prefer to consider this ordered material as a compound rather than a true solution. This is discussed in greater detail in Sec. 7.4.

7.3
Interstitial solid solutions

In normal close-packed lattices of spherical atoms there are spaces between the contact points of the spheres. If four spheres are on the corners of a tetrahedron (Fig. 7.1a), a tetrahedral void is formed. A sphere with a radius of 0.225 of the radius of the lattice spheres can fit into this void without causing distortion of the lattice. Two adjacent close-packed layers also form octahedral voids when six spheres are centered on the corners of an octahedron (Fig. 7.1b). A sphere with a radius of 0.414 of the radius of the lattice spheres can fit into this void without causing distortion of the lattice. Two types of voids are also present in body-centered cubic packings. An octahedral void, centered on the face of a unit cell, is formed by the four corner spheres and the two body-centered spheres of the two cells sharing that face (Fig. 7.2a). A sphere with a radius of 0.154 of the radius of the lattice spheres can fit into the void without causing distortion. A tetrahedral void is formed by the two corner spheres and two body-centered spheres of two adjacent unit cells (Fig. 7.2b). A sphere with a radius of 0.291 of the radius of the lattice spheres can fit into the void without causing distortion. Atoms such as hydrogen, carbon, and nitrogen, which are too small for substitutional alloying, have a tendency to dissolve in the voids of the normal lattice of a heavy metal. The most important of the interstitial solid solutions are those of carbon in iron. The maximum solubility at 1333°F of elemental carbon in face-centered cubic iron is about 1.4 percent, while the maximum solubility of elemental carbon in body-centered cubic iron at 1333°F is about 0.02 percent. The difference is attribut-

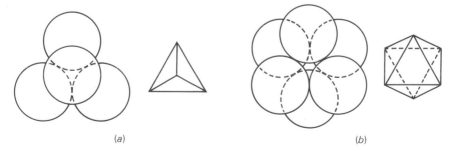

(a)   (b)

Fig. 7.1 When spheres are arranged in close-packed structures, voids exist between the points of contact. Tetrahedral- and octahedral-shaped voids exist in cubic close-packed structures. (a) Tetrahedral void; (b) octahedral void.

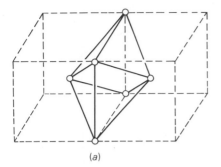 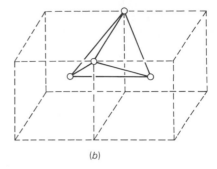

(a)   (b)

Fig. 7.2   Tetrahedral and octahedral voids are also present in body-centered cubic structures.   (a) Octahedral void; (b) tetrahedral void.

able to the larger octahedral voids of the face-centered cubic (close-packed) structure.   The diameter ratio of carbon to iron is about 0.63, which results in too serious a lattice distortion for solubility in the body-centered structure (largest voids are $0.291D$) and a small enough distortion for limited solubility in the face-centered structure (largest voids are $0.414D$).   Since iron transforms from one *polymorphic* form to the other on heating or cooling, carbon may be dissolved or precipitated by temperature changes in the region of 1333°F (see Fig. 7.16).   This reaction is the basis of all steel-hardening processes.

7.4
Intermetallic compounds

Most of the transition metals can also form stable (or metastable) carbides, nitrides, borides, and hydrides.   Small atoms such as C, N, B, and H fit into the voids of the metal lattice to form compounds of fixed composition such as Fe_3C, Fe_2N, or, in general, structures of the form M_xN_y, where M is the metal, N is the nonmetal, and x and y are usually integers between 1 and 4.   The crystal structure is often unique to a particular compound and is generally complex. Iron carbide, Fe_3C, for example, is an orthorhombic structure with lattice parameters $a = 4.524$ Å, $b = 6.743$ Å, $c = 5.089$ Å.   Each carbon atom is in a void formed by six iron atoms at the corners of a distorted trigonal prism as shown in Fig. 7.3.   The distortion in the lattice complicates the spatial arrangement of the iron atoms so that nearest-neighbor distances may vary from 2.49 to 2.68 Å and the packing is not quite close-packed.

In general, carbon and nitrogen tend to fill octahedral voids in a metallic lattice, while the smaller hydrogen and boron atoms tend to fill tetrahedral voids.   The distinction between an interstitial solid solution and an interstitial intermetallic compound is not sharply defined; rather, it is more a matter of regularity of the interstitiality.   In general, the intermetallic compounds are more brittle and have sharper melting (or decomposition) points.

A substitutional solid solution may also develop into a material which may

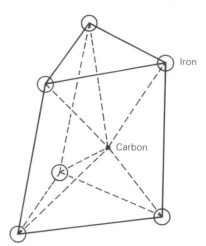

Fig. 7.3 The unit cell for the crystal structure of iron carbide, Fe_3C, has a carbon atom embedded in a distorted trigonal prism formed by six iron atoms.

be classified as an intermetallic compound. Alloys of copper and gold, for example, can form random solid solutions over the whole composition range above 500°C, while below 500°C there is a tendency for an ordering into a more specific space lattice. The 50-50 alloy can form an ordered compound with a face-centered cubic structure containing gold atoms in the eight corners and at the centers of the two base planes, while the copper atoms are at the centers of the four faces. This gives a compound $CuAu$. The 75-25 Cu-Au alloy also forms an ordered, face-centered cubic structure with gold atoms in the eight corners and copper atoms in the centers of the six faces. This gives the compound Cu_3Au. Although perfect ordering can occur only at these exact compositions, partial ordering can occur at intermediate compositions. The mechanical properties of the ordered compound are seldom very different than those of the random solution from which it was formed. Electrical and magnetic properties, however, can be noticeably different. Electrical conductivity, for example, can be greater in the ordered structure.

Alloy systems that do not meet the Hume-Rothery criteria for a wide range of substitutional solutions show very limited mutual solubility. In the copper-zinc system, for example, the maximum solubilities are 2.5 atomic percent copper in zinc and 38 atomic percent zinc in copper. On the other hand, alloys in the ranges 45 to 50 percent Zn, 60 to 70 percent Zn, and 80 to 85 percent Zn appear to be homogeneous, single-phase alloys. These are a form of intermetallic compound called an *intermediate phase.* Below about 470°C, an ordered body-centered cubic structure containing eight zinc atoms at the corners and a copper atom in the center ($CuZn$) is formed. The ordering need not be perfect to maintain an apparently homogeneous phase, so this intermediate exists over a modest composition range. At 61.5 atomic percent Zn, the intermediate Cu_5Zn_8 forms in a complex cubic crystal with 52 atoms per unit cell. At about 80 percent Zn, an intermediate with the approximate formula $CuZn_3$ is formed.

Hume-Rothery has also formulated rules for the stability of intermediates based on the ratio of electrons to atoms in the compound. If the normal valencies are assigned to the two metals in the compound (for example, +2 for Zn and +1 for Cu), intermediate phases will be stable when the electron-to-atom ratio has the following values: $3/2$, $21/13$, and $7/4$. The stable intermediates are called β, γ, and ϵ, respectively. The materials CuZn, AgMg, Cu_3Al, and Cu_5Sn are all examples of β-type intermediates. The materials Cu_5Zn_8, Cu_9Al_8, and $Cu_{31}Si_8$ are examples of γ-type intermediates, and $CuZn_3$, Ag_3Sn, Cu_3Si and $CuCd_3$ are examples of ϵ-type intermediates.

7.5
Multiphase materials

Many useful engineering materials are mixtures of two or more phases. An annealed steel at room temperature, for example, is an intimate mixture of ferrite (an interstitial solid solution of elemental carbon in body-centered cubic iron) and cementite (the intermetallic compound Fe_3C). The gross properties of the steel, or any other multiphase material, depend on the relative amounts, the degree of dispersion, and the shape of the individual phases as well as their crystal structures. These factors depend on the mutual solubilities of the individual phases and on the mode of formation of the solid.

It would be most desirable to predict the properties from the molecular structure of the constituents and the nature of the molecular interactions between phases. At our present state of knowledge, however, this mechanistic approach is virtually impossible. One must therefore depend on general thermodynamic principles and experimental data. In the next section we shall discuss free-energy calculations for simple solid systems, and in the following two sections we shall discuss equilibrium diagrams for some simple binary alloys.

7.6
Free-energy changes in alloys

A homogeneous system in equilibrium with its surroundings at constant temperature and pressure will be in a state of minimum free energy. Thus, when iron atoms are arranged in a body-centered cubic lattice at room temperature and one atmosphere of pressure, a stable minimum free-energy state is attained. The free energy of a face-centered cubic arrangement under the same environmental conditions will be higher, and thus the close-packed lattice (γ-iron) is less stable than the body-centered cubic lattice (α-iron). Figure 7.4 shows the effect of temperature on the free energy G and enthalpy H of the α and γ forms of pure iron. Below 1670°F, α is the stable phase, since it has the lower free energy, while above 1670°F, γ is the stable phase for the same reason. At 1670°F both phases have the same free energy and are therefore equally stable. This temperature is the *polymorphic transformation temperature,* and the two polymorphic forms of iron can exist in equilibrium at this temperature. A polymorphic transformation is known as a *first-order transition,* since it is characterized by a discontinuity of enthalpy. The difference in enthalpies, ΔH, is the *heat of transformation.*

Consider the formation of two substitutional solid solutions: a small amount of copper dissolved in silver (α solid solution) and a small amount of silver dissolved in copper (β solid solution). Suppose we were able to calculate the free energies of copper-silver alloys as a function of composition (at fixed temperature and pressure) and obtained the results shown in Fig. 7.5. In the range 0 to x_1 weight percent copper, where the curve is concave upward, α solid solution is stable; in the range x_2 weight percent to 100 percent copper, β solid solution is stable; and in the range $x_1 < x < x_2$, where the curves are concave downward, mixtures of α (composition x_1) and β (composition x_2) give the most stable states. If there is no free-energy change on mixing, the free energy of the mixture may be obtained from the free energies of the components:

$$WG_M = W_1G_1 + W_2G_2 \tag{7.1}$$

The symbol G represents the free energy per unit weight, W_1 is the weight of α, W_2 is the weight of β, and W is the total weight of the mixture. If the overall composition of the mixture is x, material balances give

$$\frac{W_1}{W} = \frac{x_2 - x}{x_2 - x_1} \tag{7.2}$$

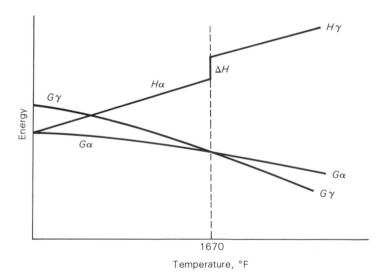

Fig. 7.4 A polymorphic change occurs at 1670°F where the free energies of the two phases are equal. An enthalpy change accompanies the transformation.

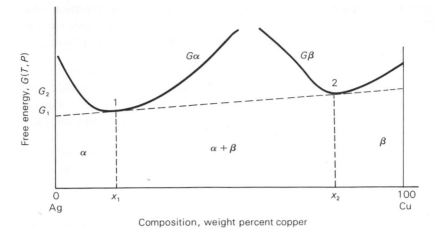

Fig. 7.5 The free-energy mapping for copper-silver alloys fixes the limits of solubility at a given temperature and pressure.

$$\frac{W_2}{W} = \frac{x - x_1}{x_2 - x_1} \tag{7.3}$$

Substituting (7.2) and (7.3) into (7.1) and rearranging, one obtains

$$G = \frac{G_2 - G_1}{x_2 - x_1} x + \frac{G_1 x_2 - G_2 x_1}{x_2 - x_1} \tag{7.4}$$

Equation (7.4) is the equation for the straight line joining points 1 and 2 and represents the lowest free energies for all possible combinations of copper and silver within that region.

This free-energy mapping tells us that the maximum solubility of copper in silver, at T and p, is x_1 and the maximum solubility of silver in copper is x_2. Furthermore, if an alloy has an overall composition between these two limits, a two-phase mixture of solid solutions is present at equilibrium. If mappings are made at different temperatures, one can then determine solubility as a function of temperature.

7.7
Equilibrium diagrams

Free-energy mappings may be calculated for random solid solutions if one has data on the specific heats of the components as a function of temperature and also information on the potential energies of interaction between like and unlike pairs of atoms. For the most part, however, equilibrium structures are determined experimentally and the results are plotted in the form of an *equilibrium diagram*. Various complex techniques of thermal analysis, supplemented by microscopic examination, may be used to find phase changes and determine compositions.   The behavior of some systems is so complex, however, that portions of diagrams for some of the most important alloys, such as iron-carbon, copper-tin, copper-zinc, and copper-aluminum, are still not known with complete certainty.

Figures 7.6 and 7.7 illustrate an oversimplified scheme for determining the phase diagrams for binary alloys.   A series of cooling curves for alloys of different composition are followed from the molten state.   The first change in slope marks the start of precipitation, and the second change marks the completion of the freezing process.   One may obtain the phase diagram by plotting a liquidus line (start of precipitation) and a solidus line (end of freezing) on a graph with temperature as the ordinate and composition as the abscissa.   The single-phase and multiphase regions are clearly shown.   Diagrams such as these serve as the basis for interpreting the behavior of alloy systems.   They are useful because they describe the equilibrium structures of alloys at a given temperature and indicate the direction toward which a reaction will go if equilibrium does not exist.   They will not indicate anything about rates of change of unstable structures, nor can they be used to predict the behavior of other, similar systems.   A large collection of most commercially important binary

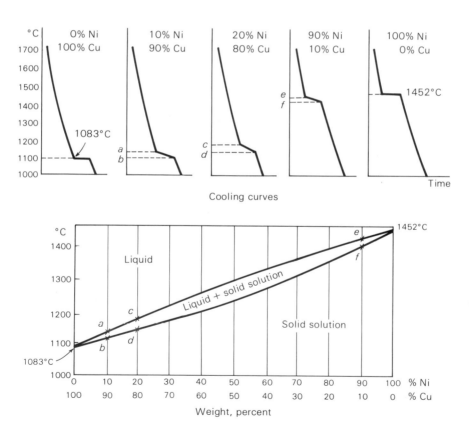

Fig. 7.6 Derivation of the copper-nickel equilibrium diagram.

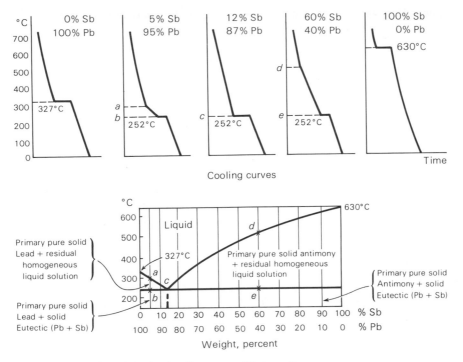

Fig. 7.7   Derivation of the lead-antimony equilibrium diagram.

alloys can be found in the "Metals Handbook" [5] and "Hansen's Constitution of Binary Alloys" [4].

A complete thermodynamic description of any system is obtained when all independent variables are specified. The number of independent variables (or degrees of freedom) associated with a system can be obtained from the Gibbs phase rule [2]:

$$F_D = C + 2 - P \tag{7.5}$$

where F_D is degrees of freedom, C is number of components, and P is number of phases. Since a binary alloy has two components and since there must be a minimum of one phase, there will be a maximum of three degrees of freedom. Since molten and solid alloys are nearly incompressible, the effect of pressure may be neglected over reasonable ranges. A graphical representation of the thermodynamic properties may therefore be obtained by plotting two other variables on rectangular coordinates. Likewise, ternary alloys have three degrees of freedom, which means that a graphical representation of the thermodynamic behavior requires three coordinates. Binary alloys are usually characterized by plotting temperature and composition on rectangular coordinates. Ternary alloys are characterized by either plotting two composition variables on triangular coordinates with temperature as a parameter or plotting temperature and one composition variable on rectangular coordinates with the other composition variable as a parameter. Equilibrium diagrams for alloys with more than three components are both rare and complex.

7.8
Binary alloys

The interpretation of apparently complex equilibrium diagrams is very simple once a few basic types are mastered. We shall first discuss a few of these "basic" diagrams and then tackle the iron-carbon phase diagram, which is more complex and is of great commercial importance, since it serves as the basis for the description of plain carbon steels.

The simplest type of alloy system is the substitutional solid solution which shows complete solubility over the whole composition range. The copper-nickel system is shown in Fig. 7.8. Consider an alloy of x percent nickel being cooled slow enough for "equilibrium" to establish at any temperature. At temperature t_1, the alloy is a homogeneous, single-phase liquid. At temperature t_2, freezing starts with the precipitation of small crystals of a substitutional solid solution of composition x_1 percent. As the temperature is further decreased, more solid forms. Since the solid solution is richer in nickel than the liquid, the percent nickel in the remaining liquid decreases. If the system is kept at equilibrium, the two phases must each remain homogeneous. As the percent nickel in the liquid decreases, the percent nickel in the precipitate must also decrease. One may determine the compositions of the two phases at,

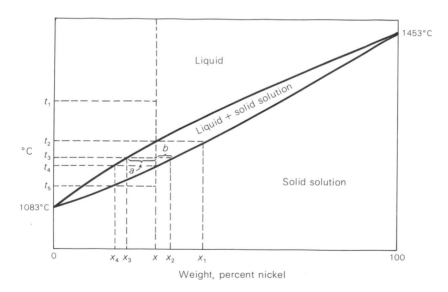

Fig. 7.8 The copper-nickel equilibrium diagram shows ideal solid-solution behavior. (Data by permission from M. Hansen, "Constitution of Binary Alloys," 2d ed., p. 602, McGraw-Hill Book Company, New York, 1958.)

for example, t_3 by drawing an isotherm through the boundaries of the region. The intersection with the liquidus line, x_3, marks the composition of the liquid, and the intersection with the solidus, x_2, marks the composition of the solid. The relative amounts of the two phases may be found by a material balance. Let W_T equal the total mass, W_S equal the weight of precipitated solid, and W_L equal the weight of saturated liquid. Then, from an overall weight balance and a nickel balance:

$$W_T = W_S + W_L \tag{7.6}$$

$$xW_T = x_2 W_S + x_3 W_L \tag{7.7}$$

The weight fractions of the two phases may then be obtained:

$$\frac{W_S}{W_T} = \frac{x - x_3}{x_2 - x_3} = \frac{a}{a + b} \tag{7.8}$$

$$\frac{W_L}{W_T} = \frac{x_2 - x}{x_2 - x_3} = \frac{b}{a + b} \tag{7.9}$$

$$\frac{W_S}{W_L} = \frac{x - x_3}{x_2 - x} = \frac{a}{b} \tag{7.10}$$

These equations form the basis of "the lever rule" for quickly determining the relative amounts of two phases in a binary alloy. The length of the isotherm from the liquidus to the solidus, $a + b$, is analogous to a stationary, balanced beam with a weight W_L at one end, a weight W_S at the other end, and the fulcrum located at the point representing the overall composition of the system. If the beam is in equilibrium, bending moments about the fulcrum may be balanced.

$$W_L a = W_S b \tag{7.11}$$

Equations (7.10) and (7.11) are identical. Thus, the weight of liquid divided by the weight of solid is equal to the length of the isotherm between the points representing the overall and solid compositions divided by the length of the isotherm between the points representing the overall and liquid compositions. As cooling continues, more solid forms and the compositions of the liquid and solid follow the liquidus and solidus lines, respectively. The freezing process is complete at temperature t_4. The resulting alloy is a homogeneous solid solution with a composition x. Further cooling does not result in any structural changes.

A second relatively simple type of alloy is one in which there is almost complete insolubility in the solid state. The lead-antimony system is shown in Fig. 7.9. An alloy of composition x_2 and at temperature t_1 is a homogeneous liquid solution. On very slow cooling, precipitation of minute crystals of pure antimony starts at t_2. (Note that the solidus line is nearly the 100 percent vertical.) Further cooling produces more pure antimony, and the composition of the saturated liquid phase decreases along the liquidus line. At t_3, the relative weights of the two phases are given by Eq. (7.12).

$$\frac{W_{Sb}}{W_{liquid}} = \frac{x_2 - x_3}{100 - x_2} = \frac{a}{b} \tag{7.12}$$

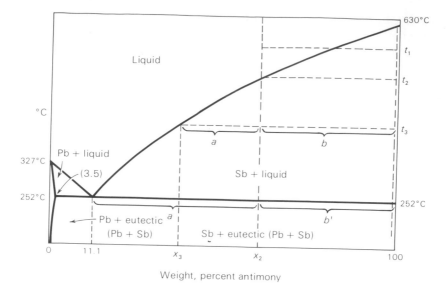

Fig. 7.9   The lead-antimony system is one in which there is almost no mutual solubility in the solid state. (By permission from M. Hansen, "Constitution of Binary Alloys," 2d ed., p. 1101, McGraw-Hill Book Company, New York, 1958.)

On just reaching 252°C we have pure antimony and saturated liquid with 11.1 percent antimony. The relative weights are

$$\frac{W_{\text{Sb}}}{W_{\text{liquid}}} = \frac{x_2 - 11.1}{100 - x_2} = \frac{a'}{b'} \tag{7.13}$$

Further cooling results in the freezing of the remaining liquid at constant temperature. A relatively fine mixture of a solid solution of 3.5 percent Sb in Pb and pure solid antimony, called the eutectic solid, is deposited. The eutectic solid must have the same composition as the liquid solution from which it was formed (11.1 percent Sb). Further cooling will reduce the solid solution to nearly pure lead. If this alloy were examined under a microscope at about 100 times magnification, one would see areas of primary antimony (the antimony which crystallized between t_2°C and 252°C) and areas of eutectic solid. Magnification of over 1,000 times would reveal that the eutectic was actually a very finely divided, two-phase mixture of pure antimony and pure lead.

Unlike the nickel-copper system, the nature of the Pb-Sb alloy differs markedly with changes in overall composition. In the composition range 0.0 to 11.1 percent Sb, the primary crystal is almost pure lead. The relative amounts of lead and eutectic depend on the overall composition of the alloy. At 11.1 percent, the alloy is 100 percent eutectic solid. In the composition range 11.1 to 100 percent Sb, the primary crystal is pure antimony. Figures 7.10 to 7.12 are photomicrographs of Pb-Sb alloys of different compositions. The light-colored areas are pure antimony, while the darkened areas are the eutectic crystals.

Fig. 7.10 A photomicrograph of a 60-40 lead-antimony alloy in the as-cast state.

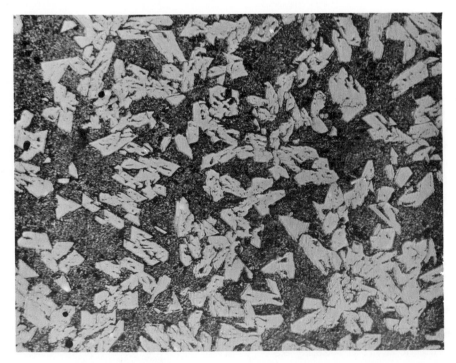

Fig. 7.11 A photomicrograph of a 70-30 lead-antimony alloy in the as-cast state.

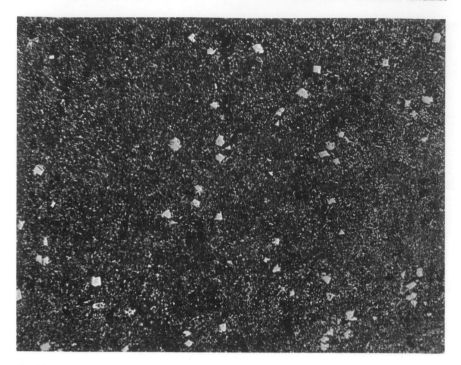

Fig. 7.12   A photomicrograph of an 87-13 lead-antimony alloy in the as-cast state.

Thermodynamically, it is impossible to have complete insolubility at equilibrium. The criterion for equilibrium between two phases is that the chemical potentials of each component are the same in all phases. This requires atoms of all components in each phase at equilibrium. In the lead-antimony system, the amounts of lead dissolved in antimony, and vice versa, are small enough to be neglected.

When two fairly similar substances, such as silver and copper, are mixed, there is a certain amount of mutual solubility in the solid state. Since solubility is almost always a function of temperature, changes in the solid phases will occur with changes of temperature. This both complicates the equilibrium behavior of the system and has important effects on the physical properties of the material. The copper-silver alloy system is shown in Fig. 7.13. The maximum solubility of copper in silver (α solid solution) is 8.8 percent at 779°C, and the maximum solubility of silver in copper (β solid solution) is 8 percent at 779°C. In both cases the solubility decreases with decreasing temperature. A eutectic reaction occurs at 779°C as a homogeneous liquid with 28.1 percent copper precipitates to a eutectic solid containing minute crystals of both α and β substitutional solid solution. The relative weights of the two solid solutions in the eutectic solid may be obtained from the lever rule:

$$\frac{\text{Wt. of } \alpha \text{ in eutectic at 779°C}}{\text{Wt. of } \beta \text{ in eutectic at 779°C}} = \frac{92.0 - 28.1}{28.1 - 8.8} \qquad (7.14)$$

Consider an alloy with 5 percent copper. Precipitation of solid solution from a homogeneous liquid starts at t_4, and freezing is complete at t_5. No further structural changes will occur until t_6 is reached. At this temperature, the α solid solution becomes saturated with respect to copper (or a copper-rich phase) and starts to precipitate crystals of β solid solution. For the most part, the precipitation will occur on the surfaces (grain boundaries) of the primary α crystals. As cooling continues, more β precipitates and the compositions of both solid solutions change along their respective solubility lines. The α phase contains 1.8 percent copper at 500°C, and the β phase contains 98 percent copper at 500°C. The relative weights of the primary and precipitated phases at 500°C may be evaluated by using the lever rule:

$$\frac{\text{Wt. of primary } \alpha \text{ in 5\% alloy at 500°C}}{\text{Wt. of precipitated } \beta \text{ in 5\% alloy at 500°C}} = \frac{98 - 5}{5 - 1.8} \qquad (7.15)$$

Next consider a homogeneous liquid alloy with 75 percent copper at t_1. Precipitation of β solid solution, composition g, will start at t_2. Continued cooling results in more β precipitation as the saturated liquid changes composition along line 1083-h-d and the solid solution changes composition along line 1083-g-f-e. On just reaching 779°C, the system contains saturated liquid, 28.1 percent copper, and β solid solution, 92 percent copper. The relative weights of the two phases are

$$\frac{\text{Wt. of liquid at 779°C}}{\text{Wt. of } \beta \text{ at 779°C}} = \frac{92 - 75}{75 - 28.1} = \frac{b'}{a'} \qquad (7.16)$$

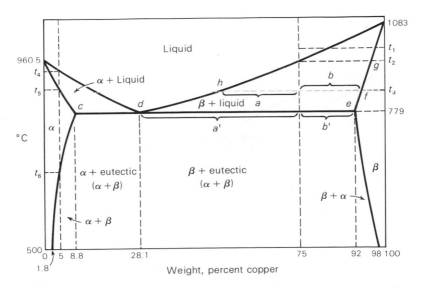

Fig. 7.13 The phase diagram for the copper-silver system shows a partial mutual solubility in the solid state. (By permission from M. Hansen, "Constitution of Binary Alloys," 2d ed., p. 18, McGraw-Hill Book Company, New York, 1958.)

Further cooling results in the freezing of a eutectic liquid, 28.1 percent copper, at constant temperature. When the freezing process is complete, further cooling will lower the temperature. This will result in a precipitation of α solid solution at the surfaces of the saturated, primary β crystals. Independently, the eutectic will be modified, since the composition of the two phases, α and β, must change with temperature. At 500°C, three distinct regions can be seen under a microscope: the modified eutectic (28.1 percent copper), the remaining primary β crystals (98 percent copper), and the precipitated α crystals (1.8 percent copper). The relative amount of each can be obtained by using the lever rule:

$$\frac{\text{Wt. of precipitated } \alpha \text{ at } 500°C}{\text{Wt. of remaining primary } \beta \text{ at } 500°C} = \frac{98 - 92}{92 - 1.8} \qquad (7.17)$$

$$\frac{\text{Wt. of modified eutectic at } 500°C}{\text{Total weight of alloy at } 500°C} = \frac{92 - 75}{92 - 28.1} \qquad (7.18)$$

$$\frac{\text{Wt. of remaining primary } \beta \text{ plus precipitated } \alpha \text{ at } 500°C}{\text{Total weight of alloy at } 500°C} = \frac{75 - 28.1}{92 - 28.1} \qquad (7.19)$$

Keep in mind that although three distinct regions are seen under a microscope, the alloy consists of only two different phases: α solid solution of composition 1.8 percent copper and β solid solution of composition 98 percent copper. The eutectic solid is merely a very intimate, physical mixture of minute crystals of α and β.

The cadmium-mercury system (Fig. 7.14) is typical of alloys that show peritectic reactions. Alloys in the composition range between 35 and 50 percent mercury are different than those previously considered in that they

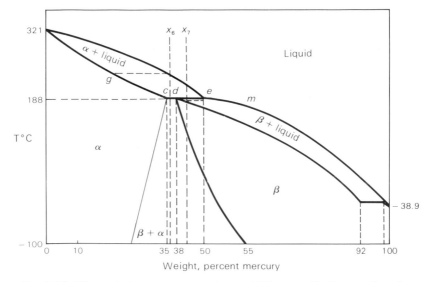

Fig. 7.14 The cadmium-mercury system exhibits a peritectic reaction at 188°C. (By permission from M. Hansen, "Constitution of Binary Alloys," 2d ed., p. 420, McGraw-Hill Book Company, New York, 1958.)

experience a peritectic reaction at 188°C. Let us summarize the behavior of alloys with composition x_6 percent, 38 percent, and x_7 percent mercury as they are cooled through the peritectic reaction temperature (see Table 7.1). By calculating the differences between the amounts of α and liquid before and after the peritectic reaction, it can be shown that in each of the three cases the reaction ratio is the same:

$$\frac{\text{Wt. } \alpha \text{ reacting}}{\text{Wt. liquid reacting}} = \frac{50 - 38}{38 - 35} \tag{7.20}$$

Thus the peritectic reaction can be characterized in the same manner as an ordinary chemical reaction; that is, the "reactants" always participate in the reaction in fixed amounts.

$$\alpha \text{ (ss)} + \text{liquid} \rightleftharpoons \beta \text{ (ss)}$$

It should be noted that a peritectic reaction differs from a eutectic reaction in two ways: liquid exists below the peritectic reaction temperature, and the horizontal (isotherm) is intersected by the phase boundaries from below rather than above.

The nickel-zinc alloy system is typical of alloys that show more complex behavior in the solid state (Fig. 7.15). Six different types of solid solutions, α, β, β_1, γ, γ_1, and δ, have been found. The maximum solubility of zinc in nickel is

Table 7.1

	x_6	Alloy, %Hg 38	x_7
On just reaching 188°C			
Comp. of α, %	35	35	35
Wt. fraction α	$\dfrac{50 - x_6}{50 - 35}$	$\dfrac{50 - 38}{50 - 35}$	$\dfrac{50 - x_7}{50 - 35}$
Comp. of liquid, %	50	50	50
Wt. fraction liquid	$\dfrac{x_6 - 35}{50 - 35}$	$\dfrac{38 - 35}{50 - 35}$	$\dfrac{x_7 - 35}{50 - 35}$
After completing the reaction at 188°C			
Comp. of α, %	35		
Wt. fraction α	$\dfrac{38 - x_6}{38 - 35}$	0.0	0.0
Comp. of β, %	38	38	38
Wt. fraction β	$\dfrac{x_6 - 35}{38 - 35}$	1.0	$\dfrac{50 - x_7}{50 - 38}$
Comp. of liquid, %			50
Wt. fraction liquid	0.0	0.0	$\dfrac{x_7 - 38}{50 - 38}$

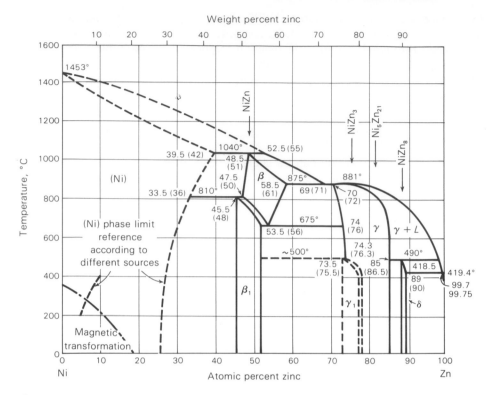

Fig. 7.15 The nickel-zinc binary alloy system exhibits a variety of complex transformations from one ordered solid solution to another. (By permission from M. Hansen, "Constitution of Binary Alloys," 2d ed., McGraw-Hill Book Company, New York, 1958.)

42 percent, while there is no significant solubility of nickel in zinc. Four different ordered solutions, $NiZn$, $NiZn_3$, Ni_5Zn_{21}, and $NiZn_8$, have been observed (the latter structure is only tentatively established). A eutectic reaction occurs at 881°C; a peritectic reaction occurs at 1040°C; a eutectoid reaction occurs at 675°C; and peritectoid reactions occur at 810, 500, and 490°C. (A eutectoid reaction is identical with a eutectic reaction except that the single phase is a homogeneous solid solution rather than a homogeneous liquid solution.) The dotted lines are tentatively assigned solubility lines. The interpretation of the figure and the use of the lever rule are identical with the previous diagrams.

7.9
The iron–iron carbide diagram

Commercial steels are alloys of up to about 1.5 percent carbon in iron plus other alloying elements. These materials have been the most important structural materials in the world in this century and will probably remain so for many years to come. There are many different types of steels. Among the most important are plain carbon steels, which are alloys of carbon in iron; stainless steels, which are alloys of iron, carbon, chromium, and (in certain grades of stainless) nickel; and a large number of special-grade iron alloys containing molybdenum, vanadium, tungsten, manganese, and silicon. The iron–iron carbide diagram (Figs. 7.16 and 7.17) indicates the equilibrium structures for the plain carbon steels. *Pure molten iron* freezes to a body-centered cubic solid (delta iron) at

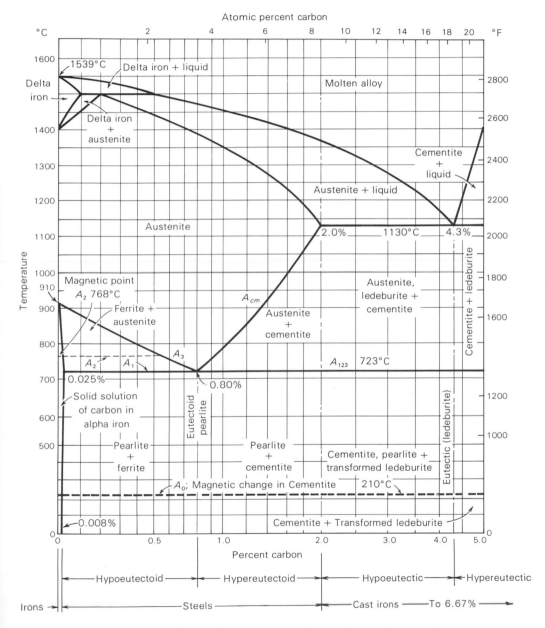

Fig. 7.16 The iron-carbon equilibrium diagram is the basis for understanding the behavior of the plain carbon steels.

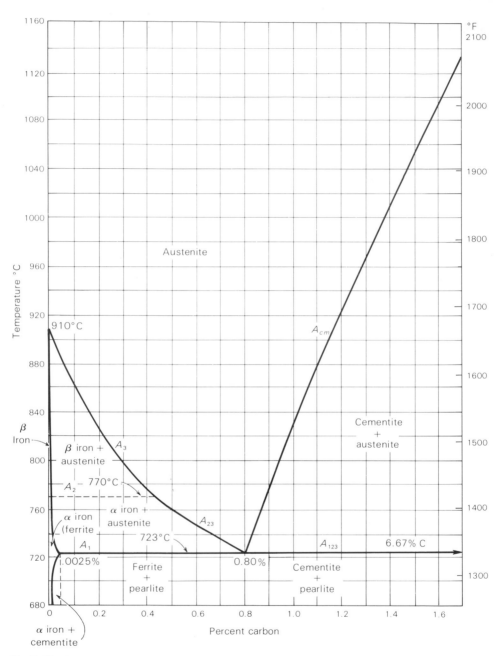

Fig. 7.17   The iron-carbon alloy system exhibits a eutectoid reaction at 723°C and 0.8 percent carbon.

1539°C. At 1400°C delta (δ) iron transforms to a face-centered cubic structure (γ-iron) and then at 910°C back to a body-centered structure (α-iron). An electronic change occurs at 768°C which produces a magnetic α-iron below 768°C. The following constituents appear on the equilibrium diagram.

Delta iron An interstitial solid solution of carbon in body-centered cubic iron. The maximum solubility of carbon is about 0.1 percent at 1493°C.

Austenite An interstitial solid solution of carbon in face-centered cubic iron. The maximum solubility of carbon is about 2 percent at 1130°C.

Ferrite An interstitial solid solution of carbon in body-centered cubic iron. Above 768°C it is nonmagnetic; below 768°C it is magnetic. The maximum solubility of carbon is about 0.025 percent at 723°C. The light-colored areas in Fig. 7.18 are ferrite.

Cementite The intermetallic compound, Fe_3C. The unit cell is orthorhombic, with each carbon atom surrounded by six iron atoms at the corners of a distorted prism. It is magnetic below 210°C, melts or decomposes somewhere

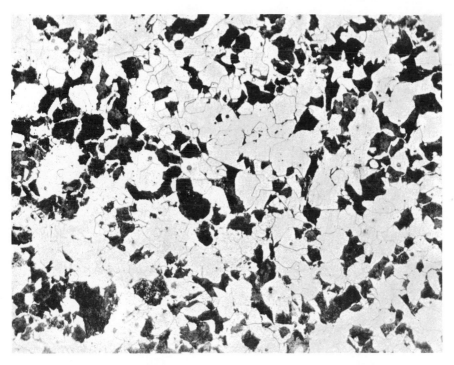

Fig. 7.18 A photomicrograph of a double-annealed (heated at 981°C, furnace-cooled, reheated at 842°C, furnace-cooled) 1023 cast steel (0.23%C). The dark areas are pearlite, the light areas ferrite.

above 1900°C, and is unstable, partially transforming to iron and graphite, below 1200°C.

Ledeburite A eutectic mixture of austenite and cementite in about a 1-to-1 ratio. The overall composition is 4.3 percent carbon.

Pearlite A eutectoid mixture of ferrite and cementite in about a 7-to-1 ratio. The cementite is arranged as thin laminar (or platelike) layers in a matrix of ferrite. The overall composition is 0.8 percent carbon. The dark areas in Fig. 7.18 are pearlite; and Fig. 7.19 shows pearlite at magnification of about 1,000 times, so that the two phases are visible. The darkened areas at the grain boundaries are cementite.

The equilibrium diagram shows a peritectic reaction at 1493°C, a eutectic reaction at 1130°C, and, most important, a eutectoid reaction at 723°C. The eutectoid transformation of austenite (0.8 percent C) to pearlite serves as the basis for most heat-treating procedures for plain carbon steels. The equilibrium diagram is not too useful for characterizing the cast irons because of the tendency of cementite to decompose to graphite and ferrite.

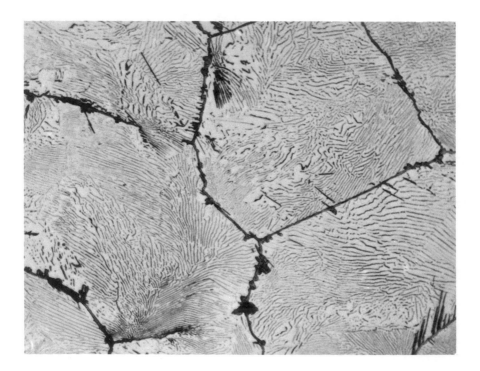

Fig. 7.19 A 1.12 percent carbon steel heated at 950°C, furnace-cooled and etched with hot sodium picrate. At magnifications of 1,000 the lamellar plate of Fe_3C embedded in a matrix of ferrite are visible.

7.10
The eutectoid reaction in steels

A eutectoid reaction is one in which a solid solution decomposes into two phases on cooling. The analysis of this process is very similar to the analysis of a freezing process in that nucleation and growth are the rate-determining factors. In solid-state transformations, these rates are slow enough to be conveniently measured.

The decomposition of austenite into ferrite and iron carbide has been particularly well studied because of its importance to the heat-treating of steel. If an SAE 1080 steel is slowly cooled from 1000°C, no changes will occur until the eutectoid temperature of 723°C is reached. At this temperature, further cooling causes the formation of the two-phase, lamellar aggregate known as pearlite. The interlamellar spacing and the nature of the particles depend upon the original austenite grain size, the homogeneity of the austenite, the temperature of formation, and the presence of impurities and alloying elements.

The reaction has been studied under isothermal conditions. The steel is heated into the stable austenite region and "soaked" until a stable, homogeneous structure is attained. It is then quenched to a temperature below the eutectoid temperature. Samples of solid material are then removed from the environment at specific intervals and quenched further to stop the decomposition of the austenite. A sample is then examined microscopically to determine the amount of pearlite (or other reaction products) that has been formed. The percent transformation may then be plotted as a function of time. A typical transformation curve is shown in Fig. 7.20. The description of this S-shaped curve has been the object of many theoretical kinetic analyses. If a random distribution of spherical nuclei, a constant rate of nucleation, and a constant growth rate are assumed, a kinetic equation may be derived [8]:

$$\text{Percent transformed} = \mathcal{F}(t) = 100 \left[1 - \exp\left(-\frac{\pi}{3} \mathcal{N} \mathcal{G}_r^3 t^4 \right) \right] \tag{7.21}$$

$$\mathcal{N} = \text{rate of nucleation} = K \exp\left(-\frac{\Delta E_D}{RT} \right) \exp\left(-\frac{A(T)}{RT} \right) \tag{7.22}$$

The quantity $\mathcal{G}_r$ is the rate of growth of particle diameter and is almost always a constant for a given set of conditions. Although this equation can curve-fit an S-shaped curve of the type shown in Fig. 7.20, it has been found that the rate of nucleation is not constant, but rather, varies markedly with time (Fig. 7.21). Both rate of growth and "average" rate of nucleation are functions of temperature. Near the eutectoid temperature, the ratio, $\mathcal{N}/\mathcal{G}_r$, is very small, resulting in a coarse-grained pearlite, while at lower temperatures $\mathcal{N}/\mathcal{G}_r$ becomes much larger, resulting in a much finer grained product.

These results are best summarized by an *isothermal transformation dia-*

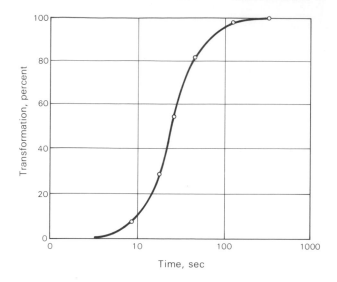

Fig. 7.20 A typical isothermal reaction curve. (By permission from R. Smoluchowski, J. E. Mayer, and W. A. Weyl (eds.), "Phase Transformations in Solids," p. 549, John Wiley & Sons, Inc., New York, 1951.)

gram. Temperature and time are plotted on rectangular coordinates. The locus of points representing the start (say, 1 percent reaction) and the end (say, 99 percent reaction) of an isothermal reaction are plotted. The C-shaped curves shown in Figs. 7.22 and 7.23 are typical. The eutectoid steel shows a maximum rate of reaction at about 1000°F. A coarse-grained pearlite is formed near the eutectoid temperature of 1333°F (723°C), while a fine-grained pearlite forms near the knee of the curve. Pearlite does not form when the reaction is

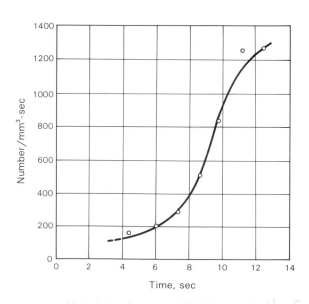

Fig. 7.21 The rate of nucleation of pearlite as a function of time for a eutectoid steel reacted at 680°C. (By permission from R. Smoluchowski, J. E. Mayer, and W. A. Weyl (eds.), "Phase Transformations in Solids," p. 549, John Wiley & Sons, Inc., New York, 1951.)

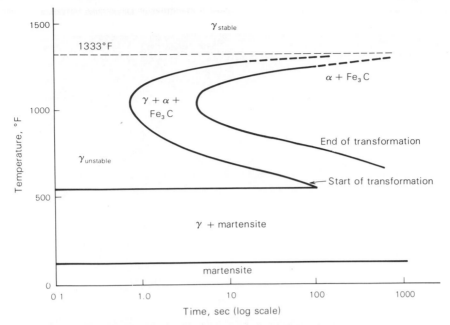

Fig. 7.22 The isothermal transformation curves for a eutectoid steel (SAE 1080) indicate the times at which the eutectoid reaction starts and ends. Note that martensite forms instantaneously. (Data from "Atlas of Isothermal Transformation Diagrams," U.S. Steel Corporation, Pittsburgh, 1951.)

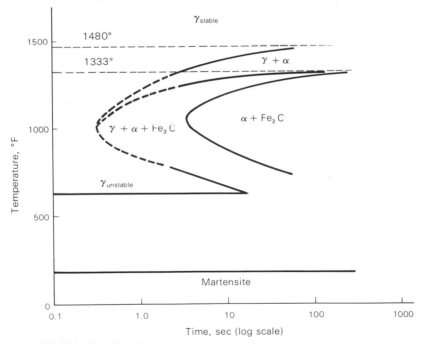

Fig. 7.23 The isothermal transformation curve for an SAE 1045 steel has an additional branch associated with the precipitation of ferrite. (Data from "Atlas of Isothermal Transformation Diagrams," U.S. Steel Corporation, Pittsburgh, 1951.)

Fig. 7.24 A coarse, single-phase, needlelike structure called martensite forms when steel is rapidly quenched. The photomicrograph is of a 1.12 percent carbon steel, heated at 920°C and quenched in water (magnification 2550).

carried out much below the knee of the curve but, rather, bainite or martensite is formed. The SAE 1045 steel shows an additional line which represents the precipitation of ferrite from the unstable austenite phase.

Pearlite and bainite are both two-phase aggregates of ferrite and cementite. At high temperatures, the cementite nucleates first, at the austenite grain boundary, and grows to a platelike structure. The ferrite then precipitates along the cementite plates, thus producing a lamellar structure. At lower temperatures the ferrite precipitates first, followed by the precipitation of cementite particles. The resulting bainite structure is not lamellar, but has a very complicated morphology. As the isothermal reaction temperature is lowered, the structure comes closer to the martensite structure.

The martensite transformation is completely different in that it is a "diffusionless" transformation. It has been reported that, upon quenching a eutectoid steel to below the "martensite transformation temperature," a martensite structure will develop within 10^{-4} sec.

The extremely rapid rate is associated with the fact that the transformation does not involve a nucleation and growth process, but rather occurs because of the trapping of carbon atoms in solution. At low temperatures, the rate of diffusion of carbon is low enough to slow down the precipitation of ferrite and cementite. The carbon remains interstitially in solution as the lattice transforms from a face-centered to a body-centered lattice. The supersaturation produces a severe lattice strain and distorts the structure into a tetragonal lattice. Martensite is a single-phase structure which is generally much harder and more brittle than the corresponding pearlitic or bainitic structures. Since the hardness is a result of the severe lattice strain produced by the super-saturation, it must increase with increasing carbon content. A photomicro-graph of martensite is shown in Fig. 7.24. When reheated, martensite can be made to revert to a two-phase aggregate of ferrite and cementite by inducing the diffusion of carbon. The softening or "tempering" of hardened steels is associated with this change in the original martensite structure.

7.11
The stainless steels

One of the most widely used groups of materials is the stainless steels. They are essentially low-carbon steels with the alloying elements chromium and, in some varieties, nickel. Their chief characteristic is greater corrosion resistance than the plain carbon steels. They may be broadly classified into the following three types:

1. Martensitic or hardenable (type 400). These usually contain from 11 to 18 percent chromium and from 0.1 to 0.8 percent carbon. These materials undergo a polymorphic change from a face-centered to a body-centered iron structure in the vicinity of 900°C. (The exact temperature depends on the composition.) They also have a tendency to precipitate complex chromium-iron carbides on slow cooling. They thus respond to temperature changes in much the same way as plain carbon steels. They are resistant to a wider variety of corroding atmospheres than the plain carbon steels but are the least corrosion-resistant of the stainless varieties.

2. Ferritic alloys (type 400). These usually contain between 16 and 27 percent chromium and 0.05 to 0.15 percent carbon. Ferrite (body-centered cubic iron) is stable from low temperatures right up to the melting points of the alloys, so that no polymorphic changes occur. There is a tendency, however, for complex chromium-iron carbide precipitation. These alloys do not respond to temperature in the same way as the martensitic alloys in that they are not "hardened" by quenching through a polymorphic transition temperature. The stability of ferrite depends primarily on the amounts of chromium and carbon. The higher the chromium-to-carbon ratio, the better the chance for a stable ferrite phase. Figure 7.25 illustrates the phase behavior of martensitic and ferritic alloys with a fixed carbon content of 0.1 percent carbon. Above about 17 percent chromium, ferrite is completely stable, so that this is the lower limit of the ferritic range. Figure 7.26 illustrates that the extent of the aus-tenite region is a function of carbon content. Above 19 percent chromium there is very little chance of austenite formation at any carbon content. At zero carbon content, the upper limit for austenite stability is only 12 percent

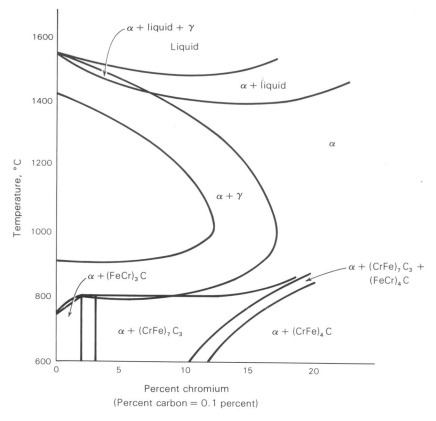

α + liquid + γ

1600

Liquid

α + liquid

1400

α

1200

α + γ

1000

α + (FeCr)₃C

α + (CrFe)₇C₃ + (FeCr)₄C

800

α + (CrFe)₇C₃

α + (CrFe)₄C

600

0   5   10   15   20

Percent chromium
(Percent carbon = 0.1 percent)

Fig. 7.25 A planar section at 0.1 percent carbon of an iron-chromium-carbon ternary system. (Do not use the simple line-segment principles discussed in prior sections.) (Sketched from data in "Metals Handbook," p. 1249, ASM, Cleveland, 1948.)

chromium. The transformation temperatures are obviously also a function of composition.

3. Austenitic alloys (type 300). These have a combined nickel plus chromium content of at least 24 percent, with a minimum of 7 percent of each alloying element. The carbon content is generally below 0.25 percent. Nickel has a tendency to stabilize a face-centered cubic lattice over wide ranges of temperature, but there is still a tendency for complex chromium-iron carbide precipitation. Figure 7.27 shows a phase diagram for chromium-nickel alloys with 0.1 percent carbon at an elevated temperature. Austenite is stable beyond about 7 percent nickel. At chromium contents above 20 percent, a hard, brittle intermetallic phase, called the σ phase, forms, which has adverse effects on the ductility and corrosion resistance of the steels. Figure 7.28 is a section of the phase diagram for the specific chromium content of 18 percent. The 18-8 Cr-Ni alloy is one of the most widely used of the stainless steels. At true equilibrium, ferrite is the stable phase at room temperature.

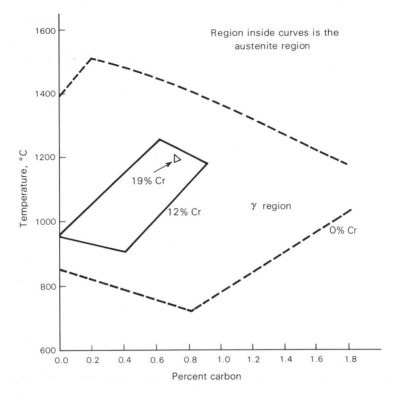

Fig. 7.26 Austenite is unstable in type 400 stainless steels at all temperatures and compositions when more than about 20 percent chromium is present.

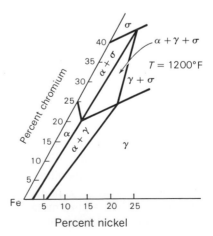

Fig. 7.27 An isothermal (1200°F) section from the phase diagram for the austenitic stainless steels. (Data from "Metals Handbook," p. 1261, ASM, Cleveland, 1948.)

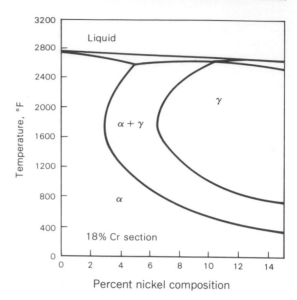

Fig. 7.28 The phase diagram for stainless steels containing 18 percent chromium [3] p. 389.

The transformation from austenite to ferrite is so slow, however, that in practice the steel remains in a metastable austenitic state. Prolonged use at elevated temperature can promote the precipitation of chromium carbide complexes and the formation of ferrite.

The corrosion resistance of the stainless steels is directly related to the dissolved chromium content; the more chromium in solution, the better the corrosion resistance. Thus, the austenitic stainless steels are the most corrosion-resistant variety. Also, the precipitation of chromium-rich intermetallic compounds lowers the dissolved chromium content and is one of the many reasons for corrosion failure in these materials. The chemical properties of alloys will be discussed in Chap. 15.

7.12
Nonequilibrium conditions and their effects on structure

For the most part in this chapter, we have examined the structure of alloys under conditions of heating or cooling that were slow enough to permit equilibrium structures. Normally, however, industrial heat-treating operations occur at rates fast enough to promote deviations from equilibrium behavior. In this section we shall consider the effects of nonequilibrium conditions on the structure and composition of alloys.

Rapid heating or cooling modifies the freezing range of an alloy, inhibits the precipitation of secondary phases, and causes thermal hysteresis of allotropic changes. When a pure metal freezes rapidly, the initial effect is on the rate of nucleation; the faster the cooling the more rapid the nucleation.

This generally leads to a finer-grained material, since there are more nuclei around which precipitation can occur, and will often lead to a complex, dendritic-grain structure, since equiaxed grains will not have time to develop. A pure metal freezes at a fixed temperature, however, and this value cannot be changed to any extent by the rate of cooling.

When solid solutions are cooled from the molten state, a freezing range exists. Referring back to Fig. 7.8, we see that the equilibrium cooling of an alloy of composition x causes freezing to start at t_2 and end at t_4. The composition of the precipitating solid changes from x_1 to x, while the composition of the liquid changes from x to x_4. In order to maintain a true equilibrium, time must be allowed for the nucleation and precipitation of the solid and also for the redistribution of solvent and solute by diffusion in order to maintain homogeneous phases with no concentration gradients. With rapid cooling, less time is available for precipitation, with the result that there is less solid, but with higher nickel content than would be expected at equilibrium at a given temperature. This shows up as a shifting of the solidus line, as shown in Fig. 7.29, with subsequent broadening of the freezing range. In the limit of infinitely fast cooling, one expects the freezing range to be extended to the melting point of the low-melting constituent. This means that at infinite cooling rate the last bit of liquid to freeze will be pure copper. Another important effect of rapid cooling is "coring" of the solid. At fast rates there is not enough time for diffusion to homogenize the precipitating solid and the resulting materials will have a central core which approaches x_1 in composition and a skin which is less rich in nickel (perhaps even pure copper in the extreme case). The importance of this phenomenon is great, especially if such an alloy is used at around the melting point of pure copper. In such a situation, intergranular

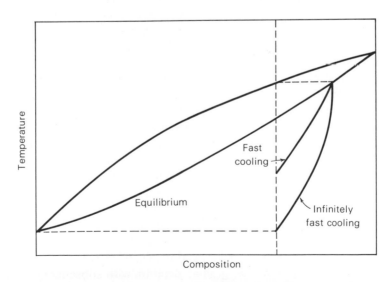

Fig. 7.29 Nonequilibrium cooling of binary alloys has a tendency to broaden the freezing range of the alloys.

fusion is quite possible. Essentially the same effects occur with alloys that form eutectics, but in these cases the freezing range cannot be broadened beyond the eutectic temperature.

Another important factor is the effect on precipitation of secondary phases. Referring back to the Ag-Cu alloy system shown in Fig. 7.13, we see that when a 5 percent Cu alloy is slowly cooled below temperature t_6, a precipitation of a copper-rich β solid solution occurs at the grain boundaries of the α-solid-solution phase. The rate-controlling step for this reaction is the slow diffusion of copper to the grain boundaries. Since diffusion is highly temperature-sensitive, rapid cooling to a low temperature has a tendency to inhibit the precipitation. A fast enough cooling rate can even prevent any secondary phase from precipitating, thus forming a metastable, supersaturated solid solution. This is the basis of many of the hardening processes used in heat-treating materials.

A third factor is the suppression of allotropic transformations that are diffusion-controlled. An important example is the transformation of austenite to ferrite in alloys of iron and carbon. This is a transformation from a face-centered cubic to a body-centered cubic structure and a subsequent redistribution of the excess carbon in the austenite. It is essentially a precipitation of a low-carbon phase with the subsequent enrichment in carbon of the carbon-rich phase. Its rate depends upon the diffusion of carbon away from the interface. On rapid cooling, the temperature at which the transformation becomes noticeable is suppressed and the amount of ferrite formed is decreased, as shown in Fig. 7.30a. Similarly, on rapid heating, the temperature at which austenite forms at a noticeable rate is higher and the amount of austenite at a given temperature is less. Again, very rapid cooling can suppress all phase changes and produce a metastable, supersaturated solution (martensite in this case). The eutectoid transformation temperature can be modified in a similar manner, as shown in Fig. 7.30. On the fast cooling of a hypoeutectoid steel (less than 0.8 percent C), the precipitation of free ferrite is suppressed and the resulting pearlite has a carbon content of less than the "equilibrium" value of 0.8 percent. On the fast cooling of a hypereutectoid steel (more than 0.8 percent C), the precipitation of free cementite is suppressed and the resulting pearlite has a carbon content greater than 0.8 percent.

A common way to modify the properties of a material is to use the effects of cooling rates on microstructure by suitably *heat-treating* the material. A *full-annealing* process is used mainly to remove strain hardening and thereby soften a material by keeping it at elevated temperatures and slowly cooling in a furnace, generally at the rate of about 0.1°F/sec. The annealing of a low-carbon steel is shown schematically in Fig. 7.31a. The "soaking" temperature is so chosen that it is above the transformation temperature, and the cooling rate is so chosen that a coarse-grained pearlitic structure is obtained. (The isothermal transformation diagram is superimposed on the cooling curve in Fig. 7.31a.) One can form a finer-grained pearlite, with subsequently greater hardness, by cooling at a faster rate, of the order of 60°F/sec, so that the transformation is complete closer to the knee on the isothermal transformation dia-

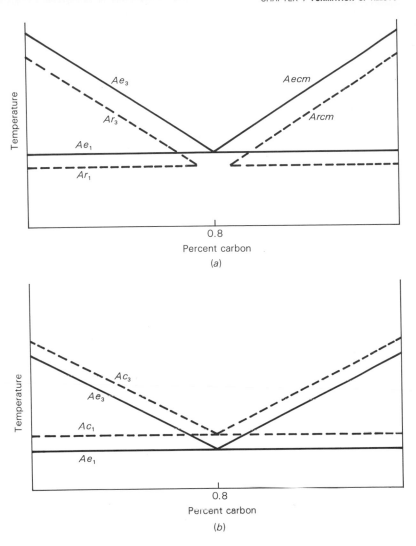

Fig. 7.30 Nonequilibrium temperature changes have a tendency to suppress allotropic modifications in binary alloys. (a) Suppression of transformation temperatures, rapid cooling (Ae are equilibrium lines); (b) suppression of transformation temperatures, rapid heating.

gram. This modified annealing treatment is sometimes known as *normalizing*.

In these treatments on steel, the eutectoid constituent is lamellar with plates of cementite in a matrix of ferrite. It is also possible to transform the platelike cementite into a more stable globular shape by heating for long periods of time just below the transformation temperature (Fig. 7.31b). This allows for a maximum of diffusion without actually carrying out a transformation to austenite. This is called *spheroidization.*

As we have discussed in preceding sections, the quenching of a steel can

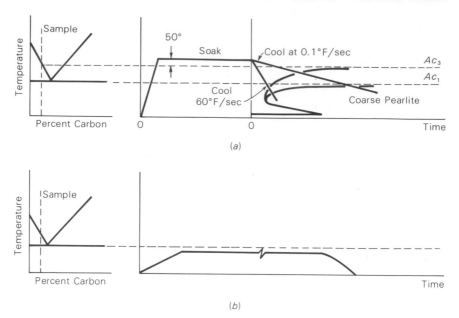

Fig. 7.31 The structure and properties of steel may be controlled by controlling the annealing treatment. (*a*) Full annealing for a plain carbon steel; (*b*) spheroidizing a low-carbon steel.

lead to the diffusionless transformation to martensite. When a given material, say, a rod, is quenched in oil or water, the surface is cooled rapidly enough to form martensite, while the subsurfaces, where the rates are limited by conduction, are cooled slowly enough to allow pearlite to form (Fig. 7.32). Since martensite is hard and brittle, the surface of the rod is said to have been *hardened*.

If one wishes to relieve internal strains in martensite and thereby resoften the material to a certain extent, the structure can be reheated to the temperature range 200 to 400°F and soaked for a given period of time. Diffusion processes permit strain relief without a major change in the martensite structure. This is known as *tempering*. Tempering at temperatures in the range of 400 to 1300°F enables one to transform the martensite to a more stable mixture of ferrite and cementite. Again, the nature and structure of the final product depends on the tempering conditions used.

The heat treatment of metals and alloys is a very complex art. In this section we have merely tried to illustrate that one can control the properties and structure of a material by subjecting it to a variety of thermal conditions. More detailed discussions of this subject can be found in the references at the end of the chapter [3,7] and in the ASM "Metals Handbook."

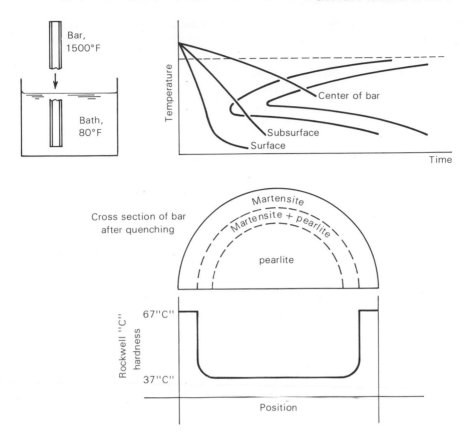

Fig. 7.32   When a steel bar is quenched, the cooling rate is maximum at the surface and minimum at the center.   This causes a variation of microstructure through the cross section of the bar.

References

1   Cottrell, A. H.: "Theoretical Structural Metallurgy," St. Martin's Press, Inc., New York, 1960. *Chapters X and XI give a more complete discussion of free-energy changes and the relation to equilibrium phase diagrams.*

2   Glasstone, S.: "Textbook of Physical Chemistry," 2d ed., D. Van Nostrand Company, Inc., Princeton, N.J., 1946. *Chapter VI is an easily read discussion of the physical chemistry of phase change.   Polymorphic changes, phase equilibria, and the phase rule are considered.*

3   Guy, A. G.: "Elements of Physical Metallurgy," Addison-Wesley Publishing Company, Inc., Reading, Mass., 1959. *Chapters 5 and 6 are complete discussions of phase transformations in metallic systems and phase diagrams.*

4 Hansen, M.: "Constitution of Binary Alloys," 2d ed., McGraw-Hill Book Company, New York, 1958. *A complete up-to-date collection of phase diagrams and other available data on binary metallic alloys.*

5 American Society for Metals, "Metals Handbook," ASM, Cleveland, 1960. *The standard reference for all types of information on metallic materials.*

6 Rhines, F. N.: "Phase Diagrams in Metallurgy," McGraw-Hill Book Company, New York, 1956. *A text on the theory and application of phase diagrams with an emphasis on metallic systems.*

7 Samans, C. H.: "Engineering Metals and Their Alloys," The Macmillan Company, New York, 1953. *Descriptive material on the structure and properties of many commercial alloys.*

8 Smoluchowski, R., J. E. Mayer, and W. A. Weyl (eds.): "Phase Transformations in Solids," John Wiley & Sons, Inc., New York, 1951.

Questions

7.1 Which of the following pairs of elements would probably form a wide range of substitutional solid solutions: Ag-Bi, Al-Cd, Au-Ni, Cu-Fe, Cu-Pd, Fe-V, Ni-Zn? Give reasons for your answers. Look through Ref. 4 to verify your answers.

7.2 Show that a sphere with a radius of 0.414 of the radius of the lattice spheres can fit into an octahedral void of a face-centered cubic lattice. Calculate the diameter of a tetrahedral void in a face-centered cubic lattice.

7.3 Repeat Question 7.2 for octahedral and tetrahedral voids in a body-centered cubic lattice.

7.4 Calculate the volume change for the polymorphic transformation of α-iron (bcc) to γ-iron (fcc). Explain why carbon is more soluble in γ-iron than α-iron.

Atomic radius bcc structure $= 1.248$ Å

Atomic radius fcc structure $= 1.292$ Å

7.5 Consider the equilibrium-phase diagram for copper-silver alloys (Fig. 7.13). Sketch typical free-energy vs. composition diagrams at temperatures t_1, t_3, 779°C, and t_5.

7.6 The addition of chromium to iron raises the α to γ polymorphic transformation temperature. Sketch this effect on a free-energy vs. temperature diagram and qualitatively explain the changes in terms of lattice distortion and bond formation.

7.7 Describe the changes that occur on the very slow cooling, from 1000°C, of a nickel-zinc alloy containing 70 weight percent zinc. Show all phase changes and determine the compositions and weights of all phases at room temperature.

7.8 Use Fig. 7.16 to describe the very slow cooling of the following steels from 1600°C to room temperature: SAE 1020, 0.2 percent C; SAE 1080, 0.8 percent C; and SAE 10100, 1.0 percent C. Describe all phase changes and determine the compositions and relative weights of all phases at room temperature. Also sketch the microstructures at room temperature.

7.9 Use the following experimental data [4] to draw the equilibrium phase diagram for iron-molybdenum alloys.

Pure iron melting point   1534°C
$\alpha \rightleftarrows \gamma$ transformation   1390°C
$\gamma \leftrightarrows \alpha$ transformation   910°C
Magnetic transformation   769°C
Pure molybdenum melting point   2625°C

Alloys

Maximum solubility of Mo in molten Fe:
     51 weight percent Mo at 1540°C
     55 weight percent Mo at 1640°C
     60 weight percent Mo at 1800°C

Maximum solubility of Fe in Mo; β solid solution:
     2.7 percent Fe at 1100°C
     3.6 percent Fe at 1200°C
     4.8 percent Fe at 1300°C
     6.7 percent Fe at 1400°C
   10.5 percent Fe at 1480°C
   14   weight percent Fe at 1540°C
   13   weight percent Fe at 1640°C
   10   weight percent Fe at 1800°C

Maximum solubility of Mo in Fe; α solid solution:
   37.5 percent Mo at 1450°C
   30.0 percent Mo at 1370°C
   20.0 percent Mo at 1225°C
   15.0 percent Mo at 1100°C
   10.0 percent Mo at 950°C
    6.7 percent Mo at 650°C

Solubility of α in saturated liquid solutions

Temp	*Percent Mo in solid solution*	*Saturated liquid*
1520	3	8
1500	12	19
1475	20	28
1440	35	35 (a minimum)
1450	37.5	37

γ-loop

α-γ transformations in a solid solution form a γ loop with a vertex at 3 percent Mo at 1100°C

Peritectic reactions

1540°C liquid (51% Mo) + β (86% Mo) $\rightleftarrows$ σ (63.2% Mo)

1480°C liquid (42% Mo) + σ (55% Mo) $\rightleftarrows$ ϵ (53.4% Mo)

1450°C liquid (37% Mo) + ϵ (51.4% Mo) $\rightleftarrows$ α (37.5% Mo)

7.10 Table 7.2 gives the isothermal rate of nucleation and rate of growth of pearlite in a eutectoid steel (0.78 percent carbon and 0.63 percent manganese) with an ASTM grain size of $5\frac{1}{4}$:

Table 7.2

$T, °C$	$\mathcal{N}, nuclei/mm^3\text{-}sec$	$\mathcal{G}_r, mm/sec$
550	1,000	10^{-2}
575	620	9×10^{-3}
600	290	7.4×10^{-3}
625	110	5.7×10^{-3}
650	27.0	3.9×10^{-3}
675	2.2	1.9×10^{-3}
700	10^{-3}	3.0×10^{-4}
703	10^{-4}	2.4×10^{-4}

Approximate the isothermal transformation diagram for this steel.

7.11 Use the isothermal transformation diagram for an SAE 1045 steel to predict the minimum rates of cooling that are required to produce the following structures:
(a) a mixture of ferrite and coarse pearlite
(b) a mixture of ferrite and fine-grained pearlite
(c) martensite
Start at 1550°F and assume a linear rate of cooling. Sketch the cooling curves directly on the isothermal-transformation diagram.

7.12 Explain why martensite forms almost instantaneously upon cooling while pearlite and bainite require a finite "induction" period.

8
Polymers

8.1
Introduction

In the preceding chapter we discussed the crystal structures of solids composed of spherical atoms. Polymer molecules in solids, however, are never hard spheres, and an understanding of the nature of molecular packing can come only after a more detailed analysis of the geometry of the molecule. A typical molecule of polymethylene, for example, might be represented by a cylindrical chain with a length of 50,000 Å (corresponding to 40,000 —CH_2— units) and a diameter of less than 5 Å. This corresponds to a rope that is 45 m long and 4.5 mm in diameter. When a molecule such as this is in a mass of material, it can, like the corresponding rope, become knotted and entangled with surrounding molecules. Since a crystalline polymer is an aggregate in which the molecules have some kind of organized, or ordered, arrangement, the ability of a polymer molecule to go into a crystal must be related to the ease with which it can disentangle from its surroundings and take on such an ordered arrangement. This ability is, of course, related to the size and geometry of the molecule and also to the nature of the intermolecular forces that are present.

A *crystalline polymer* is one which is made up of molecules that are capable of disentangling and reorganizing into a simple geometry. An *amorphous polymer* is one which is made up of molecules that can neither disentangle nor remain in a simple (and permanent) geometry. The purpose of this chapter is to discuss the molecular factors that control the structure of polymeric solids.

8.2
Configurations of a polymer molecule

One of the prime factors in determining whether a polymer can crystallize is the steric regularity of the molecules. It stands to reason that if we want a molecule to go into some kind of an ordered, repetitive pattern, its structure must also have a regularly repeating pattern.

Linear polymers are found in nature or may be formed by either addition or condensation polymerization of simple monomers. A typical addition polymerization is a free-radical reaction in which a free-radical initiator, such as a peroxide, accelerates the polymerization of an unsaturated, ethylenic compound.

$$P_2 \rightleftarrows 2P \cdot \tag{8.1}$$

$$P \cdot + X_2C{=}CX_2 \rightarrow P{-}CX_2{-}CX_2 \cdot \tag{8.2}$$

$$P{-}CX_2{-}CX_2 \cdot + nCX_2{=}CX_2 \rightarrow P({-}CX_2{-}CX_2{-})_nCX_2{-}CX_2 \cdot \tag{8.3}$$

$$P({-}CX_2{-}CX_2{-})_nCX_2CX_2 \cdot + P({-}CX_2{-}CX_2{-})_mCX_2{-}CX_2 \cdot \rightarrow$$
$$P({-}CX_2{-}CX_2{-})_{m+n+2}P \tag{8.4}$$

The actual reaction mechanism may be more complicated than that shown above. Some commercially important monomers are ethylene, $CH_2{=}CH_2$, vinyl chloride, $CHCl{=}CH_2$, and styrene, $CH_2{=}CH(C_6H_5)$. Condensation polymerization proceeds by a stepwise intermolecular reaction between two monomers with the splitting out of a simple molecule such as water. The formation of nylon 6-6 is typical:

$$xHOOC({-}CH_2)_4{-}COOH + xNH_2({-}CH_2{-})_6NH_2 \rightarrow$$
$$HO[{-}OC{-}(CH_2)_4{-}CONH({-}CH_2{-})_6NH{-}]_xH + (x-1)H_2O \tag{8.5}$$

These types of polymers are very seldom perfectly linear but rather have some branching from the main chain. The nature of the structural units, the size of the molecules and the amount of branching all influence the gross physical properties of the polymer.

When monosubstituted ethylenic monomers such as vinyl chloride, $CH_2{=}CHCl$, or, in general, $CH_2{=}CHR$, polymerize, the addition reaction may be head-to-tail, head-to-head/tail-to-tail, or a random mixture of the two:

These various configurations of the molecule cannot be changed without break-ing and reforming primary carbon-to-carbon bonds. The less regular the posi-tioning of the substituted groups, the less probable it is that long-range crystallinity can be attained. The head-to-tail configuration is normally pre-ferred to the virtual exclusion of the other two because of two factors. If the substituent R is bulky, steric hindrance will favor head-to-tail reactions. More important is the fact that a free electron has a different stability on a sub-stituted carbon atom because of a resonance effect. Thus, for a resonance-stabilizing group, the reaction

$$M_x \cdot + CH_2 = CH \rightarrow M_x CH_2 - CH \cdot \atop \quad\quad\quad | \quad\quad\quad\quad\quad | \atop \quad\quad\quad R \quad\quad\quad\quad\quad R$$

(8.6)

is more probable than any other.

Another aspect of stereoregularity is the question of *tacticity.* Let us again use a monosubstituted vinyl monomer as an example. Figure 8.1 shows an ex-tended conformation of a single polymer chain in which all of the $-CH_2-$ units are in the same plane. Three different configurations can be obtained. If all the substituted groups R lie on the same side of the main chain, the polymer molecule is said to be *isotactic.* If the substituted groups regularly alternate from one side to the other, the polymer molecule is said to be *syndiotactic,* and, finally, if the positioning is random, the molecule is said to be *atactic.* These configurations are shown in both three dimensions and in Fischer pro-jections in Fig. 8.1. Polymers containing multiple substitutions and double

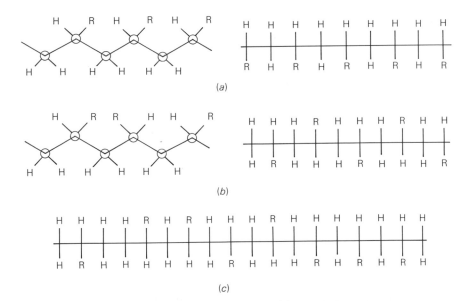

Fig. 8.1 Monosubstituted ethylenic polymers have three potential configurations. (*a*) Isotactic configuration; (*b*) syndiotactic configuration; (*c*) atactic configuration.

bonds along the main chain have many different stereoregular forms, and thus the number of potential configurations is higher than three. The point is that some configurations produce a molecule with a regular, repetitive spatial geometry and others do not. The former type are usually more susceptible to forming crystals. This does *not* mean that molecules that are atactic or molecules that have some irregularity in the normal head-to-tail configuration will not crystallize; it means only that regularity increases the chance of crystallization. In some cases, however, the tacticity *can* make the difference between crystallizing and not crystallizing. For example, commercial, general-purpose polystyrene is an amorphous substance and the molecules are atactic. Under certain reaction conditions, isotactic polystyrene molecules can be formed and the resulting solid does show some degree of crystallinity. In recent years, *stereospecific catalysts* have been developed which promote the polymerization of isotactic and syndiotactic polymers. This has added a new dimension to the polymer industry and brings us a big step closer to the possibility of "tailor-making" a molecule with a specific set of properties.

8.3
Conformations of a polymer molecule

We have said that a typical polymethylene molecule might be of the order of 50,000 Å long with a diameter of less than 5 Å. If we compare this with 45 m of 4.5-mm rope, we know that there are many different *conformations* possible. One can stretch the rope out, fold it back on itself, curl it up into a ball, entangle it, knot it, and so forth. Likewise, a polymer molecule can take on many conformations. Since each atom in the molecule is always in a state of rapid thermal motion (i.e., Brownian motion), the whole molecule may continually change from one conformation to the next. If one wants to know about the behavior of a given polymeric substance, he must determine what the most probable, or the average, conformation of each molecule is. These calculations have been carried out for flexible linear molecules. Consider a molecule as a chain of N links, each of length l_0, and each attached to the preceding one by a rotating joint. If the joints are completely free and each link is a thin line so there is no steric hindrance, we have what is called a freely orienting polymer chain (Fig. 8.2). The average conformation is characterized by the mean square distance

Fig. 8.2 The end-to-end distance of a freely orienting polymer chain is considerably less than the length of the extended chain.

$\langle r^2 \rangle$ between the ends of the chain. This is calculated by letting each link be a vector and adding vectors from one end to the other:

$$\mathbf{r} = \mathbf{l}_1 + \mathbf{l}_2 + \mathbf{l}_3 + \cdots + \mathbf{l}_N \tag{8.7}$$

The mean-square end-to-end distance is then

$$\langle r^2 \rangle = \mathbf{r} \cdot \mathbf{r} = l_1 \cdot l_1 + l_2 \cdot l_2 + \cdots + l_N \cdot l_N + 2 \sum_{i<j}^{N} \mathbf{l}_i \cdot \mathbf{l}_j$$

$$= N l_0^2 + 2 \sum_{i<j}^{N} \mathbf{l}_i \cdot \mathbf{l}_j \tag{8.8}$$

If the chain is freely orienting, all angles for the segments are equally probable, so that the summation term in Eq. (8.8) is zero. Thus for a *freely orienting chain*:

$$\langle r^2 \rangle = N l_0^2 \tag{8.9}$$

One reason why a polymer chain cannot be freely orienting is that the covalent bonds along the main chain are directed at a specific angle. The bonds in a tetrahedral carbon unit, for example, are at 109.5° to each other. If we assume that adjacent links in the chain form fixed angles θ with each other, but *rotate freely* about that angle (Fig. 8.3), Eq. (8.8) reduces to

$$\langle r^2 \rangle = \frac{1 - \cos\theta}{1 + \cos\theta} N l_0^2 \doteq 2N l_0^2 \qquad \text{for carbon chains} \tag{8.10}$$

In real chains the rotation about a valence bond is not completely free. Because the atoms take up volume and can exert mutual repulsions, there are certain positions that have lower potential energy than others. Figure 8.3 shows the case where there are three preferred conformations; the fully extended, trans conformation, $\phi = 0°$, is the most stable, and the two gauche conformations, $\phi = \pm 120°$, are metastable. The least stable position is the cis conformation, $\phi = \pm 180°$. In a polymethylene chain, the trans conformation would be as shown in Fig. 8.1 with the two hydrogens alternating from one side of the main chain to the other. The cis conformation would be the one in which all the hydrogens crowd in one plane on one side of the main chain. It is this crowding that makes the cis conformation less stable. If we consider a chain which has three preferred conformations, as shown in Fig. 8.3, with an energy difference ϵ between the trans and gauche states, it can be shown that Eq. (8.8) reduces to [12]:

$$\langle r^2 \rangle = \left(\frac{2}{3} + \frac{4}{3} \exp \frac{\epsilon}{RT} \right) N l_0^2 \tag{8.11}$$

When ϵ is large, the chain tends to assume a fully extended conformation and the end-to-end distance is very large. When ϵ is zero or negative (i.e., the gauche conformations are more stable), the square end-to-end distance is of the same order of magnitude as in the freely rotating case.

Suppose a polymethylene chain of 40,000 —CH_2— units is held in a fully

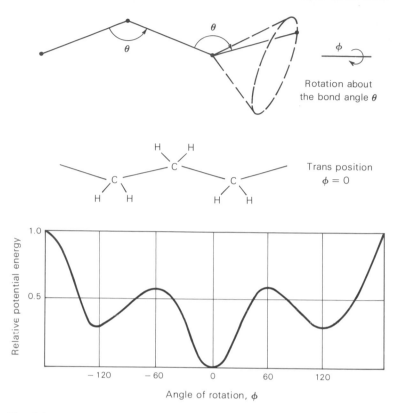

Rotation about
the bond angle θ

Trans position
$\phi = 0$

Fig. 8.3 A hindered rotation about a bond angle means that certain
angular positions are energetically more favorable than others. [Sketched
from data by W. J. Taylor, *J. Chem. Phys.*, **16**: 257, (1948).]

extended trans conformation.   The end-to-end distance $\sqrt{\langle r^2 \rangle}$ would be
50,000 Å. On the other hand, if it were freely rotating, the end-to-end distance
would be equal to $\sqrt{2N}\, l_0$, from Eq. (8.10), or approximately 375 Å. Thus it
is clear that when free rotation about bonds is possible, the tendency is for a
molecule to curl up into a ball which has a diameter that is much smaller than
the overall length of the chain. This is precisely the situation in molten polymers, where the molecules are at a high enough temperature to be mobile, and
also in rubberlike solids, where the molecules are close to freely orienting.
To anticipate a relationship between structure and properties, let us think
about what happens when we stretch a rubber band. In the unstretched state
the molecules are coiled up, and as we stretch we tend to force the molecules closer to a fully extended conformation. This accounts for the extreme
extensibility of rubber when compared with metals or other nonpolymeric
materials. We shall pursue this point in later chapters.

Real polymer molecules are not line segments without volume, but rather
take up space. The fact that they do take up space excludes many of the conformations that we have assumed to be equally probable in the previous de-

velopment. This "excluded volume" effect has a tendency to increase the end-to-end distance and, in general, we may say that

$$\langle r^2 \rangle = K N^a l_0^2 \tag{8.12}$$

where K is a constant near 2 and a is a constant between 1 and 2. Equation (8.12) is empirical, and the constants must be determined experimentally. Values of $\langle r^2 \rangle$ can be inferred from light-scattering measurements on dilute polymer solutions or from stress-birefringence measurements on the polymer in the solid state.

8.4
Crystal structure of polymers

When a polymer chain is made up of a single type of repeating unit (for example, —CH_2— units of polyethylene) or of similar-size units (for example, CH_2CHOH units of polyvinyl alcohol) and does not have too much branching, a relatively simple crystal structure will result. Polyethylene is typical of structures that have the "planar zigzag" conformation of a fully extended chain. X-ray analysis can give the position of the carbon atoms in a unit cell and also the electronic density around the chains [10]. Figure 8.4 schematically illustrates the orthorhombic arrangement of polyethylene molecules. There are four (—CH_2—) units per unit cell. A perfect crystal of polyethylene thus has a density of about 1.01 g/cm³.

No one has yet made a perfect crystal of polyethylene, but by using special techniques, one can come within 97 percent of the maximum density. The

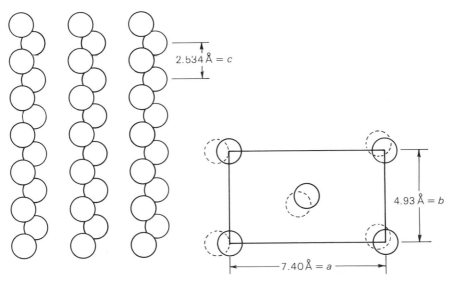

Fig. 8.4 A polyethylene crystal has an orthorhombic structure [4].

lowering of the density is attributable to a variety of physical imperfections. Figure 8.5 schematically shows the electronic density around each carbon atom. Notice that the electronic clouds are flattened at the back of the CH_2 groups and that they are elliptical near the carbon atoms. Imperfections in the unit cell and distortions of charge distributions result from thermal vibrations normal to the chain axis (c axis), kinks in the extended chains, and the nonspherical nature of the electron clouds about the tetrahedral carbon atoms. Branching along the main chain can create the most serious distortions in the unit cell and thus limit the crystallizability of commercial products.

The structures of certain polyamides are typical of those that have fully extended chains which are joined together into sheetlike crystals by hydrogen bonds. Figure 8.6 schematically illustrates the arrangement of chains in a hydrogen-bonded sheet of nylon 6-6. (A hydrogen bond is an electrostatic bridge between a proton and two strongly electronegative elements on different molecules. The $N \cdots H \cdots O$ bond is typical and is of the order of 4 to 6 kcal/g

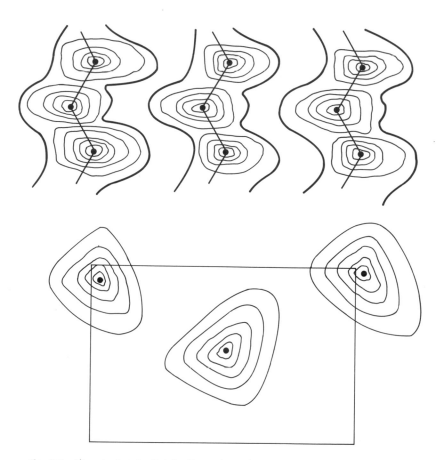

Fig. 8.5 The electronic distributions about the carbon atoms in a polyethylene crystal can be determined by interpretation of x-ray diffraction photographs [4].

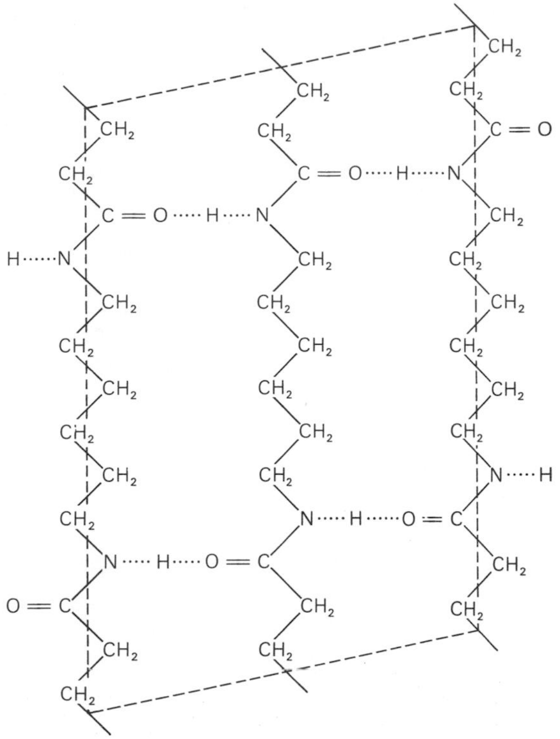

Fig. 8.6 Hydrogen bonding to electronegative groups causes nylon 6-6 molecules to form sheetlike crystals.

mole.) The juxtaposition of polyamide chains produces extended sheets, considerable hydrogen bonding, and, thus, materials of exceptionally high strength. The sheets can then arrange into a triclinic unit cell.

Figure 8.7 illustrates the very important crystal structure of cellulose, in which complex anhydroglucose units are joined in chains which are held together by extensive hydrogen bonding between adjacent hydroxyl groups. There are many known forms of cellulose in which the chains pack in different ways. The geometry of the structure is such that rotation about the oxygen units bridging two rings is impossible because of both steric hindrance and extensive hydrogen bonding. The chains are not fully extended but, rather, are mildly spiraled.

Spiraling of a polymer chain is very common when there are closely spaced, bulky substituents along the chain. Polymer molecules of the type $-CH_2-CHR-$ are typical. In these cases, the trans conformation places the neighboring R groups within 2.5 Å of each other, causing a strong repulsion (or steric hindrance). The gauche conformations are thus more stable, causing the chain to have a helical conformation which permits the close packing of these bulky groups with a minimum of distortion. If the R groups are not too bulky, the normal gauche positions at $\pm120°$ are occupied, forming a helix with three chemical groups per repeating geometric group. When the side groups are large, different-shaped helices are formed. Figure 8.8 shows a

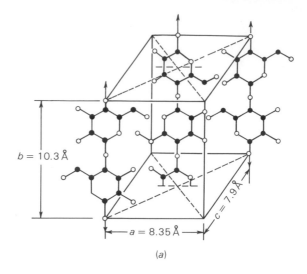

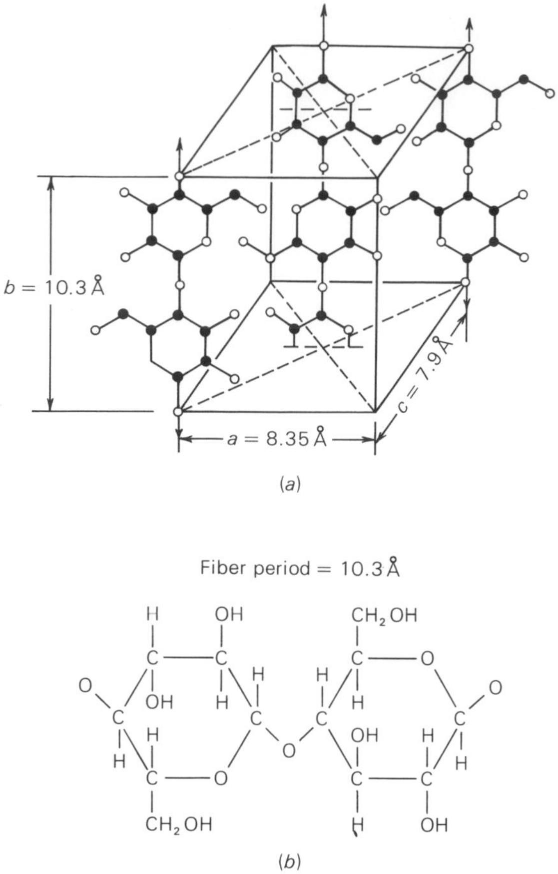

b = 10.3 Å
a = 8.35 Å
c = 7.9 Å
(a)
Fiber period = 10.3 Å
(b)

Fig. 8.7 Native cellulose has an orthorhombic crystal structure [Ref. 8, pp. 206–207]. (*a*) Orthorhombic unit cell for cellulose; (*b*) repeating unit of cellulose molecule.

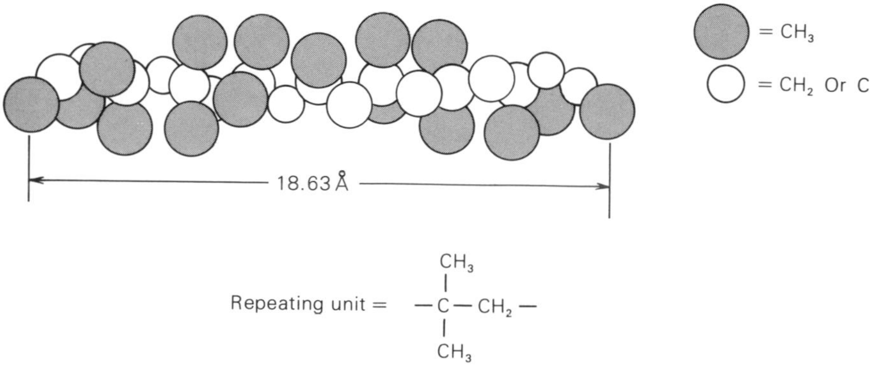

18.63 Å
= CH_3
= CH_2 Or C
Repeating unit = $-C(CH_3)_2-CH_2-$

Fig. 8.8 Steric hindrance of adjacent methylene side groups causes the polyisobutylene molecule to have a helical conformation [8].

helical form of polyisobutylene, $-CH_2-C(-CH_3-)_2$, in which every ninth iso-butylene unit repeats the spiral pattern. The crystal structures for polymer molecules can thus become very complicated because of the large number of stable geometric conformations. One can, however, find the unit cells with the aid of x-ray diffraction analysis. From information on the size of the unit cell and the type of chemical groups along the chain, one can deduce the molecular configurations in the crystal. Table 8.1 lists crystallographic data for a few important polymers.

8.5
Amorphous polymers

Materials that form simple crystals usually have a well-defined crystallization temperature. Above this temperature the material is liquid and the molecular structure does not have any well-defined space lattice. Although the molecular state is not completely random, as in a gas, there is a lack of any long-range order. Below the crystallization temperature we find the well-defined spatial geometry of the crystalline state. Some polymer structures, as we have just discussed, also exhibit this kind of behavior. As long as the polymer molecules have a repetitive pattern and they can stretch out into an extended conformation, the material can become crystalline below a given temperature.

Many structures, however, do not exhibit a tendency to rearrange into the regular geometry of the crystalline state. Rather, the solid material tends to retain the lack of molecular order that is characteristic of the liquid state.

Consider a linear polymer which is at a high enough temperature to be fluid. Each atom in the chain has a certain amount of translational, vibrational, and rotational freedom. At high enough temperatures, the kinetic energy of the whole chain is sufficiently high to provide a limited mobility of the molecule. Thus, the chain has enough freedom to diffuse through the whole volume of the fluid. The resistance to this molecular motion is caused by interaction and entanglement of the molecules. As the temperature (i.e., thermal energy) is decreased, the potential energy of interaction of atoms with their surroundings tends to restrict the mobility of the chain and, if the structure is symmetric enough, the molecules will line up in a crystalline pattern. Many polymeric structures, however, are not symmetric enough to exhibit long-range molecular order. Organic molecules such as atactic polystyrene (Fig. 8.9) have bulky side groups, and sometimes extensive branching, which makes it very difficult to develop a geometric lattice. On cooling such materials, there is no sudden rearrangement of the molecules, as in crystallization, but rather a steady loss of mobility until the material can no longer be considered a fluid. The resistance to molecular motion becomes so high that the material is a solid in every sense of the word. If one examines the molecular order under x-ray diffraction, however, it is very difficult to distinguish between the solid and the liquid states. Since molecular mobility and rotational freedom are high in the liquid state, the polymer chains normally take on a highly coiled conformation, rather than the extended conformations characteristic of crystals. Thus the amorphous state

Table 8.1

Unit cells for polymer crystals *

Polymer	Repeating unit	Crystal type	Unit cell parameters [†] a,b,c, [‡] Å angles [§]	Chain conformation
Polyethylene	$-CH_2-$	Orthorhombic	7.40, 4.93, 2.534	Planar zigzag
Polypropylene	$-CH-CH_2-$ with CH_3	Monoclinic	6.65, 20.96, 6.5 $\beta = 99°$	Helix
Polybutadiene (syndiotactic)	$-CH_2-$ $CH=CH$ CH_2-	Orthorhombic	10.98, 6.60, 5.14	Planar zigzag
Polybutadiene (isotactic)	$-CH_2-$ $CH=CH$ CH_2-	Rhombohedral	17.3, 17.3, 6.5	Helix
Polyvinylchloride	Cl $-CH-CH_2-$	Orthorhombic	10.6, 5.4, 4.1	Planar zigzag
Polytetrafluoroethylene (>20°C)	$-CF_2-$	Hexagonal	5.61, 5.61, 16.8	Helix
Nylon 6–6	$(-NH(-CH_2)_6-NH-\overset{O}{\overset{\|}{C}}-(CH_2)_4-\overset{O}{\overset{\|}{C}}-)$	Triclinic	4.9, 8.0, 17.2 $\alpha = 90$ $\beta = 77$ $\gamma = 67$	

* Extracted from Eric Baer (ed.), "Engineering Design for Plastics," p. 122, Reinhold Publishing Corporation, New York, 1964.

[†] Refer to Table 5.1 for unit cell types.   [‡] c is the axis along the polymer chain.   [§] Angles are 90° unless otherwise stated.

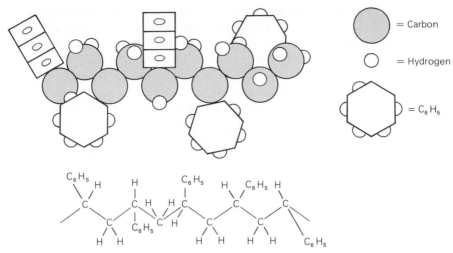

= Carbon

= Hydrogen

= C_6H_5

Fig. 8.9 The bulkiness of the benzene rings in a polystyrene molecule inhibits the crystallization of atactic polystyrene.

of a polymeric material is visualized as a disordered mass of coiled-up, entangled polymer molecules. This is schematically shown in Fig. 8.10. "From the point of view of longer-range distances, the structure of an amorphous polymer might be considered as comparable to the contents of a bowl of cooked spaghetti. The spaghetti-like molecules, of course, are in a state of wriggling motion whose amplitude and speed depend on temperature" [12, p. 45]. Polystyrene, $-CH_2-CH(C_6H_5)-$, polyvinylacetate, $-CH_2-CH(O-\overset{\overset{\displaystyle O}{\|}}{C}-CH_3)-$, and polymethylmethacrylate, $-CH_2-C(CH_3)(\underset{\underset{\displaystyle O}{\|}}{C}-O-CH_3)-$, are three commercially important examples of atactic polymer materials that are normally in an amorphous state.

Lack of molecular symmetry is not the only factor that leads to an amor-

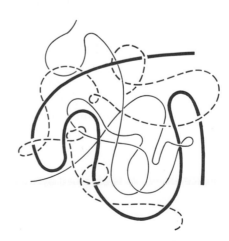

Fig. 8.10 A schematic drawing of the random molecular state of an amorphous polymer, showing the entanglement of three molecules.

phous state. Even if a molecule has good symmetry, as polybutadiene, ($-CH_2-CH=CH-CH_2-$), for example, has, the amorphous state might still be more stable than the crystalline state. In this case, an extended conformation is possible, but there is not sufficient intermolecular interaction to keep the molecules in a close packing. The mobility and rotational freedom of the molecules are sufficient to overcome the forces tending to hold the molecules in an extended conformation and force them back into a coiled-up state. Such a material is called an *elastomer* or a *rubber*. Many of the unique properties of elastomers are associated with the fact that although the amorphous state is the most stable, an oriented or crystallized state can easily be induced. The effects on mechanical properties are elaborated in Chap. 12.

8.6
Bonding in polymers

Calculation of the lattice energy in crystalline polymers is very difficult because the interaction potentials between polymer molecules are not simple functions. A $-CH_2-$ unit along a polymer chain, for example, has a spheroidal shape with the two ellipsoid axes normal to the chain being about 4.0 Å, while the axis along the chain is only about 1.25 Å. Since the unit is not symmetric, it also has a dipole moment, which means that the potential-energy function is angle-dependent. More complex units have odder shapes, and the possibility of different conformations makes the equation for the interaction potential very complicated. Furthermore, only a few polymer molecules [e.g., polymethylene, ($-CH_2-)_x$], are truly pure, and all others contain at least two kinds of chemical groups. Very little information is available on interactions between dissimilar particles.

Some calculations have been made for linear crystalline polymers by assuming the polymer chain is a line of dipolar dispersion centers, as shown in Fig. 8.11 [2]. The directions of the atomic dipoles are perpendicular to and alternate along the chain axes. A point center on an adjacent chain then interacts with each center, and the total interaction energy of a given point is obtained by summing over all possible interactions. The simplest reasonable potential-energy function would be

$$\psi_{IC} = \sum_j 4\epsilon \left[\left(\frac{\sigma}{r_{ij}}\right)^{12} - \left(\frac{\sigma}{r_{ij}}\right)^6 \right] + \frac{\mu^2 g(\theta_{ij})}{r_{ij}^3} \qquad (8.13)$$

where $g(\theta)$ is the angular dependence of the dipole term. The total potential energy of interaction of a single-point center with all surrounding chains is then obtained by adding the interactions with all other chains in the lattice:

$$\psi_{IR} = \sum_{\substack{\text{all} \\ \text{chains}}} \psi_{IC} \qquad (8.14)$$

and the lattice energy ψ_T is obtained by summing over all points in the lattice:

$$\psi_T = \frac{1}{2} \sum_i \psi_{iR} \qquad (8.15)$$

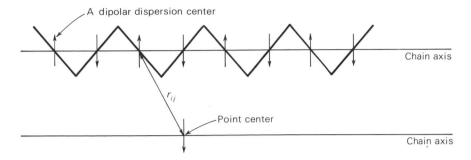

Fig. 8.11 A lattice model can be used to idealize the interaction between a polymer chain and a chemical group on an adjacent chain.

In order to make a numerical calculation of the lattice energy, one must know the geometry of the crystal and have values for the molecular constants ϵ, σ, and μ. Brandt [2] has estimated these constants for a few polymers by using a modified version of the Slater-Kirkwood equation (1.23). Some of his calculations are summarized in Tables 8.2 and 8.3. An experimental value of 2.88 kcal/g mole of —$(CH_2)_2$— (12.1 × 10⁶ joules/kg mole) for the lattice energy in paraffins shows that these calculations are not perfect. Similar techniques have been applied to amorphous structures [7], but the uncertainty of the geometry creates an even more difficult problem.

The simplest practical method of getting lattice energies for polymeric substances is to use the empirical group-contribution technique of Small [9]. The total lattice energy per unit volume of material is called the *cohesive energy density* E_{CD}. This is usually very nearly equal to the energy required to transfer a molecule from the condensed to the gaseous state and is thus related to the latent heat of vaporization of the substance.

$$E_{CD} = \frac{\Delta H_v - RT}{Mv} \tag{8.16}$$

The quantity ΔH_v is the molar heat of vaporization, M is molecular weight, and

Table 8.2

Molecular constants for polymer chain groups [2]

Chain group	Effective length along chain, Å	μ, debyes	α, Å³	ϵ/k, °K	σ, Å
—CH_2—	1.27	0.40	1.82	34.3	4.19
—CF_2—	1.23	1.85	2.06	18.7	5.40
—CFCl—	1.27	1.71	3.58	27.2	6.08
—CCl_2—	1.07	1.74	5.29	52.8	6.08
—O—	0.65	1.20	0.67	4.2	4.36

Table 8.3

Calculated lattice energies for some linear high polymers [2]

Polymer	Recurrent unit	Chain-to-chain distance from density measurements, Å	Lattice energy,* kcal/mole of recurrent unit
Polyethylene	$(-CH_2-CH_2-)$	4.63	2.50
Polytetrafluoroethylene	$(-CF_2-CF_2-)$	5.28	2.03
Polychlorotrifluoroethylene	$(-CF_2-CFCl-)$	6.15	2.65
Polyvinylidene chloride	$(-CH_2-CCl_2-)$	6.32	4.21
Polyoxymethylene	$(-CH_2-O-)$	4.39	1.85

* Multiply by 4.186×10^6 to get joules/kg mole.

Table 8.4

Molar attraction constants at 25°C *

Group	Δ, $(cal-cm^3)^{1/2}/g\ mole$	Group	Δ, $(cal-cm^3)^{1/2}/g\ mole$
$-CH_3$ (single-bonded)	214	H (variable)	80–100
$-CH_2-$ (single-bonded)	133	O ethers	70
		CO ketones	275
$-CH$ (single-bonded)	28	COO esters	310
		CN	410
		Cl (mean)	260
$-C-$ (single-bonded)	−93	Cl single	270
		Cl twinned as in CCl_2	260
$CH_2=$ (double-bonded)	190	Cl triple as in $-CCl_3$	250
$-CH=$ (double-bonded)	111	Br single	340
		I single	425
$C=$ (double-bonded)	19	CF_2 / CF_3 n fluorocarbons only	150 / 274
$CH\equiv C-$	285	S sulfides	225
$-C\equiv C-$	222	SH thiols	315
Phenyl	735	$O\cdot NO_2$ nitrates	~440
Phenylene (o,m,p)	658	NO_2 (aliphatic nitro compounds)	~440
Naphthyl	1146	PO_4 (organic phosphates)	~500
Ring five-membered	105–115		
Ring six-membered	95–105		
Conjugation	20–30		

* By permission from P. S. Small, J. Appl. Chem., **3:** 75 (1953).

v is specific volume. For simple substances, the cohesive energy density can be evaluated from latent heat data, but, since polymers do not vaporize, their cohesive energy must be obtained from group-contribution methods. Small, by various experimental techniques, has estimated that each chemical group contributes a fixed amount to the total cohesive energy density. These contributions are summarized in Table 8.4. Equation (8.17) may then be used to calculate the cohesive energy density of a given substance

$$E_{CD} = \left(\frac{\Sigma \Delta}{Mv}\right)^2 \qquad (8.17)$$

Thus, if a crystal of polymethylene, $(-CH_2-CH_2-)_x$ has a specific volume of 0.99 cm³/g, its cohesive energy density is $(2 \times 133/28 \times 0.99)^2$ or 90.2 cal/cm³. In terms of lattice energy, it is 90.2 cal/cm³ $\times$ 0.99 cm³/g $\times$ 28 g/mole of recurring unit, or 2,500 cal/mole of recurring unit, which is the same as the value in Table 8.3.

References

1 Billmeyer, F. W.: "Textbook of Polymer Science," Interscience Publishers, Inc., New York, 1962. *An introductory text on the structure and properties of polymer molecules.*

2 Brandt, W.: Calculation of Compressibilities of High Polymers from the Energy of Interaction between Chain Groups, *J. Chem. Phys.,* **26:** (2) 262–270 (1957).

3 Bueche, F.: "Physical Properties of Polymers," Interscience Publishers, Inc., New York, 1962. *A text that emphasizes the molecular concepts used in polymer science. The first chapter is a good discussion of chain conformations.*

4 Bunn, C. W.: *Trans. Faraday Soc.,* **35:** 482 (1939).

5 Danusso, F.: Stereoregular Polymers and Polymerization, *Polymer,* 3(3): 423 (1962). *A short summary of the fundamentals of stereoregularity.*

6 Flory, P. J.: "Principles of Polymer Chemistry," Cornell University Press, Ithaca, N.Y., 1953. *A basic reference for those interested in advanced study on polymers. There are several chapters on structure, configuration, and the statistical thermodynamics of polymer chains.*

7 Paul, D. R., and A. T. DiBenedetto: The Thermodynamic and Molecular Properties of Amorphous High Polymers, paper presented at the International Symposium on Macromolecular Chemistry, IUPAC, Prague, 1965.

8 Schmidt, A. X., and C. A. Marlies: Principles of High-polymer Theory and Practice," McGraw-Hill Book Company, New York, 1948. *A very readable introduction to the behavior and properties of high polymers. The first five chapters are recommended for those who want a simple, but more detailed, discussion of the principles emphasized in this chapter.*

9 Small, P. S., *J. Appl. Chem.,* **3:** 75 (1953).

10 Stokes, A. R.: The Theory of X-Ray Fibre Diagrams, *Progr. Biophys. and Biophys. Chem.,* **5:** 140 (1955).

11 Tanford, C.: "Physical Chemistry of Macromolecules," John Wiley & Sons, Inc., New York, 1961. *Chapters 2 and 3 have detailed discussions on polymer structure and chain statistics.*

12 Tobolsky, A. V.: "Properties and Structure of Polymers," John Wiley & Sons, Inc., New York, 1960. *Chapter 2 is a summary of the aspects of polymer physics discussed in this chapter.*

Questions

8.1 By what kind of reactions are the following monomers polymerized?

Styrene, $CH_2\!=\!CH(C_6H_5)$

Divinylbenzene, $CH_2\!=\!CH(C_6H_4)CH\!=\!CH_2$

An hydroxy-carboxylic acid, $HO\!-\!R\!-\!COOH$

Vinylchloride $CH_2\!=\!CHCl$

Phenol plus formaldehyde, $C_6H_5OH + H_2C\!=\!O$

Show the reaction mechanisms and classify the resulting polymers as either linear or space polymers.

8.2 Distinguish between isotactic, syndiotactic, and atactic linear polymers. How does tacticity affect the crystallizing tendencies of linear polymers?

8.3 Find the mean-square end-to-end distance for a normal butane molecule, $CH_3\!-\!CH_2\!-\!CH_2\!-\!CH_3$. Use Eq. (8.8) directly. Assume that there is free rotation about the valence-bond angle $\theta = 109.5°$. *Hint:*

$$\mathbf{l}_i \cdot \mathbf{l}_{i+n} = l^2 \cos^n (180 - \theta)$$

8.4 The size of a polyisobutylene molecule in the pure material is given experimentally as

$$\left(\frac{\langle r^2 \rangle}{M}\right)^{1/2} = 0.795 \text{ at } 24°C$$

$$= 0.757 \text{ at } 95°C$$

where r is in angstroms and M is molecular weight. Compare these results to those obtained by assuming free rotation about the valence bonds. Explain why the experimental values are higher. Explain why the experimental values decrease as the temperature increases.

8.5 Explain why a polyethylene chain can take on a planar zigzag (i.e., fully extended) conformation, while polyisobutylene is always helical.

8.6 At room temperature, atactic polystyrene is amorphous and cannot be highly oriented by stretching, while natural rubber ($-CH_2\!-\!CH\!=\!C(CH_3)\!-\!CH_2\!-)_x$ is amorphous but crystallization can be temporarily induced by stretching. Explain the difference in behavior in terms of molecular structure.

8.7 Calculate the maximum densities of the crystals listed in Table 8.1. Compare your results with typical densities of commercial polymers.

8.8 The repeating unit for chlorinated rubber is $[-CH_2CH\!=\!C(Cl)\!-\!CH_2-]$, and its specific volume is $0.81 \text{ cm}^3/\text{g}$. Calculate its cohesive energy density.

8.9 Calculate the cohesive energy densities of natural rubber, $v = 1.07 \text{ cm}^3/\text{g}$; polyvinylchloride, $v = 0.71 \text{ cm}^3/\text{g}$; polystyrene, $v = 0.95 \text{ cm}^3/\text{g}$; and nylon 6-6, $v = 0.88 \text{ cm}^3/\text{g}$. What molecular factors should control the magnitude of the cohesive energy density?

9
Formation of polymeric materials

9.1
Introduction

During the past thirty or forty years, organic and inorganic polymers have become increasingly important as a source of engineering materials. The plastics, fiber, rubber, and paint industries, in the United States alone, account for over 5 billion kg of synthetic polymer materials. These materials, although basically made up of the same types of molecules, range in properties from very thin liquids used as thinners, release agents, coating materials, and the like to very strong crystalline solids used as constructional materials.

Natural polymers have always been a part of our normal environment. Starch, cellulose, and other polysaccharides are the main constituents of plant life, while keratin (wool), myosin (in muscle), serum globulin (in blood serum) and other proteins are the essential constituents of all animal life. Polymers of graphite, silica, clay, asbestos, and other inorganic materials are a substantial part of the earth's crust.

From a knowledge of the molecular structure of polymers comes an understanding of why they behave as they do and, perhaps more importantly, how they may be synthesized. In this chapter we shall consider the formation of *synthetic* organic polymers, since by virtue of numbers they are the most important industrially.

One convenient way to classify these materials is to consider them as either *thermoplastic, thermosetting,* or *nonmoldable.* A thermoplastic material is one that can be melted and resolidified in a reversible manner. The ability of thermoplastic materials to flow is associated with the fact that they are basically linear or branched polymers without any extensive primary bonding between molecules. A thermosetting material is one that under heat and/or pressure may be changed from a fusible, flowable material to an infusible, nonmoldable material by a chemical change. The chemical reaction is the *cross-linking* of the linear molecules. A familiar example of cross-linking is the vulcanization of rubber. *Nonmoldable* polymers are those that cannot be made to flow without decomposition occurring. All thermosetting resins are nonmoldable *after* they have been cross-linked. Some linear polymers, such as cellulose and asbestos, are always non-moldable and are often used as *fillers* to strengthen moldable materials.

Another useful classification is to consider polymers as *rubbers, fibers,* or *plastics.* A rubber, or *elastomer,* is a polymeric material that has a high degree of reversible extensibility and generally a low strength. A typical rubber might be stretched elastically up to 400 to 500 percent of its original dimensions before it breaks with a tensile strength of 2×10^6 to 5×10^6 kg_w/m^2. These properties are associated with highly coiled conformations and low cohesive energy density. A "fiber" is a material that has a very low reversible extensibility and a relatively high strength. A typical drawn fiber might have a tensile strength of 10×10^6 to 80×10^6 kg_w/m^2 and will exhibit elastic deformation of less than 1 or 2 percent. These properties are associated with very high cohesive energy density and an extended, highly organized conformation along the chain (or fiber) axis. A *plastic* is a polymeric material that has neither the high extensibility of a rubber nor the high strength of a fiber, but rather has properties intermediate between the two. The most general characteristic of plastics is that they can usually be shaped by flow at moderate temperatures and pressures. In reality, there is no sharp distinction between these materials, and so there is overlapping between classes as well as a wide variety of properties within each class.

9.2
Synthesis of polymers

Synthetic polymers are made by the chemical reaction of small molecules, called monomers. There are basically two different kinds of reactions, called *condensation polymerization* and *addition polymerization.* These reactions may be carried out under a wide variety of conditions and in the presence of a number of different catalysts. In this section, we shall consider a few illustrations of polymer formation.

Condensation polymerizations occur between *bifunctional* or *polyfunctional* monomers with the splitting out of a simple molecule as a by-product. A functional unit is simply a chemical group which is susceptible to reaction. The hydroxyl groups, —OH, of alcohols, R—OH, or carboxylic acids, $R-\overset{\overset{\displaystyle O}{\|}}{C}-OH$, and the —$NH_2$ groups of amines, R—NH_2, are examples of functional groups. When a monomer contains *two* functional units, as in hexamethylene diamine, $NH_2-(CH_2)_6-NH_2$, it is bifunctional. When a monomer contains *three or more* functional units, as in glycerol, HO—CH_2—CH(OH)—CH_2OH, it is polyfunctional. Reactions between bifunctional monomers lead to the formation of linear polymers, while reactions involving at least one polyfunctional monomer lead to the formation of branched polymers or, under the proper conditions, three-dimensional space polymers. Table 9.1 lists some commercially important types of condensation polymers.

The process proceeds in a stepwise manner with the average molecular weight slowly building up. The sequence of events is illustrated by the reaction between bifunctional glycols and bifunctional acids to form a linear polyester:

$$\text{HOR-OH} + \text{HOCR}_1\overset{\text{O}}{\underset{\|}{\text{C}}}\text{-OH} \rightarrow \text{HOR-O-}\overset{\text{O}}{\underset{\|}{\text{C}}}\text{-R}_1\overset{\text{O}}{\underset{\|}{\text{C}}}\text{-OH} + \text{H}_2\text{O}$$

$$\text{HOROCR}_1\overset{\text{O}}{\underset{\|}{\text{C}}}\text{-OH} + \text{HOROH} \rightarrow \text{HOROCR}_1\text{C-OROH} + \text{H}_2\text{O}$$

$$\text{HOROCR}_1\text{C-OROH} + \text{HO-}\overset{\text{O}}{\underset{\|}{\text{C}}}\text{-R}_1\overset{\text{O}}{\underset{\|}{\text{C}}}\text{-OH} \rightarrow$$

$$\text{HOROC-R}_1\overset{\text{O}}{\underset{\|}{\text{C}}}\text{-OR-O-}\overset{\text{O}}{\underset{\|}{\text{C}}}\text{-R}_1\text{C-OH} + \text{H}_2\text{O}$$

or, in general,

$$x\text{HOR-OH} + x\text{HOC-R}_1\overset{\text{O}}{\underset{\|}{\text{C}}}\text{-OH} \rightarrow$$

$$\text{HO}(\text{-ROC-R}_1\overset{\text{O}}{\underset{\|}{\text{C}}}\text{-O-})_x\text{H} + (x-1)\text{H}_2\text{O}$$

This kind of a reaction ideally leads to linear polymers, but a variety of molecular interchanges often causes some branching from the main chains. As is clear from Table 9.1, substitution of glycerine for the bifunctional alcohol will promote growth in three dimensions. It has been experimentally proved that the reactivity of the functional groups is independent of the chain length for all degrees of polymerization greater than 2 to 8. (The degree of polymerization is the number of repeating units on the chain x.) Since this is true, the functional groups react at random with one another and the polymer formation follows the laws of probability. It can be shown [3] that the "average degree of polymerization" of simple condensation polymers, D_P, is related to the average functionality of the monomers, f, and the extent of reaction, p, by the following equation:

$$D_P = \left(1 - \frac{f}{2}p\right)^{-1} \tag{9.1}$$

The average degree of polymerization in commercial polymers varies from small numbers like 5 to 10 up to very high numbers like 1,000 to 10,000.

Table 9.1

Typical condensation polymers

Type	Interunit linkage	Example
Polyester	$-\overset{\displaystyle O}{\overset{\displaystyle \|}{C}}-O-$	$HO(CH_2)_xOH + HOOC(CH_2)_{x'}COOH \rightarrow HO[-(CH_2)_xO\overset{\displaystyle O}{\overset{\displaystyle \|}{C}}(CH_2)_{x'}\overset{\displaystyle O}{\overset{\displaystyle \|}{C}}-]_xH + H_2O$ $\begin{array}{c} CH_2OH \\ \| \\ CHOH \\ \| \\ CH_2OH \end{array} + HOOC(CH_2)_xCOOH \rightarrow$ three-dimensional network $+ H_2O$
Polyacetal	$-O-\overset{\displaystyle H}{\underset{\displaystyle R}{\overset{\displaystyle \|}{\underset{\displaystyle \|}{C}}}}-O-$	$HO(CH_2)_xOH + CH_2(OR)_2 \rightarrow HO[-(CH_2)_xOCH_2O-]_y(CH_2)_xOH + ROH$
Polyamide	$-\overset{\displaystyle O}{\overset{\displaystyle \|}{C}}-NH-$	$NH_2(CH_2)_xNH_2 + HOOC(CH_2)_{x'}COOH \rightarrow H[-NH(CH_2)_xNHCO(CH_2)_{x'}CO-]_yOH + H_2O$
Polyurethane	$-O-\overset{\displaystyle O}{\overset{\displaystyle \|}{C}}-NH-$	$HO(CH_2)_xOH + OCN(CH_2)_{x'}CNO \rightarrow [O(CH_2)_xOCONH(CH_2)_{x'}NHCO-]_y$
Polyurea	$-NH-\overset{\displaystyle O}{\overset{\displaystyle \|}{C}}-NH-$	$NH_2(CH_2)_xNH_2 + OCN(CH_2)_{x'}CNO \rightarrow [-NH(CH_2)_xNHCONH(CH_2)_{x'}NHCO-]_y$
Phenol-aldehyde	$-CH_2-$ $-CH_2OCH_2-$	(phenol rings) $+ CH_2O \rightarrow$ [structure] $+ H_2O$ (phenol ring) $+ CH_2O \rightarrow H_2O +$ three-dimensional network with $-CH_2-$ and $-CH_2OCH_2-$ bridges between positions on rings ortho and para to hydroxyls

Urea-aldehyde

$$—\text{NH—CHR—NH—}$$
$$—\text{CHR—N—CHR—}$$
$$\qquad\qquad |$$
$$\qquad\qquad \text{CHR}$$

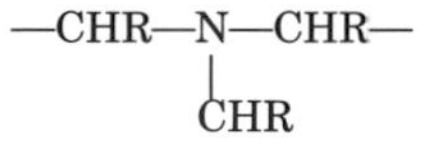

$\text{NH}_2\text{CONH}_2 + \text{CH}_2\text{O}$ (1-to-1 ratio) $\rightarrow$ —NHCONH—CH_2—NHCONH—CH_2— + H_2O

With excess CH_2O, three-dimensional network + H_2O

Polysiloxane

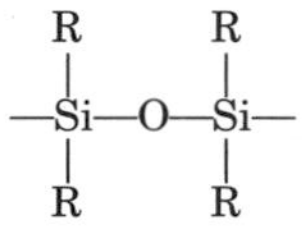

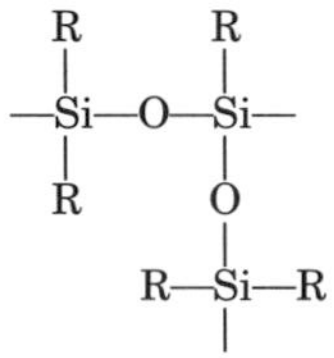

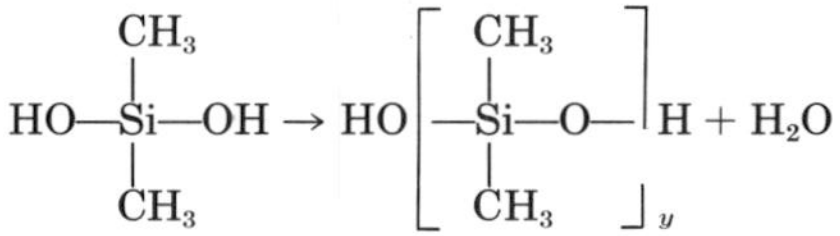

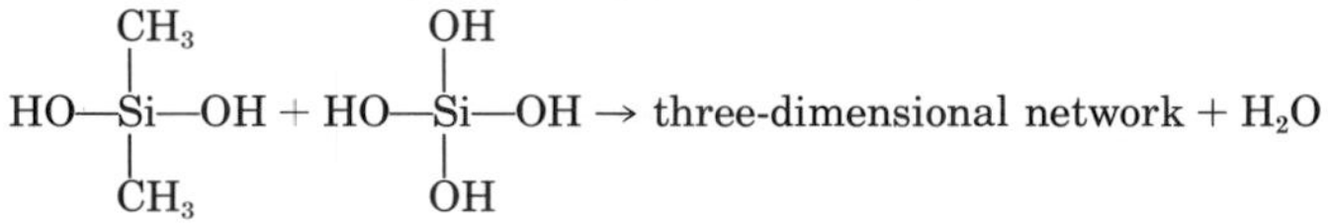

$$\begin{array}{ccccc}
& \text{R} & & \text{R} & \\
—\text{Si} & —\text{O}— & \text{Si}— & & \\
& \text{R} & & \text{R} & \\
& \text{R} & & \text{R} & \\
—\text{Si} & —\text{O}— & \text{Si}— & \text{O} & \\
& \text{R} & & \text{R}—\text{Si}—\text{R} &
\end{array}$$

$$\begin{array}{c}
\text{CH}_3 \\
\text{HO—Si—OH} \rightarrow \text{HO}\left[\begin{array}{c}\text{CH}_3\\—\text{Si—O}—\\\text{CH}_3\end{array}\right]_y \text{H} + \text{H}_2\text{O} \\
\text{CH}_3
\end{array}$$

$$\begin{array}{c}
\text{CH}_3 \qquad\qquad \text{OH} \\
\text{HO—Si—OH} + \text{HO—Si—OH} \rightarrow \text{three-dimensional network} + \text{H}_2\text{O} \\
\text{CH}_3 \qquad\qquad \text{OH}
\end{array}$$

Addition polymerization occurs with unsaturated olefins, aldehydes, and cyclic oxides and proceeds without the splitting of a by-product. A tabulation of some of the more important commercial addition polymers is given in Table 9.2.

Unsaturated molecules are reactive because the π bond is susceptible to attack. We can specify some rough rules of thumb regarding the reactivity of these monomers. Often, the greater the degree of unsaturation, the greater the reactivity. Thus, acetylenic monomers, $-C\equiv C-$, are more reactive than the ethylenic, $-C=C-$, and the conjugated ethylenic, $-C=C-C=C-$, are also more reactive than the ethylenic. Another rule is that the higher-molecular-weight olefins are less reactive than the low-molecular-weight olefins. Thus butene, $CH_3-CH_2-CH=CH_2$, is less reactive than ethylene, $CH_2=CH_2$. Olefins with molecular weights higher than butene are very slow reacting and are thus not commercially important. In general, the addition of electronegative groups makes a monomer more reactive. Thus, vinylchloride, $CH_2=CHCl$, is more reactive than ethylene, $CH_2=CH_2$, and chloroprene, $CH_2=C(Cl)-CH=CH_2$, is more reactive than isoprene, $CH_2=C(CH_3)-CH=CH_2$. The introduction of a second electronegative group will make the monomer more reactive if it makes it less symmetric but will tend to stabilize the double

Table 9.2

Some important addition polymers

Name	Type of repeating unit
Polyethylene	$-CH_2-CH_2-$
Polypropylene	$(-CH_2-CH-)$
	$\quad\quad\quad\;\;\;	$
	$\quad\quad\quad\; CH_3$
Polybutadiene	$(-CH_2-CH=CH-CH_2-)$
Polytetrafluoroethylene	$(-CF_2-CF_2-)$
Polychlorotrifluoroethylene	$-CF_2-CFCl-$
Polyvinylchloride	$-CH_2-CHCl-$
Polyvinylacetate	CH_2-CH
	$\quad\quad\quad	$
	$\quad\quad\; OOCCH_3$
	$\quad\quad\; CH_3$
	$\quad\quad\quad	$
Polymethylmethacrylate	$-CH_2-C-$
	$\quad\quad\quad	$
	$\quad\quad\; OOCH_3$
Polyacrylonitrile	$-CH_2-CH-$
	$\quad\quad\quad	$
	$\quad\quad\quad CN$
Polychloroprene	$-CH_2-CCl=CH-CH_2-$
Polystyrene ·	CH_2-CH-
	$\quad\quad\quad	$
	$\quad\quad\; C_6H_5$

bond if it improves the symmetry. Thus 1,2-dichloroethylene, $CH(Cl)\!=\!CHCl$, is less reactive than vinyl chloride, $CH_2\!=\!CHCl$, which is less reactive than vinylidene chloride, $CH_2\!=\!CCl_2$. The introduction of three or four electronegative elements tends to stabilize monomers, and therefore a material like trichloroethylene, $CHCl\!=\!CCl_2$, is inert.

Addition reactions may be triggered by the formation of a free radical. Some covalent bonds are especially weak; typical of these are the O—O bonds of organic peroxides, ROOR, and the C—N bonds of azo compounds, R—C—N=N—CR. These bonds have strengths of 30 to 100 kcal/g mole, and the absorption of electromagnetic radiation in the wavelength range of 3,000 to 6,000 Å can cause the formation of free radicals:

$$ROOR \rightarrow 2RO\cdot$$

The extra electron on the free radical can then interact with the π electrons of a double bond to initiate the formation of a polymer chain. The chain propagation proceeds very rapidly in the following manner:

$$RO\cdot + CH_2\!=\!CHX \rightarrow ROCH_2\!-\!CHX\cdot$$

$$ROCH_2CHX\cdot + CH_2\!=\!CHX \rightarrow RO(CH_2\!-\!CHX)_2\cdot$$

or in general,

$$RO\cdot + xCH_2\!=\!CHX \rightarrow RO(CH_2\!-\!CHX)_x\cdot$$

The propagation step will terminate when two growing free-radical chains interact. One type of interaction is coupling:

$$RO(CH_2\!-\!CHX)_x\cdot + \cdot(CHX\!-\!CH_2)_yOR \rightarrow RO(CH_2\!-\!CHX)_{x+y}OR$$

Reactions of this type are usually highly exothermic and difficult to control. The polymer chains grow very rapidly, and high-molecular-weight polymer appears immediately on the first sign of reaction. The reacting system will always contain monomer and high polymer, with only traces of intermediate-size products. The solid material will either precipitate from the reacting fluid or will stay in solution, causing the reacting medium to get more and more viscous until it hardens to a solid material (below the melting point, of course). A typical degree of polymerization is of the order of 10^3 to 10^5.

There are many techniques used to carry out reactions on a commercial scale. In *bulk polymerization*, pure monomer with dissolved catalyst is placed in a reactor and allowed to polymerize. The resulting product is pure polymer with some trapped monomer. The major difficulties with such a technique are heat removal and the increased resistance to flow or mixing as the polymer forms. In *solution polymerization*, the monomer is dissolved in a solvent, so that the reaction can proceed without an excessive increase in resistance to flow. In *emulsion* and *suspension* polymerization an inert medium such as water is used to absorb the heat of reaction and to keep the system fluid. All of these techniques are used commercially, and each has its own particular advantages and disadvantages.

A particularly important method of synthesis is the polymerization of olefins on the surfaces of metal-oxide catalysts. The mechanism is probably the interaction of the monomeric π bonds with the electrons at the metal surface. Chain propagation occurs at a particular ionic site on the surface, and polymer chains simultaneously form and break away from the metal. The important feature of the reaction is that the surface causes the reacting monomer to approach at a definite orientation. This enables one to control the stereospecificity of the chain and thereby exercise some control over the configuration of the final product. The whole field of stereospecific catalysis has had a strong impact on the polymer industry, and to some extent enables one to tailor-make a polymer material to a predetermined set of specifications.

9.3
Molecular weight of polymers

When a polymer is synthesized in either addition or condensation polymerization, the length of a given chain is determined by a set of random reactions. The final product will contain molecules of many different sizes. In other words, a polymer product will possess a molecular-size distribution such as that shown in Fig. 9.1. The *average degree of polymerization* is defined as the average number of repeating units per chain. Since the physical properties of a material will depend on both average degree of polymerization and the distribution, it is important to characterize both.

The nature of the distribution can be determined experimentally by fractionating the different-size molecules and then weighing and measuring the

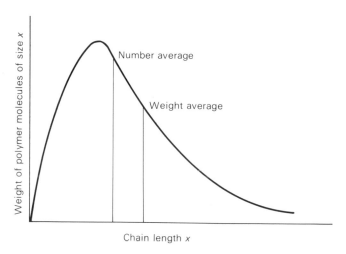

Fig. 9.1 A polymeric material contains a distribution of molecules with different sizes. An "average" molecular weight is defined relative to this distribution.

average molecular size of each narrow cut. This is always a very tedious job. The development of a variety of chromatographic techniques (e.g., gel permeation) has made this a more routine analysis, however. Another way is to make several different kinds of measurements on dilute solutions of the polymer. Certain physical-chemical measurements, such as the osmotic pressure of a dilute solution, essentially measure the number of molecules in the solution, regardless of size. From such measurements, one gets a *number-average molecular weight*:

$$\bar{M}_n = \sum_i N_i M_i \tag{9.2}$$

where N_i is the mole fraction of molecules with the molecular weight M_i. In other experiments, such as light scattering and ultracentrifuging, the size of the molecules determines the effects. From these measurements one gets a *weight-average molecular weight*:

$$\bar{M}_w = \sum w_i M_i = \frac{\sum N_i M_i^2}{\sum N_i M_i} \tag{9.3}$$

where w_i is the weight fraction of molecules with molecular weight M_i.

There are also other types of averages one can define. The main point is that when there is a distribution of sizes, the different averages will have different values and the differences are a measure of the breadth of the molecular-size distribution. Commercial polymers generally have values of $\bar{M}_w/\bar{M}_n$ ranging from 1.5 to 2.0 for simple condensation and free-radical polymerized products to 2 to 50 for polymers made in the presence of stereo-specific catalysts. The larger this ratio, the broader the spread of molecular weights.

One of the important aspects of tailor-making polymers has been the ability to control molecular-weight distribution, even to the point of producing a virtually monodisperse polymer (that is, $\bar{M}_w/\bar{M}_n \doteq 1$). This enables one to have an additional control on the mechanical properties of a final product.

In these three sections, we have considered how a polymeric material is formed during a chemical reaction. The resulting mass may be a fluid or a solid and will most likely have a distribution of molecular sizes. In the paragraphs that follow, we shall consider some of the physical changes that affect the morphology of such materials.

9.4
Amorphous polymers and second-order transitions

The transformation of a fluid polymer to a solid material can be either a first- or a second-order transition. A first-order transition is associated with an abrupt change in molecular order. The condensation of vapor, the freezing of pure metals, and the polymorphic changes in metals are typical examples. The changes occur at a constant temperature and are accompanied by sudden changes in volume, thermal-expansion coefficient, enthalpy, heat capacity, and other thermodynamic properties. A second-order transition is associated with a more gradual change from one state to another. The phenomenon occurs over a range of temperature, and there are no abrupt discontinuities in the thermodynamic properties. The nature of the transformation, however, is such that relatively large changes of thermal-expansion coefficient, viscosity, ductility, and other properties occur over a narrow temperature range.

In Chap. 8, we discussed the molecular structure of amorphous polymers. On cooling materials that retain an amorphous character, there is no sudden rearrangement of the molecules, as in crystallization, but rather a steady loss of mobility until the material can no longer be considered a fluid. The apparent viscosity becomes so high that the material is a solid in the usual sense of the word. Figure 9.2 shows the changes in viscosity and specific volume for polystyrene as it cools from 500 to 300°K. As it cools, it goes from a viscous fluid to a soft rubbery solid and, finally, to a brittle, glassy solid. The most

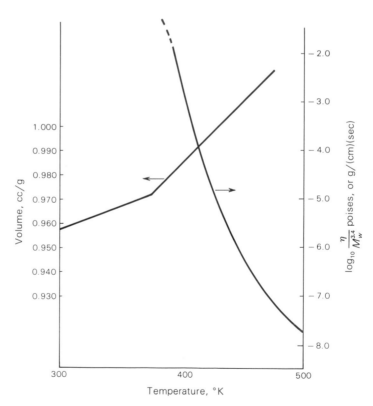

Fig. 9.2 Sharp changes in viscosity and thermal-expansion coefficient of polystyrene at about 373°K are manifestations of the second-order transition from a glassy to a rubbery polymer.

sudden changes in both viscosity and thermal-expansion coefficient occur in a narrow temperature region, the center of which is called the glass-transition temperature, T_g. What probably happens at the glass transition is that the benzene rings on the polystyrene molecules, no longer possessing enough thermal energy to retain their rotational freedom, "freeze" into a configuration which is fixed by strong inductive and dispersive attractions. (The electronic cloud within a benzene ring is highly polarizable.) The flexibility is therefore inhibited and the polymer behaves as a brittle, glassy solid. This type of behavior is typical of most high-molecular-weight materials. Although there is probably no simple quantitative relationship between T_g and the structure, a material with a low molar cohesion and a streamlined molecular structure usually has a low glass-transition temperature because of the difficulty in stopping molecular rotation. Table 9.3 compares the glass-transition tem-

Table 9.3

Effect of structure on glass-transition temperature *

Atactic polymer	Structure of repeat. unit	Nature (with no external stress)	Specific molar cohesion, kcal/5 Å chain	Approx. glass-transition temp, °C
Polybutadiene	—CH_2—CH=CH—CH_2—	Some forms amorphous, others crystallizable	1.1	−85
Polyethylene	—CH_2—	Crystallizable	1.0	−68
Polyisobutylene	[—C—CH_2—] with CH_3 above and CH_3 below	Mostly amorphous	1.2	−70
Natural rubber	—CH_2—C=CHCH_2— with CH_3	Mostly amorphous	1.3	−72
Polyvinylchloride	—CH—CH_2— with Cl	Mostly amorphous	2.6	80
Polyvinylacetate	—CH—CH_2— with $OCOCH_3$	Amorphous	3.2	29
Polyamide 6-6	—$OC(CH_2)_4CONH(CH_2)_6NH$—	Crystallizable	5.8	47
Polystyrene	—CH—CH_2— with C_6H_5	Amorphous	4.0	100

* For a complete survey of the subject of glass transitions see R. F. Boyer, *Rubber Chem. Tech.*, **36** (5): 1303–1421 (1963).

perature with the structure and molar cohesion of some simple linear polymers.

Second-order transitions have also been observed in crystalline solids such as HCl, NH_4Cl, and $NaNO_3$. Upon heating, the thermal-expansion coefficient and heat capacity rise gradually, reach a sharp peak and then decrease toward a more constant value (Fig. 9.3). There is essentially no change in the geometry of the space lattice, and there is no measurable latent heat change. The transition is again associated with a change in rotational freedom of the ions. Crystalline polymers (Sec. 9.5) also exhibit second-order transitions below their "freezing points." The changes in physical properties are similar to those occurring in amorphous polymers. Thus, polyethylene is a relatively ductile, crystalline polymer above 205°K but a brittle, crystalline polymer below 205°K.

Silicate structures behave in the same way as organic polymers. If molten silica, SiO_2, is cooled very slowly, an ordered crystal structure will develop, at the freezing point, through a definite arranging of silicate tetrahedra. On the other hand, a faster cooling rate will result in a poorly ordered arrangement

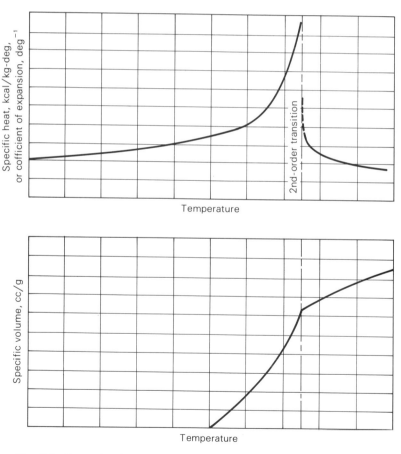

Fig. 9.3 Second-order transitions in crystalline solids are marked by discontinuities in specific heat capacity and thermal-expansion coefficient.

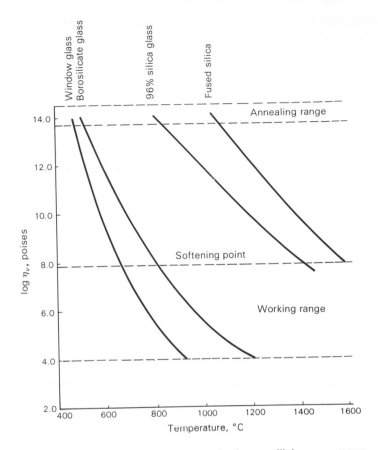

Fig. 9.4 The viscosities of inorganic glasses will decrease many orders of magnitude with relatively small increases in temperature. (Data from Ref. 5 and "Properties of Selected Commercial Glasses," Corning Glass Company, Corning, N.Y., 1949.)

which might show some localized, short-range order but no long-range, regular lattice structure. Pure vitreous or fused silica is molten above 1800°C, a soft workable solid in the range 1600 to 1800°C, and a rigid, brittle solid below 1400°C. The mobility of the silicate tetrahedra is so low below 1000°C that the amorphous state is, for all practical purposes, stable (i.e., is metastable). Note the similarity in the viscosity curves for silicate glasses (Fig. 9.4) and polystyrene (Fig. 9.2).

As the viscosity of the glass increases above the *annealing range,* the mobility of the silicate tetrahedra becomes so low that further changes in the structure become inhibited and the molecular arrangement present at the higher temperature becomes "frozen in." The actual structural arrangement will thus be a function of any variable that is related to the mobility (e.g., composition). For the same reason, the rate of cooling or the thermal history, in general, will determine the behavior of the material in the glassy state. This is an important difference between a supercooled liquid and a glass. Whereas the thermodynamic behavior of a supercooled liquid is a function of only temperature, pressure, and composition and is independent of thermal history, a glass can exist in many metastable states depending upon the thermal history of the material.

Above 1000°C, fused silica will tend to crystallize (i.e., devitrify) at a measurable rate. The stable crystalline forms are quartz, trydymite, and crystabolite. Second-order transitions may also occur in the crystals. Quartz, for example, undergoes a gradual change from α-quartz to β-quartz upon heating from room temperature to above 575°C (Fig. 9.5). No chemical bonds are broken and no latent heat changes are apparent, but the silicate tetrahedra change from a distorted SiO_4 unit giving trigonal symmetry to an undistorted SiO_4 unit giving hexagonal symmetry.

Glass-forming operations on fused silica must be carried out above the softening point of 1700°C and are difficult and very expensive. The glass-transition temperature may be lowered by disrupting the molecular order even further and by breaking some of the Si—O bonds. This is done commercially

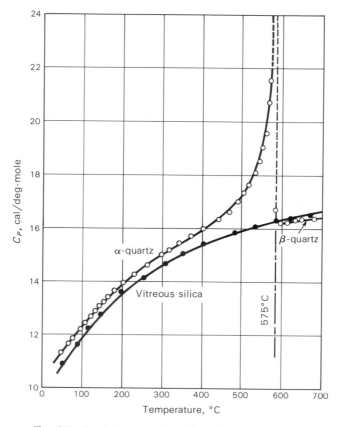

Fig. 9.5 Crystalline quartz will undergo a second-order transition at 575°C that is not apparent in vitreous silica. [From H. Moser, *Physik. Z.,* **37:** 737 (1936).]

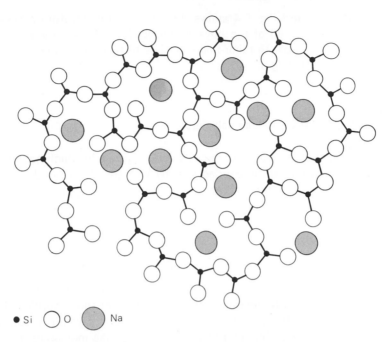

● Si   ◯ O   ⬤ Na

Fig. 9.6 A schematic representation in two dimensions of the structure of soda-silica glass showing the sodium nuclei embedded in a matrix of silicate units. (After Ref. 12.)

by adding simple metallic oxides to SiO_2. In this way, some of the Si—O—Si bonds, joining the corners of two tetrahedra, are broken and the oxygen atoms from the oxide are then attracted to the "freed" silicon atoms. The metallic cations then take up positions in the interstices to balance the negative charges of the oxygen atoms. A two-dimensional representation of a sodium oxide–substituted glass is shown in Fig. 9.6. Table 9.4 gives the compositions of some

Table 9.4

Average compositions of some commercial glasses [5]

Component	Window glass	Borosilicate glass (Pyrex)	High-silica glass
SiO_2	70–75	73–82	96
Na_2O	12–18	3–10	
K_2O	0–1	0.4–1.0	
CaO	5–14	0–1	
PbO		0–10	
B_2O_3		5–20	3
Al_2O_3	0.5–2.5	2–3	
MgO	0–4		

commercial glasses, and Fig. 9.4 shows the viscosity-temperature curves for these materials. Since all of the physical properties will be affected by the composition, it is possible to tailor-make glasses to fit certain specifications. The analogies with alloying are obvious.

9.5
The formation of linear crystalline polymers

Sheet molecules, such as graphite, form lamellar crystals in which each sheet lies parallel to the next and is bonded to it by Van der Waals bonds. These lamellar, single crystals often aggregate into spherical shapes in which the lamella radiate from a small central region called a *nucleus.* These aggregates, called *spherulites,* are somewhat analogous to the grains of polycrystalline metals. The normal polycrystalline state is then a random arrangement of spherulites which are all bonded together by interleaving of the lamellar units from adjacent spherulites. The interleaved regions might be thought of as analogous to the grain boundaries in metals. The physical properties of the material must, of course, be related to the morphology of the spherulite struc-ture and the nature of the spherulite boundaries. Linear, crystalline polymers also possess a spherulitic character in which the chainlike molecules fold into lamellar crystals which, in turn, aggregate into spherulitic arrangements.

In the molten state, the polymer molecules are in a random conformation. Figure 9.7 illustrates a typical cooling curve for a crystallizable polymer. Very rapid quenching can inhibit crystallization to give a metastable amorphous polymer. Crystallization can then proceed at any temperature below the maxi-mum crystallization temperature, T_c. Very slow cooling, on the other hand, will promote the first nuclei very close to T_c.

As with metals, the rate of crystallization of polymers depends on the formation of nuclei and the growth of crystallites. In the absence of external stress, the nucleation rate is primarily a function of the amount of supercooling (that is, $T - T_c$). The rate first increases with degrees of supercooling because of an increase in the free-energy difference between the liquid and crystalline states and then decreases again because of a decrease in the mobility of the molecules. Thus a maximum nucleation rate is attained at a certain tempera-ture below T_c. The growth rate depends primarily on the greater stability of larger crystals and increases with temperature right up to T_c. At constant temperature, the spherulite diameter will normally increase linearly with time.

Over most of the range where crystallization is observed, experimental data may be represented by [7]:

$$-\ln \left(1 - \frac{v_t - v_0}{v_\infty - v_0}\right) = -\ln \frac{v_\infty - v_t}{v_\infty - v_0} = k_R t^n \tag{9.4}$$

The quantities v_∞, v_t, and v_0 are specific volumes at the times indicated by the subscripts. The quantity k_R is a temperature and molecular-weight-dependent *rate constant.* At a fixed temperature k_R will decrease with increasing molecu-

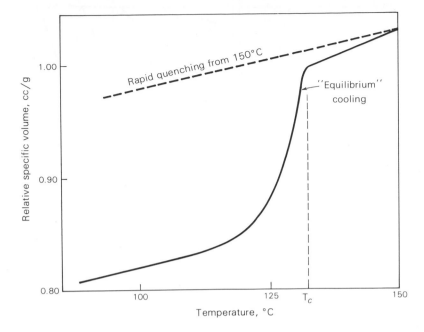

Fig. 9.7 A very rapid decrease in specific volume will normally accompany the crystallization of a polymer. Crystallization can be inhibited, however, by very rapid quenching.

lar weight, reaching a molecular-weight-independent constant value. The temperature dependence is about the same as for the temperature dependence of rates of nucleation of metals (i.e., log k_R is a linear function of (T_c^2/T) $[1/(T_c - T)]$). The quantity n is a constant, usually found to be between 1 and 4, and is dependent on the type of nucleation process. Very often, the best fit of experimental data indicates that the crystallization proceeds through a primary stage which constitutes a large percentage of the total crystallization in a relatively short period of time (characterized by n_1), followed by a secondary crystallization of the remaining material over a very long period of time (characterized by n_2). Figures 9.8 and 9.9 illustrate some isothermal rate data for the crystallization of polypropylene at various temperature levels.

Two thermodynamic factors will affect the "equilibrium" crystallization temperature T_c. When the chains align into a crystalline pattern, a latent heat of crystallization ΔH_c is evolved and a loss in entropy ΔS_c occurs which is associated with a decrease in the freedom of the chains as they enter the crystallites. Since the free-energy change ΔG_c is zero at T_c,

$$\Delta G = 0 = \Delta H_c - T_c \, \Delta S_c \tag{9.5}$$

$$T_c = \frac{\Delta H_c}{\Delta S_c} \tag{9.6}$$

At first glance one would expect that high molecular symmetry and strong

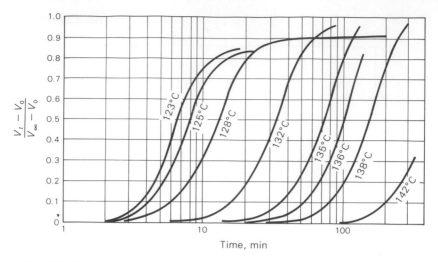

Fig. 9.8 Volume changes on isothermal crystallizations of polypropylene. [Data from L. Marker, P. M. Hay, G. P. Tilley, R. M. Early, and O. J. Sweeting, *J. Polymer Sci.,* **38:** 33 (1959).]

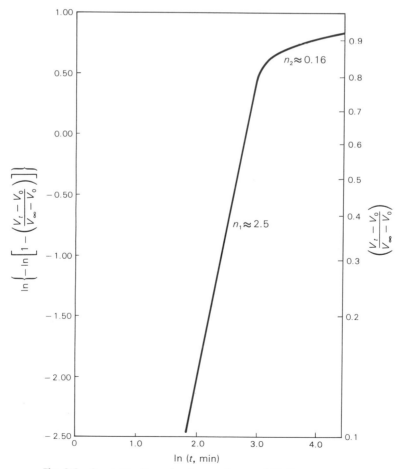

Fig. 9.9 Crystallization of polypropylene at 128°C.

intermolecular forces would lead to a high crystallization temperature. It is extremely difficult, however, to separate these factors and correlate the molecular parameters with observed crystallization temperatures. Heats of crystallization are not necessarily proportional to molar cohesion, because they depend also on the change in molar volume during crystallization. If the crystal structure has about the same molar volume as the liquid (at the same temperature), the heat of crystallization will be small, regardless of the molar cohesion. Entropy of crystallization depends on the change in the freedom of molecules in the two states. Thus a highly streamlined molecule may have limited freedom in a crystallite but may tend to be extremely flexible in the molten state, thus leading to a large entropy change and a low crystallization temperature. The crystallization temperatures and glass-transition temperatures are listed in Table 9.5 for a number of organic polymers. The glass-transition temperature is usually of the order of one-half to three-fourths of the crystallization temperature, indicating that the effects of molecular structure on the two are similar.

In general, one may say that high-intensity intermolecular attractions and close packing of molecules will tend to raise the crystallization temperature, while low-intensity intermolecular attractions, poor packing, and a high degree of chain flexibility in the molten state will tend to lower, or even eliminate, crystallization. It is extremely difficult to predict the effect of some structural changes because competing processes can come into play. Side-chain substitution on linear polyethylene, for example, will at first decrease the crystallization temperature because of the loosening of the crystal structure, but as the bulkiness of the side chain increases, the crystallization point rises again because of loss of mobility in the molten state (ΔS_c decreases).

Nucleation can start homogeneously or, more commonly, in the presence of an impurity surface. The chainlike molecules fold back on themselves to form

Table 9.5

Transition temperatures for some organic polymers *

Polymer	T_m, °K	T_g, °K	T_g/T_m
Silicone rubber	215	150	0.70
Natural rubber	301	203	0.67
Polyvinylidene fluoride	483	234	0.49
Polyvinylchloride	453	355	0.78
Polystyrene	503 (isotactic)	373	0.74
Polyethylene	408	163	0.40
Polypropylene	449	255	0.57
Nylon 6	498	350	0.70

* These are average values from the literature and should be considered only approximate.

a flat platelike disk which is of the order of 100 Å thick and several microns in diameter (Fig. 9.10). Crystallization continues by the addition of chain segments to the 100-Å-thick faces and can continue as long as the interface is in contact with amorphous polymer. Screw dislocations (Fig. 6.19) can develop normal to the folding planes [(001) planes], and the disk can thicken by a spiral growth about the screw dislocation. A good deal of research on single crystals of this type has been carried out in recent years [4]. An electron micrograph of a polyethylene (Marlex 6050) single crystal is shown in Fig. 9.11. The crystal was isothermally grown from a 0.05 weight percent polymer in xylene solution at 80°C. The cracks, with the fibrils pulled across, suggest that the crystal was once a hollow pyramid. The thin lozenge-shaped platelets are each about 140 Å thick and spiral about a single screw dislocation. Although the growth and morphology of crystallites formed from a melt are undoubtedly much more complex than from dilute solutions, the mechanism is indicative of what one would expect in melts.

When a polymer is crystallized from a melt, large numbers of lamella group together into spherulites. A spherulite starts by the thickening of a "primary" lamellar crystallite. Secondary lamella then grow rapidly, normal to the screw dislocation and approximately parallel to the primary crystallite. These form a sheaf of crystallites, as is shown schematically in Fig. 9.12. The secondary lamella do not stay parallel to the primary one, but rather begin to twist and branch away from the central region. The usual pattern is that the platelike crystallites radiate in all directions, with a particular lattice vector lying consistently along the radius of a sphere. In polyethylene, for example, the b axis (Fig. 8.4) is always parallel to the radius. The chain axis (c axis), on the other hand, is always normal to the spherulite radius, and thus the growth continues outward along the radii of the sphere. Sometimes the unit cells within each radiating crystallite also tend to spiral in a helical pattern. In polyeth-

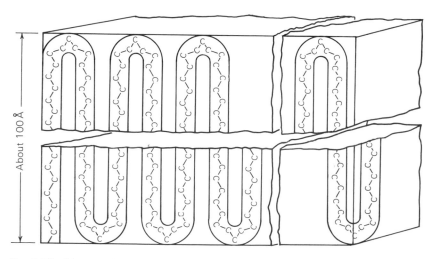

Fig. 9.10 Linear polymer chains will crystallize by chain-folding into a plate-like polymer crystal.

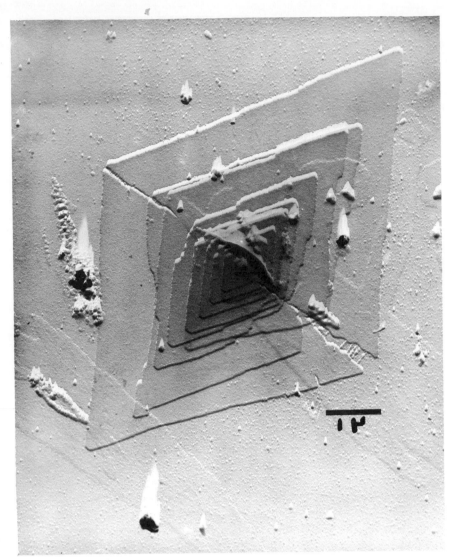

Fig. 9.11 An electron micrograph of a single crystal of polyethylene (Marlex 6050) isothermally grown from a 0.05 weight percent polymer in xylene solution at 80°C. (Micrograph courtesy of C. A. Garber and P. H. Geil, Case Institute of Technology, Cleveland.)

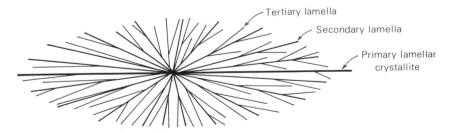

Tertiary lamella

Secondary lamella

Primary lamellar crystallite

Fig. 9.12 A schematic drawing of the cross section of a spherulite that forms by the aggregation of lamellar crystallites (each on the order of 50 to 150 Å thick) into a specific orientation.

ylene, for example, going out along the radius of a spherulite, the unit cell twists in a helical path about the b axis. In order to fill a spherical volume, tertiary lamella branch off from screw dislocations in the secondary lamella and fill the spaces between the radiating crystallites.

This process occurs simultaneously from many nuclei in the melt, and spherulites continue to grow in this way until two growing surfaces meet. Then the secondary lamella of each spherulite interleave and continue to grow until little or no amorphous polymer remains. The interleaving locks adjacent spherulites together into a mechanically strong mass.

When the structure is viewed under x-ray diffraction, it is apparent that there is a significant amount of disorder and imperfection. Lattice defects can arise from terminal groups on the chains, branching, improper folding, twisting, and, as mentioned, screw dislocations. In short, the lattice defects are similar to those that exist in simpler crystals. Another possibility, which does not occur in simple crystals, is the trapping of amorphous polymer between growing crystallites. It is not unreasonable to suppose that, because of chain entanglement, low mobility, complex chain structure, and complex chain conformation, some amorphous polymer may not get the opportunity to reorient into a crystalline geometry. A 100 percent crystalline polymer has never been produced, but whether the noncrystalline portion is truly amorphous or is merely imperfect crystal is still open to conjecture.

There is really no sharp distinction between crystalline polymers and amorphous polymers. Some materials, such as polyvinylchloride, natural rubber, and others that have relatively weak intermolecular forces and slightly bulky side groups, exhibit very low degrees of crystallinity. When a material appears to be only 10 to 20 percent crystalline, it is difficult to avoid the concept of a crystalline and an amorphous phase existing together at equilibrium. Under these conditions, the "fringed micelle" model, shown in Fig. 9.13, is useful. In the crystalline region, the polymer chains have a well organized parallel alignment with unit cell dimensions. These crystallite packets, which may be bundles several microns thick, mesh completely with disordered regions. Some polymer molecules pass through a crystallite and fold back on themselves, while others pass into a less dense, amorphous region. Any one polymer molecule can pass through many regions of order and disorder, since it is relatively long when compared with the average length of any one region. This gives the picture of a composite structure of amorphous and crystalline regions bonded together by the primary carbon-to-carbon bonds along the main chains of the molecules.

As is the case with simpler polycrystalline materials, a crystalline polymer will appear isotropic on a gross scale as long as the spherulites are randomly arranged. When a molten polyamide (nylon) is crystallized in the absence of any external stress, for example, an apparently isotropic structure of randomly arranged spherulites is formed. If the material is then stretched (cold-drawn), the crystallites will align and develop along a common "fiber" axis. The polyamide will then have the anisotropic character typical of all "fibrous" materials. The alignment probably develops through interlamellar slipping

Fig. 9.13 The fringed crystallite (micelle) model for partially crystalline polymers shows polymer chains extending from one crystalline region to another through contiguous amorphous regions.

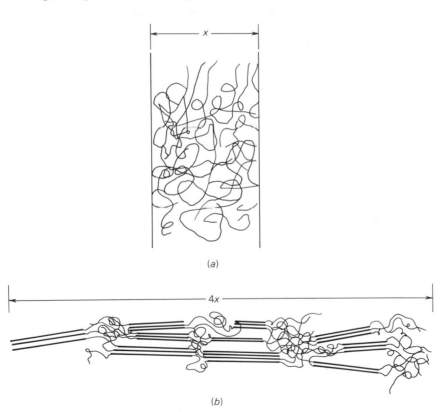

(a)

(b)

Fig. 9.14 Cold-drawing tends to increase the length of the polymer in the direction of drawing and changes the structure from isotropic to anisotropic. (a) Isotropic, amorphous polymer; (b) anisotropic, crystalline polymer.

within a given spherulite and also by the unfolding of chains in the lamella. Although the precise morphology of drawn fibers is very complicated, the fringed-micelle model can be used to visualize the difference between an amorphous polymer and what it might look like after cold-drawing (Fig. 9.14).

9.6
Formation of copolymers

By reacting two or more monomers together, it is possible to form a polymer chain which contains all the reactants. These *copolymers* may be formed by addition or condensation polymerization and may be produced as either random or stereoregular structures. A *random copolymer* is one in which the different monomers have no definite order or configuration in the chain. A *block copolymer* is one that contains polymer chains with long sequences of one monomer followed by long sequences of another. A *graft copolymer* is one in which the backbones of the polymer chains are made up of one monomer and other monomers are "grafted" on as branch chains off the main chain. These types are shown schematically in Fig. 9.15 for copolymers of two monomers.

The physical properties of copolymers will depend on the types of monomers involved and the basic structure of the polymer chains. Thus, from a limited number of monomers and a few different reaction mechanisms, one may produce a very wide spectrum of useful products; the potentialities are much the same as the alloying of metals.

An important illustration of the effects of copolymerization is the GRS rubbers, which are random copolymers of butadiene and styrene. Pure, atactic

A — B — B — A — B — A — B — A — B — A —

(*a*)

— A — A — A — A — A — A — A — A — A — A — B — B — B — B — B — B — B — B — B — A —

(*b*)

A — A — A — A — A — A — A — A — A — A — A — A — A — A —
  | |
  B   B
  | |
  B   B
  | |
  B   B
  | |
  B   B

(*c*)

Fig. 9.15 Monomers A and B can be copolymerized to form a variety of different types of copolymer chains. (*a*) Random; (*b*) block; (*c*) graft.

butadiene is a soft rubbery solid at room temperature with a glass-transition temperature in the vicinity of 193°K. Pure atactic polystyrene is an amorphous, brittle glass at room temperature with a glass-transition temperature of about 373°K. A whole range of copolymers can be made by an addition polymerization in an emulsion of butadiene and styrene. Table 9.6 shows the effect of composition on the glass-transition temperature. The crystallizing tendencies of these materials also vary from the high crystallizability (on stretching) of polybutadiene to the noncrystallinity of polystyrene.

When one or more of the monomers form crystalline polymers in the pure state, the copolymers may or may not be crystalline depending on the composition and on the type of copolymer formed. Generally, as a second structural unit is added to a pure, crystalline polymer, both the maximum degree of crystallinity and the melting point are decreased. This is due to the disruption of the symmetry and regularity of the pure chain. In many cases, noncrystalline elastomers can be produced in the intermediate composition range. This lessening of crystallinity and lowering of melting point will continue until a sufficient amount of the second monomer is present to restore the symmetry, with the second monomer controlling the crystal geometry. This is illustrated in Fig. 9.16 for copolymers of hexamethylene sebacamide,

$$-NH(-CH_2)_6-NH-\overset{\overset{\displaystyle O}{\|}}{C}(-CH_2)_8-\overset{\overset{\displaystyle O}{\|}}{C}-NH(-CH_2)_6-NH-$$

and terephthalamide,

$$-NH-\overset{\overset{\displaystyle O}{\|}}{C}-\!\!\!\left\langle\bigcirc\right\rangle\!\!\!-\overset{\overset{\displaystyle O}{\|}}{C}-NH(-CH_2)_6-NH_2-$$

On the other hand, if the comonomer has about the same geometry as the other and can replace it without seriously distorting the crystal lattice, the degree

---

Table 9.6

Effect of copolymer composition on the glass-transition temperature

Butadiene-styrene	Glass-transition temp T_g, °K
100-0	193
75-25	216
60-40	235
50-50	252
30-70	291
10-90	341
0-100	373

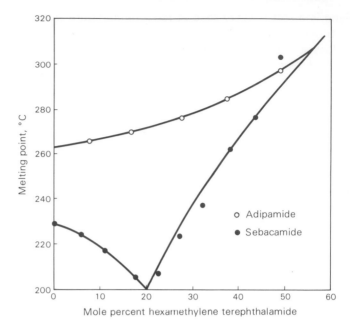

Fig. 9.16 The melting point of a polyamide copolymer is a function of comonomer concentration and type. [By permission from O. B. Edgar and R. Hill, *J. Polymer Sci.,* **8**:1 (1952).]

of crystallinity may not be too strongly affected and the melting point may vary smoothly with composition.   This is also illustrated in Fig. 9.16 for copolymers of hexamethylene adipamide,

$$-NH(-CH_2)_6-NH-\overset{\overset{\displaystyle O}{\|}}{C}(-CH_2-)_4\overset{\overset{\displaystyle O}{\|}}{C}-NH$$

and terephthalamide [the (—CH$_2$)$_4$— unit is replaced by

$$-C\underset{CH=CH}{\overset{CH-CH}{\diagup\diagdown}}C-].$$

When block or graft copolymers are formed, the behavior becomes much more complex.   If, for example, a block copolymer has long sequences of two crystallizable structural units, the copolymer might exhibit *two* distinct melting points and have *two* different unit cells describing the crystal geometry. Grafting side chains, on the other hand, can disrupt the crystal structure of the main chain; but at the same time, if the grafted units are in long enough sequences, they might develop their own crystal structure.

The polymerization of copolymers and the morphology of their structures are very broad areas of polymer science that incorporate all of the principles we have discussed for pure materials, in addition to a number of unique characteristics associated with the presence of a number of monomers.   We shall not attempt to discuss the problems here; instead, the reader should consult the references listed at the end of this chapter.

References

1 Billmeyer, F. W.: "Textbook of Polymer Science," Interscience Publishers, Inc., New York, 1962. *Parts III and IV, pp. 235–484, discuss polymerization and the properties of commercial polymers.*

2 Doremus, R. H., B. W. Roberts, and D. Turnbull: Growth and Perfection of Crystals, sec. VI, "Crystallization of Polymers," pp. 465ff., John Wiley & Sons, Inc., New York, 1958.

3 Flory, P. J.: "Principles of Polymer Chemistry," Cornell University Press, Ithaca, N.Y., 1953.

4 Geil, P. H.: "Polymer Single Crystals," Polymer Reviews, No. 5, Interscience Publishers, Inc., New York, 1963. *A treatise on the morphology and properties of polymeric crystals.*

5 Jastrzebski, Z. D.: "Nature and Properties of Engineering Materials," pp. 308–313, John Wiley & Sons, Inc., New York, 1959.

6 Keller, A.: Polymer Single Crystals, *Polymer,* **3** (3): 393 (1962). *A short review article on the morphology of polymer crystals.*

7 Mandelkern, L.: "Crystallization of Polymers," McGraw-Hill Book Company, New York, 1964. *A reference text on all aspects of crystalline polymers.*

8 Morey, G. W.: "The Properties of Glass," Reinhold Publishing Corporation, New York, 1954.

9 Morey, G. W., and N. L. Bowen: *J. Soc. Glass Technol.,* **9:** 232 (1925).

10 Schmidt, A. X., and C. A. Marlies: "The Principle of High-polymer Theory and Practice," McGraw-Hill Book Company, New York, 1948.

11 Stille, J. K.: "Introduction to Polymer Chemistry," John Wiley & Sons, Inc., New York, 1962. *An introductory text to the physical chemistry of polymers and polymer chemistry.*

12 Warren, B. E., et al.: *J. Appl. Phys.,* **8:** 645 (1937); *J. Am. Ceram. Soc.,* **21:** 259, 287 (1938).

Questions

9.1 Differentiate between a thermoplastic polymer and a thermosetting polymer. List some examples of each.

9.2 Natural rubber, $(-CH_2-CH=C(CH_3)-CH_2-)_x$, is a linear, thermoplastic polymer which may be melted and shaped any number of times. When it is heated in the presence of sulfur, however, it is converted to a nonmoldable material by a process called *vulcanization.* Can you describe what the most likely cause of this change is?

9.3 Rubbers, plastics, and fibers have many characteristics in common because they all belong to the same families of organic compounds. Discuss the factors that determine the class for a given polymeric material. Describe the differences in behavior and structure for the three classes of materials.

9.4 (a) Describe the reaction between hexamethylene diamine, $NH_2-(CH_2-)_6NH_2$, and adipic acid, $HOOC-(CH_2)_4-COOH$.

(b) Suppose one mole of amine is reacted with one mole of acid. What is the degree of polymerization when the extent of reaction, p, is 0.5, 0.9, 0.99, 0.999, and 1.000?

(c) Suppose 1.1 moles of diamine is reacted with 1.0 mole of dicarboxyacid. What is the maximum degree of polymerization?

9.5 Use any reference text for further information on bulk polymerization, suspension polymerization, and emulsion polymerization. Describe each of these techniques.

9.6 A polystyrene produced in a bulk polymerization has been fractionated into a series of sharp cuts of different molecular weight. The weight fraction and "average" degree of polymerization of each cut are given in Table 9.7. Calculate the number and weight-average molecular weights for the material.

Table 9.7

Cut	Wt. frac.	Avg deg of polymerization	Cut	Wt. frac.	Avg deg of polymerization
1	0.10	250	6	0.15	1,800
2	0.15	750	7	0.15	2,250
3	0.10	1,100	8	0.05	2,750
4	0.10	1,300	9	0.05	3,500
5	0.10	1,500	10	0.05	6,000

9.7 Distinguish between a first-order and a second-order transition.

9.8 Why does the addition of metallic oxides lower the softening point of silica?

9.9 Polytetrafluoroethylene and polyethylene are crystalline polymers at room temperature, while polystyrene and polymethylmethacrylate are amorphous and glassy at room temperature. Discuss the structural and energy factors that contribute to this behavior.

9.10 Atactic polystyrene can be slightly oriented by stretching, but it will not crystallize. Natural rubber can be highly oriented by stretching and crystallization will be temporarily induced (removal of the external force removes the induced crystallization). Polyamides (e.g., nylon 6-6) can be highly oriented by stretching and permanent crystallization will be induced. Explain these facts in terms of molecular structure and intermolecular bonding.

9.11 Describe, in your own words, the morphology of a spherulite.

9.12 What molecular factors will affect the degree of crystallinity and the crystallization temperature of a linear polymer?

9.13 List all of the possible lattice defects that you can think of that might be in a lamellar crystallite.

9.14   Use the curve of Fig. 9.8 to evaluate the temperature dependence of the initial rate constant for the crystallization of polypropylene.

9.15   Styrene, $C_6H_5CH=CH_2$,   can   be   copolymerized   with   divinylbenzene, $CH_2=CH(-C_6H_4-)CH=CH_2$.   What structural changes would you predict for the copolymer relative to pure polystyrene?

9.16   Vinyl chloride and vinylidene chloride may be correacted to form Saran copolymers. Vinylidene chloride has a crystalline melting point of about 190°C.   Polyvinylchloride does not develop a very well-formed crystal structure, but "melts" at about 210°C.   Sketch the kind of curve you would expect for softening point as a function of polymer composition.   Explain your reasoning.

Part C
Properties of
engineering materials

10
Thermodynamic properties

10.1
Introduction

The equilibrium thermodynamic properties of materials are, for the most part, insensitive to the presence of a small number of structural imperfections. Properties such as internal energy, specific heat, thermal-expansion coefficient, and compressibility are thus called *structure-insensitive* properties.

For simple crystals, approximate relationships can be derived that express the thermodynamic properties in terms of the intermolecular force constants for the material. The general idea is to consider each atom in the crystal structure as vibrating about a fixed point in the lattice and then obtain the partition function for the vibrator. Since the partition function is written in terms of the vibration frequency of the atom, or the force constant, one thus has a relationship between the thermodynamic properties and the molecular parameters. The purpose of this chapter is to show how one can interrelate thermodynamic properties, crystal geometry, and intermolecular forces for simple crystalline solids and to indicate how these ideas might be applied to more complex structures.

10.2
Internal energy

In Chap. 5, we calculated the total lattice energy of a crystalline solid by assuming that each particle was at rest at a point in the space lattice. For a molecular solid in which the pair potential is $\psi_{ab} = -a/r^n + b/r^m$, the total lattice energy is given as

$$\psi_T = \frac{N(\psi_{aT})_{r=r_0}}{2(m-n)} \left[m \left(\frac{r_0}{r}\right)^n - n \left(\frac{r_0}{r}\right)^m \right] \qquad \text{cf. (5.11)} \qquad (10.1)$$

and the potential energy of interaction for *a single particle* in the lattice is

$$\psi_{aT} = -\mathfrak{z} \left(\frac{s_a a}{r^n} - \frac{s_b b}{r^m}\right) \qquad \text{cf. (5.9)} \qquad (10.2)$$

In addition to potential energy, each atom has a certain amount of kinetic energy associated with the Brownian motion of the particles. In an ideal crys-

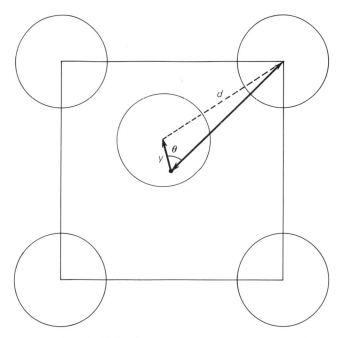

Fig. 10.1 The interaction potential between two particles can be expressed as a function of the displacement of one of the particles from its rest position (i.e., as a function of *y*).

tal, one may calculate this *internal energy* by assuming that each atom vibrates about its lattice point with a vibration frequency that is determined by the magnitude of the potential energy. The simplest approximation to the real behavior of the material is to assume that a given particle vibrates in an average field that is created by all of the other particles at rest in their equilibrium positions. This is shown schematically in Fig. 10.1. The drawing shows only one plane and four nearest neighbors, but actually the vibrating particle is moving in three dimensions and is confined to a small "caged" volume bounded by $\hat{3}$ nearest neighbors. The potential energy of this central particle when it is displaced a distance y from its rest point is actually a very complicated function of position, since even the simplest crystal is anisotropic. An average, spherically symmetric potential may be obtained, however, by averaging over all possible orientations of the particle when it is displaced by an amount y:

$$\langle \psi_{aT}(y) \rangle = \frac{\int_0^{2\pi} \int_0^{\pi} \psi(d) \sin \theta \, d\theta \, d\phi}{\int_0^{2\pi} \int_0^{\pi} \sin \theta \, d\theta \, d\phi} \tag{10.3}$$

It can be shown [5,7] that

$$\langle \psi_{aT}(y) \rangle - \psi_{aT}(0) = -\frac{(\psi_{aT})_{r=r_0} m}{m-n} \left(\frac{r_0}{r}\right)^n \left[\frac{(1+y/r)^{2-n} - (1-y/r)^{2-n}}{2(n-2)(y/r)} + 1\right]$$

$$+ \frac{(\psi_{aT})_{r=r_0} n}{m-n} \left(\frac{r_0}{r}\right)^m \left[\frac{(1+y/r)^{2-m} - (1-y/r)^{2-m}}{2(m-2)(y/r)} + 1\right] \tag{10.4}$$

This equation can be expanded in a series of y/r by using a binomial expansion:

$$\langle \psi_{aT}(y) \rangle - \psi_{aT}(0) = \frac{(\psi_{aT})_{r=r_0} mn}{6(m-n)} \left[(n-1)\left(\frac{r_0}{r}\right)^n - (m-1)\left(\frac{r_0}{r}\right)^m\right]\left(\frac{y}{r}\right)^2$$

$$+ (\cdots)\left(\frac{y}{r}\right)^4 + \cdots \tag{10.5}$$

When y/r is small, only the first term need be retained and thus the vibration is approximately harmonic:

$$\langle \psi_{aT}(y) \rangle - \psi_{aT}(0) \doteq 2\pi^2 m_R \nu^2 y^2 \tag{10.6}$$

The vibration frequency for the oscillator is thus

$$\nu = \left\{\frac{(\psi_{aT})_{r=r_0} mn}{12 m_R \pi^2 (m-n) r^2}\left[(n-1)\left(\frac{r_0}{r}\right)^n - (m-1)\left(\frac{r_0}{r}\right)^m\right]\right\}^{1/2} \tag{10.7}$$

A crystal consisting of N particles has $3N - 6 \approx 3N$ internal degrees of freedom. In a monoatomic crystal, all of these are vibrational degrees. If it is assumed that all of these are harmonic vibrations with a single frequency ν_E given by Eq. (10.7), the energy levels available to each atom are

$$\epsilon = (n + \tfrac{1}{2})h\nu_E \qquad n = 0, 1, 2, 3, \ldots \tag{10.8}$$

and the atomic partition function is

$$z = \exp\left(-\frac{h\nu_E}{2kT}\right) \sum_{n=0}^{\infty} \exp\left(-\frac{nh\nu_E}{kT}\right)$$

$$= \left(2 \sinh \frac{h\nu_E}{2kT}\right)^{-1} \tag{10.9}$$

The total internal partition function Z is thus

$$Z = \left(2 \sinh \frac{h\nu_E}{2kT}\right)^{-3N} \tag{10.10}$$

From the definitions given in Chap. 2, the Helmholtz free energy is

$$A = -kT \ln Z$$

$$= \tfrac{3}{2}Nh\nu_E + 3RT \ln\left[1 - \exp\left(-\frac{h\nu_E}{kT}\right)\right] \tag{10.11}$$

and the internal energy is

$$U = kT^2 \left(\frac{\partial \ln Z}{\partial T}\right)_V$$

$$= \frac{3}{2} Nh\nu_E + \frac{3Nh\nu_E}{[\exp\,(h\nu_E/kT)] - 1} \tag{10.12}$$

The first term on the right side represents the ground-state vibrational energy (i.e., the energy at absolute zero), while the second term represents vibrational energy relative to the ground state.

The heat of sublimation of the solid at any temperature is the difference between the lattice energy and the internal energy. The maximum energy of sublimation, at absolute zero, is, from Eqs. (10.12), (10.7), and (10.1):

$$\Delta U_s = \frac{N}{2} (\psi_{aT})_{r-r_0} + \frac{3 \, Nh}{2 \, \pi r_0} \left(\frac{mn(-\psi_{aT})_{r=r_0}}{12m_R}\right)^{1/2} \tag{10.13}$$

For a face-centered cubic crystal of neon, $n = 6$, $m = 12$, $a = 128$, $b = 59{,}100$ (see Chap. 3) and also $s_a = 1.2045$ and $s_b = 1.011$ to give $r_0 = 3.03$ Å, $(N/2)(\psi_{aT})_{r=r_0} = -0.60$ kcal/g mole and $\nu_E = 1.29 \times 10^{12}$ sec^{-1}. The ground-state vibration energy is thus 0.184 kcal/g mole and the maximum energy of sublimation is -0.416 kcal/g mole. The observed sublimation energy for neon, extrapolated to absolute zero, is -0.448 kcal/g mole.

At high temperatures, $h\nu_E/kT \ll 1$, sinh $(h\nu_E/2kT) \doteq h\nu_E/2kT$, and $z \doteq h\nu_E/kT$. The high-temperature limits of Helmholtz free energy and internal energy are thus

$$A = -3RT \ln \frac{kT}{h\nu_E} \qquad (10.14)$$

and

$$U = 3RT \qquad (10.15)$$

At low temperatures $h\nu_E/kT \gg 1$, 2 sinh $(h\nu_E/2kT) \doteq \exp (h\nu_E/2kT)$, and $\ln z \doteq h\nu_E/2kT$. The low-temperature limit of the internal energy is thus

$$U = 3Nh\nu_E \left[\frac{1}{2} + \exp \left(-\frac{h\nu_E}{kT} \right) \right] \qquad (10.16)$$

If one has information on the intermolecular-force parameters, the thermodynamic properties of the material may be estimated. When the molecular data are not available, these equations can be used to curve-fit experimental data. The molecular parameters are then determined experimentally, and the resulting equations are used to predict properties in other ranges of the variables. This simplified approach gives the proper high-temperature limits of the thermodynamic properties but does not predict the correct temperature dependence near absolute zero.

The major difficulty with Eqs. (10.9) to (10.16) is the assumption, known as the Einstein approximation [2], that all $3N$ vibrational degrees of freedom have the same frequency. Actually, each particle does not vibrate independently in a lattice with all other particles fixed, but rather each is coupled to mobile neighbors and must move together with them. The most general representation is to assume $3N - 6$ different modes of vibration, which would result in the following partition function:

$$Z = \prod_{i=1}^{3N-6} z_i$$

$$= \prod_{i=1}^{3N} \left[\exp \left(-\frac{h\nu_i}{2kT} \right) \right] \left[1 - \exp \left(-\frac{h\nu_i}{kT} \right) \right]^{-1} \qquad (10.17)$$

This complicated product of $3N$ terms reduces to Eq. (10.9) when all the ν_i are identical. We shall consider a more satisfactory solution to Eq. (10.17) after a brief discussion of specific heat.

10.3
Specific heat

The specific heat of a material is the heat required to raise a unit weight of the substance one degree of temperature at either constant pressure (c_p) or constant volume (c_v). The specific heat at constant volume is related to the internal energy by

$$c_v = \left(\frac{\partial U}{\partial T}\right)_v \qquad (10.18)$$

and the difference between c_p and c_v is

$$c_p - c_v = TV\frac{\alpha_v^2}{\kappa_T} \qquad (10.19)$$

where α_v is the volume coefficient of thermal expansion and κ_T is the isothermal compressibility (see next section). For most solids, c_v is of the order of 6 kcal/kg mole-°K at elevated temperature, while the difference $c_p - c_v$ is of the order of 0.1 kcal/kg mole-°K.

The specific heat at constant volume, in the Einstein approximation, is obtained by differentiating Eq. (10.12):

$$c_v = \frac{3R(h\nu_E/kT)^2 \exp{(h\nu_E/kT)}}{\{[\exp{(h\nu_E/kT)}] - 1\}^2} \qquad (10.20)$$

At high temperatures, $h\nu_E/kT \ll 1$, the specific heat approaches $3R$ kcal/kg mole-°K, and at low temperatures, $h\nu_E/kT \gg 1$, the specific heat approaches

$$c_v \doteq 3R\left(\frac{h\nu_E}{kT}\right)^2 \exp{\left(-\frac{h\nu_E}{kT}\right)} \qquad (10.21)$$

The upper limiting value of $3R = 5.9612$ kcal/kg mole–°K is in good agreement with the observed values for many crystalline solids at room temperature and above. The specific heat capacities of various inorganic crystals are listed in Table 10.1. This limiting value is also the basis for the empirical law of Dulong and Petit, which states that the specific heat of crystals at elevated temperature is approximately $3R$ kcal/kg atom–°K.

Experimentally, the specific heat of most simple crystals exhibits a cubic temperature dependence at very low temperatures, rather than the exponential dependence predicted by Eq. (10.21). The Einstein approximation of a single vibration frequency is thus inadequate. The proper temperature dependence may be obtained by using Eq. (10.17):

$$\ln Z = -\frac{h}{2kT} \sum_{i=1}^{3N} \nu_i - \sum_{i=1}^{3N} \ln\left[1 - \exp\left(-\frac{h\nu_i}{kT}\right)\right] \tag{10.22}$$

Debye assumes [1; see also 3,5] that the sum of the vibration frequencies can be replaced by an integral over a distribution of frequencies:

$$\sum_{i=1}^{3N} \nu_i \doteq \int_0^{\nu_m} \nu \, df \tag{10.23}$$

The upper limit ν_m is a maximum cutoff frequency which is characteristic of a specific material. The quantity df is the number of oscillators with frequencies in the range between ν and $\nu + d\nu$, and is assumed to be a parabolic function of frequency. Since the total number of vibrational degrees is $3N$, the relationship is

$$df = \frac{9N}{\nu_m^3} \nu^2 \, d\nu \tag{10.24}$$

and

$$\sum_{i=1}^{3N} \nu_i \doteq \int_0^{\nu_m} \frac{9N}{\nu_m^3} \nu^3 \, d\nu = \frac{9}{4} N\nu_m \tag{10.25}$$

In a similar manner,

$$\sum_{i=1}^{3N} \ln\left[1 - \exp\left(-\frac{h\nu_i}{kT}\right)\right] = \frac{9N}{\nu_m^3} \int_0^{\nu_m} \ln\left[1 - \exp\left(-\frac{h\nu}{kT}\right)\right] \nu^2 \, d\nu \tag{10.26}$$

so that the partition function is

$$\ln Z = -\frac{9}{8} N \frac{\Theta_D}{T} - 9N \left(\frac{T}{\Theta_D}\right)^3 \int_0^{\Theta_D/T} x^2 \ln\left[1 - \exp\left(-x\right)\right] dx \tag{10.27}$$

where $x = h\nu/kT$ and Θ_D is the *Debye characteristic temperature* for the material, $\Theta_D = h\nu_m/k$.

    The internal energy, specific heat, and other thermodynamic properties may then be obtained from Eq. (10.27). Except in the limits of high and low temperature, the definite integral must be evaluated numerically.

At high temperatures, $x \to 0$, Eq. (10.27) reduces to

$$\ln Z = 3N \ln \left(\frac{T}{\Theta_D}\right) + N \qquad (10.28)$$

and thus $U = 3RT$ and $c_v = 3R$, in agreement with the Einstein approximation. The extra factor N, however, is not in the Einstein approximation and adds a factor RT to the high-temperature limit of the Helmholtz free energy A.

At low temperature, the upper limit of integration in Eq. (10.27) approaches infinity and the integral approaches $-\pi^4/45$. The partition function is thus

$$\ln Z \doteq -\frac{9}{8} N \frac{\Theta_D}{T} + \frac{\pi^4}{5} N \left(\frac{T}{\Theta_D}\right)^3 \qquad (10.29)$$

Table 10.1

Specific heats of some crystalline solids *

Solid	c_p, kcal/kg mole-°K; T,°K	c_p at 300°K
Aluminum	$4.80 + 0.00322T$	5.77
Cadmium	$5.46 + 0.002466T$	6.20
Carbon (diamond)	$2.162 + 0.003059T - 130{,}300/T^2$	1.63
Chromium	$4.84 + 0.00295T$	5.73
Copper	$5.44 + 0.001462T$	5.88
α-Iron	$4.13 + 0.00638T$	6.05
Lead	$5.77 + 0.00202T$	6.38
α-Manganese	$3.76 + 0.00747T$	6.00
Manganese oxide (MnO)	$7.79 + 0.0421T + 9 \times 10^{-6}T^2$	9.86
α-Nickel	$4.26 + 0.00640T$	6.18
Nickel oxide (NiO)	$11.3 + 0.00215T$	12.0
Platinum	$5.92 + 0.00116T$	6.25
Silicon	$5.74 + 0.000617T - 101{,}000/T^2$	4.80
Silicon carbide (SiC)	$8.89 + 0.00291T - 284{,}000/T^2$	6.46
Silver	$5.60 + 0.00150T$	6.05
Sodium	$5.01 + 0.00536T$	6.62
Sodium chloride (NaCl)	$10.79 + 0.00420T$	12.05
Sulfur (rhombic)	$3.63 + 0.00640T$	5.55
Tin	$5.05 + 0.00480T$	6.49
Tungsten	$5.65 + 0.00866T$	8.25
Tungsten oxide(WO$_3$)	$16.0 + 0.00774T$	18.30
Zinc	$5.25 + 0.00270T$	6.06

* By permission from J. H. Perry, "Chemical Engineers' Handbook," 3d ed., McGraw-Hill Book Company, 1950.

The internal energy and specific heat at low temperature are thus

$$U = \frac{9}{8} R\Theta_D + \frac{3\pi^4}{5} R \frac{T^4}{\Theta_D^3} \qquad (10.30)$$

$$c_v = \frac{12}{5} \pi^4 R \left(\frac{T}{\Theta_D}\right)^3 \qquad (10.31)$$

Equation (10.31) gives the proper temperature dependence for the specific heat of crystals at low temperatures. The characteristic temperature Θ_D may be estimated theoretically from the elastic properties of the solid or experimentally by curve-fitting specific-heat data. The experimental characteristic temperatures for a number of crystals are given in Table 10.2.

At intermediate temperatures the specific heat of a Debye crystal is

$$c_v = 9R \left(\frac{T}{\Theta_D}\right)^3 \int_0^{\Theta_D/T} \frac{x^4 \exp x \, dx}{[(\exp x) - 1]^2} \qquad (10.32)$$

This equation may be solved numerically once Θ_D is known.

At ordinary temperatures, the contribution to specific heat by lattice vibrations is by far the most important. At very low temperatures, however, orientation effects, rotational effects, and contributions from valence electrons may also be important. The latter contribution, for example, is estimated to be on the order of $(c_v)_{\text{electrons}} \approx 10^{-3} T$ to $10^{-4} T$ kcal/kg atom–°K for simple metals. At room temperature this is only of the order of 0.03 to 0.3 kcal/kg atom–°K and is thus usually only a small fraction of the total of about 6 kcal/kg atom–°K. Since the temperature dependence is linear, however (compared with cubic for lattice vibrations), this contribution will be significant at very low temperatures.

Any kind of polymorphic transition will result in a sudden change in the specific heat because of either latent heat changes (first-order transitions) or the more gradual changes in first-derivative properties (second-order transitions). Figure 10.2 illustrates specific-heat changes during an electronic transition in nickel and during an order-disorder transition in β-brass. Figure 9.5 shows the change during a second-order transition.

Table 10.2

Characteristic temperatures of some crystalline solids

Solid	Θ_D, °K	Solid	Θ_D, °K
Aluminum	418	Lead	94.5
Cadmium	300	Nickel	456
Carbon (diamond)	2000	Platinum	229
Chromium	402	Silicon	658
Copper	339	Silver	225
Iron	467	Zinc	308

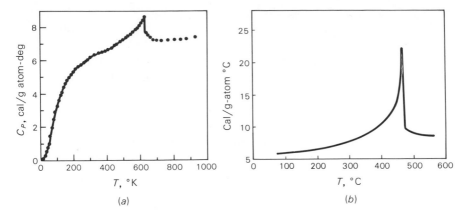

Fig. 10.2 Polymorphic transitions in crystals are accompanied by sharp changes in specific-heat capacity. (a) The atomic heat of nickel; (b) observed specific heat of β-brass (CuZn). (Data from Ref. 5, pp. 665, 685.)

10.4
Equations of state

An "equation of state" is a relationship that connects pressure, volume, and temperature. It is directly related to the Helmholtz free energy and the partition function by

$$p = -\left(\frac{\partial A}{\partial V}\right)_T = -kT\left(\frac{\partial \ln Z}{\partial V}\right)_T \qquad (10.33)$$

The usual representation is to write the product, pV/RT, as a function of either pressure, volume, or temperature. Experimental data are often reported in terms of the *volumetric thermal-expansion coefficient*, $\alpha_v = (1/V)(\partial V/\partial T)_p$, and the *isothermal compressibility*, $\kappa_T = -(1/V)(\partial V/\partial p)_T$, since these are often constant over wide ranges of variables for most solids.

Equation (10.22) may be used to obtain the Helmholtz free energy of a perfect crystal with $3N$ modes of vibration, *relative to the rest state of the crystal lattice*. In order to get the energy relative to N separated atoms, one must add the total binding energy of the lattice:

$$A = \psi_T + A(\nu)$$
$$= \psi_T + \sum_{i=1}^{3N} \frac{h\nu_i}{2} + kT \sum_{i=1}^{3N} \ln\left[1 - \exp\left(-\frac{h\nu_i}{kT}\right)\right] \qquad (10.34)$$

The pressure p is then

$$p = -\left(\frac{\partial \psi_T}{\partial V}\right)_T + \frac{1}{V}\sum_{i=1}^{3N}\left[\frac{h\nu_i}{2} + \frac{h\nu_i}{\exp(h\nu_i/kT) - 1}\right]\left(-\frac{d \ln \nu_i}{d \ln V}\right)_T \qquad (10.35)$$

If we then use the Grüneisen assumption [3] that $(d \ln \nu_i/d \ln V)_T$ is the same for all vibration frequencies, Eq. (10.35) reduces to

$$\frac{pV}{RT} = -\frac{V}{RT}\left(\frac{\partial \psi_T}{\partial V}\right)_T - \frac{U(\nu)}{RT}\frac{d\ln \nu}{d\ln V} \tag{10.36}$$

where $U(\nu)$ is the total internal (vibrational) energy of the solid. Thus we have the equation of state in terms of the intermolecular forces in the crystal. The potential energy of interaction [Eq. (10.1)] and a characteristic vibration frequency [Eq. (10.7)] are functions of the distance between nearest neighbors, r, which is in turn a function of volume. For a body-centered-cubic crystal, for example, $V = 4Nr^3/3^{3/2}$, and for a face-centered-cubic structure $V = Nr^3/2^{1/2}$.

Relatively simple relationships may be developed between thermodynamic and molecular properties by expanding the first derivative of the intermolecular potential in a Taylor series about the minimum at r_0:

$$\frac{d\psi}{dV} = \left(\frac{d\psi}{dV}\right)_{\substack{r=r_0 \\ V=V_0}} + (V - V_0)\left(\frac{d^2\psi}{dV^2}\right)_{V=V_0} + \cdots \tag{10.37}$$

Since the first derivative at the minimum is zero and since V is always very nearly equal to V_0,

$$\frac{d\psi}{dV} \doteq (V - V_0)\frac{d^2\psi}{dV^2} \doteq (V - V_0)\left(\frac{d^2\psi}{dV^2}\right)_{V=V_0} \tag{10.38}$$

From Eq. (10.36), the isothermal compressibility, at temperature T, is

$$\left(\frac{1}{\kappa}\right)_T = V\left(\frac{\partial^2\psi_T}{\partial V^2}\right)_T + V\frac{\partial}{\partial V}\left[\frac{U(\nu)}{V}\frac{d\ln \nu}{d\ln V}\right]_T \tag{10.39}$$

or at very low temperatures

$$\left(\frac{1}{\kappa}\right)_{T=0} \doteq V_0\left(\frac{\partial^2\psi_T}{\partial V^2}\right)_{V=V_0} = -\frac{Nmn(\psi_{aT})_{r=r_0}}{18V_0} \tag{10.40}$$

The volumetric thermal-expansion coefficient at low pressure (less than a few atmospheres usually) is obtained by setting the left side of Eq. (10.36) equal to zero. Then, using (10.38) and (10.40),

$$V\left(\frac{\partial\psi_T}{\partial V}\right)_T \doteq \frac{V - V_0}{(\kappa)_{T=0}} \doteq -U\frac{d\ln \nu}{d\ln V} \tag{10.41}$$

Differentiating Eq. (10.41) with respect to temperature gives

$$\alpha_v \doteq \frac{1}{V_0}\left(\frac{\partial V}{\partial T}\right)_p = -\frac{(\kappa)_{T=0}}{V_0}\frac{d\ln \nu}{d\ln V}\left(\frac{\partial U}{\partial T}\right)_p$$

$$\doteq \frac{(\kappa)_{T=0}c_p}{V_0}\left(-\frac{d\ln \nu}{d\ln V}\right) \doteq \frac{(\kappa)_{T=0}c_v}{V_0}\left(-\frac{d\ln \nu}{d\ln V}\right) \tag{10.42}$$

To a very good approximation the derivative $\left(-\dfrac{d\ln \nu}{d\ln V}\right)$ is a constant, called the

Grüneisen constant γ, so that,

$$\frac{\alpha_v V_0}{(\kappa)_{T=0} c_v} \doteq \gamma \qquad (10.43)$$

Some experimental values of γ, calculated from Eq. (10.43), are given in Table 10.3 for a number of simple crystals.

Table 10.3

Values of the Grüneisen constant *

Substance	γ	Substance	γ
Na	1.25	Ag	2.40
K	1.34	Pt	2.54
Al	2.17	NaCl	1.63
Mn	2.42	KF	1.45
Fe	1.6	KCl	1.60
Co	1.87	KBr	1.68
Ni	1.88	KI	1.63
Cu	1.96		

* Data from Ref. 3, p. 155.

The volume coefficent of thermal expansion is approximately proportional to the specific heat and is reasonably constant at high temperatures (at least over moderate temperature ranges). A tabulation of volumetric-expansion coefficients at room temperature is given in Table 10.4. A *linear*-expansion coefficient may be defined as $(1/L)(\partial L/\partial T)_p$ and, for isotropic solids, is approximately one-third of the volumetric coefficient. Linear coefficients are more frequently measured in the laboratory. It should be remembered that all single crystals are really *anisotropic* and therefore have different properties in different directions. A single zinc crystal, for example, has a linear coefficient of $0.634 \times 10^{-4} °\text{K}^{-1}$ normal to the close-packed (001) planes, while parallel to the close-packed planes it is $0.125 \times 10^{-4} °\text{K}^{-1}$. This compares to an average value of $0.358 \times 10^{-4} °\text{K}^{-1}$ for a polycrystalline sample.

Average values of isothermal compressibility are also listed in Table 10.4. The reciprocal of the compressibility, $1/\kappa_T$, called the "bulk modulus" K is a measure of the resistance of the solid to a volume change caused by external pressure. In the next chapter, we shall relate the bulk modulus to a number of mechanical (i.e., elastic) properties of the solid.

Table 10.4

Equation of state data for crystalline solids *

Solid	Density M_w/V_0, g/cm³ at 20°C	Average cubical exp. coeff. $\alpha_v \times 10^4$ °K⁻¹ at 20°C	Average compress. $\kappa_T \times 10^{12}$, cm²/dyne	$\kappa_T \times 10^{10}$ m²/kg_w at 20°C	Cohesive energy, kcal/mole
Aluminum	2.7	0.672 †	1.36	1.33	74.4
Cadmium	8.65	–	2.32	2.27	27
Carbon (diamond)	3.51	0.0354	0.163	0.160	252
Chromium	7.1	0.204 †	0.618	0.605	80
Copper	8.92	0.4998	0.72	0.705	81
α-Iron	7.86	0.355	0.618	0.605	97
Lead	11.337	0.8399	0.243	0.238	46
Manganese	7.2	0.699 †	0.806	0.790	68
Manganese oxide	5.18				
α-Nickel	8.90	0.378	0.582	0.542	101
Nickel oxide	7.45				
Platinum	21.45	0.265	0.379	0.371	122
Silicon	2.40	0.2289	0.331	0.324	
Silicon carbide	3.17				
Silver	10.5	0.5831	1.04	1.02	69
Sodium	0.97	2.13	15.9	15.6	26
Tin: cubic	5.750	0.6889	2.06	2.01	72
Tungsten	19.3	0.1332 †	0.31	0.303	201
Zinc	7.14	0.8928	1.79	1.75	31

* From a variety of literature sources.

† Three times the linear expansion coefficient.

10.5
Thermodynamic properties of polymeric materials

A theoretical analysis of thermodynamic properties of polymers has not been developed to any great extent because of the difficulty in describing the degrees of freedom of the molecule. Consider the simplest case of a linear hydrocarbon, $CH_3(-CH_2)_{x-2}-CH_3$, containing x tetrahedral carbon atoms joined axially by high-energy valence bonds. Imagine that we were able to take one such molecule and place it randomly into a polymeric mass. The first carbon on the chain may be placed anywhere in the mass and thus has three translational degrees of freedom. Once the position of the first is fixed, the second atom, with two translational degrees of freedom, is limited to the surface of a sphere whose radius is equal to the carbon-carbon bond length. Since the primary valence bonds have fixed lengths and angles, the third carbon atom is limited to one rotational degree of freedom on the circumference of a circle whose radius is fixed by the geometry of the bond. The positioning of all subsequent carbon atoms is further limited as a result of a preference for specific isomeric conformations. If there were no hindrance to rotation, each subsequent carbon unit would have one rotational degree of freedom. In reality, steric hindrance limits it to some fraction of this, $3C_m$. The total number of degrees of freedom of this type is then $3C = 6 + (x-3)(3C_m)$. The linear hydrocarbon molecule contains x carbon atoms and $2x + 2$ hydrogen atoms, which result in a total of $3x + 2$ degrees of freedom. The difference, $3x + 2 - 3C$, must be the number of degrees of freedom associated with the internal vibration, stretching, bending, and twisting of the primary bonds. The former degrees of freedom, called *external degrees,* are dependent on the temperature and volume of the material (i.e., they depend on the nature of the intermolecular forces), while the latter degrees, called *internal degrees,* are dependent on the temperature only (i.e., they depend on the nature of the primary bonding). The partition function for the material may usually be written as the product of an internal and an external function:

$$Z = Z_{int}(T)Z_{ext}(T,V) \tag{10.44}$$

Properties such as internal energy and specific heat can be predicted only from a detailed knowledge of distribution frequencies of both internal and external degrees of freedom. Since the internal motions depend on the primary bonding and the external motions depend on Van der Waals (intermolecular) bonding, the characteristic frequencies are of different orders of magnitude. Recalling the discussion in Chap. 4 (specifically Figs. 4.18 and 4.19), one can appreciate the difficuly of estimating the partition functions analogous to those in Sec. 10.2. A serious complication is that the intermolecular potentials cannot be spherically symmetric because of the directional nature of the linear chain and, therefore, the averaging processes developed in earlier sections are not completely valid.

The most important difficulties in predicting thermodynamic properties beyond the range of actual experimental data arise from the fact that a number of different structural changes are bound to occur. The two most common transitions are the glass transition and crystallization, and any one polymer may have a number of different transitions associated with different degrees of freedom in the chain. Further complications arise in the glassy state because of the extremely low mobility of the polymer chains. Very often, cooling a polymer below its glass-transition temperature freezes it in a nonequilibrium (or metastable) state. The "thermodynamic" behavior on subsequent reheating will then be a function of the past history of the material.

All of this leads us to the conclusion that it is very difficult to state generalizations about the behavior of organic solids and, further, each material must be considered separately in the light of information concerning its past history. Figure 10.3 shows a relatively simple specific heat curve for Marlex 50 polyethylene (79 percent crystallinity). At temperatures below 25°K, the data can be curve-fitted to the Debye equation, $c_v = Af(\Theta_D/T)$, with $\Theta_D = 136°K$. This is to be expected, since in this temperature range the atomic groups would tend to vibrate in much the same way as in simpler crystals. As the temperature increases, the specific heat continues to increase, and above 200°K, the curve has a sharp increase in slope. This might be interpreted as a continuous devitrification of the solid above about 200°K. Thus one would expect a glassy, brittle solid below 200°K and a softer, more rubbery solid above 200°K. As the melting point is approached, the crystallites absorb energy, accounting for a sharp rise in specific heat; and then, above 410°K, the molten polymer has an approximately constant specific heat of 2.1 to 2.5 joules/°K-g. The curve shown in Fig. 10.3 is good *only* for that particular material, and the actual behavior of other polyethylenes will be determined by percent crystallinity, degree of branching, and other structural characteristics. Figure 10.4 shows the observed specific heat for a *cis*-1,4-polybutadiene. The material was rapidly quenched from room temperature to 20°K, and the specific heat was then determined on reheating. Below 50°K the curve fits the Debye equation with $\Theta_D = 112$. The specific heat increases linearly and then increases very sharply at the glass-transition temperature of 165°K. The curve then takes a sharp drop in the vicinity of 170 to 200°K, followed by another sharp rise. The interpretation is that the polybutadiene is in an unstable amorphous state. Above the glass-transition temperature, the crystallization rate is fast enough to cause

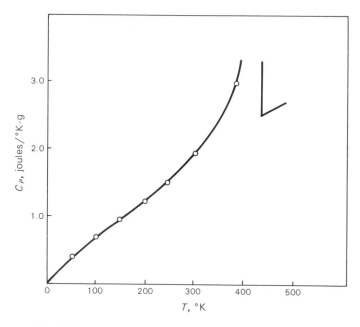

Fig. 10.3 The specific-heat capacity of Marlex 50 polyethylene increases sharply and then decreases equally as fast in the vicinity of the melting point. [Data from F. S. Dainton et al., *Polymer*, **3:** 277 (1962) and B. Wunderlich and M. Dole, *J. Polymer Sci.*, **24:** 201 (1957).]

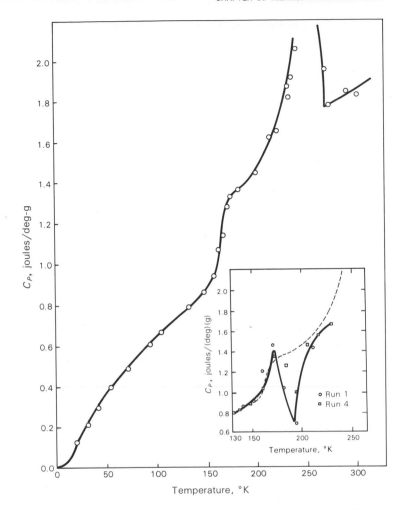

Fig. 10.4 The nature of the specific-heat-capacity curve for *cis*-1,4-polybutadiene is influenced by transition temperatures and the state of the structure. [By permission from F. S. Dainton, D. M. Evans, F. E. Hoare, and T. P. Melia, *Polymer,* **3**(3): 297–309 (1962).]

a noticeable amount of crystallite to form. This results in an evolution of heat and an apparently low specific heat in this region. As the melting point of 262°K is approached, the specific heat again increases very rapidly, as expected.

It should be clear from these two illustrations that generalizations that have a high degree of reliability cannot be developed. One useful rule of thumb, however, for obtaining an approximate value of specific heat near room temperature is *Kopp's rule.* It may be stated that the specific heat of a substance is estimated by adding contributions from each of the atoms in the structure. At ordinary temperatures, the following values, in kilocalories per kilogram atom, may be used: carbon, 1.8; hydrogen, 2.3; silicon, 3.8; oxygen, 4.0; fluorine, 5.0; phosphorus, 5.4; sulfur, 5.4; all other elements 6.2.

Thus, polyethylene ($-CH_2-$)$_x$, has a specific heat of $(1.8 + 4.6)/14 = 0.46$ kcal/°K-kg, which is, in fact, close to the experimental values near room temperature. A number of other values are given in Table 10.5 and are seen to compare favorably with experimental data.

Table 10.5

Specific heats of some polymeric substances at ordinary temperatures

Material	c_v/M, kcal/°K-kg	
	Kopp's rule	Experimental
SiC	0.14	0.17
Asbestos ($-Ca_2Mg_5Si_8O_{24}H_2-$)$_x$	0.21	0.20
Clay ($-Al_2(OH)_4Si_2O_5-$)$_x$	0.24	0.20
Polyvinylchloride ($-CH_2-CHCl-$)	0.27	0.20-0.28
Polyethylene ($-CH_2-$)$_x$	0.46	0.4-0.6
Polystyrene ($-CH_2-CHC_6H_5-$)$_x$	0.32	0.3-0.4
Teflon ($-C_2F_4-$)$_x$	0.25	0.28
Phenolics ($-C_9H_9O-$)	0.31	0.3-0.4
Epoxies	0.32	0.25

10.6
Equations of state for polymeric materials

There are presently no general equations of state that can be used to curve-fit experimental data through the first- and second-order transition temperatures. Generally, one must consider the perfect crystal, the amorphous polymer, and the glassy state separately and measure thermal-expansion coefficients and compressibilities for each state.

The prediction of an equation of state depends on being able to evaluate the configurational partition function for the molecule [Eq. (2.31)]. The first step is to assume that the internal and external degrees of freedom are separable, as shown in Eq. (10.44). If the total potential energy is the sum of pair potentials and if the pair potential is a function of two molecular parameters, such as

$$\psi_{ij} = \epsilon^* f\left(\frac{r^*}{r}\right) \tag{10.45}$$

(the Lennard-Jones 12-6 potential is an example), then the configurational partition function can be shown to be a function of only two reduced variables:

$$\mathcal{Q} = r^{*3N} f\left(\frac{kT}{\epsilon^*}, \frac{v}{r^{*3}}\right) = r^{*3N} f(T_R, V_R) \tag{10.46}$$

or in terms of pressure

$$p_R = \frac{pr^{*3}}{\sqrt{2}\epsilon^*} = p(T_R, V_R) \qquad (10.47)$$

Any materials that can be described by the same type of intermolecular potential-energy function [Eq. (10.45)] will then conform to the same reduced equation of state. This is known as the *theorem of corresponding states* and is widely used to describe the behavior of simple gases and liquids. One would expect all similar-type polymers to also conform to a corresponding-states theorem; but the difficulty arises in determining the proper reduced variables, since the "correct" intermolecular potential-energy function has to be a very complex function. The few published efforts in this area [7] are beyond the scope of this text, but they will probably become important when the molecular theory of liquids is improved.

A typical volume-temperature curve for a polymeric material is shown in Fig. 10.5. Thermoplastic, crystalline materials are usually molten in the temperature range 150 to 300°C. Upon cooling, the volume of the material decreases because of a decrease in the amplitude of thermal vibration. Since the volume change produces a slight increase in the cohesive energy of the solid, the thermal-expansion coefficient tends to decrease slightly with decreasing temperature. At the crystallization temperature, an abrupt decrease in volume is associated with the formation of a regular, ordered structure. (The details of the crystallization process were discussed in Chap. 9.) When the crystallization is complete, the material continues to shrink at a somewhat lower

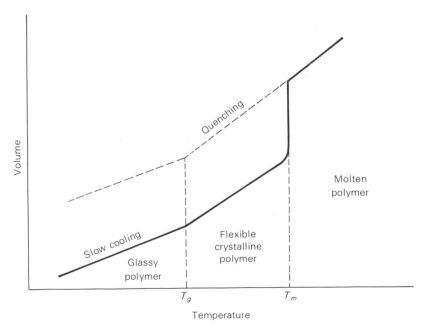

Fig. 10.5 The volume-temperature curve for a crystalline polymer.

rate than that above T_m. Although the thermal-expansion coefficient continues to decrease slightly, the quantity $(\partial V/\partial T)_p$ is usually constant over restricted temperature ranges. On cooling below T_g, an abrupt change in the thermal expansion coefficient occurs. Generally, α_v may be decreased by as much as one-half the original value. This "second-order" transition is usually associated with the loss of external degrees of freedom for the polymer chain. If, for example, a vinyl polymer, CH_2—CHX, has a side chain capable of rotation, the glass transition might be associated with the change of this rotational degree to a vibrational rocking degree of freedom. When these organic molecules are complex, as in polyvinylacetate or polymethylmethacrylate, there might be more than one second-order transition. These would also show up as rapid changes in the thermal-expansion coefficient.

If a molten polymer is quenched, the crystallization can be suppressed, forming an amorphous, isotropic solid below T_m. In the temperature range between T_g and T_m, this amorphous phase is not stable and crystallites will form. Below T_g the molecular mobility is so restricted that the amorphous phase can stay unchanged for long periods of time. This is identical with a rapidly cooled silica glass; although quartz is more stable, the vitreous product remains the same for long periods of time at low temperature. Heating into the annealing range, however, can promote devitrification of the glass.

Table 10.6 lists thermal-expansion coefficients, highest glass-transition temperatures, and crystallization temperatures for a variety of commercially important polymers. These values should be considered only as averages for the wide variety of products each name represents. It should be noted that, in general, the expansion coefficients are an order of magnitude larger than those of the metals. This is to be expected, since the intermolecular forces in polymers are of the Van der Waals type, which are an order of magnitude weaker than the metallic bonds. Also notice that the highest crystalline melting point is 600°K for tetrafluoroethylene and that most of the others are in the range of 400 to 500°K. This marks the upper temperature limit of these materials as useful solids and illustrates one of the prime weaknesses of organic solids: their thermal instability.

In regions where there are no phase transitions (induced by either temperature or pressure), the pVT behavior of a polymer can often be represented empirically by a modified form of the Van der Waals equation of state [8]:

$$(V - b)(p + \pi) = \frac{RT}{M} \tag{10.48}$$

The quantities b, π, and M are experimentally determined constants. The net volume, $V - b$, may be interpreted as the free volume of a polymer unit in the solid, and the quantity π is equivalent to the internal pressure of the solid. Thermodynamically, the internal pressure p_i is

$$p_i = T \left(\frac{\partial p}{\partial T}\right)_v = \frac{\alpha_v T}{\kappa_T} \doteq \pi \tag{10.49}$$

where α_v is the volume coefficient of thermal expansion and κ_T is the isothermal

Table 10.6

Thermal properties of various thermoplastic polymers

Material	Glass-transition temp T_g, °K	Crystalline melting point T_m, °K	Volumetric thermal-expansion coeff. at 25°C $\alpha_v \times 10^4$, °K^{-1}
Polyamide 6-6	350	498	3.0
Polybutadiene	160–180	260–320	6.7
Polychloroprene	235	353	5.2
Polyethylene	205	390–410	3.5–5.5
Polyisobutylene	203		5.8
Polymethylmethacrylate	378		2.0
Natural rubber	203	301	5.7
Polypropylene	255	449	3.0
Silicone rubber	150	215	8.0–10.0
Polystyrene	373	503 (isotactic)	2.5
Polytetrafluoroethylene		600	1.7
Polyvinylidene fluoride	234	483	3.6
Polyvinylacetate	302		2.5
Polyvinylchloride	355	453	3.0

compressibility. The internal pressure π is always much larger than a few atmospheres, so that the external pressure p can generally be neglected. Differentiating Eq. (10.48) with respect to temperature then gives the expansion coefficient as

$$\frac{1}{V}\left(\frac{dV}{dT}\right)_p = \alpha_v \doteq \frac{R}{M\pi V} \tag{10.50}$$

which shows that the expansion coefficient is inversely proportional to internal pressure. Table 10.7 shows some experimental values for the constants of (10.48).

Another interesting relationship based on experimental data is that the internal pressure is directly proportional to the cohesive energy density, as defined by Eq. (8.16). For most polymers:

$$\pi \doteq 1.1 - 1.6 \times E_{CD} \tag{10.51}$$

This means that one may use the group-contribution techniques of Small to estimate the compressibility, using Eq. (10.49) (see Chap. 8).

The purpose of this chapter has been to relate the measurable thermodynamic properties of a material to the nature of the intermolecular forces between atoms. In the next two chapters, we shall consider the relationships between mechanical properties, structure, and these same forces.

Table 10.7

Constants for the Van der Waals equation of state [8]

Material	M	π atm	$10^{-7}\ kg_w/m^2$	$b,\ cm^3/g\ (or\ 10^3\ m^3/kg)$
Polystyrene	104	1,840	1.90	0.822
Polymethylmethacrylate	100	2,100	2.20	0.734
Ethylcellulose	60.5	2,370	2.45	0.720
Cellulose acetate butyrate	54.4	2,810	2.90	0.688
Polyethylene	28.1	3,240	3.35	0.875

References

1   Debye, P.: *Ann. Physik,* **39,** 789 (1912).

2   Einstein, A.: *Ann. Physik,* **22,** 180 (1907).

3   Kittel, C.: "Introduction to Solid State Physics," 2d ed., John Wiley & Sons, Inc., New York, 1956. *Chapter 6 is a readable but detailed discussion of the thermal properties of crystals.*

4   Moelwyn-Hughes, E. A.: "States of Matter," John Wiley & Sons, Inc., New York, 1961. *Chapter III is a summary of the ideas used in studying crystalline solids.*

5   Moelwyn-Hughes, E. A.: "Physical Chemistry," 2d ed., The Macmillan Company, New York, 1961. *Chapters VII, VIII, and XIII thoroughly discuss the principles of this chapter.*

6   Mott, N. F., and H. Jones: "The Theory of the Properties of Metals and Alloys," Dover Publications, Inc., New York, 1958. *Chapter I considers the thermal properties of crystals, with specific reference to metals, in a clear, concise manner.*

7   Prigogene, I.: "The Molecular Theory of Solutions," Interscience Publishers, Inc., New York, 1957. *Chapter VII discusses simple lattice theories for condensed states. This chapter considers the details of using angle-averaged spherically symmetric potentials for describing thermodynamic properties. Essential reading for those who want a deeper understanding of the principles presented in this chapter.*

8   Spencer, R. S., and G. D. Gilmore: *J. Appl. Phys.,* **21,** 523 (1950).

Questions

10.1   Show that the maximum vibration frequency for an atom in a monoatomic crystal is $\nu_0 = (1/\pi r_0)\ \sqrt{6\epsilon/m_R}$ if the pair potential can be approximated by the Lennard-Jones 12-6 potential. Calculate the vibration frequencies in the inert-gas crystals using the data of Table 2.1.

10.2   Calculate the ground-state vibrational energies of the above crystals and compare them with the maximum potential energy.

10.3 Show that at high temperatures $U = 3RT$. Discuss the limitations of the law of Dulong and Petit.

10.4 The volumetric thermal-expansion coefficient of copper is 5×10^{-5} °K^{-1}, and its isothermal compressibility is 0.705×10^{-10} m^2/kg$_w$. Calculate the percent difference between C_p and C_v at 800°K.

10.5 Show that the atomic specific heat for a Debye solid is

$$c_v = 9R \left(\frac{T}{\Theta_D}\right)^3 \int_0^{\Theta_D/T} \frac{x^4 \exp x}{[(\exp x) - 1]^2} \, dx$$

10.6 The Debye temperature Θ_D is 94.5°K for lead and 2000°K for diamond. Plot the specific heat of these materials as a function of temperature between 0 and 500°K.

10.7 Use the data in Table 10.4 to calculate the Grüneisen constants for aluminum, copper, and nickel.

10.8 Draw an isotherm (p versus V at 20°C) for a monoatomic crystal. Assume that the intermolecular forces follow a 12-6 dependence. Use reduced variables in your plot.

10.9 Values for the specific heat of atactic and isotactic polypropylene are given in Table 10.8. Evaluate the entropy, $S_T - S_0$, and the enthalpy, $H_T - H_0$, at 310°K from the specific-heat data. (The subscript 0 refers to absolute zero.) Explain the difference in entropy and enthalpy of the isotactic and atactic polymers on the basis of molecular configuration. Specific heat below 25°K curve fits to the Debye equation in the form $C = Af(\Theta_D/T)$

Isotactic $\Theta_D = 113$ $A = 0.327$ Atactic $\Theta_D = 100$ $A = 0.320$

Table 10.8

T,°K	c_p isotactic, joules/°K-g	c_p atactic, joules/°K-g	T,°K	c_p isotactic, joules/°K-g	c_p atactic, joules/°K-g
0	0.000	0.000	160	0.9507	0.9965
10	0.0175	0.0243	170	0.9993	1.044
20	0.0975	0.1180	180	1.046	1.091
30	0.1813	0.2003	190	1.093	1.137
40	0.2568	0.2798	200	1.140	1.184
50	0.3275	0.3564	210	1.188	1.231
60	0.3935	0.4267	220	1.237	1.279
70	0.4565	0.4929	230	1.287	1.327
80	0.5190	0.5566	240	1.338	1.385
90	0.5797	0.6182	250	1.392	1.708
100	0.6397	0.6778	260	1.452	1.901
110	0.6972	0.7349	270	1.535	1.952
120	0.7520	0.7909	280	1.646	2.004
130	0.8044	0.8451	290	1.752	2.068
140	0.8541	0.8974	300	1.851	2.145
150	0.9029	0.9477	310	1.931	2.229

Data from F. S. Dainton, D. M. Evans, F. E. Hoare, and T. P. Melia, *Polymer*, **3:** 286–296, September, 1962.

10.10 Use Kopp's rule to estimate the specific heat of polyamide 6-6, polychloroprene, natural rubber, polymethylmethacrylate, and polyvinylacetate. Use the Modern Plastics Encyclopedia Charts or any other source of data to compare your predictions with experiment.

10.11 A rod of polystyrene is extruded from the molten state into a water bath at 300°K. Its density immediately after quenching is 1.020 g/cm³, and after 72 hr at 300°K it is 1.042 g/cm³. After one week at 300°K it apparently remains constant at 1.045 g/cm³. Discuss the changes in molecular structure that occur after quenching.

10.12 Use Small's group-contribution technique and data given in this chapter to estimate the compressibility at 25°C of polybutadiene, polychloroprene, polyethylene, polymethylmethacrylate, silicon rubber, and polystyrene. How accurate do you feel your estimates are? Why?

11
Mechanical properties of inorganic materials

11.1
Introduction

The usefulness of materials of construction depends to a large extent on the mechanical properties of the substances in the environment in which they are being used. Well-standardized mechanical tests give numerical values for tensile strength, elastic modulus, toughness, impact strength, etc. (see ASTM Standards), but very often they do not indicate the effects of environment on actual performance.

The emphasis in this chapter is placed on understanding the relationship between the structure of materials and their response to an external stress. The response is always a deformation which will be classified as either recoverable (elastic) or nonrecoverable (plastic or viscous). All structural materials show both types of deformation with, perhaps, one or the other predominating under a specific set of conditions. Metals, for example, exhibit elastic and plastic deformation at room temperature, while steady flow (creep) becomes especially important at elevated temperatures. Amorphous materials are usually *viscoelastic* in that viscous flow and elasticity are equally important in certain temperature ranges. Window glass, for example, exhibits both elasticity and viscous flow at 500 to 600°C, while at room temperature it is a brittle, low-deforming solid.

In addition to temperature, the rate of loading of a material is important. A material like asphalt at 20°C, for example, will flow under a steadily applied load, but will exhibit brittle fracture under sudden impact.

This chapter will discuss the various molecular and microstructural factors that control the mechanical properties of inorganic solids (primarily metals).

11.2
Elasticity

An ideal elastic deformation is one that takes place instantaneously upon application of a load and disappears completely and instantaneously upon release of the load. All materials will exhibit some elastic behavior. The elastic strain of simple metallic, ionic, and covalent crystals is usually directly proportional to the applied stress, and the maximum amount that can occur is normally no more than 0.10 to 1.0 percent of the original length of the material. The elastic strain in many complex linear polymers is frequently not proportional to stress and may involve as high as several hundred percent elongation (as is the case with elastomers).

In order to develop some insight into the relationship between stress (i.e., an externally applied force) and strain (i.e., the resulting deformation), let us consider the separation of two planes in a crystal. The potential energy of interaction between a single particle in plane A and a single particle in plane B is

$$\psi_{1i} = \frac{(\psi)_{r=r_0}}{m-n} \left[m \left(\frac{r_0}{r_{1i}}\right)^n - n \left(\frac{r_0}{r_{1i}}\right)^m \right] \tag{11.1}$$

where $(\psi)_{r=r_0} = b/r_0^m - c/r_0^n$ and r_{1i} is the distance between point 1 and point i (Fig. 11.1). The total potential energy of interaction between point 1 and all the nearest neighbors to 1 in plane B is then

$$\psi_{1B} \doteq \frac{\langle\psi\rangle_{r=r_0}\mathfrak{z}_p}{m-n} \left[m \left(\frac{r_0}{a}\right)^n - n \left(\frac{r_0}{a}\right)^m \right] \tag{11.2}$$

where $\mathfrak{z}_p$ is the number of nearest neighbors in the adjacent plane and a is the nearest-neighbor separation. [If the plane in question is the close-packed

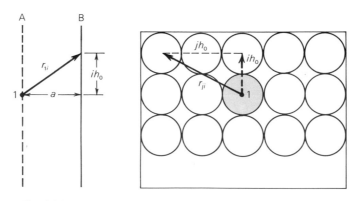

Fig. 11.1 The interaction between a particle and an adjacent plane is obtained by adding the interactions with each atom in the plane. This is expressed in terms of a set of r_{ij} vectors which are, in turn, geometrically related to the nearest-neighbor distance.

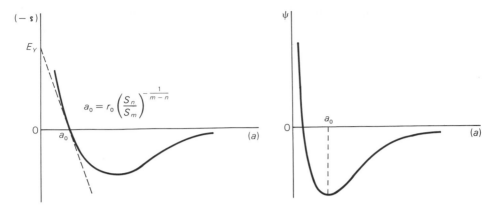

Fig. 11.2 The interaction potential between two planes in a simple crystal is qualitatively similar to the pair potentials discussed in Chap. 1.

plane (111) of a face-centered cubic structure, $\delta_p = 3$.] The potential energy of interaction between a square centimeter of plane A and all of plane B, neglecting non-nearest neighbors, is then $\psi_{1B} \times \rho_s$, where ρ_s is the number of atoms per unit area on plane A. The total attraction of the solid below plane A for the solid above plane B can then be obtained by including the interactions between the non-nearest neighbors in the remaining planes of the set. The total potential energy of interaction per unit area is then approximately

$$\psi_T \doteq \frac{(\psi)_{r=r_0}\rho_s\delta_p}{m-n}\left[mS_n\left(\frac{r_0}{a}\right)^n - nS_m\left(\frac{r_0}{a}\right)^m\right] \qquad (11.3)$$

where S_n and S_m are geometric factors. The force of attraction, in kilograms weight per square meter, $-s$, can then be obtained by differentiating Eq. (11.3).

$$-s = \frac{mn(\psi)_{r=r_0}\delta_p}{m-n}\frac{\rho_s}{a}\left[S_n\left(\frac{r_0}{a}\right)^n - S_m\left(\frac{r_0}{a}\right)^m\right] \qquad (11.4)$$

Equation (11.4) is plotted in Fig. 11.2 and shows that the equilibrium separation ($s = 0$) occurs at $a_0 = r_0\,(S_n/S_m)^{1/(n-m)}$. Suppose an external stress s that causes a displacement $a - a_0$ is applied. A relation between the *applied* stress and the displacement may be obtained by expanding Eq. (11.4) in a Taylor series of the displacement $a - a_0$:

$$s = \frac{mn(-\psi)_{r=r_0}\delta_p\rho_s}{a_0^2}\,S_n\left(\frac{r_0}{a_0}\right)^n\left[(a-a_0) - \frac{n+m-5}{2a_0}(a-a_0)^2 + \cdots\right] \qquad (11.5)$$

Thus, one sees that for small displacements, the total deformation $a - a_0$ is directly proportional to the applied stress s. If a straight line is drawn tangent to the stress curve at a_0, its intercept with the ordinate, E_Y, is given by the relation $E_Y = s/[(a - a_0)/a_0]$, which is the ratio of the applied stress to the strain. This property is a measure of the resistance to deformation normal to a set of parallel planes. In cubic crystals, this direction is the same as the Miller indices for the planes, so that the *elastic modulus* is symbolized by $E_{[hkl]}$. As long as the deformation is small, $E_{[hkl]}$ will remain constant and may be approximated, from Eq. (11.5), as

$$E_{[hkl]} \doteq \frac{mn\delta_p}{a_0} \rho_s S_n \left(\frac{r_0}{a_0}\right)^n (-\psi)_{r=r_0}$$

$$\doteq (30 - 300) \frac{(-\psi)_{r=r_0}}{a_0^3} \tag{11.6}$$

The range of the numerical constant is for reasonable values of n, m, S_n, and S_m and assuming $\rho_s \doteq 1/a_0^2$. The elastic modulus is seen to be proportional to the intensity of the intermolecular forces, $(-\psi)_{r=r_0}$, and will increase as the density of the packing increases (i.e., as $1/a_0$ increases). For simple molecular crystals, Van der Waals bond strengths are of the order of $\psi \doteq 0.1$ kcal/g mole and molecular separations are of the order of $a_0 \doteq 4$ Å, yielding $E_{[hkl]} \doteq 4 \times 10^8$ kg$_w$/m^2. For crystals with high-intensity primary bonds, $\psi \doteq 50$ kcal/g mole and molecular separations are of the order of 2 to 3 Å, yielding $E_{[hkl]} \doteq 2 \times 10^{11}$ kg$_w$/m^2. Thus Eq. (11.6) predicts that the elastic moduli of materials should lie in the range 10^8 to 10^{11} kg$_w$/m^2. Experimentally, most crystalline solids have moduli in this range.

In general, the magnitude of $E_{[hkl]}$ will depend on the shape of the potential-energy curve. Covalent and ionic solids, whose atoms are in very deep potential troughs, will have the highest elastic moduli; metallic solids, with fractional covalent bonding and shallower potential troughs, have lower elastic moduli; and molecular solids, which have only weak Van der Waals bonding, have the lowest values of the elastic moduli.

An exact relationship between the elastic moduli and the intermolecular forces in crystals is usually not attainable. All crystals are three-dimensional and anisotropic, and thus the true potential-energy functions are too complex to evaluate. A phenomenological description, however, can be given by a generalized form of Hooke's law. Consider a cubic volume subjected to an arbitrary stress. This stress may be resolved into nine components as is shown in Fig. 11.3. Three components are pure tension along each axis, while the other six are shearing stresses. Of the six shearing stresses, only three are independent, since $\tau_{ij} = \tau_{ji}$.

Hooke's law states that each component of the stress is directly proportional to the resulting strain. The generalized Hooke's law may then be written in terms of six independent stresses:

$$s_{xx} = E_{11}\epsilon_{xx} + E_{12}\epsilon_{yy} + E_{13}\epsilon_{zz} + E_{14}\epsilon_{xy} + E_{15}\epsilon_{xz} + E_{16}\epsilon_{yz}$$
$$s_{yy} = E_{21}\epsilon_{xx} + E_{22}\epsilon_{yy} + E_{23}\epsilon_{zz} + E_{24}\epsilon_{xy} + E_{25}\epsilon_{xz} + E_{26}\epsilon_{yz}$$
$$s_{zz} = E_{31}\epsilon_{xx} + E_{32}\epsilon_{yy} + E_{33}\epsilon_{zz} + E_{34}\epsilon_{xy} + E_{35}\epsilon_{xz} + E_{36}\epsilon_{yz}$$
$$\tau_{xy} = E_{41}\epsilon_{xx} + E_{42}\epsilon_{yy} + E_{43}\epsilon_{zz} + E_{44}\epsilon_{xy} + E_{45}\epsilon_{xz} + E_{46}\epsilon_{yz}$$
$$\tau_{xz} = E_{51}\epsilon_{xx} + E_{52}\epsilon_{yy} + E_{53}\epsilon_{zz} + E_{54}\epsilon_{xy} + E_{55}\epsilon_{xz} + E_{56}\epsilon_{yz}$$
$$\tau_{yz} = E_{61}\epsilon_{xx} + E_{62}\epsilon_{yy} + E_{63}\epsilon_{zz} + E_{64}\epsilon_{xy} + E_{65}\epsilon_{xz} + E_{66}\epsilon_{yz} \tag{11.7}$$

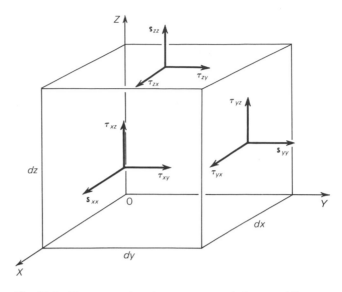

Fig. 11.3 There are nine stress components for an arbitrary stress on a body.

The quantities E_{ij} are the elastic moduli and are constants if the solid is "Hookeian." An important property of these equations is that $E_{ij} = E_{ji}$. Thus, an arbitrary elastic solid can have a maximum of 21 independent elastic moduli. Fortunately, the symmetry properties of real crystals reduce the number of *independent* constants. In cubic crystals, for example, only E_{11}, E_{12}, and E_{44} have to be specified, since all other moduli are either zero or related to these. If a material is isotropic, only *two independent moduli* must be specified. *Many simple, polycrystalline materials of construction can be well characterized with two or three moduli.* Highly anisotropic materials, such as the orthorhombic structures of cellulosic materials, have only 9 independent moduli, many fewer than the maximum of 21.

Because of the relative ease of measurement, four elastic constants are commonly used. *Young's modulus* is the ratio of a uniaxial stress to the strain in the same direction (Fig. 11.4*a*). In general, it is the slope of the elastic portion of a tensile stress-strain curve.

$$E_Y = \frac{s}{\epsilon} \qquad (11.8)$$

A Young's modulus in a single cubic crystal will vary with direction, so the Miller index of direction $[hkl]$ should be specified.

$$E_{Y[hkl]} = \frac{s[hkl]}{\epsilon[hkl]} \qquad (11.9)$$

The *shear modulus* is the ratio of a shearing stress to the shear strain in the same plane (Fig. 11.4*b*):

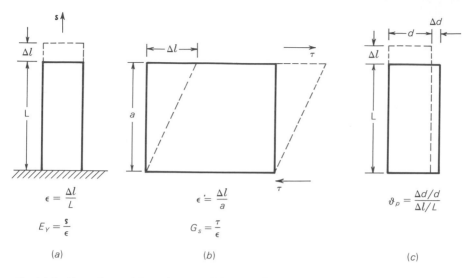

Fig. 11.4 Young's modulus, shear modulus, and Poisson's ratio are elastic moduli defined for ease of measurement. (a) Young's modulus; (b) shear modulus; (c) Poisson's ratio.

$$G_s = \frac{\tau}{\epsilon} \qquad\qquad (11.10)$$

The *Poisson ratio* is the ratio of the lateral contracting strain to the elongation strain in the direction of a uniaxial load (Fig. 11.4c):

$$\vartheta_p = -\frac{\epsilon \ \text{lateral}}{\epsilon \ \text{longitudinal}} \qquad\qquad (11.11)$$

The *bulk modulus* is the ratio of the hydrostatic pressure on a solid to the relative change in its volume because of the applied pressure:

$$K = -\frac{s}{\Delta V/V} \qquad\qquad (11.12)$$

Since the isothermal compressibility of a solid, $\kappa_T = -(1/V) \ \partial V/\partial p$, is approximately constant over a wide range of pressure, it is about equal to the reciprocal of the bulk modulus.

In truly isotropic solids and in unoriented polycrystalline solids, there are only two independent moduli of elasticity. It is thus clear that there must be relationships between the various moduli. If, for example, a unit cube of isotropic solid is stretched by a uniaxial tensile stress s, it will elongate by an amount $\epsilon_s = s/E_Y$ in the direction of loading and contract $-\vartheta_p \epsilon_s$ in each of the lateral directions. The volume after loading is thus $(1 + \epsilon_s)(1 - \vartheta_p \epsilon_s)(1 - \vartheta_p \epsilon_s)$, which is approximately $1 + (1 - 2\vartheta_p)\epsilon_s$ for small strains. The change in volume is thus $\Delta V \doteq (1 - 2\vartheta_p)\epsilon_s$. If equal uniaxial stresses are simultaneously applied along the other two axes, the total volume change is merely three times larger: $\Delta V \doteq 3(1 - 2\vartheta_p)\epsilon_s$. Equal uniaxial stresses on each of the cube faces is equivalent to a hydrostatic pressure $-s$; so the bulk modulus is

$$K \doteq \frac{s}{3(1 - 2\vartheta_p)\epsilon_s} = \frac{E_Y}{3(1 - 2\vartheta_p)} \tag{11.13}$$

Thus we have derived a simple relationship between three of the moduli for an isotropic solid. A similar relationship for the shear modulus is

$$G_s \doteq \frac{E_Y}{2(1 + \vartheta_p)} \tag{11.14}$$

When an isotropic solid is incompressible, $K = \infty$ and ϑ_p reaches its maximum value of 0.5. Most solids are slightly compressible, with ϑ_p being in the range of 0.3 to 0.4. From Eq. (11.13) the product of Young's modulus and the isothermal compressibility is thus on the order of $E_Y \kappa_T = 0.6 - 1.2$ and also, from (11.14), the ratio of Young's modulus to the shear modulus is on the order of $E_Y/G_s \approx 2.4 - 2.8$. By combining Eqs. (11.13) and (11.14), one may eliminate the Poisson ratio to give

$$\frac{E_Y}{G} = \frac{9}{3 + (G/K)} \tag{11.15}$$

In a soft, incompressible material, putty, for example, $G/K \doteq 0$, so that $E_Y = 3G$, or Young's modulus is 3 times the shear modulus.

It has been found [5] that a large number of polycrystalline and amorphous materials follow the relation

$$E_Y \alpha_v^2 \doteq 13.8 \text{ kg}_w/\text{m}^2\text{-}^\circ\text{K}^2 \tag{11.16}$$

at normal temperatures. Barker [5] showed that this relation held, with a maximum variation of from about 7 to 25 $\text{kg}_w/\text{m}^2\text{-}^\circ\text{K}^2$, for 79 different materials including metals, alloys, polymers, copolymers, and glasses. Notable exceptions were wood, granular materials, rubbery materials, certain alloys, and some inorganic glasses. Equation (11.16) is useful for estimating the properties of materials, and its simplicity bears out the interrelations between mechanical, thermodynamic, and molecular properties.

Table 11.1 gives the elastic moduli for a number of inorganic materials with different cohesive energies. In general, the moduli decrease as the cohesive energy decreases. Maximum and minimum values of the moduli for a given material are sometimes considerably different, and the average values for isotropic, polycrystalline materials are always between these values.

Since elastic moduli depend on the intensity of molecular cohesion, one would expect them to vary with temperature. Materials usually expand with increasing temperature, which causes the elastic moduli to decrease. Figure

Table 11.1

Elastic properties of some inorganic materials

| Material | Young's modulus 10^9 kg$_w$/m^2 * | | | Shear modulus 10^9 kg$_w$/m^2 * | | | Poisson's ratio | $\dfrac{E_Y}{2(1+\vartheta_P)}$ |
	Max	Min	Polycrystalline average	Max	Min	Polycrystalline average		
Tungsten carbide			63 (90)				0.23	2.9 (4.07)
Soda glass			7 (10)			2.5 (3.5)		
Tungsten	49.7 (56.5)	49.7 (56.5)	49.7 (56.5)	15.5 (22.0)	15.5 (22.0)	15.5 (22.0)	0.27	15.6 (22.20)
Nickel	29.0 (41.2)	13.5 (19.2)	21.8 (31.0)	11.9 (16.9)	6.1 (8.7)	8.1 (11.5)	0.30	8.4 (11.9)
α-Iron	19.6 (27.9)	6.8 (9.7)	21.1 (30.0)	9.8 (13.9)	3.2 (4.5)	8.4 (12.0)	0.26	8.4 (11.9)
Copper	12.7 (18.0)	3.5 (5.0)	11.3 (16.1)	5.0 (7.1)	2.8 (4.0)	4.6 (6.6)	0.36	4.2 (5.9)
Zinc			10.2 (14.5)			3.9 (5.6)	0.35	3.8 (5.37)
Aluminum	7.7 (11.0)	6.4 (9.1)	7.0 (10.0)	2.9 (4.1)	2.5 (3.5)	2.7 (3.9)	0.33	2.6 (3.76)
Cadmium	8.3 (11.8)	2.9 (4.1)	5.1 (7.2)	2.5 (3.6)	1.8 (2.6)	2.0 (2.8)	0.29	2.8 (2.79)
Lead	3.9 (5.6)	1.1 (1.6)	1.6 (2.3)	1.5 (2.1)	0.5 (0.7)	0.6 (0.9)	0.4	0.6 (0.82)
Concrete			1.4–3.5 (2.0–5.0)				0.1–0.2	
Steel (mild)			21 (30)			8.3 (11.8)	0.26	8.4 (11.9)
Brass 70–30			10.2 (14.5)			3.7 (5.3)		

* Numbers in parentheses are in units of 10^6 psi.

11.5 shows the temperature dependence of the Young's modulus of several pure materials. The decrease in Young's modulus is fairly linear over wide ranges of temperature but tends to decrease sharply as the melting point is approached. The sharp increase in E_Y for iron at 1670°F occurs at the polymorphic transformation of ferrite to austenite. The transformation of a body-centered cubic structure to a face-centered cubic structure (on heating) is also accompanied by an increase in density.

Alloying often has a relatively small effect on the absolute value of Young's modulus. A tabulation of over one hundred ferrous alloys [from "Chemical Engineer's Handbook," by J. Perry (ed.)], including plain carbon steels, stainless steels, manganese steels, vanadium steels, and many other types, shows a variation in Young's modulus of from 17 to 23×10^9 kg_w/m^2 (25 to 33×10^6 psi), almost without exception. This compares with 21×10^9 kg_w/m^2 (30×10^6 psi) for pure, annealed iron. Larger variations occur when there is a drastic change in the relative amounts of different phases in multiphase alloys. Figure 11.6 shows the variation of Young's moduli at room temperature across the binary phase diagrams for Mo-W, Pb-Sn, and Mg-Sn alloys. The changes are approximately linear with respect to the amount of a given phase (if eutectic solids are considered as separate phases).

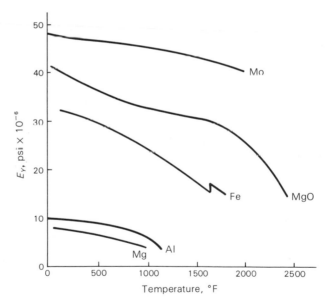

Fig. 11.5 The elastic moduli of simple metals and metal oxides generally decrease with temperature; discontinuities may occur at polymorphic transition temperatures.

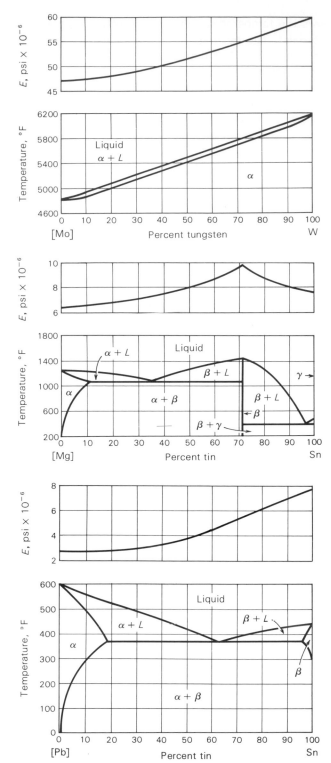

Fig. 11.6 Examples of the variation of Young's modulus across binary phase diagrams. (By permission from A. G. Guy, "Elements of Physical Metallurgy," 2d ed., p. 297, Addison-Wesley Publishing Company, Inc., Reading, Mass., 1959.)

11.3
Plastic deformation

Consider the tensile stress-strain curve for a mild steel, shown in Fig. 11.7. Up to point P on the diagram the stress is directly proportional to a completely reversible strain. This is called the *proportional limit* of the material. Beyond this point the slope of the stress-strain curve decreases. Beyond point E, the *elastic limit* of the material, the deformation is nonrecoverable. (Very often the proportional limit and the elastic limit are so close together that they are indistinguishable.) Upon removal of a uniaxial tension, s_1, for example, a test sample will be permanently stretched by an amount $\epsilon_1 - \epsilon_E$. This nonrecoverable deformation is the result of an internal flow of material. If the material is *ductile*, a yield point Y will be reached beyond which the solid will begin to flow without a further increase in stress. In polycrystalline solids this ductile

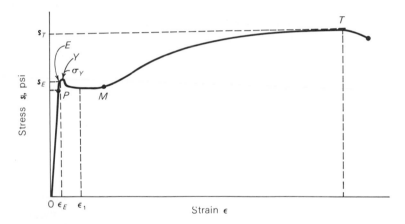

Fig. 11.7   The tensile stress-strain curve for a mild steel exhibits both an elastic and a plastic region.

Region $O \rightarrow P$ Elastic Hookeian solid: $s = E_Y \epsilon$
                                   E_Y = Young's modulus
Region $P \rightarrow E$ Elastic non-Hookeian solid: $E_Y = E_Y(s)$
Beyond E Plastic solid
Region $Y \rightarrow M$ Region of high ductility
Region $M \rightarrow T$ Strain hardening occurs
Point P *Proportional limit.* (Maximum point of linear relation-ship between s and ϵ)
Point E *Elastic limit.* The point beyond which deformation is no longer elastic. (Sometimes indistinguishable from point P).
Point Y *Yield point.* The point beyond which deformation continues without an increase in load.
Point T *Ultimate tensile strength.*
Modulus of resiliency   Area under the curve to the elastic limit.
Modulus of toughness   Total area under the stress-strain curve.

region is then followed by a region of *strain hardening,* in which it becomes increasingly difficult to further deform the material. Continued deformation will ultimately lead to a fracture. The maximum stress before fracture, s_T, is called the *ultimate tensile strength* of the material. When the ordinate of a stress-strain curve is based on the *original dimensions* of the sample, the stress is called the *engineering stress.* When the ordinate is based on the true dimensions of the minimum cross section of the deformed sample, the stress is called the *true stress.* Both definitions are widely used.

In this text, we shall use the term *plastic flow* to mean the nearly time-independent, nonrecoverable deformation that occurs very rapidly on loading and then stops, thus producing an apparently constant deformation. The terms *viscous flow* and *creep* will refer to the steady, continual deformation of a solid under stress. In other words, the total viscous deformation of a material is dependent on the length of time that the load is applied. Although convenient, this is a somewhat arbitrary classification, since both may be occurring by similar mechanisms.

Plastic deformation in crystals is the result of relative motion along specific crystallographic planes and is caused by a shearing stress parallel to the planes. The pure stretching or compressing of atomic bonds can only result in elastic deformation or brittle fracture, but a shearing stress can cause one layer of atoms to be permanently displaced relative to another layer. Crystals have families of "close-packed" crystallographic planes in which the atomic density is highest. Since the density is highest, the separation of parallel planes, in the same set, must be the greatest. Likewise, within a plane there are certain directions in which the number of atoms per unit length of vector is highest (i.e., the close-packed directions). The separation between lines of atoms pointing in the close-packed directions must therefore be the greatest. If an arbitrary stress is placed on a material, it is very probable that the shear components will cause *slip* parallel to the close-packed planes and in the close-packed directions, since there will be the least resistance to motion in these directions (because of intermolecular forces). This does not imply that slip is impossible in other directions, but only that it is less probable. Referring back to the crystal structures described in Chap. 5, we can find the number of potential *slip systems* for the three common crystal structures. The (111) planes are the close-packed planes, and the [110] directions are the close-packed directions in face-centered cubic structures. There are four nonparallel planes and three independent directions for a total of twelve independent slip systems. The close-packed planes and directions in hexagonal close-packed structures are the (001) and the [100], respectively. There is one base plane and there are three independent directions for a total of three independent slip systems. The close-packed planes and directions in body-centered structures are the (110) and [111], respectively. There are six nonparallel planes and two independent directions for a total of twelve slip systems. Since the atomic density in the close-packed planes of body-centered cubic structures is not very much more than in some of the others, slip frequently occurs in the (211) and (321) planes.

The *ductility* of metals is closely associated with the number of probable slip systems in the structure. Thus, copper, aluminum, lead, gold, silver, and γ-iron are all relatively ductile materials because they are face-centered cubic, while cadmium, magnesium, and zinc are relatively brittle because they are hexagonal close-packed. Body-centered cubic structures such as α-iron, tungsten, and molybdenum are closer in ductility to the face-centered cubic structures. This is a somewhat oversimplified picture of potential slip systems, but the general conclusions are accurate.

The plastic deformation of a crystal is also accompanied by the appearance of *slip bands* in the microstructure. Figure 11.8 is a photomicrograph of slip bands in brass. Electron microscope studies have shown that *each single line* in the slip band consists of a series of parallel steps, as is shown schematically in Fig. 11.9. Each step represents a slippage of about 1,000 to 2,000 atomic units on a specific plane. Slipped planes are separated by about 100 to 200 planes. At relatively low stresses (10^5 to 10^6 kg_w/m^2 or 150 to 1,500 psi), slip bands first begin to appear as thin, parallel lines. As the deformation proceeds, the number of bands increases and the existing ones broaden. The material also *strain hardens* by becoming progressively more difficult to deform. Any theory describing the mechanism of the plastic flow must explain all of these features.

Fig. 11.8 When brass (70-30 Cu-Zn) is stressed beyond the elastic limit, slip bands will appear in the microstructure.

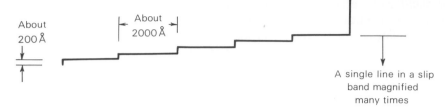

About
200 Å

About
2000 Å

A single line in a slip
band magnified
many times

Fig. 11.9 The schematic drawing of a single slip band shows that it consists of a series of discrete, parallel steps.

First, let us suppose that the deformation occurs through the en masse movement of one crystallographic plane over another. The theoretical yield stress may be approximated by assuming a sinusoidal relationship between the stress and the resulting strain (Fig. 11.10). This is reasonable, since the net shear stress at equilibrium positions 0 and d must be zero and the stress must also be zero when atom 1 is directly over atom 2 (i.e., at $d/2$). The shear stress is approximately

$$\tau = \tau_m \sin \frac{2\pi x}{d} \tag{11.17}$$

For a Hookeian solid and a unidirectional shear stress,

$$\tau = G_s \frac{x}{a} \tag{11.18}$$

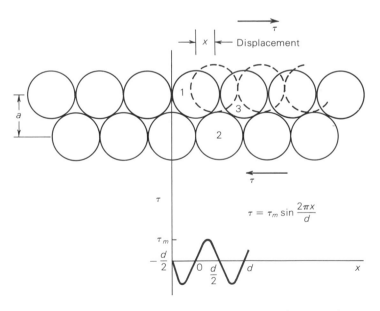

Fig. 11.10 The theoretical yield stress of a perfect crystal may be estimated by assuming that the stress varies sinusoidally when one plane moves en masse over another.

Combining Eqs. (11.17) and (11.18) and considering small deformation, one obtains an expression for the *yield stress* τ_m:

$$\frac{G_s x}{a} = \tau_m \sin \frac{2\pi x}{d} \approx \frac{2\pi x}{d} \tau_m \qquad (11.19)$$

$$\tau_m \approx \frac{G_s d}{2\pi a} \qquad (11.20)$$

For typical crystals, $d/a \approx 1$, $G_s \approx 10^9$ to 10^{10} kg$_w$/m^2 (10^6 to 10^7 psi), and thus $\tau_m \approx 10^8$ to 10^9 kg$_w$/m^2 (10^5 to 10^6 psi). Experimental values of τ_m are of the order of 10^5 to 10^7 kg$_w$/m^2 (10^2 to 10^4 psi), or low by two or three orders of magnitude. The calculations are very rough but should not be that poor. The only conclusion that can be drawn is that the deformation is *not* an en masse movement of one crystallographic plane over another.

The presence of dislocations in a crystal plane can serve as the nucleus for relative motion within the plane. Suppose a shear stress is applied perpendicular to an edge dislocation (Fig. 11.11). A considerable amount of elastic strain is generated in the region around the dislocation. A good deal of this strain may be relieved if the atoms in line AB move to positions defined by line AC. This is equivalent to moving the edge dislocation *from* position C *to* position B. If this stepwise movement continued from one end of the crystal to the other, it would result in a permanent deformation of one Burger's vector length (Fig. 11.11c).

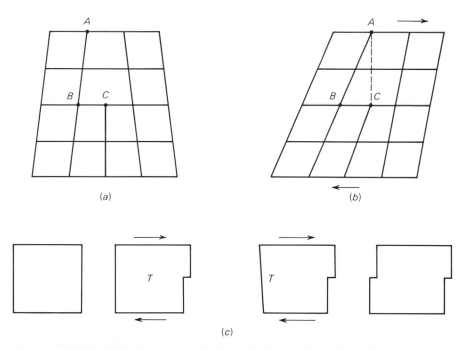

Fig. 11.11 Dislocations can move in a stepwise manner through a crystal plane. (a) Unstressed; (b) stressed; (c) movement of an edge dislocation.

Figure 11.12 shows that the edge dislocation will move in the direction of the shearing force, while a screw dislocation moves perpendicularly to the direction of the shearing force. In any case, the dislocation loop on a crystallographic plane (cf. Chap. 6) is the boundary line between the part of the plane that has moved and the part that has not. This is shown in Fig. 11.13. The displacement within the dislocation loop is a constant Burger's length **b**, so that the geometry is perfect within the loop as well as outside the loop. The displacement drops to zero right at the dislocation line. As the deformation proceeds, the dislocation loop expands and spreads over the whole plane.

The important thing is that the motion is described as a series of discrete steps in which only a few atoms are moving at any one time. This is bound to take considerably less force than the en masse motion of a whole plane of atoms. It has been shown [19], for example, that the shear stress required to move an edge dislocation that is parallel to a row of close-packed atoms is

$$\tau_m = \frac{2G_s}{1 - \vartheta_p} \exp\left[-\frac{2\pi a}{\mathbf{b}(1 - \vartheta_p)}\right] \tag{11.21}$$

For typical crystals, $a/\mathbf{b} \approx 1$, $G_s \approx 10^9$ to 10^{10} kg$_w$/m^2 (10^6 to 10^7 psi), $\vartheta_p \approx 0.3$, which leads to $\tau_m \approx 0.3 \times 10^6$ to 3.0×10^6 kg$_w$/m^2 (400 to 4,000 psi) in agreement with experimental values of the yield stress.

The number of dislocation lines piercing a square centimeter of an unstressed, annealed crystal is usually about 10^5 to 10^6 dislocations per square centimeter. If each of these dislocations moved out of the crystal causing only a single unit of deformation, there should be no noticeable change in dimensions. For example, a Burger's vector of 3 Å and a density of 10^6 dislocations in a 1-cm length of crystal would lead to a maximum of $3 \times 10^{-8} \times 10^6 = 0.03$ cm of deformation per centimeter. At the same time, the dislocation density would decrease toward zero. Actually, it is possible to plastically deform metals up

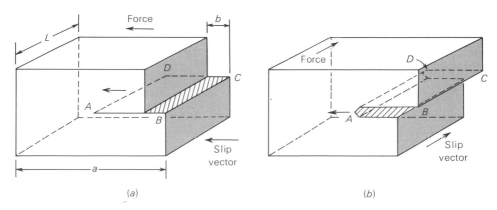

Fig. 11.12 A three-dimensional sketch showing that an edge dislocation moves in the direction of the shearing force while a screw dislocation moves perpendicularly to the direction of the shearing force. (a) Motion of edge dislocation *AD*; (b) motion of screw dislocation *AD*.

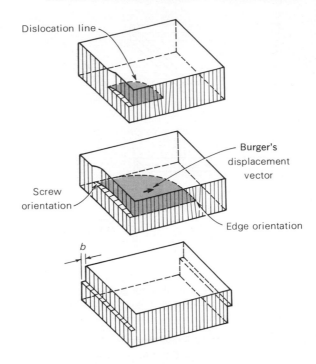

Dislocation line

Burger's displacement vector

Screw orientation

Edge orientation

Fig. 11.13 A total displacement of one Burger's vector is caused by the spread of a dislocation loop across its glide plane. (By permission from J. E. Dorn (ed.), "Mechanical Behavior of Materials at Elevated Temperatures," McGraw-Hill Book Company, New York, 1961.)

to several hundred percent elongation, and the dislocation density *increases* to as high as 10^{12} dislocations per square centimeter.

The Frank-Read mechanism for the motion of dislocations can be used to explain these observations. Consider the segment of an edge dislocation A-D shown in Fig. 11.12. If the line is free to move, a shearing stress τ can force the dislocation to the edge of the crystal plane. The total work done in moving a layer of crystal L units long through a displacement b is thus $(\tau La)b$. In order to get this deformation, the dislocation line must move through the slip plane a distance a. If the force on the dislocation line is F, the total work done on the line is Fa. Equating the two amounts of work, one can relate the total force on the dislocation line to the external stress:

$$F = \tau Lb \qquad (11.22)$$

Next consider the segment of an edge dislocation OP shown in Fig. 11.14. Suppose that the dislocation line is anchored at points O and P. The "anchors" may be intersections with other dislocations, impurities, second phases, or any other physical obstruction to the motion. If an external shear stress τ is applied, the dislocation line will experience a force τbL. Since points O and P are immobile, the line will have a tendency to bow out around these points and thus increase in length, which will require a certain amount of energy. If sufficient energy is supplied, the line will move; if not enough energy is supplied, the line OP will not move. The question is, when will the force τbL be large enough to cause a movement of the dislocation line? This can be estimated by

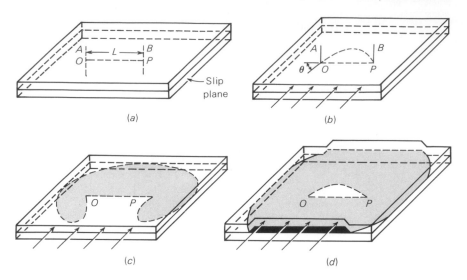

Fig. 11.14 The Frank-Read mechanism for generating dislocations explains how extensive deformation can be caused by a single dislocation.

calculating the strain energy associated with a dislocation. Consider a screw dislocation, since the strain field is easier to analyze than that around an edge dislocation. Figure 11.15 shows a thin cylinder of material of radius r and a unit length, whose axis is the screw-dislocation line. If this cylinder is distorted by an amount b, the total shear strain ϵ is $b/2\pi r$ and the total shear stress required is $G_s b/2\pi r$. The strain energy per unit volume is then

$$\gamma_s = \int \tau \, d\epsilon_s = \int G_s \epsilon_s \, d\epsilon_s = \frac{G_s \epsilon_s^2}{2}$$

$$= \frac{G_s}{2}\left(\frac{b}{2\pi r}\right)^2 \tag{11.23}$$

The total strain energy in a cylindrical shell with an inner radius r and an outer radius $r + dr$ is $d\Gamma_s = (G_s b^2/4\pi r) \, dr$, so that the total strain energy per unit length of the screw dislocation may then be obtained by integrating over all values of r:

$$\Gamma_s = \frac{G_s b^2}{4\pi} \ln \frac{R}{b} \tag{11.24}$$

The limits of integration are not easy to define in a real crystal. For a single dislocation at the center of a cylindrical crystal, the upper limit R would merely be the radius of the crystal. The other limit is usually taken to be approximately equal to the Burger's vector b. The stress field within this distance would have to be calculated from the intermolecular forces and is probably not more than 10 percent of the total strain energy. If G_s is about 10^9 kg$_w$/m^2, b is about 3×10^{-10} m, and $\ln (R/b)$ is about 8, the strain energy is about 10^{-19} joules per angstrom of dislocation. This is much higher than the thermal energy of an atom, which is of the order of $3kT \approx 10^{-20}$ joules per atom at 300°K. The strain energy for an edge dislocation is more difficult to calculate because of the nonsymmetrical stress patterns around the defect. The strain energy can be shown to be approximated by

$$\Gamma_s = \frac{1}{1-\vartheta_p} \frac{G_s b^2}{4\pi} \ln \frac{R}{b} \tag{11.25}$$

If all other structural factors are the same, the edge dislocation has a strain energy that is larger than the energy of a screw dislocation by a factor of about $1/(1-\vartheta_p) \doteq 1.5$.

For the purpose of calculation, let us assume that the strain energy for the dislocation line OP in Fig. 11.14 is about $G_s b^2$ joules/m. This is equivalent to a line tension of $G_s b^2$ newtons (analogous to surface energy and surface tension). When the segment is forced to bow out under the applied stress, there will be a restoring force of $2G_s b^2 \sin \theta$, where θ is related to the radius of curvature of the bowed dislocation line. The maximum restoring force occurs when θ is 90°, so that the minimum shearing stress required to keep the dislocation line moving is

$$\tau_m b L \doteq 2G_s b^2 \tag{11.26}$$

$$\tau_m \approx \frac{2G_s b}{L} \tag{11.27}$$

If this critical stress is exceeded, the dislocation line bows out to its maximum

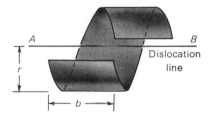

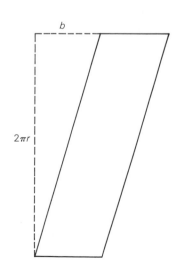

Fig. 11.15 Deformation of a thin cylinder whose axis is a unit length of a screw-dislocation line.

radius of curvature, $L/2$, then begins to spiral about fixed points O and P, coming back on itself to complete the loop. This results in a unit of permanent deformation and the generation of another dislocation line OP. The process may then be repeated any number of times, producing a large deformation from only a single dislocation. A similar analysis can be made on a complete dislocation loop in a crystal plane. The total energy of a circular loop of radius R is approximately

$$E = \left(\frac{G_s b^2}{4\pi} \ln \frac{R}{b}\right) 2\pi R - b(\pi R^2 \tau) \qquad (11.28)$$

where the first term is the strain energy of the line and the second term is the work done in causing a displacement b within the loop area πr^2. A loop will grow spontaneously if $dE/dR < 0$, so that the critical loop radius is

$$R_c = \frac{G_s b}{4\pi\tau} \left(\ln \frac{R}{b} + 1\right) \qquad (11.29)$$

In a typical crystal, $R/b \approx 10^3$, so that

$$R_c \doteq \frac{G_s b}{2\tau} \qquad (11.30)$$

Dislocation loops with a radius larger than R_c can then expand and cause plastic deformation.

If the dislocation loops reach a free surface, they will pass out of the crystal. If, on the other hand, they are prevented from leaving the crystal, they tend to pile up in the slip plane, as shown schematically in Fig. 11.16, and interfere with

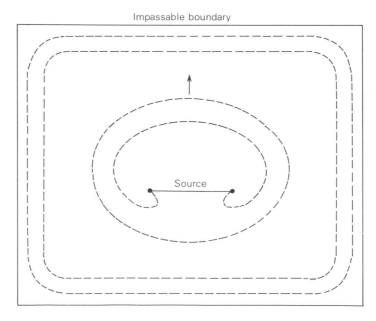

Impassable boundary

Source

Fig. 11.16 A pileup of dislocations at an impassable boundary will result in an overlapping of stress fields and an increasing resistance to the further propagation of other dislocations in that plane.

the motion of other lines. Thus, the Frank-Read mechanism is consistent with the facts that straining a material increases the dislocation density and causes further strain to become increasingly more difficult.

11.4
The hardening of polycrystalline materials

The maximum yield strength of a material is obtained when all dislocations are eliminated. Hairlike single crystals with radii on the order of 10^{-6} m, called whiskers, have been made, from iron, copper, graphite, aluminum oxide, and other substances, that are essentially dislocation-free. These materials do have strengths on the same order as the theoretical values predicted on the basis of en masse movement of planes. Commercial materials always contain dislocations, and the strengthening, or hardening of such materials involves inhibiting the motion of the dislocations that are either formed or are already present. The strengthening effects are caused by several sources in a relatively complex manner. Dislocation pileups, the crossing and tangling of moving dislocations, the clustering of impurities and alloying elements, and the presence of secondary phases are the most obvious sources for immobilizing dislocations. Quantitative descriptions of some of these effects are given by Cottrell [8], and a good deal of information is available in the current literature. In this section we shall qualitatively discuss some of these factors.

The dislocation density in an unstressed metal is normally of the order of 10^5 to 10^6 dislocation lines piercing a square centimeter of surface. The strain hardening becomes pronounced when the density increases beyond about 10^8 dislocation lines per square centimeter. The presence of a grain boundary enhances the rate of strain hardening of a material. If the grain boundary is to remain continuous, two adjacent crystals must deform similarly at their common boundary. This greatly complicates the slip process, since the preferred slip planes in adjacent crystals are not necessarily oriented in the same way. A complex motion of many slip systems is required, which leads to a higher yield stress. Since dislocations cannot easily pass through a grain boundary (except, perhaps, at high temperature), there is a tendency for them to pile up at grain boundaries, creating a large amount of internal stress and resistance to the motion of other dislocations. Grain size will thus have an effect on the strain-hardening characteristics of a material: the finer the grain size the greater the amount of strain hardening that is possible. Figure 11.17 illustrates this effect for the strain hardening of commercially pure copper.

Within a crystal, resistance to deformation can develop because of the interaction or intersection of dislocations moving in different directions. Since they can exert forces on one another, the motion of one dislocation through the field of another can create distortions of the dislocation lines. Figure 11.18 illustrates the formation of "jogs" in two intersecting edge dislocations. The jog increases the strain energy associated with the line defect and also lowers its mobility. Increasing the dislocation density increases the probability of interactions and, therefore, increases the resistance to further deformation. Fig-

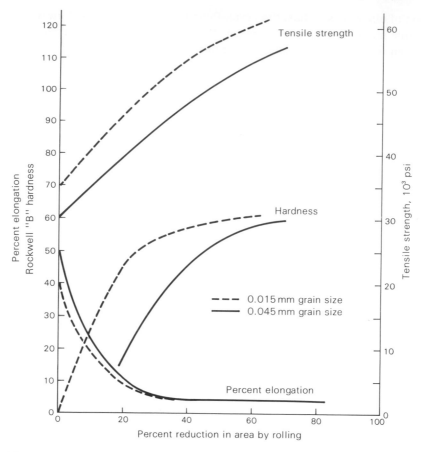

Fig. 11.17 Fine-grained, oxygen-free copper is more easily strain-hardened than coarser-grained material. (Data from Ref. 26.)

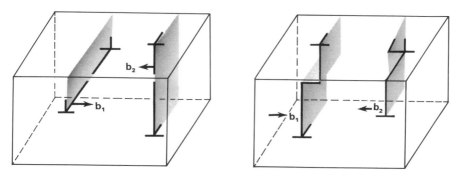

Fig. 11.18 Jog formation in two intersecting edge dislocations.

ure 11.19 illustrates the effects of *cold working* on commercially pure copper
and a copper alloy with 0.03 percent silver. The percent reduction in area by
rolling is proportional to the extent of the deformation. Generally, tensile
strength and hardness are increased, while ductility is decreased. The effects
of substitutional impurities are also illustrated by the 0.03-99.95% Ag-Cu alloy.
Generally, the presence of additional impurity makes a material more strain-
hardenable and also increases its yield stress. Very minute amounts can cause
considerable change in the properties. Approximately 10^{-4} percent of silver in
mercury crystals, for example, increases yield stress by 150 percent. The
mechanism for this effect has not been completely determined, but the formation of a Cottrell atmosphere [10] is probably an important factor. Figure
11.20*a* indicates that the region directly below an edge dislocation is in tension
and thus is a center for an excessive amount of strain energy. If large impurity
atoms are present in the system, some of this tension can be relieved if the impurities concentrate in the region below the edge of the extra half-plane (Fig.

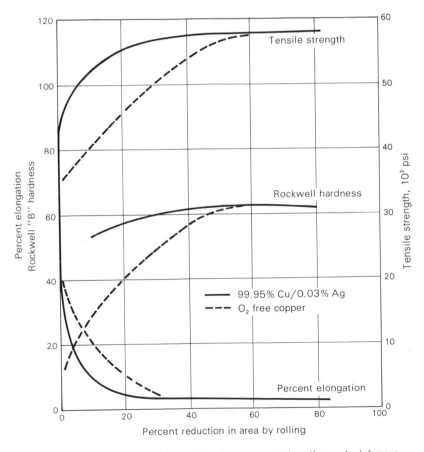

Fig. 11.19 The presence of impurities in copper makes the material more
easily strain-hardened. (Data from Ref. 26.)

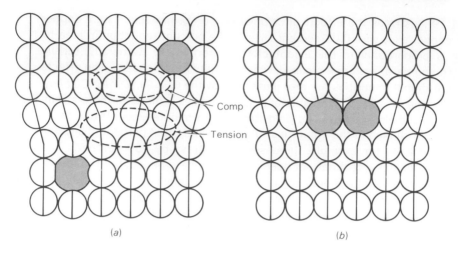

Comp

Tension

(a)

(b)

Fig. 11.20 The diffusion of foreign atoms into the region below an edge dislocation can relieve the strain energy in this region, thus making the dislocation more resistant to movement [10].

11.20b). This would then reduce the strain energy and create a more stable arrangement. An attempt to move the dislocation out of the "atmosphere" of the concentrated impurities would then require a larger force than before.

A similar effect is caused by a small amount of a second phase, finely dispersed in a matrix of the primary phase. Dislocations, not being able to move easily through the second-phase particles, tend to move around them (Fig. 11.21). Since there is a line tension associated with the dislocation, a certain critical stress $G_s b/d$, where d is the distance between the second-phase particles, is required to force the dislocation line through the obstacles. Dislocation loops are left behind after the dislocation has moved past the particles, which

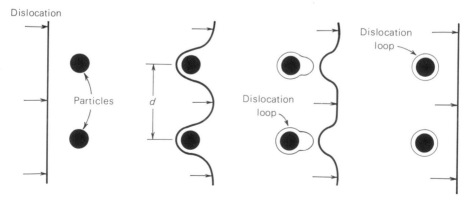

Dislocation

Dislocation
loop

Particles

d

Dislocation
loop

Fig. 11.21 When a dislocation is forced past second-phase particles lying in the slip plane, dislocation loops are generated around the particles.

decreases the effective distance between particles and thus increases the required yield stress.

This kind of behavior serves as the mechanism for the *age-hardening* of alloys. Figure 11.22 indicates the general type of phase diagram for age-hardenable alloys. In this case, alloys with less than B percent of the alloying element are hardenable. The usual procedure is to heat the alloy into the temperature region above the solubility line AB but below the eutectoid temperature. This is followed by a short annealing time, a rapid quenching, and a controlled precipitation at lower temperature. The heating dissolves all soluble precipitates; the annealing homogenizes the structure; the quenching develops an unstable, supersaturated solution; and the controlled precipitation (i.e., the age hardening) promotes a fine, uniformly dispersed second phase imbedded in the primary matrix. Figures 11.23 and 11.24 summarize the principal effects of age-hardening. They show that strength and hardness increase at the expense of ductility. The loss in ductility is not usually as great as it is in cold-working, however. The slowness of the process at low temperatures indicates insufficient atomic mobility for rapid precipitation. At a given temperature, an optimum strength is attained, after which "overaging" causes a resoftening of the material. The maximum strength develops when the number of particles and their size distribution combine to promote the smallest average interparticle separation.

Initially there is not enough precipitate to develop an effective resistance to the dislocation movement. After the optimum aging time is passed, the finely dispersed phase tends to agglomerate to a larger average particle size.

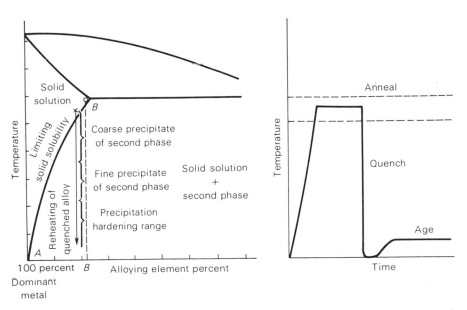

Fig. 11.22 General type of phase diagram and treating schedule for age-hardening.

Since the number of particles decreases, the average interparticle separation increases and the resistance to the movement of dislocations decreases.

There are several other types of plastic deformation that are observed in polycrystalline materials. Under rapid loading conditions and low temperature there is a tendency for the formation of mechanical twins. This occurs by a uniform shearing of successive planes of atoms, parallel to the twin boundary, sufficient to promote mirror images through the boundary (Fig. 6.24). This type of behavior is much different than normal slip in that it occurs homogeneously throughout the crystal, rather than on specific close-packed planes. Twinning is very common in most close-packed cubic crystals, but it usually accounts for only a very small fraction of the total deformation of a solid.

High temperatures and low rates of deformation encourage flow within the grain boundaries simultaneously with intergranular slip. Under certain conditions, the boundary flow may be a sizable fraction of the total deformation. It is difficult to separate the two processes, since they must interact to maintain a continuous structure between adjacent crystals. There has not been much evidence to affirm the nature of grain-boundary flow, but it is likely that it is a complex phenomenon involving both viscous flow and migration. It is not neces-

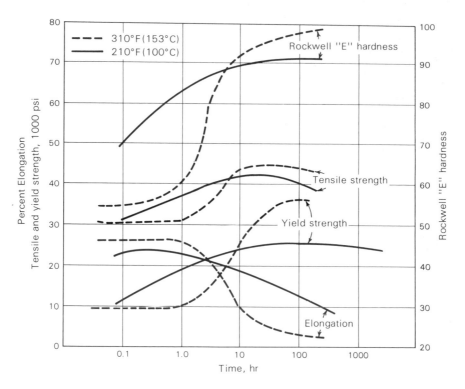

Fig. 11.23 Age-hardening a wrought aluminum alloy (4 percent Cu) after quenching from 16 hrs at 975°F increases the strength and hardness. After an optimum treating time, the properties start to degrade. [W. L. Fink and D. W. Smith, *Trans. AIME,* **128:** 223 (1938).]

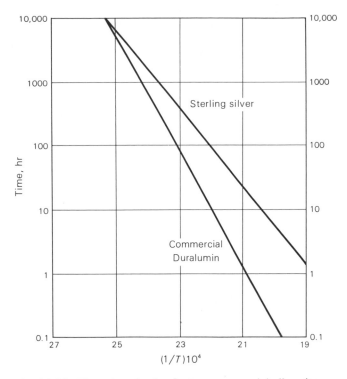

Fig. 11.24 The rates of aging for two commercial alloys (as time to reach maximum tensile strength) follow an Arrhenius-type equation. (Data from Ref. 24.)

sarily a continuous or steady process, and it may vary from one part of the grain boundary to another. The nature of the stress concentration on either side of the boundary must also influence the deformation.

11.5
Annealing, recovery, recrystallization

Cold-work is plastic deformation under conditions such that strain hardening persists for a long period of time. If a cold-worked material is annealed (i.e., kept at an elevated temperature), its properties and microstructure will be affected; the changes will depend on the degree of cold working, the *annealing* temperature, and the annealing time. Figure 11.25 shows the *recovery* of a typical metal as a function of time at a constant annealing temperature. The overall effect is that the properties are returned toward their pre-cold-worked levels. At a given temperature, the initial rate of recovery is rapid and decreases as the process proceeds. The higher the temperature and the greater the amount of cold-work, the greater is the recovery in a given period of time.

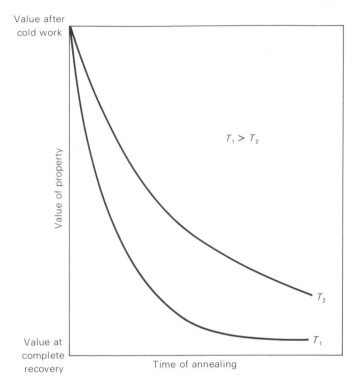

Fig. 11.25   The rate of recovery of a typical metal increases rapidly with temperature.

The final microstructure of the recovered material is about the same as that of the strain-hardened material.

The recovery process may be described in terms of dislocation movements. When a metal is cold-worked, distortional energy is stored by the multiplication and interaction of the dislocations. Since the metal is not in its minimum free-energy state, it is not thermodynamically stable. Annealing increases the self-diffusivity of the atoms, thereby providing a mechanism for the system to move to a more stable state. Immediately after cold working, there is a high dislocation density and the dislocations are concentrated in slip planes and are piled up near obstacles such as grain boundaries. The distortional energy is associated with the strain energy of the individual dislocations and also the energy of interaction between piled-up dislocations.

Initially, the dislocations may move out of their original positions by two types of motion. Screw dislocations are able to "cross-slip" into another slip plane by moving normal to the Burger's vector. Edge dislocations can "climb" into a new slip plane by having a row of vacancies replace the edge of the half-plane. When the defect moves out of its original slip plane, it bypasses obstacles, thus making it more mobile than it was previously. The initial change in properties is associated with the randomizing of the positions of the dislocations. This minimizes the interaction energy and reduces the internal stresses within the material. Since the dislocation density remains high, the hardness and the high strength are, for the most part, retained. This much of the heat treatment is known as a *light anneal*.

As annealing is continued, mobile dislocations can be attracted to one another and annihilated. Figure 11.26 shows three simple interactions that can lower the dislocation density. If two dislocations of opposite sign come together on the same plane, a perfect lattice will result; if they are on adjacent planes, either a row of vacancies or a row of interstitial atoms will result. As the number of dislocations decreases, the material softens, until it has returned to its "normal" annealed state.

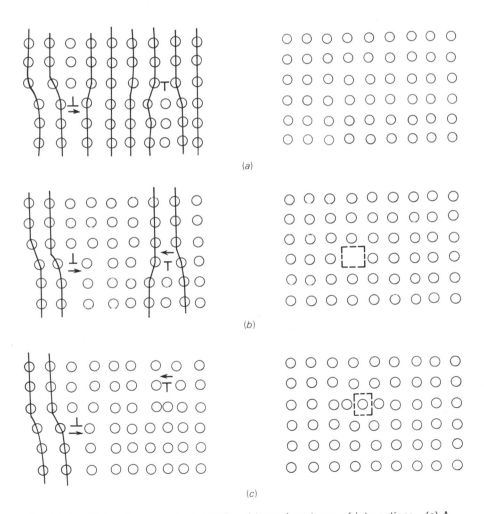

Fig. 11.26 Dislocations can be annihilated by various types of interactions. (a) A positive and negative dislocation cancel one another; (b) edge dislocations on adjacent planes form a row of vacancies; (c) edge dislocations on adjacent planes form a row of interstitial atoms.

At temperatures which are high enough to promote the rapid recovery of a strain-hardened material, *recrystallization* occurs simultaneously with the recovery process. Recrystallization is very much analogous to the freezing of a melt, but in this case the change is from a distorted, elongated grain structure to an undistorted, strain-free, equiaxed grain structure (Figs. 11.27, 11.28). The process takes place in stages, starting with the formation of nuclei in regions of high strain energy. Strain-free, equiaxed grains grow at almost a constant rate until adjacent grains begin to come together. The remaining strained material absorbs into the new grains to form new grain boundaries.

A recrystallization nucleus grows by absorbing dislocations into its boundary. In contrast with aggregates formed in liquids, subcritical nuclei cannot break up, because once the dislocations have been absorbed, they cannot be returned to their original positions. Thus, a nucleus will develop slowly, at first, until a critical size is reached, and then a continuous, more rapid growth rate will characterize the formation of equiaxed grains. Severely deformed copper has a distortional energy of about 800 joules/kg ($\Delta G_f \approx 800$ joules/kg) and a grain-boundary energy of about 0.300 joule/m^2. The critical radius r^* is therefore about 10^{-7}m, and ΔG^* is about 10^{-14} joules per nucleus. The overall rate of recrystallization of pure copper at various annealing temperatures is shown in Fig. 11.29. The similarity to the isothermal crystallization of polypropylene (Fig. 9.8) should be noticed.

The rate depends, of course, on temperature, degree of cold work, grain size, and impurity content. It is convenient to define a *recrystallization temper-*

Table 11.2

Approximate recrystallization temperatures of commercially pure metals and their alloys

	Recrystallization temp T_R, °K	Melting point T_m, °K	T_R/T_m
Lead	270	600	0.45
Tin	270	502	0.54
Magnesium	340	923	0.37
Magnesium alloys	500		
Aluminum	420	933	0.45
Aluminum alloys	600		
Copper	470	1356	0.35
Copper alloys	610		
Iron	700	1866	0.38
Low carbon steel	810		
Nickel	640	1728	0.37
Monel (30-70 Cu-Ni)	860		
Tungsten	1500	3683	0.41

Fig. 11.27 The microstructure of cold-drawn low-carbon steel wire, reduced from 0.223 to 0.053 in. in six draws, shows a highly elongated grain structure in the direction of drawing.

Fig. 11.28 The low-carbon steel wire of Fig. 11.27, reduced from 0.223 to 0.053 in., after annealing at 950°C and air cooling, shows a reestablishment of a fine-grained equiaxed structure.

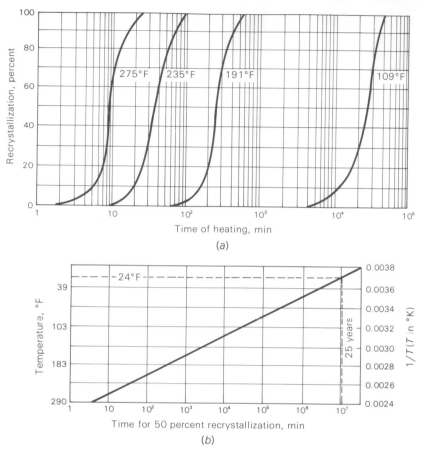

Fig. 11.29 The isothermal recrystallization of 99.999 percent pure copper (after Decker and Harker). (*a*) Isothermal recrystallization of pure copper cold-rolled 98 percent; (*b*) plot for extrapolation from the data given by the four curves of (*a*). (By permission from A. G. Guy "Elements of Physical Metallurgy," 2d ed., p. 430, Addison-Wesley Publishing Company, Reading, Mass., 1959.)

ature as the temperature at which an extensively cold-worked material will completely recrystallize in one hour. Table 11.2 lists the approximate recrystallization temperatures for several commercially pure metals and their alloys, along with the melting points of the pure metals. It is interesting that the recrystallization temperature is usually between one-third and one-half of the melting point.

When a material is deformed above the recrystallization temperature, the strain hardening is very rapidly removed by spontaneous recrystallization. This, in contrast to cold working, is called *hot working*. Materials such as lead and tin are hot-worked at room temperature (300°K), while tungsten, on the other hand, can be cold-worked at 1000°K.

11.6
Creep

Creep in crystalline materials is a complicated phenomenon which most likely involves a number of different flow mechanisms. Typical creep curves are shown in Fig. 11.30. Upon application of a load, an instantaneous elastic deformation occurs, followed by a plastic deformation and strain hardening. At low temperatures the rate of deformation continues to decrease until the strain hardening limits further deformation to very small amounts. At elevated temperatures, a sustained deformation at constant load is more apparent. Very often, the creep curve levels out to a constant rate of deformation, $d\epsilon_s/dt$, and this linear deformation continues for long periods of time. This stage of the process is called steady-state, or secondary, creep. In general, the slope increases with increasing temperature and increasing stress. As the material deforms, a slow decrease in cross section occurs, which results in a steadily increasing true stress (at constant external stress). If this is allowed to continue, the creep rate will accelerate and lead to fracture of the material. Fracture can occur, of course, even if a constant true stress is maintained. In some

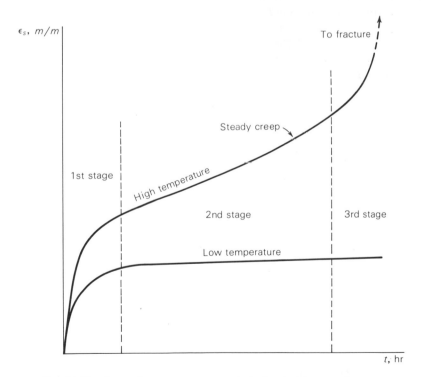

Fig. 11.30 Creep is more pronounced at elevated temperatures, sometimes leading to failure of the material.

situations, steady-state creep may never be attained and fracture may occur at any stage of the process. At low temperatures and stresses the primary zone may persist over long periods of time, while at high temperatures and stresses the third stage may occur rapidly and lead to the propagation of submicroscopic cracks and, therefore, early fracture.

A number of molecular processes undoubtedly occur during creep. The formation and gliding of dislocations during work-hardening, the gliding and climbing of dislocations during recovery, the diffusion of vacancies and impurities and the movement of atoms within grain boundaries, all must be considered. The relative importance of these mechanisms will depend on the temperature, stress, and type of structure involved.

It is experimental fact that regardless of the flow mechanism, creep is a thermally activated process that can be represented by the following equation (cf. Sec. 2.7):

$$\frac{d\epsilon}{dt} = A_f(T,\tau, \text{structure}) \exp\left[-\frac{\Delta E(T,\tau, \text{structure})}{RT}\right] \tag{11.31}$$

All thermally activated processes are characterized by a preexponential factor which may be interpreted as being a measure of the frequency at which the molecular phenomenon occurs. In creep, it would vary with temperature, stress, and the state of the structure. As long as the molecular process controlling the creep rate remained the same, one would not expect large changes in this quantity. If the mechanism changes, however, the frequency factor could be quite different. The rate of deformation also depends on the exponential factor, $\exp(-\Delta E/RT)$. The quantity ΔE is known as the *activation energy* for the process. Figure 11.31 indicates a physical interpretation of

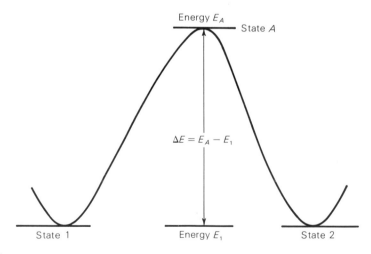

Fig. 11.31 The activated-state concept may be applied to creep by postulating that a dislocation may glide from one metastable state to another by absorbing an amount ΔE of activation energy.

this quantity. The system can exist in two stable states, 1 and 2. The process of going from state 1 to state 2 is the molecular-creep mechanism. For example, the process of a dislocation gliding from one stable position in the glide plane to another might represent the two stable states. In thermally activated processes this change is not spontaneous but rather requires an energy ΔE to first bring the system to the activated state A. The rate of going from state 1 to state 2 is then directly proportional to the fraction of systems that can attain energy level E_A, as was discussed in Sec. 2.7. The magnitude of the activation energy must also depend on temperature, state of the structure, and, indirectly, stress level.

Although a number of different mechanisms can contribute to the creep in a crystalline solid, the formation, movement, and annihilation of dislocations are the most important. At low temperatures, the gliding of dislocation lines in their slip planes is the rate-controlling mechanism, while at high temperatures it is the rate of annihilation of dislocations during recovery that is most important. A relatively simple analysis of these phenomena leads to equations relating the total deformation to the time of the applied stress.

At low temperatures, creep occurs predominantly by the movement of dislocation lines. As a dislocation line moves, it encounters obstacles to its motion. These obstacles might, among others, be the passage of a dislocation through the strain field of others, the passage by solute atoms, and the intersection with precipitated secondary phases. Some of these local obstacles can be overcome with the aid of thermal fluctuations. Assume that the overall creep rate $d\epsilon_s/dt$ at constant stress and temperature is proportional to the rate at which these obstacles can be overcome by a thermally activated mechanism:

$$\left(\frac{d\epsilon_s}{dt}\right)_{s,T} = A_f \exp\left(-\frac{\Delta E}{RT}\right) \tag{11.32}$$

where A_f is an approximately constant frequency factor and ΔE is the activation energy. As the deformation proceeds, more and more strain energy is concentrated in the solid and it becomes increasingly difficult to continue the deformation. In other words, the activation energy for overcoming obstacles increases with deformation. Let us assume that the activation energy increases linearly with deformation and decreases linearly with the level of stress:

$$\Delta E = \Delta E_0 - as + b\epsilon_s \tag{11.33}$$

where ΔE_0 is the activation energy at zero stress and strain. Substituting Eq. (11.33) into (11.32) and solving the resulting differential equation, one gets:

$$\epsilon_{s,T} = \frac{RT}{b} \ln\left\{1 + \left[\frac{Ab}{RT}\exp\left(-\frac{\Delta E_0}{RT}\right)\exp\frac{as}{RT}\right]t\right\} \tag{11.34}$$

This is known as the logarithmic time law of creep; it has been found to curve-fit a good deal of creep data at temperatures below about 0.3 to 0.5 of the melting point of the crystalline material. Comparing this with the recrystallization temperatures given in Table 11.2, one sees that the logarithmic time law is valid *below* the range of rapid recovery and recrystallization.

At higher temperatures, especially above 0.5 T_m, the creep rate is controlled by the rate of recovery of the material. Suppose a solid has been placed under stress and the dislocations have moved until they pile up at grain boundaries, precipitates, and other obstacles in the glide planes. When the internal back stress balances the applied stress, no further deformation will occur. At higher temperatures, vacancies can diffuse to the edge of a dislocation, causing the dislocation to "climb" from its glide plane. Also, dislocations can annihilate each other in recovery processes (Fig. 11.26). Thus, by random movement of dislocations, the internal back stresses at any point can be changed in a random manner. If the stress near a dislocation is decreased sufficiently, it is possible for more deformation to occur. The rate of creep at elevated temperature is thus controlled by a competition between recovery and work-hardening phenomena. Consider a point in the structure and suppose some event occurs which changes the stress at that point by an amount Δs_i. The change is completely random, so the stress may either increase or decrease. Now suppose n similar events occur one after the other so that the total change in stress, Δs, is large enough to release a dislocation for further glide. According to the laws of statistics (compare with random walk of a polymer chain, Chap. 8), $\Delta s = n^{1/2} \Delta s_i$, and thus the number of events required to cause the release of a dislocation is $n = (\Delta s/\Delta s_i)^2$. Let us again assume that the amount of stress required increases linearly with the total deformation, so that

$$\Delta s = b_w(\epsilon_s - \epsilon_{s0}) \tag{11.35}$$

The rate of release of dislocations, and hence the rate of creep, will be inversely proportional to the number of events required to build up the stress change to Δs, so that

$$\left(\frac{d\epsilon_s}{dt}\right)_{s,T} = \frac{k}{n} = \frac{k(\Delta s_i)^2}{b_w^2}(\epsilon_s - \epsilon_{s0})^{-2} \tag{11.36}$$

$$\epsilon_{s_s,T} = \left(\frac{3k(\Delta s_i)^2}{b_w^2} t\right)^{1/3} + \epsilon_{s0}$$

$$= Bt^{1/3} + \epsilon_{s0} \tag{11.37}$$

where B is a constant at constant temperature and external stress. This is called *Andrade creep,* and it has been widely observed for many crystalline materials at higher temperatures. The quantity B generally increases exponentially with both stress and temperature, as expected.

A special case of high-temperature creep occurs when the recovery rate is fast enough to *just balance* the work-hardening effect caused by the deformation. Under these conditions the stress change Δs required to move a dislocation is independent of the total strain and Eq. (11.35) reduces to $\Delta s = k_s$, where k_s is a constant at a given temperature and stress. Then

$$\left(\frac{d\epsilon_s}{dt}\right)_{s,T} = \frac{k(\Delta s_i)^2}{k_s^2} \tag{11.38}$$

$$\epsilon_s = B_s t + \epsilon_{s0} \tag{11.39}$$

which give an expression for the steady-state creep, shown as the second stage in Fig. 11.30. The coefficient B_s is the steady-state creep rate of the material. It has been found that B_s varies with stress and temperature in the following way:

$$B_s = C_S{}^m \exp\left(-\frac{\Delta E_D}{RT}\right) \qquad \text{at low stress} \tag{11.40}$$

and

$$B_s = C \exp D_S \exp\left(-\frac{\Delta E_D}{RT}\right) \qquad \text{at high stress} \tag{11.41}$$

The quantities C and D are constants and depend on structure; the quantity m is a constant and is often of the order of $m \approx 4$; and ΔE_D is the activation energy for the process and is usually about equal to the activation energy for vacancy diffusion (or self-diffusion) in the crystal lattice. The activation energy in kilocalories per kilogram mole is generally 30 to 40 times the melting point of a metal in degrees Kelvin:

$$\Delta E_D = 30 \text{ to } 40(T_m, {}^\circ\text{K}) \tag{11.42}$$

The third stage of creep involves a rapidly increasing true stress and the propagation of submicroscopic cracks and is thus more difficult to characterize with a semiempirical equation. Fracture processes will be considered next.

11.7
Fracture

Fracture is the separation of a cohesive solid into two or more parts. For obvious reasons, it is desirable to understand the nature and causes of such failure. As was the case with yield stress and plastic deformation, it is experimental fact that materials usually fracture at only a small fraction of their theoretical strength. It is virtually impossible to develop analytical relations between molecular structure and "ultimate tensile strength," because the criteria for completion of the process do not necessarily depend on the nature of the cohesive structure *before* the start of the phenomenon. Incipient fracture is, however, dependent on submicroscopic defects in the structure, and a qualitative understanding may be developed by considering the possible types of imperfections that could lead to a loss of cohesiveness.

Three basically different types of fracture have been observed. *Ductile fracture* can occur by an almost uninterrupted plastic deformation. In one extreme case, tension can cause a continual necking down to a wedge or a point. More commonly, the necking down is accompanied by the development of structural flaws in the necked portion, which then propagate through the remaining cross section. In general, the fracture surface is rough and dull and a considerable amount of slip is apparent. The cup-and-cone fractures shown in Fig. 11.32 are typical of polycrystalline materials. *Cleavage fracture*

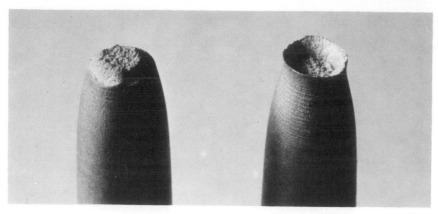

(*a*) Mild steel

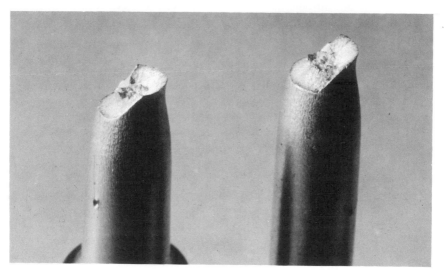

(*b*) Aluminum

Fig. 11.32 These cup-and-cone fractures are typical of materials that show plastic deformation before fracture.

occurs by a perfect separation normal to a specific crystallographic plane. Perfect cleavage surfaces are shiny, bright, and perfectly smooth. This type of fracture can be achieved in body-centered cubic and hexagonal close-packed single crystals at very low temperatures and also in sheetlike crystals of graphite, talc, and mica. Normally, a cleavage fracture does not occur on a single crystallographic plane, but rather the surface shows a stepwise pattern which indicates a whole set of closely spaced, parallel cracks rapidly propagating and overlapping. The appearance of the fracture surface is uniform, and the cracks converge in the direction of propagation. Cleavage fractures do not show very much visible deformation and are thus called *brittle fractures.*

Brittle fracture, however, very often requires some plastic deformation to initiate the process. Many structural materials will exhibit brittle fracture at low temperatures and/or high rates of straining, but tend toward ductile fracture at higher temperatures and/or lower rates of straining. Steels, for example, are normally brittle below −150 to −250°C but can exhibit considerable plastic deformation prior to fracture at room temperature in the absence of sharp notches and high strain rate. A sharp ductile-brittle transition is typical of most body-centered cubic and hexagonal close-packed metals, but the type of failure is also very sensitive to rate of loading and other environmental conditions. Figure 11.33 shows typical brittle failures in cast iron. The third type of fracture, which can occur in any polycrystalline material, is *intercrystalline fracture.* It is a brittle fracture within the grain boundary, which often nucleates at a point where impurities or second-phase elements accumulate.

Figures 11.34 to 11.36 are examples of some tensile stress-strain curves for structural materials. Figure 11.34 is a typical curve for a strain-hardenable polycrystalline metal. A large amount of plastic deformation, a high ultimate tensile strength, and a high modulus of elasticity result in a relatively hard, strong material. Figure 11.35 shows the behavior of an annealed mild steel and a "tough" thermoplastic polymer (for comparison). Both exhibit a sudden yielding of the material whereby a large deformation is accompanied by a slightly decreasing stress level. After yielding, the steel then strain-hardens because of the resistance to dislocation movement. The fracture is thus preceded by an extensive plastic deformation. (The cellulose acetate, on the other hand, yields and continues its plastic deformation without appreciable strain-hardening.) The tensile stress-strain curve for MgO is shown in Fig. 11.36 in order to illustrate the behavior of a hard, brittle ceramic. The tensile strength is low relative to the metals, and the total deformation before fracture is almost negligible.

Fig. 11.33 The grainy surface and uniform cross section are typical of brittle failure in cast iron. Above is a rod-tensile failure; below, a bar-shear failure.

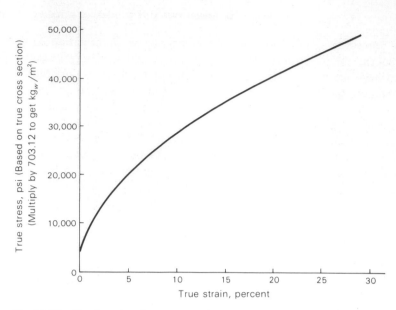

Fig. 11.34 The true tensile stress-strain curve for polycrystalline copper at 25°C shows that copper exhibits considerable plastic deformation and strain-hardening.

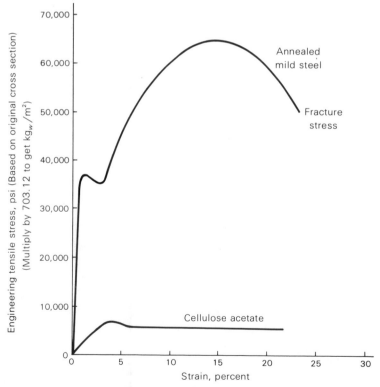

Fig. 11.35 These engineering tensile stress-strain curves show that a strain-hardenable material with a high elastic modulus will be strong and tough relative to a low-modulus, non-strain-hardenable material.

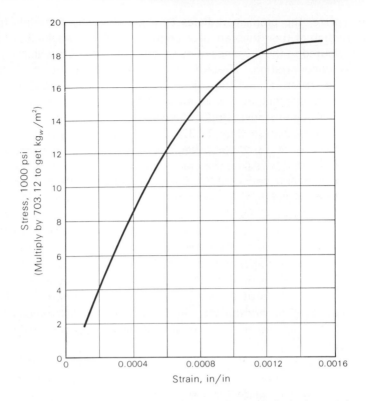

Fig. 11.36 The stress-strain curve for an MgO single crystal in tension shows that very little plastic deformation occurs prior to fracture. This is typical of brittle solids [4, 12, 16].

Table 11.3 lists approximate values for the ultimate tensile strengths of a variety of structural materials. The theoretical ultimate tensile strength is the maximum stress required to separate two adjacent planes of molecules completely. One can roughly calculate this quantity from the intermolecular potential function in the same way that the elastic modulus was estimated (cf. Sec. 11.2). The maximum force of attraction between two particles may be obtained from Eq. (11.4) by evaluating the stress s_s at the minimum of the force curve (i.e., find s_{max} at $ds/da = -d^2\psi/da^2 = 0$). The result is

$$s_{max} \doteq \frac{E_{[hkl]}}{m+1} \left(\frac{n+1}{m+1} \right)^{(1+n)/(m-n)} \tag{11.43}$$

Since values of m are generally 9 to 12 and values of n are generally 1 to 6, the theoretical strength is on the order of 0.05 of the elastic modulus.

$$s_{max} \approx 0.05 E_{[hkl]} \tag{11.44}$$

Table 11.3 also shows the theoretical values of ultimate tensile strength for a variety of materials. Generally, the theoretical strength is an order of magnitude or more greater than the actual strength of the material.

As before, the problem reduces to explaining why materials fracture at only a fraction of their theoretical strength. Again, the weakness of the material is attributed to the presence of submicroscopic defects which act as points of stress concentration. Fracture starts at these points and propagates through the structure until the cohesive cross section is reduced sufficiently to cause complete failure. There are a number of potential sources of such defects. Surface roughness and surface scratches can serve as the "notches" for stress concentration (Fig. 11.37a). The maximum stress concentration occurs at the apex of the notch. When the stress exceeds the cohesive strength of the bonding in this region, the crack can extend itself. It is not unusual to have stress concentrations orders of magnitude greater than at a normal cross section. Internal "cracks" or voids may also develop during the formation of the solid. Impurities, blowholes, voids, clusters of vacancies, dislocation clusters, and incompletely fused grain boundaries can all serve as the source of submicroscopic cracks within crystals. Particles of dirt, other impurities, and dissolved gas are all potential sources of submicroscopic cracks in amorphous solids. Flaws within crystals may also develop as a result of plastic deformation. A pileup of dislocations at a grain boundary is one potential source (Fig. 11.37b), and an intersection of moving dislocations is another (Fig. 11.37c). The surfaces of secondary phases are ideal locations for structural defects.

A considerable amount of research has been done on producing defect-free "whiskers" of crystalline materials. These are hairlike single crystals with radii of the order of 10^{-6} m. Whiskers of iron, copper, potassium halides, graphite, and aluminum oxide, among others, have been made. The tensile strength of these flaw-free structures actually does approach the theoretical

---

Table 11.3

Tensile strength for a variety of solid materials

Material	Average value of ultimate tensile strength		Theoretical tensile strength	
	psi	$10^6 \, kg_w/m^2$	psi	$10^6 \, kg_w/m^2$
Dense silicon carbide	25,000	17.6	3,400,000	2,400
Silica glass	15,550	10.9	500,000	352
Pyrex glass	10,000	7.0	500,000	352
Sodium chloride	14,000	9.8	350,000	246
Tungsten	500,000	352.	2,800,000	1,970
Nickel	90,000	63.3	1,600,000	1,130
α-Iron	50,000	35.2	1,500,000	1,050
Copper	40,000	28.2	800,000	563
Lead	2,500	1.76	115,000	81

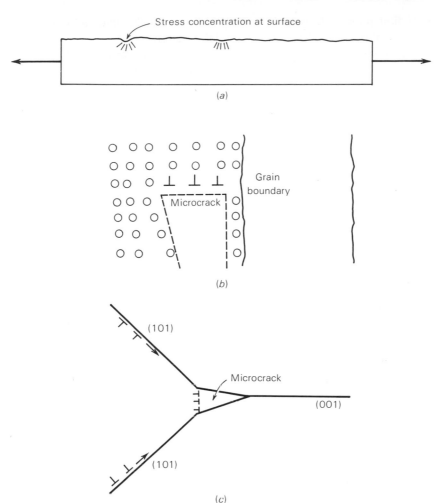

Fig. 11.37 There are many types of structural defects that can concentrate stresses and cause premature fracture. (a) Stress concentration at surface; (b) microcrack from pileup of dislocations; (c) microcrack from coalescence of dislocations (for body-centered cubic structures).

strength of the material. It is, therefore, well established that the formation and propagation of microscopic "defects" are responsible for the normal fracture behavior of materials.

There are two factors that must be analyzed in order to explain fracture phenomena; the first is the stress distribution in the vicinity of a structural defect, and the second is the conditions under which the crack may propagate at a constant or an accelerating velocity. This is still a very active research area, and a complete understanding of the problems is far from being attained. A good qualitative understanding may be developed, however, by examining the concepts first proposed by A. A. Griffith [14] for brittle solids and later modified by several people to include plastic deformation.

Consider a submicroscopic crack with length $2l$ as shown in Figure 11.38. A stress s is applied, causing it to take an approximately elliptical shape. There is a complicated stress distribution about the crack with the maximum stress at points M. It can be shown [23] that

$$s_{\max} = s \left(1 + \frac{2l}{a} \right) \tag{11.45}$$

so that, if $2l/a$ is large, there will be a considerable region about the crack which is at a much higher stress than the applied stress. When the crack grows, as a result of the applied stress, a number of energy changes will occur. Two high-energy surfaces must develop, requiring a surface energy which is proportional to both the length of the crack and the surface tension of the material:

$$\Gamma = A\gamma l \tag{11.46}$$

Since the volume within the crack cannot support any stress, its growth must result in a release of elastic strain energy. The total strain energy in a stressed elastic solid is

$$\Gamma_s = V \int_0^{\epsilon_s} s \, d\epsilon_s = V \int_0^{\epsilon_s} E_Y \epsilon_s \, d\epsilon_s$$

$$= \frac{V E_Y \epsilon_s^2}{2} = \frac{V s^2}{2 E_Y} \tag{11.47}$$

An exact calculation of how much strain energy is released by the growth of the crack is very complicated. Let us approximate that the strain energy in a cylindrical volume, slightly larger than the crack, has been released.

$$\Gamma_s = -B\pi l^2 \frac{s^2}{2 E_Y} \qquad B \approx 1 \tag{11.48}$$

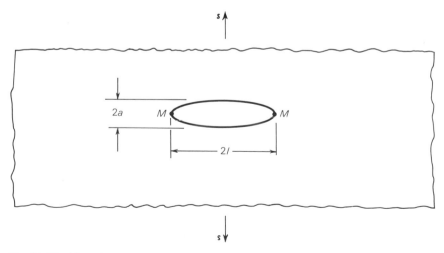

Fig. 11.38 The microcrack is elliptical causing a maximum stress at M.

If the true stress at any point in the solid exceeds the yield strength of the material, plastic deformation, which requires a considerable absorption of energy, can occur. The amount of energy absorbed as the crack propagates will depend on the interaction of a number of factors. The applied stress s is an obvious factor — the higher the applied stress, the more likely is plastic deformation. The size and shape of the crack determine the stress concentration in the structure and, therefore, must also be important. The yield point of a material will generally increase with increasing rate of strain, so that both the yield point and the velocity of propagation also affect this term. Plastic deformation is the movement of dislocations, so that the dislocation density, dislocation mobility, and atomic mobility are also factors. The way in which a crack propagates through a solid and the interactions of all of these factors are very complex and not completely understood. Let us express the energy absorption because of plastic deformation as an unknown function of these variables:

$$\Gamma = Df(l, s, \dots) \tag{11.49}$$

A reasonable criterion for spontaneous growth of a crack is that the total energy released by an advance of the crack is greater than the energy absorbed by both the newly formed surface and plastic deformation.

$$\frac{dG}{dl} = \frac{d}{dl}\left[A\gamma l + Df(l, s, \dots) - B\pi l^2 \frac{s^2}{2E_Y}\right] < 0 \tag{11.50}$$

$$\left(A\gamma + D\frac{df}{dl} - \frac{B\pi l s^2}{E_Y}\right) < 0 \tag{11.51}$$

Equation (11.51) may be examined from two points of view. There is probably some critical value of crack size, l^*, above which Eq. (11.51) is satisfied. One may then imagine that cracks with lengths less than l^* cannot accelerate, while cracks with lengths greater than l^* can start to accelerate. Since the plastic deformation term depends on velocity of propagation, yield stress, etc., the criterion for whether a crack can *continue* to accelerate depends on many interacting factors. The other way to look at (11.51) is to suppose that some minimum stress s_f can cause a crack of length l to spontaneously grow. Setting Eq. (11.51) equal to zero, one gets

$$s_f = \sqrt{\frac{E_Y}{B\pi l}\left(A\gamma + D\frac{df}{dl}\right)} \tag{11.52}$$

Thus, the stress required for fracture decreases as the crack length increases, decreases as the amount of plastic deformation decreases, and decreases as the elastic modulus decreases. For very brittle materials:

$$s_f \approx \sqrt{\frac{A\gamma E_Y}{B\pi l}} \tag{11.53}$$

For Pyrex glass $s_f \approx 7.6 \times 10^6 \ kg_w/m^2$ (10,000 psi), $\gamma \approx 0.02 \ kg_w/m$ (10^{-3} lb$_f$/in.), $E_Y \approx 10^{10} \ kg_w/m^2$, $l \approx (A/B\pi) \ 10^{-6} \ m \approx 10^{-6}$ to 10^{-7} m. For zinc crystals $s_f \approx 2 \times 10^5 \ kg_w/m^2$, $\gamma \approx 0.08 \ kg_w/m$, $E_Y \approx 3 \times 10^9 \ kg_w/m^2$, and $l \approx 0.007$ m. In the case of glass, it is apparent that brittle fracture can be caused by submicroscopic cracks, while in zinc the required crack size is so large that visible cracks must develop before a normal tensile specimen would be expected to fail.

11.8
Fatigue and endurance

When a material is subjected to a cyclic or fluctuating stress (or strain), it will fracture, after a period of time, at stresses well below the tensile strength of the material. This is known as *fatigue failure* and almost always ends in a brittle fracture. Figure 11.39 is a photograph of a typical fatigue failure. In this case, submicroscopic cracks originated at the surface of the smooth region and propagated outward, through the cross section of the rod. The crack velocity was probably intermittent and the motion was accompanied by plastic deformation. When the cohesive cross section was reduced sufficiently, the remaining material fractured suddenly and in brittle fracture.

An understanding of the factors that promote fatigue failure are essential to the proper design of piston rods, axles, gears, airplane wings, or any other

Fig. 11.39 A typical fatigue failure in steel with the cracks originating at the surface in the upper part of the photograph and propagating downward through the cross section of the rod.

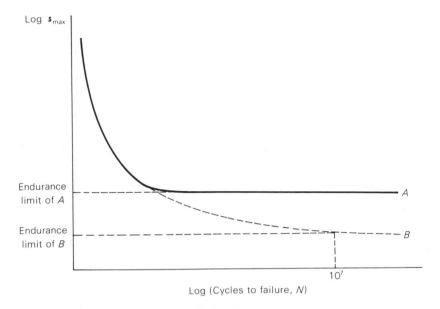

Fig. 11.40 Typical fatigue test results show that the number of stress cycles without failure of the material increases as the magnitude of the stress decreases.

structure that experiences cyclic or fluctuating loads. One standard laboratory test for measuring fatigue characteristics is the *rotating beam* test. A mirror-polished cylindrical rod is subjected to a cyclic load by rotating a stressed specimen in such a way that a point on the surface of the rod undergoes a sinusoidal change in stress from maximum tension to maximum compression every 180° of rotation (Ref. 25, chap. 5). The usual technique is to test a number of samples to failure at a fixed stress and then repeat the test at several stress levels. One can then plot the maximum fiber stress versus the average number of cycles required to cause a fatigue failure. Typical results are plotted in Fig. 11.40. In general, decreasing stress permits a longer life before fatigue failure. Many materials exhibit a sharp break in the curve to an almost horizontal line. This defines the *endurance limit* of the material. The endurance limit is the cylic stress that a solid can withstand for an infinite number of cycles. Some materials do not show a very sharp knee, so that the endurance limit must be defined as the cyclic stress which can be supported for a fixed number of cycles (for example, 10^7 cycles). The purpose of this section is to discuss the factors that influence the shape of these curves.

The endurance limit of a metal is normally a fraction of the ultimate tensile strength. Annealed steels (tensile strengths less than 10^8 kg_w/m^2 (180,000 psi) and annealed aluminum alloys, for example, have endurance limits of the order of one-half of the static tensile strengths of the materials. The nature of the fracture is determined by the cumulative effects of the continually reversing strains. An important factor to understand is the *Bauschinger effect.* When a metal is stressed in one direction only, the yield stress increases because of strain hardening. Figure 11.41 shows the effect of repeated unidirectional loading. The material is stressed for the first time, yields at s_1, and is deformed to ϵ_{sa}. The stress is then removed; the elastic deformation is recovered; and a permanent set results. The sample is then restressed. The elastic modulus remains the same in the second cycle, but the yield point increases to s_2. Repeated cycles continue to show an increase in yield strength. Bauschinger discovered that although the tensile yield strength is increased, the compressive yield strength is decreased. Likewise, unidirectional compressing will increase the compressive yield stress and decrease the tensile yield stress. This means that when cyclic loads are applied, the strain hardening picked up in one half cycle will be partially lost in the next half cycle.

Thus, strain-hardening during cyclic loading occurs more slowly than for an equivalent amount of unidirectional straining. The significance of this is illustrated in Figs. 11.42 and 11.43. An annealed α-brass was subjected to alternating torsional strains $\pm\epsilon_s$, and the torque required to produce this much strain was recorded as a function of the number of cycles. The required torque was then plotted as a function of the total strain (irrespective of sign). Figure 11.42 shows that the accumulation of strain-hardening depends on the amplitude of the cyclic strain. At large amplitudes, the hardening effect increases rapidly and continues to accumulate up to relatively high total deformations. The gradual reduction in ductility promotes the formation of submicroscopic cracks, which then tend to propagate through the cross section of the material and result in the typically granular fatigue fracture. This effect is similar to the results of unidirectional stressing except that the strain hardening is slower in cyclic loading. At very small amplitudes of cyclic strain, a little hardening occurs in the first few cycles, but after that there is no noticeable change. This means that the hardening occurring in a half cycle of tension is just balanced by that which is lost in the next half cycle. Thus, large amounts of deformation occur with no noticeable hardening effects.

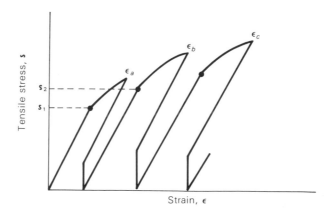

Fig. 11.41   Yield strength will increase under a repeated unidirectional stress.

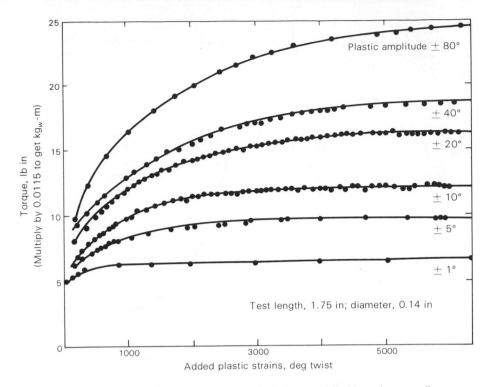

Fig. 11.42 Cyclic stress-strain curves for annealed α-brass subject to various amplitudes of alternating torsion. (By permission from B. L. Averbach, D. K. Felbeck, G. T. Hahn, and D. A. Thomas, "Fracture," p. 416, The M.I.T. Press, Cambridge, Mass., 1959.)

Figure 11.43 shows the amplitude of the strain plotted against the total strain to fracture. Large amplitudes cause a relatively short life until the range is reached where there is little strain-hardening. Then, the life of the sample increases very rapidly. The relationship to the fatigue curve (Fig. 11.40) is clear. At large amplitudes of stress, strain hardening is rapid and cumulative with a subsequent embrittlement of the solid. The fatigue life is thus relatively short. At lower stress levels, the cycling strain does not produce a cumulative hardening, and thus very large strains (and long life) are permissible before the material fractures. The actual mechanism of the fatigue failure for the latter case is still not well understood, but there is evidence to indicate that the high total plastic strain produces abnormally high lattice distortions in certain regions of the slip planes. These active regions, at a very early stage of the process, generate submicroscopic defects which then turn into observable cracks in the structure. The mechanism of formation and propagation of these cracks is still a matter of conjecture.

The best way to determine the fatigue life of an actual material in service is to reproduce the system perfectly. Thus the size, shape, surface, etc. of the material, the complete loading spectrum, the environment, and any other

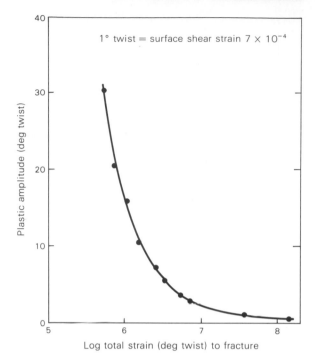

Fig. 11.43 Total plastic strain to fracture of brass un-
der various plastic amplitues of alternating torsion.
(By permission from B. L. Averbach, D. K. Felbeck, G.
T. Hahn, and D. A. Thomas, "Fracture," p. 416, The
M.I.T. Press, Cambridge, Mass., 1959.)

important factors must be considered. Even then, the fatigue life would not
be exactly known, since no two pieces of the same material will behave in
exactly the same way. (That is, fatigue failure has a statistical nature and one
can only hope to find the most probable behavior.) The life of a material under
fatigue conditions can only be approximated, and laboratory tests can only be
used as a guide for the experienced designer. Field testing of the materials
(e.g., automobile, airplane, motor parts, etc.) is very valuable in this respect.
About all that can be emphasized here, is that when possible, the design for
fatigue life should be left to those who are expert in this area. We can, however,
interpret laboratory tests and understand the effects of various conditions on
the results of such tests. The following paragraphs discuss the influence of
various factors on the results of simple, rotating-beam fatigue tests.

Laboratory endurance tests are often carried out on samples with highly
polished surfaces. Figure 11.44 qualitatively shows the effect of surface
roughening on the measured endurance limit. Roughness creates notches in
the surface which concentrate stress and cause premature failure. The effect
is worse with the higher-strength, higher-hardness steels because of their
tendency to be more brittle (or more notch-sensitive).

Mean stresses are often superimposed on a fluctuating stress by service loads or by residual stresses produced during the manufacturing of a material. A mean tensile stress will usually accelerate fatigue failure. Very often, residual stresses are the limiting factor on fatigue life. Thus, for any given amplitude of fluctuation, the life of a sample will decrease with increasing mean tensile stress. Also, fatigue life for a material under a fluctuating compressive load is much greater than the fatigue life under the same magnitude of fluctuating tensile load.

Over wide ranges, the frequency of cyclic loading has virtually no effect on the endurance limit. Figure 11.45 shows that the room-temperature endurance limits of copper, iron, and steel are virtually constant up to about 5,000 to 10,000 cycles/min. This makes it possible to test such materials at relatively high speeds and get reasonable predictions of long-time behavior (at lower frequencies) from short-time tests. Similarly, rest periods have very little effect on experimental endurance limits.

Endurance limit also depends on the past history of the material. Figure 11.46 shows the behavior of differently treated aluminum alloys. For a given tensile strength, annealed alloys have the highest endurance limits, cold-worked alloys are next, and age-hardened alloys have the lowest endurance limits. The significance of this is that cold-worked or age-hardened, high-strength, alloys may be no better, or may be poorer, in fatigue than lower-strength, annealed alloys. Thus, an age-hardened, 40×10^6–kg_w/m^2 (60,000-psi) aluminum alloy has an endurance limit of about 12×10^6–kg_w/m^2 (17,000-psi),

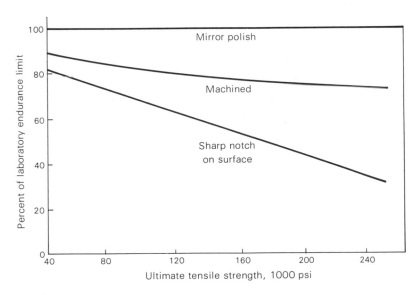

Fig. 11.44 The presence of defects on the surface of steel will lower the endurance limit of the material; the harder the material the more pronounced the effect.

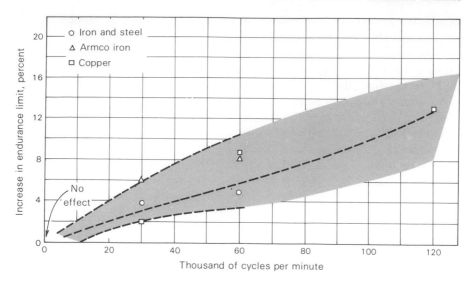

Fig. 11.45 Effect of frequency on endurance limit. There is very little effect below 5,000 cycles/min. (By permission from G. Sines and J. L. Waisman, "Metal Fatigue," McGraw-Hill Book Company, New York, 1959.)

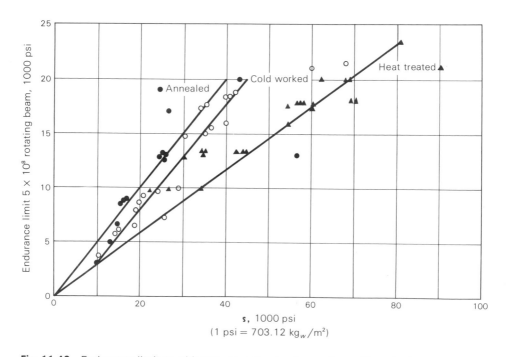

Fig. 11.46 Endurance limit vs. ultimate strength, aluminum alloys. The prior treating history has an effect on the endurance limit. (By permission from G. Sines and J. L. Waisman, "Metal Fatigue," McGraw-Hill Book Company, New York, 1959.)

while an annealed 30×10^6–kg_w/m^2 (40,000-psi) aluminum alloy has an endurance limit of about 14×10^6–kg_w/m^2 (20,000-psi).

Corrosion has a very pronounced effect on the fatigue life of a material. Appreciable decrease in endurance limit can be caused even by the corrosive influence of "clean" air. Extreme conditions, such as the effect of salt water on steel, can reduce the endurance limit to a few percent of the laboratory value. Figure 11.47 qualitatively shows the effect of environment. High-strength steels are affected to a much greater extent because of their higher degree of notch sensitivity. Thus a 100×10^6–kg_w/m^2 (160,000-psi) tensile strength steel is no more effective than a 40×10^6–kg_w/m^2 (60,000-psi) steel in fatigue service under salt water.

As temperature increases, the fatigue strength of materials decreases for several reasons. Elevated temperature accelerates corrosion and oxidation, which create surface defects. Increased atomic mobility reduces the stiffness of the material and facilitates a greater amount of creep. These, in turn, promote the formation of submicroscopic defects. Lower temperatures, therefore, will improve the fatigue strength of materials. Thus, although a material might be closer to its brittle-transition temperature (defined by a static test), it is not necessarily more notch-sensitive under cyclic stressing.

An important fact about fatigue life is that a series of test results on

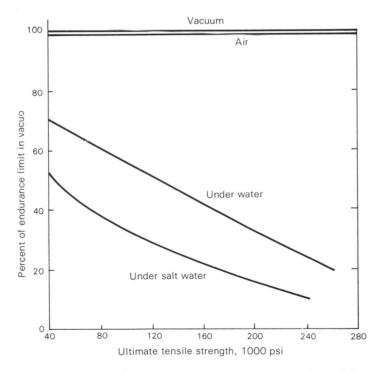

Fig. 11.47 A corroding environment will reduce the endurance limit of steel.

apparently identical samples always indicate a scattering of data. Very often the scatter approximates a log-normal distribution, and it is therefore felt that fatigue life is inherently a statistical characteristic of a material. This should not be too surprising, since fatigue damage is associated with the presence of submicroscopic flaws. It is not too difficult to visualize the nature of flaws in a substance in terms of a statistical distribution of defects. This means, however, that even if the equipment and testing procedures are perfect, the best one can hope to find is the most probable fatigue life of a material.

11.9
Thermal stresses and thermal shock

When a material is subjected to a temperature gradient, different parts will expand at different rates. If a free expansion occurs, the material will distort in a manner determined by the temperature distribution. Consider the flat strip shown in Fig. 11.48. It is initially at uniform temperature and rectangular in shape. Suppose the top side is then heated to a higher constant temperature. Heat is conducted through the strip; and when steady state is attained, there will be a linear temperature gradient across the strip. If a free thermal expansion is allowed, the warm part of the strip will expand more than the cold part, causing a warpage. If the temperature gradient is linear and there is no internal stress buildup, each horizontal length of strip will form the arc of a circle. If, on the other hand, the strip is constrained to a fixed shape, there will be an internal stress buildup because of differential expansion. The stress distribution in the constrained piece can be calculated by determining the stress distribution required to straighten the piece when it experiences free expansion.

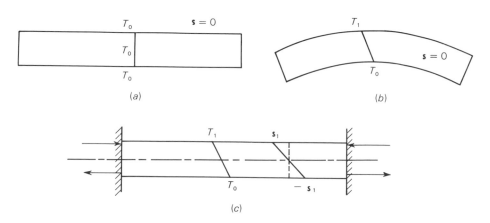

Fig. 11.48 Thermal stress in a flat bar. (*a*) Bar at uniform temperature; (*b*) free expansion under a temperature gradient; (*c*) thermal stress buildup in a constrained bar.

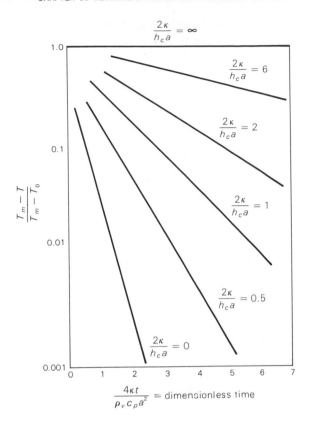

Fig. 11.49 Surface temperatures for a slab. (From D. Q. Kern, "Process Heat Transfer," p. 652, McGraw-Hill Book Company, New York, 1950.)

When a material experiences a sudden change in temperature, sharp temperature gradients will always introduce thermal stresses. The sudden quenching of a surface, for example, will introduce tensile stresses in the surface. When the thermal stress becomes higher than the ultimate tensile strength, fracture can be induced. When a material experiences cycling temperatures, cycling thermal stresses which can lead to a fatigue failure are introduced. Brittle materials are especially sensitive to such conditions. In this section we shall outline the thermal stress analysis for the quenching of a brittle flat plate.

Consider a thin flat plate of a brittle, elastic material, initially at a uniform temperature T_0, quenched in a medium at a lower temperature T_m. Assume that there are no solid-state transformations that might contribute to internal stress and that all of the stresses are due to thermal contraction. Let us calculate the tensile stresses developed *at the surface* of the flat plate as a function of time. The first piece of information that is needed is the temperature of the surface as a function of time. This heat-transfer problem has been solved, and the solution is given in various references. The information needed here is given in Fig. 11.49. The quantities κ, ρ_v, and c_p are the thermal conductivity, density, and specific heat of the slab. The quantity a is the slab thickness, and h_c is the heat-transfer coefficient at the surface of the plate. The figure gives the temperature at the surface for a variety of different combinations of variables. If the elastic plate were allowed to contract freely on cooling from T_0 to T_m, the total linear dimension change would be $\alpha_L(T_0 - T_m)$, where α_L is the linear thermal expansion coefficient. If the plate were constrained, the maximum thermal stress would be

$$s_{max} = \frac{E\alpha_L}{1 - \vartheta_p}(T_0 - T_m) \tag{11.54}$$

The actual stress at any given time will be a fraction of this, since the actual temperature gradient in the solid would be smaller than the maximum. If the surface stress is proportional to the difference between the average temperature of the solid, $\langle T \rangle$, and the surface temperature T_s, the true thermal stress s is

$$s^* = \frac{s}{s_{max}} = \frac{s(1 - \vartheta_p)}{E\alpha_L(T_0 - T_m)} = \frac{\langle T \rangle - T_s}{T_0 - T_m} \tag{11.55}$$

Since the temperature is a known function of time, the thermal stress at the surface may be calculated as a function of time. The solutions are shown in Fig. 11.50. Thermal stresses increase, reach a maximum, and then decrease as thermal gradients in the solid become less severe. The maximum stress is of prime concern, since it must stay below the tensile strength of the material. The maximum reduced stress s^*_{max} can be represented by [17]:

$$\left(\frac{1}{s^*_{max}}\right)_{surf} \doteq 1.5 + \frac{3.25\kappa}{ah_c} \qquad \frac{2\kappa}{ah_c} > 0.4 \tag{11.56}$$

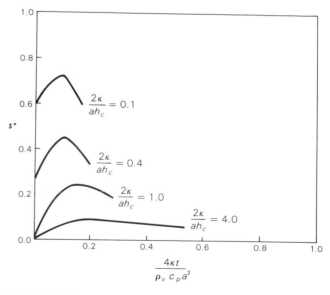

Fig. 11.50 Reduced thermal stresses at the surface of a flat plate [17].

$$\left(\frac{1}{s^*_{max}}\right)_{surf} \doteq 1.0 + 3.25 \left(\frac{\kappa}{ah_c}\right)^{2/3} \qquad \frac{2\kappa}{ah_c} < 0.4 \qquad (11.57)$$

When $\kappa/ah_c \gg 1.0$.

$$\frac{1}{s^*_{max}} \doteq \frac{3.25\kappa}{ah_c} = \frac{E\alpha_L(T_0 - T_m)}{s(1 - \vartheta_p)} \qquad (11.58)$$

One may then calculate the maximum allowable temperature gradient that the solid may experience without breaking by setting s equal to the ultimate tensile strength s_T.

$$(T_0 - T_m)_{max} \doteq \frac{ks_T}{E\alpha_L} \frac{3.25(1 - \vartheta_p)}{ah_c} \qquad (11.59)$$

The group $\kappa s_T/E\alpha_L$ is called the *thermal shock resistance parameter.* Thus, the thermal shock resistance of a brittle material is proportional to thermal conductivity and tensile strength and inversely proportional to elastic modulus and thermal-expansion coefficient. When $\kappa/ah_c \ll 1.0$, $1/s^*_{max}$ approaches 1.0 and

$$(T_0 - T_m)_{max} \doteq \frac{s_T}{E\alpha_L}(1 - \vartheta_p) \qquad (11.60)$$

The thermal shock resistance, for this situation, is independent of thermal conductivity, plate thickness, and the cooling medium. The *former* case is the more usual one.

In the last paragraphs, we have quantitatively examined the important parameters for determining the thermal shock resistance on quenching brittle solids. When a plate is suddenly heated, on the other hand, the surface stresses are compressive and the center of the plate is in tension. Since most brittle solids are weaker in tension, crack propagation could start at the center. A number of other factors have been neglected in this discussion. When a ductile solid experiences thermal stresses, it is capable of flowing to a certain extent, which tends to make the material more shock-resistant. Plastic flow results in dissipation of some of the strain energy and also promotes a strain hardening of the material. Solid-state transformations, grain-boundary precipitation, oxidation, corrosion, and grain growth will all have an effect on the actual thermal shock resistance of a material. Each material must be individually analyzed for a given set of conditions.

References

1 Almen, J. O., and P. H. Black: "Residual Stresses and Fatigue in Metals," McGraw-Hill Book Company, New York, 1963.

2 American Society for Metals, "Creep and Recovery," ASM, Cleveland, 1957.

3 American Society for Testing and Materials, ASTM Standards, many volumes of standardized testing procedures.

4   Averbach, B. L., D. K. Felbeck, G. T. Hahn, and D. A. Thomas: "Fracture," John Wiley & Sons, Inc., and The Technology Press of the Massachusetts Institute of Technology, New York, 1959.

5   Barker, R. E.: *J. Appl. Phys.,* **34:** 107 (1963).

6   Barrett, C. S., and T. B. Massalski: "Structure of Metals," 3d ed., McGraw-Hill Book Company, New York, 1966.

7   Chalmers, B.: "Physical Metallurgy," John Wiley & Sons, Inc., New York, 1959.

8   Cottrell, A. H.: "Dislocations and Plastic Flow in Crystals," Oxford University Press, New York, 1953.

9   Cottrell, A. H.: "Theoretical Structural Metallurgy," St Martin's Press, New York, 1960.

10   Cottrell, A. H.: "The Mechanical Properties of Matter," John Wiley & Sons, Inc., New York, 1964.

11   Dorn, J. E. (ed.): "Mechanical Behavior of Materials at Elevated Temperatures," McGraw-Hill Book Company, New York, 1961.

12   Gilman, J. J.: Mechanical Behavior of Ionic Crystals, in J. E. Burke (ed.), "Progress in Ceramic Science," vol. 1, Pergamon Press, New York, 1960.

13   Glasstone, S., K. J. Laidler, and H. Eyring: "The Theory of Rate Processes," McGraw-Hill Book Company, New York, 1941.

14   Griffith, A. A.: *Phil. Trans. Roy. Soc. London,* Ser. A, **221,** 163 (1920–21).

15   Guy, A. G.: "Elements of Physical Metallurgy," chaps. 4, 8, 13, Addison-Wesley Publishing Company, Inc., Reading, Mass., 1959.

16   Kingery, W. D.: "Introduction to Ceramics," John Wiley & Sons, Inc., New York, 1960.

17   Manson, S. S.: Behavior of Materials under Conditions of Thermal Stress, in "Heat Transfer: A Symposium," The University of Michigan Press, Ann Arbor, Mich., 1952.

18   McLean, D.: "Grain Boundaries in Metals," Oxford University Press, London, 1957.

19   Nabarro, F. R. N.: *Proc. Phys. Soc. (London),* **59:** 256 (1947).

20   National Physical Laboratory, "Creep and Fracture of Metals at High Temperature" Teddington, England, Feb. 1966.

21   Parker, E. R.: "Brittle Behavior of Engineering Structures," John Wiley & Sons, Inc., New York, 1957.

22   Read, W. T., Jr.: "Dislocations in Crystals," McGraw-Hill Book Company, New York, 1953.

23   Roark, R. J.: "Formulas for Stress and Strain," 3d ed., McGraw-Hill Book Company, New York, 1954.

24   Samans, C. H.: "Engineering Metals and Their Alloys," The Macmillan Company, New York, 1953.

25   Sines, G., and J. L. Waisman (eds.): "Metal Fatigue," McGraw-Hill Book Company, New York, 1959.

26   Wilkens, R. A., and E. S. Bunn: "Copper and Copper Alloys," McGraw-Hill Book Company, New York, 1943.

Questions

11.1 The bulk modulus K (modulus of compressibility) is defined as the ratio of the hydrostatic pressure to the relative change in volume $K = s/(\Delta V/V_0)$. Show that an isotropic solid has an infinite bulk modulus if its Poisson ratio equals 0.5.

11.2 A sudden decrease in the Young's modulus for pure iron occurs at 1670°F on cooling. Explain this in terms of molecular bonding.

11.3 Use Eq. (11.6) to estimate the average elastic modulus for an argon crystal and for a sodium fluoride crystal.

11.4 Show the close-packed planes and directions of a face-centered cubic crystal. Show that there are 12 different slip vectors in the lattice.

11.5 Explain in your own words why a crystalline material will yield at a fraction of its theoretical yield stress. Estimate the theoretical yield strength of a perfect copper crystal and also the yield stress required to move an edge dislocation parallel to a row of close-packed atoms.

11.6 Approximate the stress required to cause plastic deformation in copper by a Frank-Read mechanism in which a dislocation is pinned at two points. Estimate the distance between pinned points on a dislocation line from dislocation density (the number of dislocations piercing a square centimeter of surface). Make the calculations for a well-annealed material (dislocation density about 10^8 dislocations per square centimeter) and a cold-worked material (dislocation density about 10^{12} dislocations per square centimeter).

11.7 Discuss the effect of grain boundaries on the mechanism for slip and on the rate of strain-hardening of a polycrystalline metal.

11.8 Discuss the effects of impurities and alloying elements on the rate of strain-hardening of a polycrystalline metal.

11.9 Figure 11.51 is a phase diagram for the aluminum-copper alloy system. What composition range is hardenable by age-hardening techniques? Discuss the conditions that are required to age-harden an alloy and describe the hardening mechanism.

11.10 The diffusivity of copper in aluminum is given by the following equation:

$$D \frac{cm^2}{sec} = \left[2.0 \exp \left(-\frac{17,100}{T°K} \right) \right]$$

If the aging process is diffusion-controlled and it takes about 20 hr to attain maximum strength at 153°C (see Fig 11.23) in a 4 percent Cu-Al alloy, estimate the optimum time at 100°C. Compare your answers with Fig. 11.23. What other factors can control the age-hardening process?

11.11 Isothermal recrystallization data for severely cold-worked copper are given in Fig. 11.29. Try curve-fitting the data to the equation

$$\ln \frac{100 - \text{percent recrystallization}}{100} = Kt^n$$

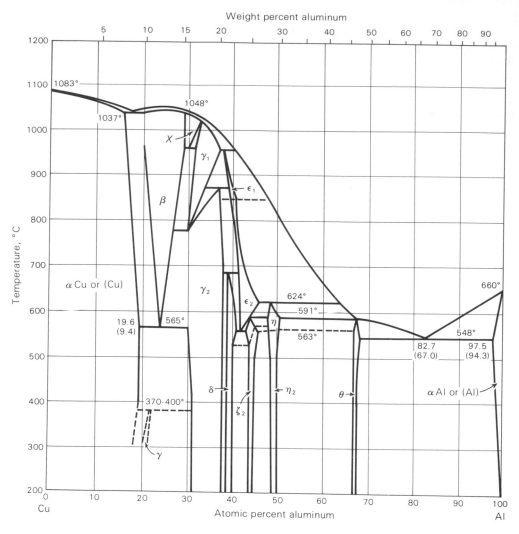

Fig. 11.51 Equilibrium phase diagram for aluminum-copper alloys. (By permission from M. Hansen, "Constitution of Binary Alloys," 2d ed., p. 85, McGraw-Hill Book Company, New York, 1958.)

Evaluate K and n for the four temperatures and investigate the temperature dependence of these quantities.

11.12 The data in Table 11.4 were taken for the creep behavior of an alloy steel at 800°F.

(a) Plot the strain vs. time on log-log coordinates.
(b) Express the creep as a function of time and stress through an empirical equation.
(c) Predict the creep curve for 34×10^6 kg$_w$/m² and 800°F.
(d) Find the total creep strain at 34×10^6 kg$_w$/m² and 800°F after 1,000 min.

Table 11.4

Stress, kg_w/m^2	$m/m \times 10^4$	Time, min	Stress, kg_w/m^2	$m/m \times 10^4$	Time, min
50×10^6	3.81	1.0		0.955	200.0
	6.77	10.0		1.05	300.0
	8.13	20.0		1.21	500.0
	9.12	30.0		1.32	700
	10.20	50.0		1.45	1000
	11.20	70.0		2.59	10000
	12.35	100.0	14×10^6	0.159	10
	14.20	200.0		0.191	20
	16.25	300.0		0.210	30
	18.65	500.0		0.240	50
	20.45	700.0		0.258	70
	22.40	1000.0		0.282	100
21×10^6	0.251	1.0		0.340	200
	0.448	10.0		0.376	300
	0.538	20.0		0.428	500
	0.590	30.0		0.458	700
	0.677	50.0		0.502	1000
	0.742	70.0		0.989	10000
	0.795	100.0		1.590	100000

11.13 Figure 11.52 is the stress-strain curve for polycrystalline copper based on the original cross section and length of the specimen.

$$s = \frac{F}{A_0} \qquad \epsilon_s = 1 - \frac{l}{l_0}$$

This does not give an indication of the true maximum stress in the test piece because of the necking effect preceding ductile fracture. Recompute the true stress-strain curve by defining:

True stress $s = F/A$

True strain $d\epsilon = dl/l$

Assume that there is no volume change during plastic deformation: $A_0 l_0 = Al$. Compare your answer with Fig. 11.34.

11.14 What are the important differences between a ductile and a brittle fracture? Under what conditions will a brittle fracture be preceded by plastic deformation? What is a brittle-ductile transition?

11.15 Use the general form of the potential-energy expression,

$$\psi = -\frac{a}{r^n} + \frac{b}{r^m}$$

to show that the theoretical tensile strength of a solid is approximately 0.05 of its elastic modulus.

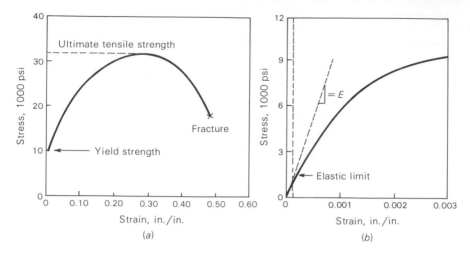

Fig. 11.52 Apparent stress-strain curve for polycrystalline copper. (a) Complete curve; (b) initial portion.

11.16 Explain why a solid will usually fracture at only a fraction of its theoretical strength.

11.17 A sheet of glass with a Young's modulus of 10^{10} kg/m² and a surface energy of 0.053 kg_w/m is scratched with a diamond tool, producing a scratch of one mil. When tested in tension, it has a strength of 3.5×10^6 kg_w/m². What is the probable strength for a piece of smooth glass if the largest surface scratch is about one micron?

11.18 What is the Bauschinger effect? Why is it important in an analysis of fatigue failure?

11.19 Why do many metals exhibit a rather sharp endurance limit?

11.20 Write a short discussion of the factors that will affect the fatigue life of a material in service. Compare laboratory results on fatigue failure with what might be expected in a particular application.

12
Mechanical properties
of polymeric materials

12.1
Introduction

The elastic response of polymeric materials is associated with both the deformation of primary bonds and a change in molecular conformation. The two extremes of behavior are illustrated by diamond and natural rubber. The elastic modulus of diamond is controlled by the resistance to deformation of the primary C—C bonds, while the elastic modulus of an elastomer is controlled by the resistance to the uncoiling of entangled chains. The extent of elastic deformation may vary from a few tenths of a percent (in diamond) to a few hundred percent (in elastomers). The elastic responses of all other polymers lie between these extremes.

Plastic deformation and strain-hardening can also occur in polymers. The deformation of amorphous polymers that do not orient is analogous to the viscous flow of a fluid. When a shearing load is applied, the material begins to flow uniformly throughout the structure until complex entanglements and molecular interactions resist further deformation. The situation in crystalline polymers is much more complicated, with some regions in the structure being more resistant to flow than others. Strain-hardening is not common to all, but rather, occurs markedly only when the material can be oriented into a fiberlike structure. Although there are dislocations and other defects in polymer crystals, their movement and interactions have not been studied to any great extent.

All polymeric materials are, to some extent, *viscoelastic,* which means that they simultaneously exhibit mechanical properties characteristic of elastic solids and viscous fluids. This enormously complicates the analysis of mechanical response, since time and rate of loading become important variables.

In this chapter we shall relate the mechanical response to polymer structure. In addition to utilizing the concepts and definitions of the preceding
chapter, we shall introduce concepts of rubber elasticity, time-dependent
moduli, and damping capacity.

12.2
Rubber elasticity

Amorphous, rubberlike polymers (i.e., elastomers) have two unusual elastic
properties. They are able to deform elastically up to many hundreds of percent
elongation and, second, when they are behaving as ideal elastomers, the modulus of elasticity increases with temperature (which is just the opposite of what
is observed for other materials). The chainlike nature of these materials is responsible for this behavior.

The long chains of an elastomer are normally in a highly coiled arrangement, approximately in the shape of a sphere whose radius is only a small fraction of the extended chain length. In an amorphous solid, these coiled chains
are randomly arranged and highly entangled. The stress-strain curves for typical elastomers at a specified strain rate are shown in Fig. 12.1. The effective
modulus of elasticity at a given stress level is just the slope of the curve at that
point. The initial value of the modulus depends on the resistance to the uncoiling of the randomly distributed chains. After the chains become oriented and
the "looser" entanglements are removed, the structure is more cohesive and is
thus capable of supporting a higher stress, which tends to raise the value of the
modulus. When the stress-induced orientation becomes extensive, the modulus approaches the same order of magnitude as for other Van der Waals–bonded
solids. An increase in temperature increases the random thermal motion of the
polymer segments, thus making it more difficult to orient the coiled chains.
This results in a *higher* modulus of elasticity. Another way to look at this phenomenon is to consider an elastomer which has been stretched by an external
force f_T. The randomly coiled molecules have been oriented to a certain extent.
If the force is constant and the temperature is increased, some of the induced
orientation will be destroyed by greater thermal motion, thus causing the elastomer to shrink. This is just the reverse of the behavior of the metals, silicates,
and other structural materials. Figure 12.2a and b shows the change of elastic
modulus for typical polymers that exhibit rubbery behavior over part of the
temperature range. The natural rubber is below its glass-transition temperature at −100°C but rapidly softens between −70 and −40°C. From −40 to 160°C
it is almost an ideal elastomer, since E_Y remains about constant (ideally, dE_Y/dT
is slightly positive). Above 160°C the material softens to a flowable state in
which elasticity is not as important. Polystyrene shows similar characteristics
except that there is no region in which it is an "ideal" elastomer. Average values for the elastic moduli are given in Table 12.5, along with a number of other
mechanical properties. As expected, the moduli of the unfilled polymers are
an order of magnitude smaller than those of metals because of the smaller re-

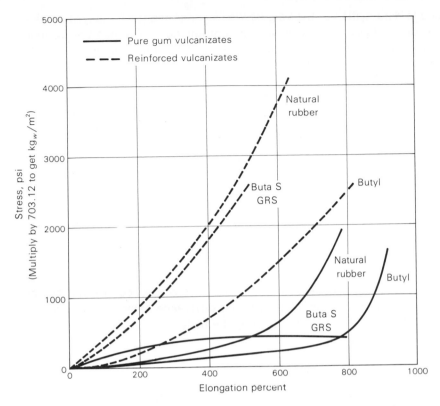

Fig. 12.1   Stress-strain curves for some rubber vulcanizates.   (By permission from A. X. Schmidt and C. A. Marlies, "Principles of High-polymer Theory and Practice," p. 573, McGraw-Hill Book Company, New York, 1948.)

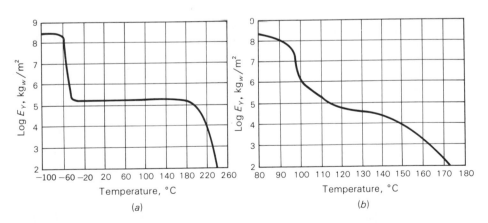

Fig. 12.2   The elastic moduli of polymers decrease very rapidly upon heating through glass-transition and crystallization temperatures.   In the "ideal rubbery" state, however, elastic moduli increase slightly with temperature.   (a) Lightly vulcanized natural rubber; (b) polystyrene.   (Data from Ref. 21, pp. 72, 77.)

sistance to deformation of the Van der Waals bonds and the initially low resistance to disentanglement and changing conformation. The addition of inorganic or cellulosic filler, on the other hand, increases the resistance to deformation and raises the moduli considerably.

Rather simple relationships exist between the mechanical and thermodynamic properties of elastomers. When the resistance to stretching is associated totally with the entropy change accompanying the deformation, a material is said to be an *ideal elastomer.* This condition may be met when the enthalpy change accompanying a deformation dl is equal to zero:

$$\left(\frac{\partial H}{\partial l}\right)_{T,p} = 0 \tag{12.1}$$

A "mechanical equation of state" may be developed by calculating the work required to stretch the elastomer. Consider a uniaxial tensile force f_T that causes a deformation dl. The work of stretching W_{el} is

$$W_{el} = f_T \, dl \tag{12.2}$$

The first law of thermodynamics states that, in the absence of other energy changes, the internal-energy change is the difference between the heat absorbed by the body and the work done by the body

$$dU = dQ - p \, dV + f_T \, dl$$
$$= T \, dS - p \, dV + f_T \, dl \tag{12.3}$$

Since the free energy G is related to internal energy by the equation $G = U + pV - TS = H - TS$, the free-energy change is

$$dG = -S \, dT + V \, dp + f_T \, dl \tag{12.4}$$

The tensile force f_T may therefore be expressed as a function of thermodynamic properties:

$$f_T = \left(\frac{\partial G}{\partial l}\right)_{T,p} = \left(\frac{\partial H}{\partial l}\right)_{T,p} - T\left(\frac{\partial S}{\partial l}\right)_{T,p} \tag{12.5}$$

The equation of state for an ideal elastomer is thus

$$f_T = -T\left(\frac{\partial S}{\partial l}\right)_{T,p} \tag{12.6}$$

This is analogous to the equation of state for an ideal gas, $p = T(\partial S/\partial V)_T$. From the properties of exact differentials, Eq. (12.4) yields $-(\partial S/\partial l)_{T,p} = (\partial f_T/\partial T)_{l,p}$, which, when substituted into Eq. (12.5), gives another form for the equation of state:

$$f_T = \left(\frac{\partial H}{\partial l}\right)_{T,p} + T\left(\frac{\partial f_T}{\partial T}\right)_{p,l} \tag{12.7}$$

Typical data are shown in Figure 12.3. For small strains, the modulus of elasticity increases linearly with temperature. Ideal elastomeric behavior, that is, $(\partial H/\partial l) = 0$, is maintained to very high percent elongation, until, above a certain

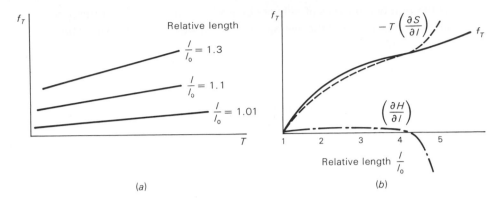

Fig. 12.3 The mechanical behavior of elastomers. (a) Effect of temperature on tensile force at constant elongation; (b) enthalphy and entropy contributions to force curve.

point, both the enthalpy and entropy decrease very rapidly. In molecular terms, this represents the onset of a stress-induced crystallization, with the rapid decrease in enthalpy indicating an exothermic heat change. It can be shown by the methods of statistical mechanics that the entropy change between a stretched and an unstretched state, *in the absence of crystallization,* is [22]:

$$S - S_0 = -\frac{1}{2} N_0 k \left[\left(\frac{l}{l_0} \right)^2 + 2 \frac{l_0}{l} - 3 \right] \tag{12.8}$$

The quantity N_0 is the number of "network chains" in the unstretched elastomer. In all synthetic rubbers the flexible chainlike molecules are entangled and randomly coiled. If the rubber has been vulcanized, there will also be occasional primary bonds linking the linear molecules into a three-dimensional network. In a typical vulcanized elastomer, there may be of the order of a primary bond every 100 to 300 chain atoms. In unvulcanized rubbers, the entanglement points are spaced in about the same manner and may be thought of as *temporary cross-links.* In the unstretched state, the molecules continually change from one conformation to another, but the spacing between cross-links remains about constant. A *network chain* is, by definition, the length of chain between two cross-linking points. Thus, there can be many network chains per polymer molecule. From Eq. (12.6), and (12.8), one can derive an equation for the tensile force:

$$f_T = \frac{N_0 k T}{l_0} \left[\frac{l}{l_0} - \left(\frac{l_0}{l} \right)^2 \right] \tag{12.9}$$

If crystallization does not occur, there is very little volume change on stretching, so that $l_0 A_0 = l A$. The relationship between true stress, $s = f_T / A$, and strain for an ideal elastomer is thus

$$s = nRT \left[\left(\frac{l}{l_0} \right)^2 - \frac{l_0}{l} \right] \tag{12.10}$$

where n is the number of moles of network chains per unit volume. If the density of the elastomer is ρ_v and the average molecular weight of a network chain is M_c, then $\rho_v = nM_c$ and

$$s = \frac{\rho_v RT}{M_c} \left[\left(\frac{l}{l_0} \right)^2 - \frac{l_0}{l} \right] \tag{12.11}$$

The Young's modulus of the elastomer may be defined as

$$E_Y = l \left(\frac{\partial s}{\partial l} \right)_T$$

$$= \frac{\rho_v RT}{M_c} \left[2 \left(\frac{l}{l_0} \right)^2 + \frac{l_0}{l} \right] \tag{12.12}$$

Thus, one sees that Young's modulus increases as the temperature, number of cross-links (or entanglements), and the percent elongation increase, as expected. For small deformations

$$E_{\lim l/l_0 \to 1.0} = \frac{3\rho_v RT}{M_c} \tag{12.13}$$

If the density is about 1 gm/cm³ at 300°K, the limiting value of Young's modulus is about $10^9/M_c$ kg$_w$/m² ($10^6/M_c$ psi). For natural rubber (Fig. 12.2), this means that $M_c \doteq 10^4$ kg/kg mole. This is, in fact, a typical number for most cross-linked natural and synthetic rubbers.

12.3
Viscous flow

The deformation of organic polymers at almost any temperature, and of most other materials at elevated temperature, is a function of both stress and time. This time-dependent deformation may be either recoverable (elastic) or non-recoverable (viscous). Indeed, many materials exhibit both types of deformation simultaneously (i.e., they are viscoelastic). Viscous flow will be discussed in this section, and viscoelasticity will be discussed in the next.

The viscosity of gases was briefly discussed in Chap. 2 from the viewpoint of kinetic theory. The resistance to flow develops when molecules from a faster-moving plane in the gas transfer some of their momentum to molecules in a slower-moving plane. Equations (2.83) and (2.95) show that the viscosity of a gas is nearly independent of pressure and increases with temperature. This simplified analysis *cannot* be applied to condensed systems because of the proximity of adjacent layers of molecules and the strength of the intermolecular forces.

By definition, the viscosity η_v is the ratio of a one-dimensional shear stress to a one-dimensional rate of strain:

$$\tau = \eta_v \left(\frac{d\epsilon_s}{dt} \right) \tag{12.14}$$

Viscosity has the units of force $\times$ time/length^2 or mass/length $\times$ time. A *poise* is defined as 1 g/cm-sec. There are many commercially available viscometers for measuring the viscosity as a function of time, temperature, and shear rate. Among the more important types are capillary tubes, cone-and-plates, rotating cylinders, falling balls, and parallel-plate plastometers [8]. The type of viscometer used depends on the viscosity range and the type of material being tested. Whereas gases have viscosities of the order of 10^{-4} poise at 20°C, liquids have viscosities in the range of 10^{-2} poise for water to 10^{10} poises for heavy tars. One may also describe the flow properties of glassy solids by a viscosity, but here the range is 10^{15} to 10^{20} poises.

There have been several molecular theories of the viscosity of liquids, but they are complex and beyond the scope of this text. A semiempirical equation proposed by Andrade [2] for liquid metals at their melting points is

$$\eta_v = 2.78 \times 10^{10} \frac{m}{v_m^{1/3}} \Theta_D \tag{12.15}$$

where m is grams per molecule, v_m is cubic centimeters per molecule, Θ_D is the Debye temperature of the material, and η_v is the viscosity in poises. Andrade found that predictions using Eq. (12.15) compared well with experimental data. An accurate semiempirical equation for the viscosity of liquids has been proposed by Doolittle [7], among others:

$$\ln \eta_v = \ln A + \frac{Bv_0}{v - v_0}$$

$$= \ln A + \frac{Bv_0}{v_f} \tag{12.16}$$

It is based on the fact that the viscosity of most liquids is nearly independent of temperature and pressure at constant specific volume. The quantities A and B are constants that depend on the material. The specific volume in cubic centimeters per gram is symbolized by v, and the specific volume at absolute zero is v_0. The increase in volume above absolute zero, $v - v_0$, is called the *free volume* (also excess volume) of the fluid.

The viscous flow of simple liquids may also be described as a "thermally activated" process [12] with a molecule jumping from one lattice point to another in the fluid. Although the liquid state cannot have any long-range geometric order, as in the crystalline state, it is not unreasonable to assume that some localized, short-range order exists. Thus, any given molecule is surrounded by a fixed number of nearest neighbors which are arranged in some specific geometry. The next layer of molecules has a less perfect geometry relative to the central molecule, while succeeding layers are increasingly more disordered relative to this central atom. This lack of long-range order can be accounted for by assuming a fixed geometry and imagining that vacancies, or "holes," are present. Thus, one can visualize a liquid (or a solid for that matter) as an almost perfect geometric lattice consisting of a mixture of holes and atoms. As was shown in Chap. 6, the number of holes in the structure will be a function of temperature. In normal liquids, the hole concentration may be of the order of 0.5 percent and may go as high as 50 percent as the liquid approaches its critical point. The hole theories of liquids can qualitatively account for many of the properties of simple liquids, including viscous flow [13].

Figure 12.4 shows a small region of a simple liquid with two adjacent vacancies in the lattice. One can visualize atom 1, for example, jumping into a vacancy by breaking the atomic bonds holding it in its initial position. If ΔE_D is the activation energy required to move from position 1 to position a, one can represent these two positions as minima in equal-potential wells (Fig. 12.4b). The "jumping frequency" is the same in both directions and is a function of the temperature and the "activation energy" for the process:

$$\dot{j}_{1\to a} = \dot{j}_{a\to 1} = A_f \exp\left(-\frac{\Delta E_D}{RT}\right) \quad \frac{\text{jumps}}{\text{sec}} \qquad (12.17)$$

where A_f is the frequency factor for the process.

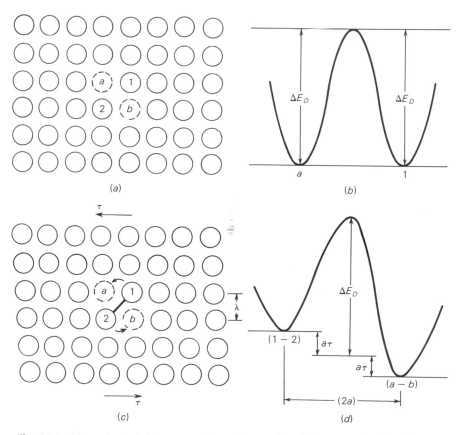

Fig. 12.4 The activated-state concept may be used to devise a mechanism for viscous flow in liquids. (a) Liquid structure with vacancies; (b) equipotential wells, no external stress; (c) shear of the liquid; (d) distortion of potential well by external stress.

Self-diffusion occurs, but over a time interval longer than the period of the motion there is no net relative movement of the molecules. If a shearing stress τ is imposed on the liquid, one can also visualize atoms 1 and 2 coupling and "rotating" into positions a and b (Fig. 12.4c). A rotation from position 1-2 to position a-b is aided by the shear stress, which reduces the required thermal energy for activation, while a rotation from a-b to 1-2 requires motion against the external stress, thus increasing the activation energy. If this extra energy is proportional to the external stress (energy = force × distance):

$$j_{1-2\to ab} = A_f \exp\left(-\frac{\Delta E_D - a\tau}{RT}\right) \tag{12.18}$$

$$j_{ab\to 12} = A_f \exp\left(-\frac{\Delta E_D + a\tau}{RT}\right) \tag{12.19}$$

(See Fig. 12.4d). This leads to a net relative motion of the atoms which is a function of temperature, shear stress, and activation energy.

$$
\begin{aligned}
j_{\text{net}} &= A_f \left[\exp\left(-\frac{\Delta E_D - a\tau}{RT}\right) - \exp\left(-\frac{\Delta E_D + a\tau}{RT}\right) \right] \\
&= \left[A_f \exp\left(-\frac{\Delta E_D}{RT}\right) \right] \left[\exp\frac{a\tau}{RT} - \exp\left(-\frac{a\tau}{RT}\right) \right] \\
&= \left[2A_f \exp\left(-\frac{\Delta E_D}{RT}\right) \right] \sinh\frac{a\tau}{RT} = \frac{\lambda}{2a}\frac{d\epsilon_s}{dt}
\end{aligned}
\tag{12.20}
$$

where the net flux is related to the net velocity by $\Delta v = j_{\text{net}}(2a)$ and the rate of strain is defined by $d\epsilon_s/dt = \Delta v/\lambda$ (see Fig. 12.4). Rewriting Eq. (12.20), one obtains the shear stress as a function of the rate of strain:

$$
\begin{aligned}
\tau &= \frac{1}{2A_f}\left(\exp\frac{\Delta E_D}{RT}\right)\tau\left(\operatorname{csch}\frac{a\tau}{RT}\right)\frac{\lambda}{2a}\frac{d\epsilon_s}{dt} \\
&= \eta_v(\tau,T)\frac{d\epsilon_s}{dt}
\end{aligned}
\tag{12.21}
$$

$$\eta_v(\tau,T) = \frac{RT\lambda}{4a^2 A_f}\left(\exp\frac{\Delta E_D}{RT}\right)\frac{a\tau}{RT}\operatorname{csch}\frac{a\tau}{RT} \tag{12.22}$$

The quantity η_v is the viscosity of the fluid and is the proportionality factor between stress and rate of strain. Just as the elastic moduli are measures of the resistance to elastic deformation, so viscosity is a measure of the resistance to viscous deformation.

In the limit of $a\tau/RT \ll 1$:

$$\eta_v(T) \doteq \frac{RT\lambda}{4a^2 A_f}\exp\frac{\Delta E_D}{RT} \tag{12.23}$$

$$\tau = \eta_v(T)\frac{d\epsilon_s}{dt} \tag{12.24}$$

Equation (12.24) is simply the definition of a *Newtonian fluid,* and $\eta_v(T)$ is the *coefficient of viscosity.* Many simple fluids are Newtonian in that their viscosities are independent of shear stress. Figure 12.5 shows viscosity data for water (polar and hydrogen-bonded) and benzene (nonpolar) in the liquid state. The viscosities of both are perfectly independent of shear stress, but their temperature dependence is not as simple as expected from Eq. (12.23). The apparent activation energy for benzene is almost constant, but for water it decreases rapidly as the temperature increases. This effect is very likely associated with the hydrogen bonding in the water. This order of agreement is not uncommon, even with simple fluids, and it points out that this kind of a mathematical model is only a rough approximation of the actual flow character. The activation energy ΔE_D is related to both the energy required to break chemical bonds and the energy required to form a large enough hole to permit a free diffusion of the particle into a new lattice position. One may thus expect to find a simple relationship between activation energy and latent heat of vaporization (which involves breaking a molecule away from the surface). Eyring has found [12] that, for many nonassociated, nonmetallic liquids, ΔE_D is a fraction of the energy of vaporization of the liquid:

$$\Delta E_D = \frac{\Delta U_{\text{vap}}}{n} \tag{12.25}$$

where n is a slightly temperature-dependent quantity with values of the order

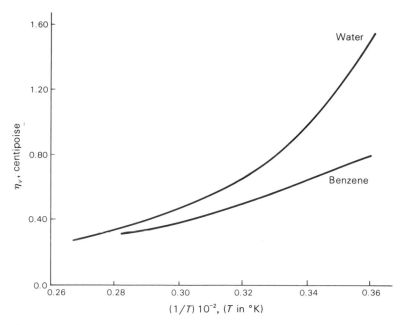

Fig. 12.5 The temperature dependence of the viscosity of benzene follows an Arrhenius rate expression, but a similar relation for water is more complex.

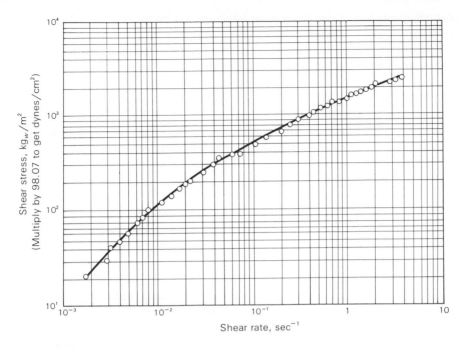

Fig. 12.6 Alathon-14 polyethylene resin is a non-Newtonian fluid at 126°C. (By permission from J. M. McKelvey, "Polymer Processing," John Wiley & Sons, Inc., New York, 1962.)

of 3 to 4. In general, for nonpolar, spherical molecules, n lies nearer 3, while for more complex molecules n lies nearer 4.

Equation (12.22) is not always a good representation of the "apparent viscosity" of "non-Newtonian" fluids. Over narrow ranges of temperature and shear stress, however, it is often adequate. Figure 12.6 shows a flow curve for molten polyethylene in steady shear at constant temperature. This is typical of a large percentage of complex fluids under *steady* shearing conditions. The "non-Newtonian" viscosity decreases as the rate of strain increases. This is termed "pseudo-plastic" behavior. One could curve-fit Eq. (12.21) to these data over some of the range, but it is usually more valuable to use empirical expressions which are easier to work with. Two such equations are the power-law model [Eq. (12.26)] and the Ellis model [Eq. (12.27)].

$$\tau = K \left(\frac{d\epsilon_s}{dt}\right)^n \qquad \text{power law} \qquad\qquad (12.26)$$

$$\tau = \frac{a}{1 + b\tau^m} \frac{d\epsilon_s}{dt} \qquad \text{Ellis model} \qquad\qquad (12.27)$$

The experimentally determined quantities K, n, a, b, and m are generally functions of temperature. Thus, one can curve-fit viscosity data at a given temperature with either a two- or a three-parameter empirical function. A molecular interpretation of non-Newtonian behavior will be given in Sec. 12.5, after the discussion of viscoelasticity.

The viscosity of polymeric materials is primarily a function of shear stress, temperature, and molecular weight. The shear-stress dependence for a given material at constant temperature has already been given by Eqs. (12.26) and (12.27). The temperature dependence of the viscosity can normally be represented by the exponential function, given by Eq. (12.22), as long as no transitions occur over the temperature range being considered. For most purposes, Eq. (12.22) may be rewritten for a specific material at constant stress as

$$\eta_v = A_f \exp \frac{\Delta E_D}{RT} \qquad (12.28)$$

where A_f is a constant. The temperature dependence of viscosity for polyethylene is shown in Fig. 12.7. In general, the activation energy is a function of both strain rate and stress and thus should be measured at either a constant strain rate or a constant stress.

The activation energy for the viscous flow of low-molecular-weight compounds is generally of the order of one-fourth the heat of vaporization, which increases roughly in proportion to degree of polymerization in a homologous series of compounds. At relatively low degrees of polymerization, however, ΔE_D becomes smaller than this, tapering off to a constant value, as shown in Fig. 12.8. At very high degrees of polymerization (where one cannot measure a heat of vaporization), the activation energy is independent of molecular weight. Under these conditions, the temperature dependence of the viscosity can be separated from the molecular-weight dependence:

$$\eta_v = f(T)g(M_w) \qquad (12.29)$$

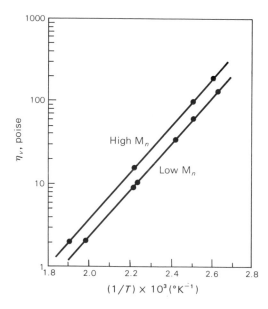

Fig. 12.7 The viscosity of polyethylene depends on both temperature and molecular weight. (Data from Ref. 4.)

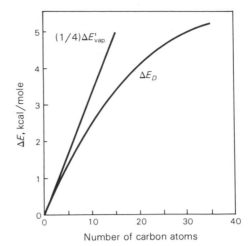

Fig. 12.8 Relation between energy of activation for viscous flow and heat of vaporization for linear hydrocarbons [12].

These two facts lead to the concept that the viscous flow of a polymer involves a coordinated sequence of segmental jumps. A small segment of the molecule is activated by a characteristic energy and "jumps" into a new position. Since adjacent segments are connected by primary valence bonds, other segments follow suit. A net motion of the whole molecule must involve a sequence of jumps. When chain length increases, the coordination becomes progressively more difficult and the viscosity increases, as is seen qualitatively in Fig. 12.7 for two different-molecular-weight polyethylenes. On the other hand, the unit jump sequence involves only a relatively small segment of the chain, and thus the activation energy is independent of the molecular weight. The experimental activation energies for various polymers indicate that segmental lengths are probably of the order of 6 to 16 carbon atoms along the polymer chain (7 to 20 Å).

The temperature dependence of viscosity may also be given by:

$$\left(\frac{\eta_v}{\eta_{v0}}\right)_{d\epsilon/dt} = \exp\left[-(b)_{d\epsilon_s/dt}(T - T_0)\right] \tag{12.30}$$

where b is a constant for a given rate of strain and the zero subscript refers to a reference state. Some experimental data are given in Table 12.1. The reciprocal of the constant, $1/b$, is a measure of the temperature sensitivity of the material. It represents the number of degrees that the temperature must be raised to decrease the viscosity by a factor of e. Lucite 140 is the most temperature-sensitive and polyethylene the least sensitive of the materials listed in Table 12.1.

The viscosity does not have an exponential temperature dependence when the polymer approaches its glass-transition temperature. This is to be expected since the nature of the segmental jumps should certainly depend on the freedom of the polymer molecules. Williams, Landel, and Ferry [23] have utilized the same equation as Doolittle (12.16) to correlate viscosity data near

Table 12.1

Viscosity characteristics of several polymers [4]

Material	Shear rate, sec^{-1}	$1/b$, °C
Polymethylmethacrylate (Lucite 140)	100	24
Cellulose acetate	100	32
Nylon 6-6	100	56
Polyethylene	100	85
Polystyrene	100	46

the glass-transition temperature.   The viscosity at temperature T relative to the viscosity at a reference temperature T_s is

$$\log_{10} \frac{\eta_v(T)}{\eta_v(T_s)} = \frac{1}{2.303} \left(\frac{1}{x_v} - \frac{1}{x_{vs}} \right) \tag{12.31}$$

where x_v is interpreted as the *fractional free volume* at temperature T, $v_f(T)/v(T)$. The fractional free volume at T relative to that at the reference temperature is approximately

$$x_v - x_{vs} = (\alpha_T - \alpha_s)(T - T_s) \tag{12.32}$$

where the α are the volumetric thermal-expansion coefficients at the two temperatures.   Then

Table 12.2

WLF equation parameters for several polymers *

Polymer	T_s, °K	T_g, °K
Polyisobutylene	243	202
Polymethylacrylate	378	324
Polyvinylacetate	349	301
Polystyrene	408	373
Polymethylmethacrylate	433	378
Polyvinylacetal	380	
Butadiene-styrene:		
75-25	268	216
60-40	283	235
50-50	296	252
30-70	328	291

* From F. R. Eirich, "Rheology," vol. 1, p. 453, Academic Press Inc., New York, 1956.

$$\log_{10} \frac{\eta_v(T)}{\eta_v(T_s)} = -\frac{1}{2.303\, x_s} \frac{T - T_s}{x_s/(\alpha_T - \alpha_s) + T - T_s} \tag{12.33}$$

It has been found experimentally that Eq. (12.33) can correlate viscosity data for many polymers in the temperature range T_g to $T_g + 100$ when

$$\log_{10} \frac{\eta_v(T)}{\eta_v(T_s)} = -\frac{8.86(T - T_s)}{101.6 + T - T_s} \tag{12.34}$$

where the temperature T_s is an adjustable parameter. Very often, $T_s \doteq T_g + 50$. Table 12.2 lists values of T_s and T_g for several polymers, and Fig. 12.9 is a plot

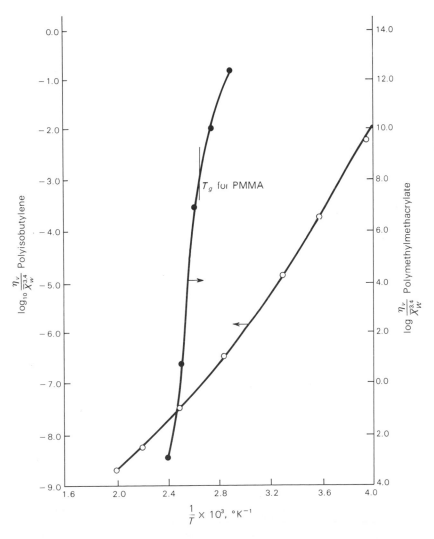

Fig. 12.9 The viscosities of polyisobutylene and polymethylmethacrylate change by many orders of magnitude over relatively narrow temperature ranges [8].

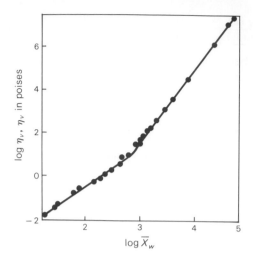

Fig. 12.10 Molecular-weight dependence of polyisobutylene at 217°C. [T. G. Fox and P. J. Flory, *J. Phys. Chem.*, **55**: 221 (1951).]

Table 12.3

Viscosity relationships for long-chain polymers *

Polymer	Empirical equation	For $\bar{X}_w$ greater than
Linear nonpolar polymers		
Polyisobutylene	$\log \eta_v = 3.4 \log \bar{X}_w + 5.5 \times 10^5/T^2 - 10.93$	610
Polystyrene	$\log \eta_v = 3.4 \log \bar{X}_w + 2.7 \times 10^{16}/T^6 - 9.51$	730
Poly(dimethyl siloxane)	$\log \eta_{v25°} = 3.4 \log \bar{X}_w - 9.0$ (stokes)	~950
Linear polar polymers		
Polymethyl methacrylate	$\log \eta_v = 3.4 \log \bar{X}_w + 4.5 \times 10^{34}/T^{13} - 7.4$	208
Polyvinyl acetate	$\log \eta_v = 3.4 \log \bar{X}_w + 9.77 \times 10^{10}/T^4 - 10.05$	
Decamethylene sebacate	$\log \eta_{v109°} = 3.4 \log \bar{X}_w - 8.2$	290
Decamethylene adipate	$\log \eta_v = 3.4 \log \bar{X}_w + 3.4 \times 10^5/T^2 - 11.2$	280
Decamethylene succinate	$\log \eta_{v109°} = 3.4 \log \bar{X}_w - 8.0$	290
Diethyl adipate	$\log \eta_v = 3.4 \log \bar{X}_w + 2.1 \times 10^{10}/T^4 - 9.1$	290
ω-Hydroxy undecanoates	$\log \eta_{v90°} = 3.4 \log \bar{X}_w - 7.5$	< 326
Effect of branching		
Poly(ε-caprolactam):		
Linear	$\log \eta_{v253°} = 3.4 \log \bar{X}_w - 8.0$	340
Tetrachain	$\log \eta_{v253°} = 3.4 \log \bar{X}_w - 8.1$	390
Octachain	$\log \eta_{v253°} = 3.4 \log \bar{X}_w - 8.7$	550

The tabulation is taken from Ref. 8, p. 456, and the data are from a variety of sources.

of viscosity vs. temperature for polyisobutylene and polymethylmethacrylate in the vicinity of T_g.

A large amount of experimental data exists to show that the molecular-weight dependence of the viscosity for high-molecular-weight polymers is

$$\log \eta_v = 3.4 \log \bar{X}_W + K(T) \qquad \text{for } \bar{M}_W > M_B \tag{12.35}$$

where $\bar{X}_w$ is the weight-average degree of polymerization, $K(T)$ is the temperature-dependent portion of the viscosity, and M_B is the lowest molecular weight at which the relationship holds. Experimentally, there is always a very sharp change in slope of a log η_v versus log M_W plot at M_B, as is shown for polyisobutylene in Fig. 12.10. Generally, the slope below M_B is roughly one, but the precise relationship is fairly complex. It is clear, however, that the abrupt change in behavior is associated with an abrupt change in the mechanism for the flow process. Values of M_B are generally of the order of 10^4 kg/kg mole, which are the same order of magnitude as the molecular weights of network chains, M_C. It is thus very likely that M_B is also associated with chain-entanglement effects. Empirical viscosity equations for a number of polymers are given in Table 12.3.

12.4
Viscoelasticity — Creep and stress relaxation

When a material exhibits both elastic and viscous characteristics simultaneously, it is said to be *viscoelastic.* The total strain on the material is then a complex function of stress, temperature, time, and the manner in which the load is applied. The simplest aspects of viscoelasticity can be characterized by examining creep and stress relaxation characteristics of a material. A *creep* (flow) curve is obtained by applying a constant stress s_0 to a body and measuring the deformation as a function of time (Fig. 12.11a). The apparent modulus of elasticity, i.e., the ratio of the stress to the strain, is a function of time and, in many cases, stress. The results of a creep experiment are generally reported in terms of a *compliance $J(t)$*, which is a function of time:

$$J(t) = \frac{\epsilon_s(t)}{s_0} \tag{12.36}$$

When the compliance is independent of stress, the material is said to be a linear viscoelastic material. The nature of the flow curve depends on the nature of the material. Raw rubber, for example, is a thermoplastic material, and thus there are no chemical cross-links between molecules. The compliance will steadily increase until the material fails. A vulcanized rubber, on the other hand, is a space polymer, and the molecules are held together by primary bonds. The compliance will increase until the network is stretched enough to resist further deformation; then it will level off to a constant value.

A *stress-relaxation* curve is obtained by stretching a material to a fixed deformation ϵ_{s0} and measuring the decrease in stress as a function of time

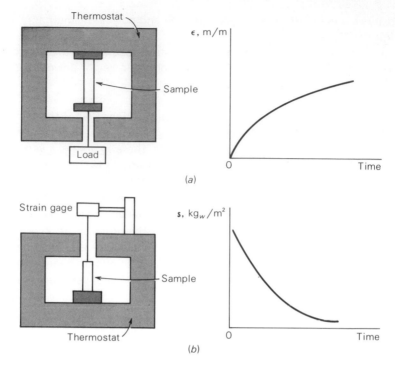

Fig. 12.11   Creep and stress-relaxation measurements are used to characterize the viscoelastic properties of materials.   (a) Creep measurement; (b) stress-relaxation measurement.

(Fig. 12.11b).   The ratio of the stress and the strain is again a function of time and, in many cases, strain.   The results of a relaxation experiment are generally reported in terms of a *relaxation modulus* $E(t)$, which is a function of time:

$$E(t) = \frac{s(t)}{\epsilon_{s0}} \tag{12.37}$$

or for a shear stress $\tau(t)$:

$$G(t) = \frac{\tau(t)}{\epsilon_{s0}} \tag{12.38}$$

When the relaxation modulus is independent of strain, the material is said to be a linear viscoelastic material.   In a raw rubber, the relaxation modulus will decrease to zero, while in a vulcanized rubber it will level off to a constant value.

Most of the theoretical analyses of viscoelasticity are restricted to linear viscoelastic behavior.   Most commercial materials are not linear, but the approximation is reasonably good for small stresses and strains.   When linear behavior is realized, the moduli may be estimated for any complex history of stresses and strains by utilizing the *Boltzmann superposition principle.*

Suppose a constant stress s_0 is applied at zero time.   The total creep strain at time t_0 is then $\epsilon_s(t_0) = J(t_0)s_0$. At t_0 an additional stress s_1 is added. The total strain at time t, for a *linear* material, may then be approximated as

$$\epsilon_s(t) = J(t)s_0 + J(t - t_0)s_1 \tag{12.39}$$

The total strain is thus caused by a superposition of the two stresses acting independently of one another. Equation (12.39) may be generalized to an arbitrary history of stresses:

$$\epsilon_s(t) = \sum_{t_i=-\infty}^{t_i=t} J(t - t_i)s_i \tag{12.40}$$

Equation (12.40) is a statement of the Boltzmann superposition principle for the creep of a linear viscoelastic material. For a continuous loading cycle, the summation may be replaced by an integral:

$$\epsilon_s(t) = \int_{-\infty}^{t} J(t - s) \frac{ds}{ds} ds \tag{12.41}$$

In general then, if one knows the compliance $J(t)$ and the loading history, one may evaluate the creep deformation as a function of time. An analogous expression may be written for the variation of stress with time in a relaxation experiment:

$$\tau(t) = \int_{-\infty}^{t} G(t - s) \frac{d\epsilon_s}{ds} ds \tag{12.42}$$

Thus, if one wishes to predict the creep or stress relaxation properties of a viscoelastic solid, the compliance and relaxation moduli must be evaluated.

One of the simplest equations used to describe viscoelastic behavior is the *Maxwell fluid model.* This model describes the total strain of a body as the sum of an elastic and a viscous component:

$$\epsilon_s(t) = \epsilon_{sE} + \epsilon_{sV} \tag{12.43}$$

If the elastic element is Hookeian and the viscous element is Newtonian,

$$\frac{d\epsilon_s}{dt} = \frac{1}{G_s} \frac{d\tau}{dt} + \frac{\tau}{\eta_v} \tag{12.44}$$

$$\tau = \eta_v \frac{d\epsilon_s}{dt} - \frac{\eta_v}{G_s} \frac{d\tau}{dt} \tag{12.45}$$

Equation (12.45) expresses the shear stress as a function of rate of strain, rate of stress, and two experimental constants. The flow curve for a Maxwell fluid is obtained by setting $d\tau/dt = 0$ (that is, $\tau = s_0$).

$$s_0 = \eta_v \frac{d\epsilon_s}{dt} \qquad \epsilon_s = \epsilon_{s0} \text{ at } t = 0 \tag{12.46}$$

$$J(t) = \frac{\epsilon_s(t)}{s_0} = \frac{\epsilon_{s0}}{s_0} + \frac{1}{\eta_v} t = J_0 + \frac{t}{\eta_v} \tag{12.47}$$

where J_0 is an instantaneous response and η_v is an effective viscosity. Equation (12.47) is plotted in Fig. 12.12a. The relaxation curve for a Maxwell fluid is obtained by setting $d\epsilon_s/dt = 0$ (that is, ϵ_s is constant).

$$G(t) = \frac{\tau(t)}{\epsilon_{s0}} = -\frac{\eta_v}{G_s}\frac{dG(t)}{dt} \qquad \tau = \tau_0 \text{ at } t = 0 \qquad (12.48)$$

$$\ln\frac{G(t)}{G(0)} = -\frac{t}{\eta_v/G_s} = -\frac{t}{\lambda_R} \qquad (12.49)$$

Equation (12.49) is plotted in Fig. 12.12b. The quantity λ_R, called the *relaxation time* for the material, is a measure of the resistance to viscous flow, and $G(0)$ is the initial modulus for the material. If a solid is suddenly stretched to a constant strain ϵ_{s0} and held, a rearrangement of molecules will cause a reduction of the stress level. The less resistance the molecules have to flow, the faster the reduction in stress (i.e., the lower the relaxation time). Simple liquids such as water have relaxation times of the order of microseconds, and thus no time effects are apparent under the usual measuring conditions. Many complex liquids and solids, on the other hand, have relaxation times of the order of minutes to years. A comparison of (a) and (b) of Fig. 12.12 with the experimental data of Figs. 12.13 and 12.14 shows a similarity in behavior, but actually a Maxwell model is far too simple to adequately describe the true behavior. The relaxation curves, for example, are somewhat broader than the theoretical curve shown in Fig. 12.12b.

Another very simple model that is commonly used to describe *retarded elasticity* is the *Voigt-Kelvin solid*. In this case, the total stress on the body is divided into an elastic and a viscous component.

$$\tau_T = \tau_E + \tau_V \qquad (12.50)$$

If the elastic element is Hookeian and the viscous element is Newtonian,

$$\tau = G_s\epsilon_s + \eta_v\frac{d\epsilon_s}{dt} \qquad (12.51)$$

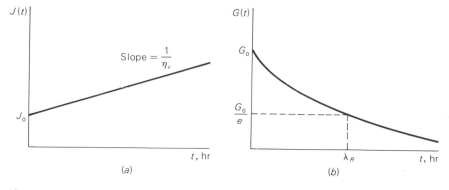

Fig. 12.12 Viscoelastic behavior of a Maxwell fluid. (a) Flow curve for a Maxwell fluid; (b) stress relaxation curve for a Maxwell fluid.

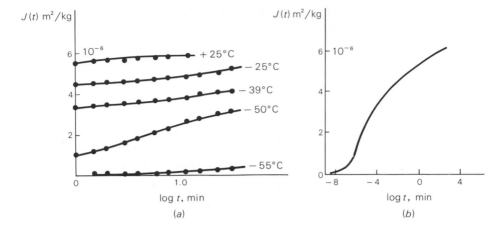

Fig. 12.13 The creep rate of a cross-linked SBR rubber is strongly dependent on temperature, but all data can be reduced to a single composite curve using the time-temperature superposition principle. (a) Creep measurements at various temperatures; (b) composite creep curve at 25°C using data of (a) and time-temperature superposition principle [5]. (By permission from F. Bueche, "Physical Properties of Polymers," Interscience Publishers, Inc., New York, 1962.)

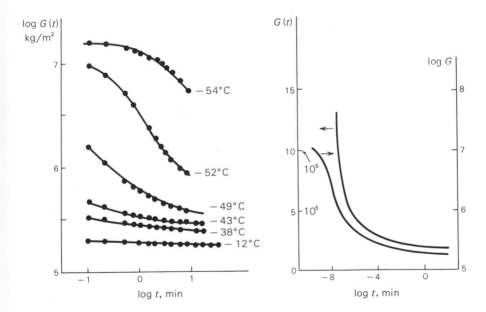

Fig. 12.14 The relaxation rate of a cross-linked SBR rubber is strongly dependent on temperature, but all data can be reduced to a single composite curve by using the time-temperature superposition principle. (a) Stress-relaxation measurements at various temperatures; (b) composite relaxation curve at 25°C using data of (a) and time-temperature superposition principle [5]. (By permission from F. Bueche, "Physical Properties of Polymers," Interscience Publishers, Inc., New York, 1962.)

The flow curve ($\tau = $ constant $= \tau_0$) is obtained by solving Eq. (12.51) with the boundary condition $\epsilon_s = 0$ at $t = 0$ to give

$$J(t) = \frac{\epsilon_s(t)}{\tau_0} = \frac{1}{G_s}\left[1 - \exp\left(-\frac{t}{\lambda_R}\right)\right]$$

$$= J(\infty)\left[1 - \exp\left(-\frac{t}{\lambda_R}\right)\right] \tag{12.52}$$

where $J(\infty)$ represents the "equilibrium compliance" of the material. Equation (12.52) is plotted in Fig. 12.15a. If a stress τ_0 is suddenly applied to a Voigt-Kelvin solid, it will exhibit a retarded elastic stretching to a constant value, and λ_R is called the retardation time of the material. This kind of material also shows "*elastic memory.*" If the solid is strained to $\epsilon_{s\infty}$ and the stress is suddenly removed, a retarded change to zero strain will occur (Fig. 12.15b). Solving Eq. (12.51) with the conditions $\tau_0 = 0$, $\epsilon_s = \epsilon_{s\infty}$ at $t = 0$, one obtains:

$$J(t) = \frac{\epsilon_s}{\tau_0} = J(\infty)\exp\left(\frac{-t}{\lambda_R}\right) \tag{12.53}$$

Voigt solids do not show stress relaxation at constant strain. From Eq. (12.51), $\epsilon_s = \epsilon_{s\infty}$ for all t, $d\epsilon_s/dt = 0$, $\tau = G\epsilon_{s\infty}$. Again, there is some similarity between the flow curve (Fig. 12.15a) and the experimental data (Fig. 12.13), but a good curve-fit is not possible.

The actual viscoelastic behavior of most materials is more complicated than the simple models just described. Figure 12.13b is a composite creep curve for cross-linked SBR at 25°C. An adequate curve-fit of the data may be obtained by combining a Maxwell fluid with a *series* of n Voigt-Kelvin elements.

$$J(t) = J_0 + \frac{t}{\eta_v} + \sum_{n=1}^{n} J_n\left[1 - \exp\left(-\frac{t}{\lambda_{Rn}}\right)\right] \tag{12.54}$$

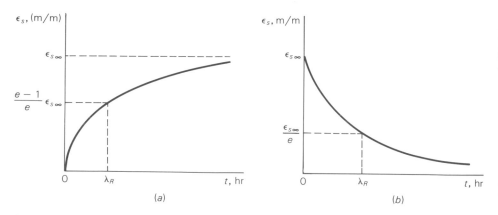

Fig. 12.15   Viscoelastic behavior of a Voigt-Kelvin solid. (a) Retarded elasticity of a Voigt-Kelvin solid; (b) plastic memory of a Voigt-Kelvin solid.

Naturally, it is clear that we are forcing a curve-fit by using a large number of experimental constants (J_0, η_v, n different J_n, and n different λ_R). These quantities do, however, have physical significance, and the molecular structure of SBR (or any polymer) makes the necessity of a large number of constants very plausible. The first term on the right side of Eq. (12.54) represents the instantaneous elastic response of the material. The magnitude of the compliance is a function of the primary carbon-to-carbon bonding along the main chains of the rubber. The second term is the viscous flow of the solid under a constant load. The magnitude of this term depends upon the resistance of the individual molecules to a relative slippage. This is a function of molecular symmetry, intensity of intermolecular attraction, and the degree of cross-linking. A higher degree of cross-linking, for example, will decrease the magnitude of this term. The last set of terms in Eq. (12.54) represents the delayed elastic response of the material. Physically it represents the uncoiling, disentangling, and temporary orientation of the chains. In a complex amorphous mass, one can visualize chains of different size, with some portions more tightly entangled than others. It is not hard to understand why some portions of the chain could have higher "retardation times" than other portions. In a very complex structure it is reasonable to expect a distribution of retardation times. If the values of λ_{Rn} are spaced closely enough, it is much more convenient to replace the summation with an integral over all possible values of λ_R. A distribution function may then replace the summation:

$$J(t) = J_0 + \frac{t}{\eta_v} + \int_{-\infty}^{\infty} L \ (\ln \lambda_R) \left[1 - \exp \left(-\frac{t}{\lambda_R} \right) \right] d \ln \lambda_R \tag{12.55}$$

The quantity $L \ (\ln \lambda_R)$ is a distribution function of retardation times.

Analogous expressions can be devised to curve-fit the relaxation data shown in Fig. 12.14. If n Maxwell elements are connected in parallel, the strain on each element is the same and the total stress is the sum of the individual stresses of the elements:

$$G(t) = \sum_{n=1}^{n} \frac{\tau_n(t)}{\epsilon_{s0}} = \sum_{n=1}^{n} G_n(0) \exp \left(-\frac{t}{\lambda_{Rn}} \right) \tag{12.56}$$

Replacing the summation with a distribution function:

$$G(t) = G(\infty) + \int_{-\infty}^{\infty} H \ (\ln \lambda_R) \left[\exp \left(-\frac{t}{\lambda_R} \right) \right] d \ln \lambda_R \tag{12.57}$$

The quantity $H(\ln \lambda_R)$ is the distribution function of relaxation times, and $G(\infty)$ is the limiting value of the relaxation modulus.

Both $L(\ln \lambda_R)$ and $H(\ln \lambda_R)$ are related to the molecular structure of the material. Molecular theory has not developed sufficiently to predict a priori these distribution functions, so they must be determined indirectly by experiment. In theory, it is not necessary to measure both $L(\ln \lambda_R)$ and $H(\ln \lambda_R)$ since they are interrelated [9]. The relationships, however, are fairly complex and contain integrals that do not converge very rapidly. In practice, the usual approach is to calculate the spectrum from the compliances and moduli. It can be shown [9], that to a good approximation

$$H(\ln \lambda_R) \doteq -\left[\frac{dG(t)}{d \ln t} - \frac{d^2G(t)}{(d \ln t)^2}\right]_{t=2\bar{\lambda}_R} \tag{12.58}$$

$$L(\ln \lambda_R) \doteq \left[\frac{dJ(t)}{d \ln t} - \frac{d^2J(t)}{(d \ln t)^2}\right]_{t=2\lambda_R} \tag{12.59}$$

Thus, it is possible to get the distribution functions by evaluating the slopes of plots of $G(t)$ and $J(t)$ as functions of $\ln t$. It is also common to evaluate the compliance from the relaxation modulus, and vice versa. It can be shown that

$$G(t) = \frac{\sin m\pi}{m\pi J(t)} \tag{12.60}$$

where

$$m = \frac{d \ln J(t)}{d \ln t} \tag{12.61}$$

It should be clear from these equations that the various modes of viscoelastic response are interrelated because of their common relationship to molecular structure. In the next section we shall consider the dynamic response of a viscoelastic material.

12.5
Viscoelasticity—Dynamic behavior

If strain were perfectly independent of time, alternate loading and unloading would not create any thermal changes in a material. However, whenever there is a change in the positions of atoms, the intermolecular potential is affected, which, in turn, causes thermal effects. Consider the free-energy change accompanying a small extension dl caused by a constant force F at constant pressure:

$$(dG)_p = (-S \, dT + F \, dl)_p \tag{12.62}$$

Since this is an exact differential equation, the following relationship exists between the coefficients on the right side of the equation:

$$-\left(\frac{\partial S}{\partial l}\right)_{p,T} = \left(\frac{\partial F}{\partial T}\right)_{l,p} \tag{12.63}$$

Equation (12.63) indicates the kind of thermal effects that can be expected. Since the elastic modulus of most materials decreases with increasing temperature, the force required to hold a solid at a given extension l must also decrease. The right-hand side of Eq. (12.63) is therefore negative, so that $(\partial S/\partial l)_{p,T}$ must be positive. This means that, as a material (e.g., a metal) is isothermally stretched at constant pressure, its entropy must increase or, in other words, it must absorb energy from its surroundings in order to maintain its temperature. If the stretching is rapid enough to be adiabatic, the material will not have time to absorb the energy and will therefore cool. Ideal elastomers behave in the opposite manner: $(\partial F/\partial T)_{l,p}$ is positive, $(\partial S/\partial l)_{p,T}$ is negative (this corresponds to an orienting of the long-chain molecules), and adiabatic stretching causes heating. The effect on the stress-strain behavior of a typical material is illustrated in Fig. 12.16a; the phenomenon is called *anelasticity*. If the material is adiabatically stretched to ϵ_{s0}, it will cool. If it is then held with a constant stress s_0, it will heat back to the temperature of the surroundings. Since most materials have positive thermal-expansion coefficients, the material will expand to ϵ_{s1}. Elongation ϵ_{s1} is merely the extension that would be attained directly if the process were carried out isothermally. An adiabatic release of the stress would result in a sudden contraction to $\epsilon_{s1} - \epsilon_{s0}$ and a heating of the material. As the material cooled, it would then contract to zero elongation. It is therefore clear that the apparent modulus of elasticity under adiabatic conditions (i.e., rapid rates of strain) is higher than the modulus under isothermal conditions (i.e., slow rates of strain). This phenomenon leads to "*elastic hysteresis*" at all intermediate rates of strain, as illustrated in Fig. 12.16b. The area within the loop represents the difference between the energy changes on loading and unloading the material. This area is therefore equal to the energy dissipation per cycle of stress. The same effects occur in com-

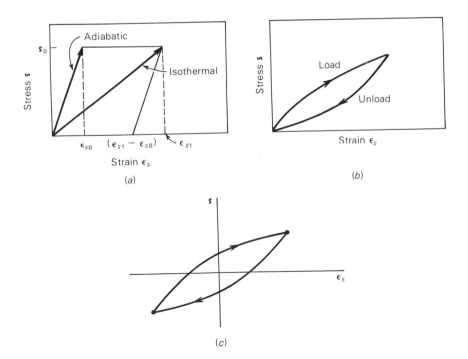

Fig. 12.16 Elastic hysteresis leads to energy dissipation upon cyclic loading. (*a*) Thermoelastic effect; (*b*) elastic hysteresis; (*c*) elastic hysteresis in cyclic loading.

pression, and a typical hysteresis loop for one cycle of alternating tension and compression is shown in Fig. 12.16c. The important fact is that, in real materials, the stress and the strain will not stay in phase, so that cyclic loading will result in a dissipation of energy. The most important results of this phenomenon, from an engineering point of view, are the generation of heat and the damping of vibrations.

We have discussed a thermal cause of elastic hysteresis because it is relatively easy to visualize the mechanism. More important causes of hysteresis are plastic deformation, viscous flow, viscoelasticity, internal diffusion, inhomogeneity, and anisotropy in the material. In general, the important variable is the relaxation time for the process, or, more specifically, the ratio of the relaxation time to the period of the oscillating stress or strain.

In order to describe some typical consequences of anelasticity, let us analyze the behavior of some ideal materials under the influence of an oscillating strain with a frequency ω.

$$\epsilon_s = \epsilon_{s0} \sin \omega t \qquad (12.64)$$

$$\frac{d\epsilon_s}{d(\omega t)} = \epsilon_{s0} \cos \omega t \qquad (12.65)$$

If the solid is ideally elastic and Hooke's law is valid, $\tau = G\epsilon_s$ and the stress and strain are always in phase. The power loss P_L per cycle of strain is calculated by integrating $\tau \, d\epsilon$ over one complete cycle:

$$P_L = \oint \tau \, d\epsilon_s = \int_0^{2\pi} G\epsilon_{s0}^2 \sin \omega t \cos \omega t \, d(\omega t) = 0 \qquad (12.66)$$

Thus, there is no power dissipation during the sinusoidal straining of an ideal Hookeian solid.

If the material is a Newtonian fluid, $\tau = \eta_v \, d\epsilon_s/dt$ and the stress is always 90° out of phase with the strain. The power loss per cycle is then

$$P_L = \oint \tau \, d\epsilon_s$$

$$= \int_0^{2\pi} \omega \eta_v \epsilon_{s0}^2 \cos^2 \omega t \, d(\omega t)$$

$$= \omega \eta_v \epsilon_{s0}^2 \pi \qquad (12.67)$$

If the material is viscoelastic, the stress and strain will be out of phase by an angle somewhere between 0 and 90°. This is known as the loss angle ϕ of the material. If the stress is also written as a sinusoidal function:

$$\tau = G_{\text{eff}} \epsilon_{s0} \sin (\omega t + \phi) \qquad (12.68)$$

$$P_L = \oint G_{\text{eff}} \epsilon_{s0}^2 \sin (\omega t + \phi) \cos \omega t \, d(\omega t)$$

$$= \pi G_{\text{eff}} \epsilon_{s0}^2 \sin \phi \qquad (12.69)$$

$$\sin \phi = \frac{P_L}{\pi G_{\text{eff}} \epsilon_{s0}^2} \qquad (12.70)$$

The sine of the loss angle is a measure of the *specific damping capacity* of the material. Hookeian solids will not dissipate energy under cyclic loading and have a zero damping capacity, while Newtonian fluids dissipate a maximum of energy and have a maximum damping capacity. Most materials will function between these limits with the damping capacity being a function of the frequency of the oscillating stress or strain. Let us look specifically at a Maxwell fluid under oscillating strain:

$$G_S \epsilon_{s0} \cos \omega t = \frac{d\tau}{d(\omega t)} + \frac{\tau}{\omega \lambda_R} \qquad \text{cf. (12.44)} \tag{12.71}$$

Solving with the boundary condition $\tau = \tau_0$ at $t = 0$, one obtains

$$G(t) = \frac{\tau}{\epsilon_{s0}} = \frac{G_S(\omega \lambda_R)^2}{1 + (\omega \lambda_R)^2} \sin \omega t + \frac{G_S \omega \lambda_R}{1 + (\omega \lambda_R)^2} \cos \omega t + \left[\frac{\tau_0}{\epsilon_{s0}} - \frac{G_S \omega \lambda_R}{1 + (\omega \lambda_R)^2} \right] e^{-t/\lambda_R}$$

$$\tag{12.72}$$

After an initial period (i.e., when $t \gg \lambda_R$), the modulus is cyclic and may be divided into in-phase and out-of-phase components. Since $\epsilon_s = \epsilon_{s0} \sin \omega t$,

$$G(t) = \frac{\tau}{\epsilon_{s0}} = \underbrace{\frac{G_S(\omega \lambda_R)^2}{1 + (\omega \lambda_R)^2} \sin \omega t}_{\text{in phase}} + \underbrace{\frac{G_S \omega \lambda_R}{1 + (\omega \lambda_R)^2} \cos \omega t}_{\text{out of phase}} \tag{12.73}$$

The power dissipation per cycle is then

$$P_L = \oint \tau \, d\epsilon_s = \frac{\pi G_S \epsilon_{s0}^2 \omega \lambda_R}{1 + (\omega \lambda_R)^2} \tag{12.74}$$

One may then define an in-phase modulus of elasticity associated with the storage of elastic energy:

$$\text{Storage modulus} = G'(\omega) = \frac{G_S(\omega \lambda_R)^2}{1 + (\omega \lambda_R)^2} \tag{12.75}$$

and an out-of-phase modulus associated with the power loss:

$$\text{Loss modulus} = G''(\omega) = \frac{G_S(\omega \lambda_R)}{1 + (\omega \lambda_R)^2} \tag{12.76}$$

Comparing Eqs. (12.74) and (12.70), one sees that the loss modulus is proportional to the sine of the loss angle (as they are defined here). Figure 12.17 shows the frequency dependence of power loss and storage modulus for a Maxwell fluid under sinusoidal straining. Even though the Maxwell model cannot be used to describe any real material accurately, the results shown in Fig. 12.17 qualitatively describe the behavior of many materials under sinusoidal stressing or straining. The dynamic moduli may also be expressed in terms of the distribution function of relaxation time, $H(\ln \lambda)$:

$$G'(\omega) = \int_{-\infty}^{\infty} H(\ln \lambda_R) \frac{(\omega \lambda_R)^2}{1 + (\omega \lambda_R)^2} \, d \ln \lambda \tag{12.77}$$

$$G''(\omega) = \int_{-\infty}^{\infty} H(\ln \lambda_R) \frac{\omega\lambda_R}{1 + (\omega\lambda_R)^2} \, d\ln \lambda_R \qquad (12.78)$$

Thus, a single elastic constant G_S and a single relaxation time λ_R are replaced by a distribution function which has the effect of broadening the curves shown in Fig. 12.17 and thereby allowing a better curve-fit of experimental data.

By analogy with electrical networks, one may express the moduli in terms of a *complex dynamic modulus* G^* using the relation

$$G^* = G' + iG'' = \frac{\tau}{\epsilon_{s0}} \qquad (12.79)$$

where $i = \sqrt{-1}$. Alternatively, one may define a *complex dynamic compliance* J^*, which is related to the retardation time distribution function $L(\ln \lambda_R)$:

$$J^* = J' - iJ'' \qquad (12.80)$$

As with the other viscoelastic properties, the dynamic properties are interrelated. It can be shown [9] that

$$J^* = \frac{1}{G^*} \qquad (12.81)$$

Thus, it should be clear that if one knows $H(\ln \lambda_R)$ or $L(\ln \lambda_R)$ from theory or simple experiments, all of the pertinent viscoelastic properties may be evaluated.

Let us momentarily return to the phenomenon of non-Newtonian viscous flow. In Sec. 12.3 it was stated that the viscosity of a pseudoplastic, non-Newtonian fluid decreases with increasing rate of strain. In general, the variation,

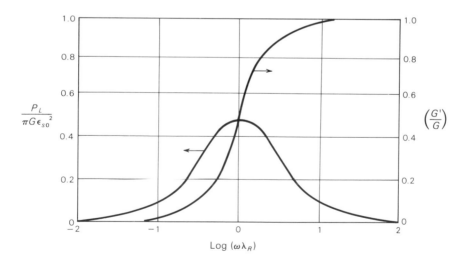

Fig. 12.17 The frequency dependence of the mechanical properties of polymers is qualitatively described by the behavior of a Maxwell model.

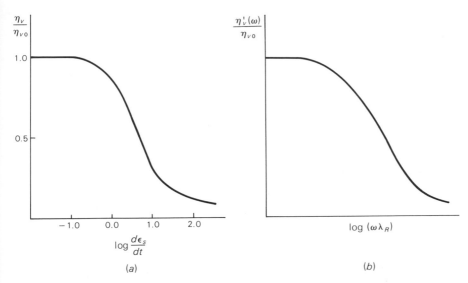

Fig. 12.18   The viscosity of non-Newtonian fluids varies with both rate of strain and frequency. (a) Variation of viscosity with strain rate; (b) variation of dynamic viscosity with frequency.

as shown in Fig. 12.18a, is often several orders of magnitude over a few decades of rate of strain. Just as one may define complex moduli, one may also define a complex viscosity η_v^* as

$$\eta_v^* = \eta_v' - i\eta_v'' \tag{12.82}$$

It can be shown that $\eta_v^* = G^*/i\omega$ and, from Eq. (12.76) for a Maxwell model:

$$\eta_v' = \frac{G''}{\omega} = \frac{G_s \lambda_R}{1 + (\omega\lambda_R)^2}$$

$$= \frac{\eta_{v0}}{1 + (\omega\lambda_R)^2} \tag{12.83}$$

The general shape of the curve of η_v'/η_{v0} versus $\log \omega\lambda_R$, shown in Fig. 12.18b, is seen to be about the same shape as for η_v/η_{v0} versus $\log d\epsilon_s/dt$. This similarity is expected, since *individual polymer molecules* experience oscillatory forces, with frequency $\frac{1}{2} d\epsilon_s/dt$, even though the fluid as a whole is experiencing a steady shearing force. This can be seen more clearly by examining Fig. 12.19. If a randomly coiled polymer molecule is immersed in a viscous matrix that is being sheared, different parts of the molecule will be experiencing different forces at the same time. The net result is that the molecule will rotate as it moves along with the viscous mass. A given segment of the polymer will be pulled away from the center of gravity of the molecule as it rotates past points A and C, while it will be pushed toward the center of gravity as it rotates past points B and D. Thus, each polymer segment is experiencing an oscillatory force with

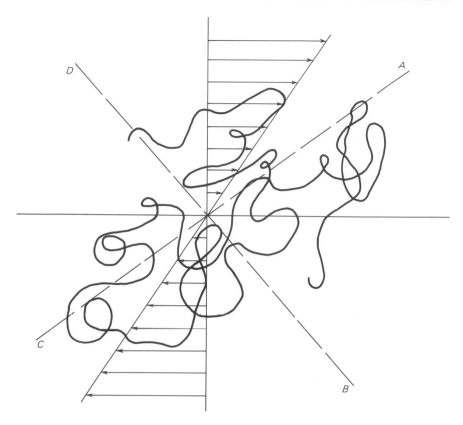

Fig. 12.19 A shear gradient on a randomly coiled polymer molecule causes the molecule to rotate.

a frequency that is double the rotational frequency of the molecule. Since the polymer molecule is rotating relative to the viscous matrix, an energy dissipation will result. When the polymer segments cannot respond instantaneously to the shearing forces, the energy dissipation will be a function of the strain rate. This kind of analysis leads to the following expression for the non-Newtonian viscosity:

$$\eta_v = nRT \sum_{i=1}^{N} \frac{\lambda_{Ri}}{1 + [(d\epsilon_s/dt)\lambda_{Ri}]^2} \tag{12.84}$$

$$\lambda_{Ri} = \frac{\lambda_{R1}}{i^2} \qquad i = 1,2,3,\ldots,N \tag{12.85}$$

The coefficient nRT is related to the elastic properties of the polymer through Eq. (12.10). The similarity between Eq. (12.84) and a series of N Maxwell models is apparent. Thus, one can relate the change in viscosity to the viscoelastic properties through the relaxation spectrum of the material.

12.6
Superposition principles and evaluation of relaxation spectra

All of the viscoelastic properties of polymers are strongly dependent on temperature. Referring to Fig. 12.2, for example, one sees that Young's modulus changes several orders of magnitude when passing through the glass-transition temperature. Most of this effect is related to the temperature dependence of the relaxation times. It can be shown [9] that the ratio of the relaxation time at temperature T to the relaxation time at temperature T_0 is:

$$\frac{\lambda_{Ri}(T)}{\lambda_{Ri}(T_0)} = \frac{\eta_{vT}}{\eta_{vT_0}} \frac{\rho_{v0}}{\rho_v} \frac{T_0}{T} = a_T \tag{12.86}$$

From the general definitions of the viscoelastic properties in terms of integrals over the different spectra [Eqs. (12.55) and (12.57)], it can also be shown that any property $f(t,T)$ at temperature T and time t is related to that same property $f(t',T_0)$ at a different time and temperature by the following expression:

$$f(t,T) = f(t',T_0) \frac{\rho_v T}{\rho_{v0} T_0} \tag{12.87}$$

where

$$t = a_T t' \tag{12.88}$$

Thus, if one has a set of data at different temperatures, as shown in Figs. 12.13a and 12.14a, it is possible to superposition the data to a single curve at a given reference temperature. If the reference temperature is T_0, the curve at temperature T is shifted by an amount $\rho_v T / \rho_{v0} T_0$ along the vertical axis and an amount a_T along the horizontal axis. A single master curve is then obtained which gives values for the viscoelastic function at T_0 and any time t. Since viscosity varies exponentially with temperature, while density is fairly constant, the shift factor a_T is by far the most important. One need not actually obtain values of a_T, since the superpositioning can be done by trial-and-error procedures. The important thing is that one can predict the behavior of a given material over many decades of time from relatively short time tests. This is obviously an important engineering design procedure.

If one assumes that $(\rho_{v0}/\rho_v)(T_0/T)$ is approximately equal to 1.0, Eq. (12.86) can be combined with Eq. (12.34) to give

$$\log a_T = -\frac{8.86(T - T_s)}{101.6 + T - T_s} \tag{12.89}$$

In other words, with the appropriate choice of a reference temperature, the shift factor is a universal function of temperature. This universal function is good only for amorphous polymers in the temperature range T_g to $T_g + 100$.

A very important limitation of the superpositioning principle is that the retardation (or relaxation) spectrum must not depend explicitly upon temperature [that is, $L(\lambda(T), T) \doteq L(\lambda_R(T)]$. This can only be true if there are no structural changes accompanying a temperature change. Thus, the application to crystalline or partially crystalline polymers must take into account the change in crystallinity and other structural factors. Superposition principles that include change in crystalline content with temperature have been proposed [20], but there is presently not enough information to make broad generalizations. Superposition principles are thus most applicable to amorphous polymers and relatively low levels of the total strain.

The theories presented in the preceding two sections are restricted to *linear* viscoelastic materials. Although many materials, especially at large total deformation, are not really linear, the general forms of the equations are useful for representing experimental data. The relationships between the various moduli would not be valid for nonlinear materials, however.

Empirical equations, like those presented in Sec. 11.6, can be used to express the stress and temperature dependence of the compliances and the relaxation moduli. One particularly useful equation for describing the creep behavior of a variety of thermoplastics and reinforced plastics is [10,11]:

$$\epsilon_s = \epsilon_{s0} + B_s t^n \qquad \text{cf. Eq. (11.39)} \tag{12.90}$$

where

$$\epsilon_{s0} = A_f \left[\exp\left(-\frac{\Delta E_c}{RT}\right) \right] \sinh \frac{s}{s_0} = \epsilon_{s0}' \sinh \frac{s}{s_0} \tag{12.91}$$

$$B_S = C \left[\exp\left(-\frac{\Delta Q}{RT}\right) \right] \sinh \frac{s}{s_m} = C' \sinh \frac{s}{s_m} \tag{12.92}$$

and n is a function of temperature and stress. Values for ϵ_{s0}', B_S, and n are reported in Table 12.4 for a number of systems.

Table 12.4

Creep data for a variety of plastics [10,11]

Material	n (t = hours)	ϵ_{s0}', m/m	C', m/m	s_0, psi	s_m, psi
Phenolic-type cross-laminated paper laminate	0.0763	0.00315	0.001176	12,000	8,000
Phenolic-type asbestos laminate	0.267	0.00311	0.0001271	4,000	2,400
Polyethylene	0.0890	0.01350	0.00397	400	185
Kel-F (crystalline) (<2,700 psi)	0.0872	0.00810	0.00099	2,600	1,475
Geon 404 annealed (PVC)	0.3109	0.01150	0.00018	6,000	2,100

12.7
Tensile strength of polymers

The stress-strain characteristics of ideal elastomers and linear viscoelastic materials have been discussed in preceding sections. The stress-strain curves at large extensions and at the rupture point are complicated by both nonlinear effects and complex stress patterns. The tensile stress-strain curves for polymethylmethacrylate (Fig. 12.20) are illustrative of the wide variety of behavior that organic solids can exhibit. Below the glass-transition region of 85 to 105°C, the material behaves as a glassy solid, breaking in brittle fracture, while above 105°C it behaves as a very ductile material with a definite yield point and extensive plastic flow. When a plastic is crystallizable on stretching, as is natural rubber (Fig. 12.1), there is also the possibility of a "strain-hardening" effect prior to fracture. Temperature, degree of cross-linking, reinforcement, percent crystallinity, rate of deformation, the condition of the sample, and many other

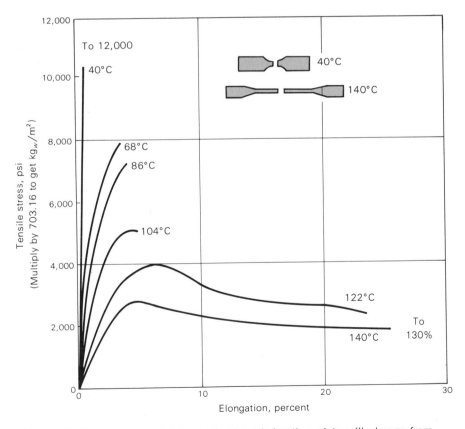

Fig. 12.20 The mechanical failure of polymethylmethacrylate will change from brittle fracture to ductile fracture by heating through the glass-transition temperature. (By permission from T. Alfrey, "Mechanical Behavior of High Polymers," p. 516, Interscience Publishers, Inc., New York, 1948.)

factors influence the fracture phenomenon. The molecular theories explaining fracture are rudimentary and limited to simple materials. We shall consider the behavior of glassy plastics and amorphous rubbers.

Since glassy polymers are isotropic and exhibit brittle fracture, the tensile strength can be estimated by using the Griffith theory $s_f \doteq (2\gamma E_Y/\pi l)^{1/2}$, where γ is specific surface energy, E_Y is Young's modulus, and $2l$ is the size of the largest crack in the material [cf. Eq. (11.53)]. Figure 12.21 is a theoretical plot of tensile strength vs. crack size for polymethylmethacrylate and polystyrene based on the data of J. P. Berry (summarized by Berry in Ref. 19). The data are characterized by a consistent scattering, with deviations of ± 20 to 25 percent from the best theoretical curves. Artificial flaws were made on the surfaces of the samples, and failure usually occurred at these flaws. The general scattering of the data is probably associated with both the minor differences in crack morphology from one sample to the next and the inherent statistical nature of fracture phenomena. A pronounced deviation from the inverse square-root dependence showed up on polystyrene samples when the crack size was below 1 mm. This was attributed to the fact that polystyrene contains inherent flaws in the structure that are of the order of 1 mm. Thus, when the artificial flaws are smaller than this, they do not control the fracture process. By curve-fitting the data, it was found that $E_Y\gamma \doteq 5.2 \pm 1.4 \times 10^9$ kg$_w{}^2$/m^3 and $\gamma = 2.1 \pm 0.7 \times 10^2$ joules/m^2 for polymethylmethacrylate and $E_Y\gamma \doteq 3.5 \pm 1.1 \times 10^{10}$ kg$_w{}^2$/m^3 and $\gamma = 1.7 \pm 0.6 \times 10^3$ joules/m^2 for polystyrene.

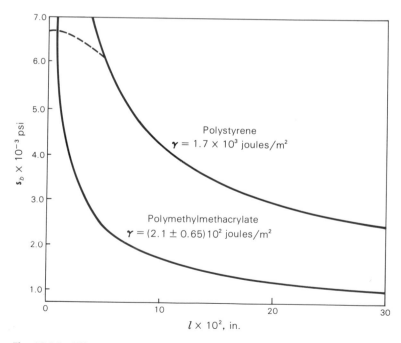

Fig. 12.21 Effect of crack size on tensile strength. [Curve fit of Griffith equation based on data of J. P. Berry, *J. Polymer Sci.* **50:** 107, 313 (1961).]

If one assumes that a crack propagates by breaking covalent bonds, the surface energy would be equal to the energy required to break enough bonds to separate two planes in the material. If we assume that the bond energy is about 90 kcal/g mole and that the chains are separated by about 5 Å, the energy required to break the bonds in a square meter of surface is about 2.4 joules, or the surface energy is 1.2 joules/m^2. The experimental values are more than a hundred times larger than this, indicating that the energy required to propagate a crack is primarily expended in promoting viscous flow. Thus, at points of stress concentration, both bond breaking and viscous flow occur. One can rationalize that stress orientation probably occurs in advance of a propagating crack, which would promote anisotropic properties on the fractured surface. Optical studies bear out these expectations [19]. The mechanical properties of a few glassy polymers are included in Table 12.5. In general, they exhibit higher tensile strength and much lower percent elongation at break than materials above their glass-transition temperatures.

Some stress-strain curves for elastomers were shown in Fig. 12.1. It was also shown that a thermodynamic analysis of rubber elasticity leads to Eq. (12.9) for the tensile force as a function of strain:

$$S_{eng} = \frac{f_T}{A_0} = nRT \left[\frac{l}{l_0} - \left(\frac{l_0}{l} \right)^2 \right] \tag{12.93}$$

At high extensions, the experimental stress-strain curve increases more rapidly than predicted by Eq. (12.93). An empirical modification of this equation has been given by Martin, Roth, and Stiehler [16]:

$$S_{eng} = nRT \left[\frac{l}{l_0} - \left(\frac{l_0}{l} \right)^2 \right] \exp \left[A \left(\frac{l}{l_0} - \frac{l_0}{l} \right) \right] \tag{12.94}$$

The quantity A is an empirical constant that is usually equal to about 0.38 and is also slightly dependent upon the rate of straining of the material.

The breaking stress generally increases with rate of straining. This effect can be qualitatively understood in terms of the viscoelastic nature of the polymer. At very low strain rates, the network of chains can reorient in the direction of the tensile force and the strength will be controlled by the amount of energy required to overcome the viscous resistance of the chains in their oriented state. At higher rates of strain, they cannot respond fast enough to reorient, but rather, remain in a coiled-up entangled mass. The material in this state acts more like an elastic solid, and the strength is controlled by the breaking of covalent bonds and the propagation of a crack during brittle fracture. The latter process invariably requires more energy, thereby resulting in a higher tensile strength. This effect has been quantitatively described by the theory of Knauss [14]. The general idea is to assume that the cross section of an amorphous, isotropic polymer consists of a group of polymer chains with a distribution of bond strengths. Fracture is initiated at the weakest bonds and propagates through the weakest regions, forming submicroscopic flaws. These cracks propagate when the stored elastic energy becomes greater than the energy dissipated in forming a new surface.

Table 12.5

Mechanical properties for some commercial polymers *

Polymer	D 256 † Impact str., 73°F ‡ 10^{-2} kg_w-m/cm	D 638 Tensile mod. of elast.§ E_Y 10^8 kg_w/m^2	D 651 or D 638 Tensile str., @ 73°F $10^8 kg_w/m^2$	D 695 Compressive mod. of elast. E_c 10^8 kg_w/m^2
Phenolic molding compound (general-purpose cellulose filled)	1.3–1.9	5.6–8.5	4.2–5.6	4.2–7.0
Epoxy resin, general purpose	0.9–3.8	2.1–7.0	1.4–8.5	2.8–12.7
Glass-phenolic laminates G-3	D-229 35	14	D-229 14–16	—
Polyester–glass-fiber mat–resins	38–82	3.5–10	5.6–17.6	—
Acrylic molding powder, grade 5	2.2–3.3	2.5–3.2	5.3–6.0	2.5–3.2
Polyethylene:				
High density	5–20	0.6–1.1	1.7–3.5	0.3–0.7
Low density	Incomplete break	0.10–0.27	1.0–1.7	—
Polytetrafluoroethylene	14–22	0.23–0.46	1.0–2.1	0.5–0.7
Polystyrene, general purpose	1.3–3.3	2.8–3.5	3.9–5.6	2.1–4.0
Nylon 6-6:				
Molding compound	5.0–11.0	1.5–2.9	5.6–7.8	—
Filament	—	4.0 flexure	44	—

* Data from "Technical Data on Plastics," Manufacturing Chemists Association, Washington, D.C., 1957.

† The D numbers refer to standard ASTM Tests.

‡ Multiply by 18.32 to get ft-lb/in.

§ Multiply by 1.422×10^{-3} to get psi.

The effect of molecular weight on the tensile strength of rubber is shown in Fig. 12.22. The curve can be qualitatively explained by showing the effect of molecular weight on the number of effective network chains n. If the polymer has an infinite molecular weight and the average molecular weight between network junctions is M_C, the number of effective network chains is ρ/M_C. If the polymer has a molecular weight M_n, however, there will be $2\rho/M_n$ chain ends. Each network chain that is terminated by a chain end will not be effective in supporting stress, so that the actual number of effective network chains, n_e, is:

$$n_e = n \left(1 - \frac{2M_c}{M_n}\right) \qquad (12.95)$$

when $M_n \gg 2M_C$, $n_e \rightarrow n$ and the tensile strength approaches a constant value. As M_n decreases toward $2M_C$, the number of effective chains decreases toward zero and thus the tensile strength should approach zero as M_n approaches $2M_C$. For butyl rubber, $M_C \doteq 37,000$, which means that the tensile strength should approach zero at about $M_n \doteq 72,000$. Figure 12.22 shows that the strength decreases rapidly at about 200,000, which is higher than expected, but this is not surprising in view of the very crude physical picture.

The effect of cross-linking is shown in Fig. 12.23. Superficially, from Eq. (12.11), one would expect that the strength should increase continuously with increasing degree of cross-linking (i.e., decreasing M_C). In fact, however, the tensile strength increases, reaches a maximum, and then decreases with in-

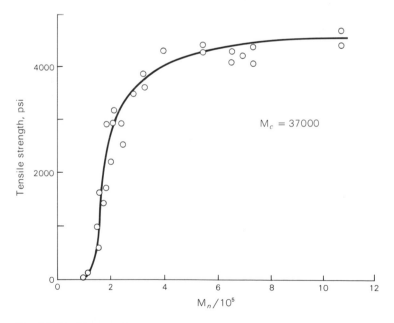

Fig. 12.22 The tensile strength of butyl rubber as a function of molecular weight. [By permission from P. J. Flory, *Ind. Eng. Chem.*, **38:** 417 (1946).]

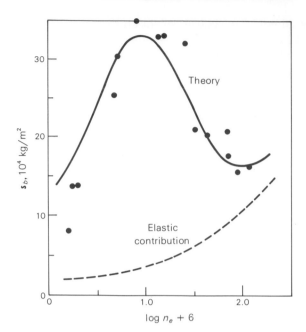

Fig. 12.23 Dependence of breaking stress on cross-linking density for SBR. Theoretical curve is Eq. (12.96) [6].

creasing degree of cross-linking. The molecular theory of Bueche and Dudek [6] can be used to explain this phenomenon. Without going into detail, the general view is that the cross-linked polymer is a distribution of network chains. Upon stretching, all the junction points move in unison, causing the shorter network segments to elongate to a relatively greater extent than the longer segments. The shorter chains thus bear a disproportionately larger share of the load. The highly elongated chains can then relax and redistribute the load to their neighbors through the motion of common junction points. This concept leads to an expression for the stress as the sum of an equilibrium component given by the expression for ideal elasticity and a time-dependent component which is proportional to the number of fully extended segments. The total strain at the rupture point is obtained by specifying a critical value for the average elastic storage energy per network bond, Γ_s, which leads to the following equation for the tensile strength:

$$s_b = n_e RT \left[\frac{l_b}{l_0} - \left(\frac{l_0}{l_b} \right)^2 \right] + n_e g(t) f \left(T, \Gamma_s, n_e, \frac{l_b}{l_0} \right) \tag{12.96}$$

The quantity $g(t)$ is a function of the rate of straining, and f is the fraction of fully extended chains, which can be evaluated in terms of the properties of the polymer and the criterion for rupture. Figure 12.23 shows that the theoretical curve can be made to approximate experimental data.

Temperature, crystallinity, reinforcement, and any other property that affects the viscoelastic properties of a solid will also affect the ultimate tensile strength of the material. There is a great deal of research that is still to be done in this very important area.

References

1 Alfrey, T. J.: "Mechanical Behavior of High Polymers," Interscience Publishers, Inc., New York, 1948. *A treatise on the viscoelastic properties of polymers and the relationship between structure and properties.*

2 Andrade, E. N.: *Phil. Mag.,* **17:** 497 (1934); *Proc. Roy. Soc. (London),* Ser. A **215:** 36 (1952).

3 Averbach, B. L., D. K. Felbeck, G. T. Hahn, and D. A. Thomas: "Fracture," John Wiley & Sons, Inc., and The Technology Press of the Massachusetts Institute of Technology, New York, 1959. *A series of up-to-date articles on fracture including several on the behavior of nonmetallic materials.*

4 Bernhardt, E. C. (ed.): "Processing of Thermoplastic Material," sec. III, by R. F. Westover, Reinhold, New York, 1959. *An SPE review of the science and technology of polymer processing. A good deal of very useful data is presented.*

5 Bueche, F.: "Physical Properties of Polymers," Interscience Publishers, Inc., New York, 1962. *Emphasizes molecular concepts in polymer science. Gives a detailed treatment of all the subjects covered in this chapter.*

6 Bueche, F., and T. Dudek: *Rubber Chem. Technol.,* **36:** 1 (1963).

7 Doolittle, A. K.: *J. Appl. Phys.,* **22:** 1471 (1951), **23:** 236 (1952).

8 Eirich, F. R. (ed.): "Rheology: Theory and Applications," vol. 1, Academic Press Inc., New York, 1956. *An advanced treatise on the rheology of all types of materials. Chapter 9, Theory of Viscosity, by A. Bondi and chap. 12, Viscosity Relationships for Polymers in Bulk and in Concentrated Solution, by T. G. Fox, et al., have been used extensively in this chapter.*

9 Ferry, J. D.: "Viscoelastic Properties of Polymers," John Wiley & Sons, Inc., New York, 1961. *A standard reference work on the theory and experimental techniques of viscoelastic studies. Essential reading for all people doing advanced work in this area.*

10 Findlay, W. N., and D. B. Peterson: *Proc. Am. Soc. Testing Mater.,* **58:** 841 (1958).

11 Findlay, W. N., and G. Khosla: *Soc. Plastics Engrs. J.,* **12** (12): 20–25 (1956).

12 Glasstone, S., K. J. Laidler, and H. Eyring: "The Theory of Rate Processes," McGraw-Hill Book Company, New York, 1941. *The standard reference for the theory of thermal activation.*

13 Hirschfelder, J. O., C. F. Curtiss, and R. B. Bird: "Molecular Theory of Gases and Liquids," 2d ed., John Wiley & Sons, Inc., New York, 1964.

14 Knauss, W. G.: "Rupture Phenomena in Viscoelastic Materials," unpublished doctoral dissertation, California Institute of Technology, Pasadena, Calif., June, 1963. *The information presented in this chapter was taken from a summary in Ref. 19, pp. 442ff.*

15 Leaderman, H.: "Elastic and Creep Properties of Filamentous Materials and Other High Polymers," Textile Foundation, Washington, D.C., 1943. *A comprehensive set of experimental data on a variety of materials.*

16 Martin, G. M., F. L. Roth, and R. D. Stiehler: *Trans. Inst. Rubber Ind.,* **32:** 189 (1956).

17 McKelvey, J. M.: "Polymer Processing," John Wiley & Sons, Inc., New York, 1962. *An introductory text on the rheology and processing techniques for non-Newtonian fluids.*

18 Nielsen, L. E.: "Mechanical Properties of Polymers," Reinhold Publishing Corp., New York, 1962. *A highly recommended survey.*

19 Rosen, B. (ed.): "Fracture Processes in Polymeric Solids," Interscience Publishers, Inc., New York, 1964. *A complete and up-to-date survey of the theory and experimental techniques for fracture phenomena. A necessary prerequisite to research in this area.*

20 Takemura, T.: *J. Polymer Sci.,* **38**: 471 (1959).

21 Tobolsky, A. V.: "Properties and Structure of Polymers," John Wiley & Sons, Inc., New York, 1960. *A survey of research in the area of viscoelastic properties.*

22 Treloar, L. R. G.: "The Physics of Rubber Elasticity," 2d ed., Oxford University Press, London, 1958.

23 Williams, M. L., R. F. Landel, and J. D. Ferry: *J. Am. Chem. Soc.,* **77**: 3701 (1955).

Questions

12.1 When an ideal elastomer is stressed, its elastic modulus increases with increasing percent elongation. Furthermore, the elastic modulus increases with increasing temperature and the elastomer heats up when it is rapidly stretched. Explain these phenomena in terms of the molecular structure of an elastomer. Compare these effects with the behavior of other elastic materials.

12.2 A natural rubber has a density of 0.93 g/cm³ and a number-average molecular weight of 68,000. Calculate the average molecular weight of a network chain, M_C, if the degree of cross-linking (i.e., the percent of double bonds that are cross-linked) is 0.5, 1.0, and 5 percent. Plot the stress-strain curves for these three cases assuming an ideal elastomer and neglecting the effects of entanglement in each case. Calculate the stress required to elongate to $\epsilon_s = 1.00$ (that is, $l/l_0 = 2$) in each case.

12.3 Viscosity data show that the molecular weight between entanglement points in an unvulcanized rubber is often of the order of 10^4 kg/kg mole. How would the predictions made in Question 12.2 be modified if the effect of entanglements was included?

12.4 A mildly cross-linked elastomer can be swollen in a good solvent. Discuss the effect of adding solvent on the stress-strain curve.

12.5 Curve fit the apparent viscosity data for Alathon-14 polyethylene resin at 126°C (Fig. 12.6) to the following models:

Eyring model $\qquad \dfrac{d\epsilon_s}{dt} = K \sinh \dfrac{a\tau}{RT}$ $\qquad$ Eq. (12.20)

Power-law model $\qquad \tau = K \left(\dfrac{d\epsilon_s}{dt}\right)^n$ $\qquad$ Eq. (12.26)

Ellis model $\qquad \tau = \dfrac{a}{1 + b\tau^m} \dfrac{d\epsilon_s}{dt}$ $\qquad$ Eq. (12.27)

Which equation gives the best curve-fit of the data?

12.6 According to the "thermally activated" model for viscous flow, the temperature dependence of the viscosity can be approximated by an equation of the form

$$\eta_v = A_f \exp\left(-\frac{\Delta E_v}{RT}\right)$$

where A_f and ΔE_V are constants and ΔE_v is the *activation energy* of the process. Figures 12.5 and 12.9 show data for water, benzene, polyisobutylene, and polymethylmethacrylate. The "apparent activation energy" (i.e., the slope of a log η_v versus $1/T$ curve) is actually nowhere near constant in any case except, perhaps, benzene. Discuss the structural or molecular characteristics of the four substances involved that might account for these facts.

12.7 The data in Table 12.6 were taken for the flow behavior of acetate rayon under very small loads (of the order of $\frac{1}{2}$ g/denier).

(a)   Evaluate the steady-state creep rate as a function of temperature and stress according to the following formulas

$$\left(\frac{d\epsilon_s}{dt}\right)_T = B\tau^n \qquad \frac{d\epsilon_s}{dt} = Ae^{-Q/RT}$$

Use the following units: $\epsilon_s = $ in./in., $\tau = $ g/denier, $Q = $ cal/mole-°K, $T = $ °K, $t = $ min.
(b)   Draw a curve of ϵ_s versus t for a total load of 0.86 g and 67°C.

12.8 The compliance of a certain polymer may be represented by the following four-constant model:

$$J(t) = J_0 + \frac{t}{\eta_0} + J(\infty)\left[1 - \exp\left(-t/\lambda_1\right)\right]$$

where $J(\infty) = 10^{-5}$ m²/kg$_w$
$\qquad \lambda_0 = 10^3$ sec
$\qquad J_0 = 2 \times 10^{-6}$ m²/kg$_w$
$\qquad \eta_v = 5 \times 10^{12}$ poises

(a)   Plot the compliance as a function of the logarithm of temperature from 1 to 10^4 sec.
(b)   Predict the percent elongation in creep at 10^4 sec with a constant load of 10^5 kg$_w$/m² and with a constant load of 10^6 kg$_w$/m².
(c)   The load is removed after 10^4 sec.   Plot the compliance as a function of log time.
(d)   Predict the percent elongation after the following loading history:

0–10^4 sec	$s_0 = 10^5$ kg$_w$/m²
10^4–2×10^4 sec	$s_0 = 0$ kg$_w$/m²
2×10^4–3×10^4 sec	$s_0 = 10^6$ kg$_w$/m²

(e)   Predict the percent elongation after 10^4 sec if the load is increased at a steady rate

$$\frac{ds}{dt} = 10^2 \text{ kg}_w/\text{m}^2\text{-sec}$$

12.9 The dynamic behavior of the four-constant model developed in Question 12.8 can be studied by placing a Maxwell model and a Voigt-Kelvin model in series:

$$\left(\frac{d\epsilon_s}{dt}\right)_{\text{Maxwell}} = \frac{\tau}{\eta_v} + J_0\frac{d\tau}{dt}$$

$$\left(\frac{d\epsilon_s}{dt}\right)_{\text{V-K}} = \frac{J(\infty)}{\lambda_R}\tau - \frac{1}{\lambda_R}\epsilon_{\text{V-K}}$$

The total rate of strain under a load τ is then

$$\frac{d\epsilon_s}{dt} = \left(\frac{d\epsilon_s}{dt}\right)_{\text{Maxwell}} + \left(\frac{d\epsilon_s}{dt}\right)_{\text{V-K}}$$

(a)   Obtain the following equation:

Table 12.6 *

Total deformation, in.	Time, min	Temp, °C
Total load = 1.05 g		
0.0250	1	51
0.0260	5	51
0.0265	10	51
0.0275	50	51
0.0280	100	51
0.0260	1	59
0.0274	5	59
0.0280	10	59
0.0293	50	59
0.030	100	59
0.0270	1	67
0.0288	5	67
0.0295	10	67
0.0313	50	67
0.0320	100	67
0.0280	1	75
0.0301	5	75
0.0310	10	75
0.0331	50	75
0.0340	100	75
Total load = 1.48 g		
0.0405	1	51
0.0427	5	51
0.0437	10	51
0.0460	50	51
0.0470	100	51
0.0415	1	59
0.0441	5	59
0.0453	10	59
0.0475	50	59
0.0490	100	59
0.0430	1	67
0.0462	5	67
0.0476	10	67
0.0509	50	67
0.0523	100	67
0.0450	1	75
0.0491	5	75
0.0508	10	75
0.0549	50	75

* Ref. 15, pp. 171ff. Filament length = 3.94 in.; filament size = 3 denier.

$$\frac{d^3\epsilon_s}{d(\omega t)^3} + \frac{1}{\omega\lambda_R}\frac{d^2\epsilon_s}{d(\omega t)^2} = J_0\frac{d^3\tau}{d(\omega t)^3} + \left(\frac{1}{\omega\eta_v} + \frac{J(\infty) + J_0}{\omega\lambda_R}\right)\frac{d^2\tau}{d(\omega t)^2} + \frac{1}{\omega\eta_v\omega\lambda_R}\frac{d\tau}{d(\omega t)}$$

(b) Consider the sinusoidal stress $\tau = \tau_0\sin\omega t$ and derive an expression for the compliance $J(t) = \epsilon(t)/\tau_0$ if $J(0) = 0$.

(c) Obtain expressions for the dynamic moduli J' and J'' in terms of the constants of the model. (Assume $t \gg \lambda$.)

12.10 Tensile-creep experiments were run on natural rubber containing 30 parts HAF black and vulcanized 60 min at 280°F with sulfur. Values of the creep compliance at a variety of temperatures were calculated (see Table 12.7).

Table 12.7 *

Time, sec	$J_T(t) \times 10^6$, m^2/kg_w, at						
	−62'C	−56°C	−44°C	−37°C	−21°C	15°C	42°C
15	0.206	0.48	3.01	3.65	3.79	3.69	3.79
30	0.226	0.51	3.24	3.70	3.83	3.76	3.84
60	0.247	0.79	3.39	3.80	3.94	3.80	3.90
120	0.319	1.09	3.53	3.89	3.99	3.82	3.94
240	0.34	1.51	3.66	3.98	4.06	3.85	3.98
480	0.40	1.96	3.78	4.09	4.12	3.91	4.05
960	0.50	2.35	3.88	4.15	4.26	3.96	4.10
1,920	0.61	2.79	4.00	4.23	4.36	4.00	4.14
3,840'	0.80	3.09	4.12	4.32	4.43	4.05	4.20

* Ref. 5, p. 176.

(a) Plot $(T/217)J(t)$ as a function of log time.
(b) Obtain a master curve of $J_{217}(t)$ versus time for the reference temperature 217°K.
(c) What will be the compliance of the material at 217°K and 10^8 sec?

12.11 Use the data of Table 12.4 to calculate the creep behavior of polyethylene and Kel-F at 42×10^4 kg_w/m^2 over the time interval 0 to 1,000 hr. Explain the difference in the curves in terms of the chemical and physical structure of the polymers.

12.12 Figure 12.20 shows the effect of temperature on the tensile stress-strain behavior of polymethylmethacrylate. Correlate the shape of the curves with the glass-transition temperature. Also discuss under what conditions brittle fracture occurs and relate this to the molecular structure of polymethylmethacrylate.

12.13 Plot a reduced stress-strain curve for an ideal elastomer and compare it to the curve obtained from the Martin-Roth-Stiehler equation. Explain the difference in terms of molecular structure. Use the variables $(s)_{eng}/nRT$ versus l/l_0.

12.14 The breaking stress of rubber increases as the rate of elongation increases (at constant temperature). Explain these effects in terms of the molecular properties of rubber.

12.15 Figure 12.22 shows the effects of molecular weight on the tensile strength of a vulcanized rubber. Explain the shape of the curve in terms of molecular structure.

13
Conduction in crystalline materials

13.1
Introduction

Just as a proper understanding of the strength of materials requires a knowledge of how aggregates of molecules respond to external stresses, so an understanding of conducting (or insulating) properties requires a knowledge of how molecules, electrons, and ions respond to electromagnetic radiation.

Consider, for example, a simple metal. In the absence of an external electric field, both the ion cores and the valence electrons move in a random Brownian motion. If an electric field is placed across the material, the electromagnetic radiation will produce a force on the particles, causing the electrons to be pushed toward the positive pole of the field while the nuclei are pushed toward the negative pole. Since the ion cores are not free to migrate and (in moderate fields) will not lose inner-shell electrons, they will tend to polarize in the field while continuing to vibrate in the vicinity of their lattice points. The valence electrons, on the other hand, being free to move, drift toward the positive pole. The electrical conductivity of a metal is determined by the resistance that these electrons (or electron waves) encounter as they pass by the vibrating atoms, the lattice defects, the grain boundaries, and other irregularities in the space lattice.

In general, the effects of electromagnetic forces can be described in terms of electrical conductivity, thermal conductivity, dielectric character, and magnetic susceptibility. The conductivities are considered in this chapter.

13.2
Electrical conductivity—Classical concepts

The electrical conductivity of a material is a measure of the ease in transporting electric charge from one point to another in an electric field. The charge may be carried by cations and anions, in which case one speaks of *ionic conductivity,* or it may be carried by electrons, in which case one uses the term *electrical conductivity.*

In most instances, it is found that the electric current is directly proportional to the electric field across the material. In the absence of other external forces and at constant temperature, Ohm's law of electrical conduction is

$$\mathscr{I} = \sigma\mathscr{E} \tag{13.1}$$

where $\mathscr{I}$ is current density in units such as amperes/per square meter, $\mathscr{E}$ is the electric field in units such as volts/per meter, and σ is the conductivity in units such as $(\text{ohm-m})^{-1}$. The conductivity may also be written as the product of the electron density, N electrons/cm³, the electron charge, e coul/electron, and the electron mobility, η_e m/sec-volt/m:

$$\sigma = Ne\eta_e \tag{13.2}$$

The mobility is the velocity per unit potential gradient in the material. The purpose of any theory of conductivity is to predict Ohm's law and to evaluate the electron mobility.

Let us consider the simplest possible model for conduction in a metal. Assume that the valence electrons are perfectly free to move throughout the volume of the metal or, in other words, that they do not interact with the ionic cores. This *free-electron* model is shown in Fig. 13.1. At equilibrium, each electron moves in a random fashion with a thermal velocity v_i. The average drift velocity v_D of the electrons is defined as

$$v_D = \frac{1}{N}\sum_{i=1}^{N} v_i \tag{13.3}$$

In the absence of an electric field, the net drift velocity is zero. If the particles are truly free, the classical equation of motion may be used to calculate the acceleration of the electrons when an external field is applied:

$$F = e\mathscr{E} = m_e\frac{dv_D}{dt} + \left(\frac{m}{\Theta}\right)v_D \tag{13.4}$$

The first term on the right is the force due to acceleration, and the second term is a drag force resulting from the resistance to the flow. The drag force is as-

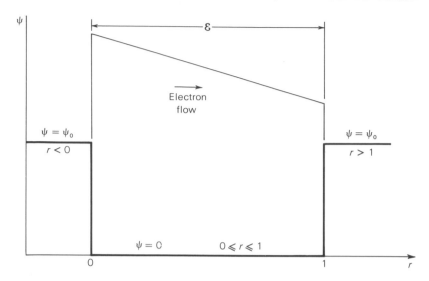

Fig. 13.1 Electrons do not interact with ionic cores in the simplified free-electron model for a valence electron in a metal.

sumed to be equal to a *frictional coefficient* times the drift velocity. Solving for the drift velocity gives

$$v_D = \frac{e\mathscr{E}\Theta}{m_e}(1 - e^{-t/\Theta}) \qquad (13.5)$$

Thus, when an electric field is imposed, the electrons accelerate to a limiting drift velocity of $e\mathscr{E}\Theta/m_e$. This is called the *steady-state drift velocity*. If the valence-electron density is N, the steady-state flux of electrons is then Nv_D electrons per unit area per unit time. The current density is then

$$\mathscr{I} = Nv_D e = \frac{Ne^2\Theta}{m_e}\mathscr{E} \qquad (13.6)$$

This is equivalent to Ohm's law with the conductivity equal to

$$\sigma = \frac{Ne^2\Theta}{m_e} \qquad (13.7)$$

From Eq. (13.5) it is clear that Θ has the units of time. The physical interpretation of Θ is that it is the average time of flight between collisions. Thus, the electron accelerates in the electric field until it collides with another particle. The collision causes it to lose its momentum and brings its drift velocity back to zero. The electron again accelerates until it experiences another collision. The frequency of these collisions determines the conductivity of the material; that is, many collisions means high resistance to flow and a low conductivity (Θ is small). If l_p is the mean free path between collisions and $\mathbf{u}$ is the average electron velocity:

$$\Theta = \frac{l_p}{\mathbf{u}} \tag{13.8}$$

$$\boldsymbol{\sigma} = \frac{Ne^2 l_p}{m_e \mathbf{u}} \tag{13.9}$$

Let us now estimate the conductivity of a typical metal, copper, for example. The density of copper is 7.1 cm^3/g mole, and there is one valence electron per copper atom, which gives a valence electron density of $N = 8.5 \times 10^{28}$ electrons/m^3. The mean free path between collisions should certainly be of the order of the lattice parameters, so let us assume that $l_p \doteq 10^{-9}$ m. The electron mass is 9.1×10^{-31} kg (at rest), and the electronic charge is 1.6×10^{-19} coul. If these are freely moving particles, their kinetic energy is about $3/2 kT$ or, in terms of thermal velocity, $\mathbf{u} = \sqrt{3kT/m} \doteq 1.2 \times 10^5$ m/sec at 300°K. Substituting into Eq. (13.9), one estimates that the conductivity of copper is of the order of 2.8×10^6 (ohm-m)$^{-1}$. This compares with an experimental value of 6.5×10^7 (ohm-m)$^{-1}$. *Thus, our prediction is an order of magnitude low.* Furthermore, if the electrons were classical particles with an internal energy $3/2 RT$, the electronic contribution to the specific heat would be about $3/2 R$. Experimental data show that the actual electron specific heat is about $10^{-4}T$ cal/g atom–°K.

These two facts are clear proof that a classical free-electron model cannot describe the electronic behavior of metals. In reality, the electrons move in a periodic potential field caused by interaction with the ion cores. The motion can be described only by application of the Schrödinger wave equation. In the following sections we shall describe the quantum behavior of electrons in metals and then return to the question of conductivity, showing how this classical picture must be modified in order to account for quantum effects.

13.3
Electronic behavior in a periodic lattice

The simplest physical model of a metal is an array of positive nuclei arranged in a regular and definite geometric lattice. Each nucleus vibrates about a mean point in the lattice and is surrounded by inner shells of tightly bound electrons. These "x-ray" shells are much the same as would be found in isolated atoms and are not significantly changed by ordinary external electric fields. The valence electrons, on the other hand, are not tightly bound to any one nucleus, but are relatively free to move in the lattice.

A complete analysis of the electronic motion within a metal is very difficult because it is impossible to account for all of the interactions between nuclei, inner-shell electrons, and valence electrons. The potential energy of interaction between a single electron and a row of ion cores is shown in Fig. 13.2. When the electron is relatively far from the ion core, it is acted on by an electrostatic attractive force which increases rapidly as the electron approaches the core. When the valence electron moves into the electronic shell surrounding

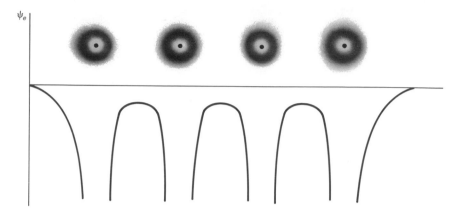

Fig. 13.2 The potential energy of an electron in the field of a line of ionic cores varies periodically.

the positive nucleus, the potential energy of interaction becomes very complicated because of the proximity of the point charges. The one-dimensional motion of a single electron in this periodic potential can be approximated by assuming that the potential is a periodic square well (Fig. 13.3). Since a valence electron moves under the influence of a periodic potential, a single wave function will describe its motion in regions $0 \rightarrow a$, $a + b \rightarrow 2a + b$, $2a + 2b \rightarrow 3a + 2b$, etc., and a different wave function will describe its motion in regions $a \rightarrow a + b$, $2a + b \rightarrow 2a + 2b$, $3a + 2b \rightarrow 3a + 3b$, etc. The Schrödinger equations for these regions (for one dimension) are

$$\frac{d^2\Psi_{1n}}{dx^2} + \frac{8\pi^2 m_e}{h^2} (E_n - \psi_0)\Psi_{1n} = 0 \qquad (13.10)$$

for $a \leqslant x \leqslant a + b$, etc.

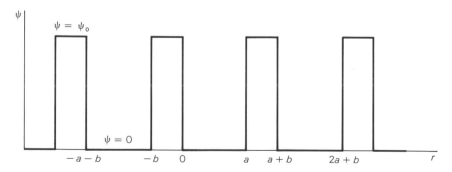

Fig. 13.3 The Kronig-Penney one-dimensional periodic square-well potential for a valence electron in a metal is an idealized model for the true periodic potential.

$$\frac{d^2\Psi_{2n}}{dx^2} + \frac{8\pi^2 m_e}{h^2} E_n \Psi_{2n} = 0 \tag{13.11}$$

$0 \leqslant x \leqslant a$, etc.

Four boundary conditions are required to solve this pair of differential equations. These are obtained by letting the wave function and its first derivative be continuous at the boundaries between the regions (for example, at $x = a$, $x = 0$).

$$\Psi_{1n}(a) = \Psi_{2n}(a) \tag{13.12}$$

$$\Psi_{1n}(0) = \Psi_{2n}(0) \tag{13.13}$$

$$\frac{d\Psi_{1n}}{dx}\bigg|_{x=a} = \frac{d\Psi_{2n}}{dx}\bigg|_{x=a} \tag{13.14}$$

$$\frac{d\Psi_{1n}}{dx}\bigg|_{x=0} = \frac{d\Psi_{2n}}{dx}\bigg|_{x=0} \tag{13.15}$$

It can be shown that solutions to these equations can exist only for certain values of the total energy E; this is analogous to the solutions of the hydrogen atom problem which gave quantized energy states for the electron. Specifically, it can be shown that only those energies which permit Eqs. (13.16) to (13.18) to be satisfied are allowable [7].

$$\cos k_x a = P \frac{\sin \alpha a}{\alpha a} + \cos \alpha a \tag{13.16}$$

$$P = \frac{4\pi^2 m_e a b \psi_0}{h^2} \tag{13.17}$$

$$\alpha = \frac{2\pi}{h} \sqrt{2 m_e E} \tag{13.18}$$

When the potential ψ_0 becomes very small, $\psi_0 \to 0$, Eq. (13.16) reduces to $\alpha = k_x$, or substituting into Eq. (13.18):

$$E = \frac{1}{2m_e} \frac{h^2}{4\pi^2} k_x^2 \tag{13.19}$$

This is merely the kinetic energy of a perfectly free electron. The constant k is thus related to the momentum by

$$m_e v = \frac{h}{2\pi} k_x \tag{13.20}$$

When the potential ψ_0 becomes very large, $\psi_0 \to \infty$, Eq. (13.16) can be satisfied only when the sine of αa approaches zero or, in other words, when the only allowable values of αa are the discrete points $n_x \pi$ ($n_x = 1,2,3,4, \ldots$). From Eq. (13.18)

$$E = \frac{n_x^2 h^2}{8 m_e a^2} \tag{13.21}$$

This is the solution for a free electron in a one-dimensional box of length a. (See Question 13.2.)

The most realistic view is to consider a finite value of P. Figure 13.4 shows the right side of Eq. (13.16) plotted as a function of αa for $P = 4\pi$ Since the left side of the equation can only take on values between $\pm 1 (-1 \leqslant \cos k_x a \leqslant 1)$, only certain values of αa (and thus E) will satisfy the equality expressed by Eq. (13.16). These ranges of allowable energy are shown by the shaded areas in Fig. 13.4. The forbidden zones of energy separate the allowable zones.

Thus we can see an important distinction between the behavior of tightly bound electrons in atoms and the behavior of loosely bound valence electrons in metals. Whereas atomic energy levels are discrete states separated by forbidden values of energy, electronic states in metals form bands of allowable energies separated by forbidden values of energy. Whereas atomic energy levels are characterized by specific quantum numbers, allowable energy zones are characterized by a range of values of the quantity k_x with the forbidden zones starting and ending at the specific values of k_x given by

$$k_x = \frac{n_x \pi}{a} \qquad n_x = \pm 1, \pm 2, \dots \qquad (13.22)$$

Whereas Eq. (3.19) shows that the atomic energy levels crowd together forming a "quasi-continuous" range of energies in the limit of high energy, the valence-electron bands broaden toward a continuum of energy as αa approaches infinity.

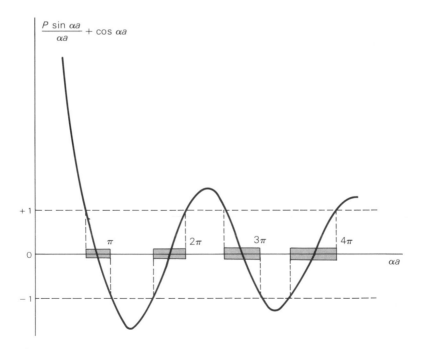

Fig. 13.4 The use of a Kronig-Penney model leads to the prediction that there are discrete bands of allowable energies for the valence electrons.

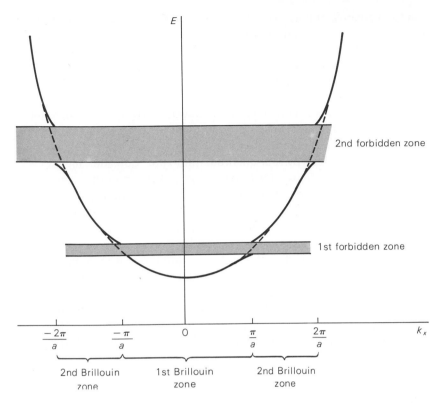

Fig. 13.5 The allowable energy bands for a linear monoatomic lattice are called Brillouin zones.

Allowable and forbidden energy zones can be seen more easily by plotting energy as a function of the quantity k_x as in Fig. 13.5. Equation (13.19) indicates that the curve would be a continuous parabola for a perfectly free electron. The darkened lines show the influence of a periodic potential. The region between $-\pi/a \le k_x \le \pi/a$ is called the *first Brillouin zone;* the region between the next discontinuities is called the *second Brillouin zone;* and so on. Each of these "zones" can be filled by a certain number of electrons. Suppose we have N atoms in a simple linear array of spacing a. If the wave function is to be periodic, the wavelength for the electronic motion must also be periodic. From Eq. (13.20), the De Broglie wavelength is

$$\frac{2\pi}{k_x} = \lambda = \frac{Na}{n} \qquad n = \pm 1, \pm 2, \pm 3, \ldots \tag{13.23}$$

Since the maximum value of k_x in the first Brillouin zone is π/a,

$$(k_x)_{\max} = \frac{\pi}{a} = \frac{2\pi n_{\max}}{Na} \tag{13.24}$$

$$n_{\max} = \frac{N}{2} \tag{13.25}$$

Since n can have positive or negative values, the total number of available electronic energy states is N. If two electrons with opposing spin can fill a given energy level, 2N *electrons are required to fill a Brillouin zone.* Since we are dealing with a limited number of k_x values and a tremendous number of states ($N \doteq 10^{24}$), each zone may be considered as essentially a continuous range of allowable energy.

The concept of a band structure can also be developed by considering what happens to the electronic energy levels of isolated atoms when the atoms are brought together. We have already seen that electronic energy states in isolated atoms are characterized by four quantum numbers. Consider, for example, two isolated hydrogen atoms. Each has a single electron in the 1s energy state. When the two atoms are brought together, a superposition of electronic fields results in a lowering of the potential energy in the region between the atoms. Since an increase in electronic density between the two particles is allowable, a more stable σ_s orbital and a less stable σ_s^* orbital are formed.

The important point is that when the two atoms are brought together, each energy level in an isolated atom can split into a more stable and a less stable energy state. When N atoms are brought together, N new levels are formed for each level of the isolated atoms. The degree of splitting increases as the amount of overlapping increases. Thus, marked splitting in the outer electronic shells occurs before the inner shells are much affected. This is illustrated in Fig. 13.6. Each of the atomic energy levels is thus associated with a band of closely related energy levels. The width of the band depends on the interatomic

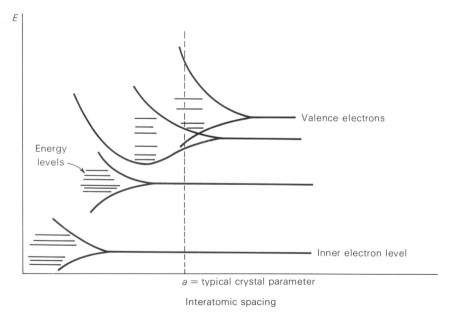

a = typical crystal parameter

Interatomic spacing

Fig. 13.6 Band theory can also be interpreted in terms of the splitting of atomic energy levels in aggregates of atoms.

spacing. At normal crystal dimensions, the inner-shell electrons are not perturbed very much from their energy states at infinite separation and thus form
very narrow bands. The valence electronic levels are spread into relatively wide
bands which may overlap to give the *appearance* of a continuous range of allowable energy. The qualitative results of this approach are much the same as the
previous one. Generally, the latter approach is most fruitful when applied to the
transition metals (with their relatively tightly bound $3d$ valence electrons), while
the former approach is most fruitful with the alkali metals (with their nearly free
s-type valence electrons).

Thus far we have limited ourselves to motion in a one-dimensional lattice.
The analogous description for a three-dimensional crystal lattice is much the
same as for the linear lattice, but in this case three quantities k_x, k_y, k_z must be
used to define the wave vector $\mathbf{k}$. Allowable and forbidden zones are also
formed, but there is the added complication that the allowable zones might
overlap, thus eliminating some of the forbidden zones. This is a direct consequence of the fact that the interatomic spacing in a crystal lattice might be different in different directions. The easiest way to see this is to examine the
properties of a two-dimensional square lattice. By analogy with Eq. (13.22), it
can be shown that energy discontinuities will appear in a two-dimensional lattice when

$$k_x n_x + k_y n_y = \frac{\pi}{a}\,(n_x^2 + n_y^2) \qquad\qquad (13.26)$$

where k_x and k_y are the components of the wave vector and n_x and n_y are integers. The first Brillouin zone is obtained by setting $n_x = \pm 1$, $n_y = 0$ and $n_x =$
$0, n_y = \pm 1$. The boundaries of the second zone are defined by $n_x = \pm 1$, $n_y = \pm 1$.
The boundaries of the third zone are defined by setting n_x and n_y equal to $0, \pm 2$,
etc. Figure 13.7 is a plot of the first three zones of a two-dimensional lattice.

In a one-dimensional lattice we found that the energy of a free electron was
proportional to k_x^2 [Eq. (13.19)], while the energy of a bound electron was a
complex function of k_x, showing marked departure from free-electron behavior
near the boundaries of the Brillouin zones (Fig. 13.5). Likewise, in a two-dimensional lattice, the energy of a free electron is proportional to $k_x^2 + k_y^2$, so
that constant-energy curves are circles, as is shown in Fig. 13.8 by the curves
near the center of the zone. When the boundaries of the zone are approached,
the curves deviate markedly from a circle, the extent of the deviation being
greater the stronger the electron binding.

The overlapping of energy bands can be seen by moving along two different
vectors in the lattice (refer to Fig. 13.8). The energy increases continuously
along vector $\mathbf{AB}$ until point B is reached. The energy then takes a discontinuous jump into zone 2. The energy also increases along vector $\mathbf{AC}$ but reaches a
value corresponding to the energy at point B well within the first zone at point
C. If the energy increase from point C to point D is *greater* than the energy increase required to cross the boundary at point B, the first and second Brillouin
zones will overlap. Thus an electron at point D in the first zone could have an
energy that is greater than that of an electron at point B in zone 2. Overlapping

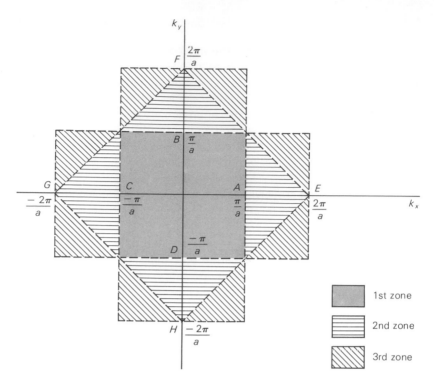

Fig. 13.7 The first three Brillouin zones for a two-dimensional square lattice.

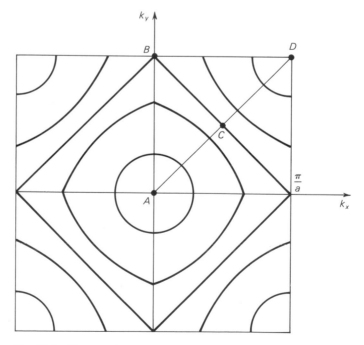

Fig. 13.8 The equal-energy contours in the first Brillouin zone of a two-dimensional square lattice depart from a circular shape on approaching the zone boundary.

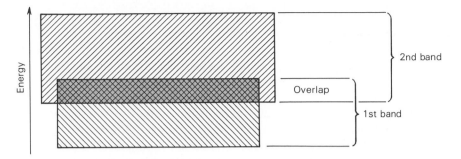

Fig. 13.9 In two- or three-dimensional lattices the energy bands may overlap.

energy bands are shown schematically in Fig. 13.9. This overlapping phenomenon has a very important effect on the electrical properties, as will be shown later.

In three dimensions, the boundaries of the Brillouin zones satisfy the condition

$$k_x n_x + k_y n_y + k_z n_z = \frac{\pi}{a} (n_x^2 + n_y^2 + n_z^2) \qquad (13.27)$$

and the boundaries are complex surfaces. The shapes of the first two zones for a body-centered cubic lattice and a hexagonal close-packed lattice are shown in Fig. 13.10. The constant-energy contours for free electrons near the center of a zone are spheres, while the contours for bound electrons, especially near the zone boundaries, are extremely complex. As in the two-dimensional lattice, overlapping of energy bands is possible under the right conditions.

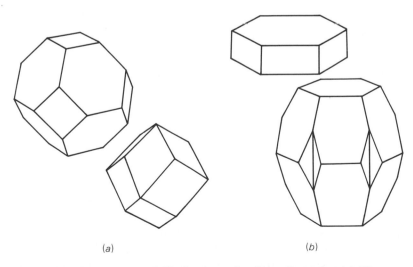

(a)   (b)

Fig. 13.10 The first two Brillouin zones for three-dimensional lattices. (a) Body-centered cubic; (b) hexagonal close-packed.

13.4
Electronic distributions in solids

In the preceding sections we have considered the behavior of a single electron in a periodic lattice and have determined the allowable energy states for that electron. In this section we shall consider how the many electrons of a real material distribute among these allowable energy states. Since we are talking about an almost continuous range of energies, we can represent the probability of occupying a given state by a continuous distribution function. The probability $\mathfrak{W}(E)$ of an electron occupying a given energy level is represented by Fermi-Dirac statistics:

$$\mathfrak{W}(E) = \frac{1}{1 + \exp\left[(E - E_F)/kT\right]} \qquad \text{cf. (2.16)} \qquad (13.28)$$

The energy E_F is called the *Fermi level* of the material. At absolute zero, $\mathfrak{W}(E) = 0$ for $E > E_F$ and $\mathfrak{W}(E) = 1$ for $E < E_F$. Thus, at absolute zero, the Fermi level divides the occupied states from the unoccupied states. It is the highest energy state for the electrons at absolute zero. In order to calculate the number of electrons with energy E, $N(E)$, one must multiply the probability function by the number of states with that energy, $s(E)$. Then,

$$N(E)\ dE = s(E)\mathfrak{W}(E)\ dE \qquad (13.29)$$

Calculation of the electron distribution over the whole Brillouin zone is a very complicated problem, since the energy is a complicated function of position in the zone. It may be easily evaluated at the center of a zone, however, where the free-electron model is adequate. The energy of a free electron in a three-dimensional box is, by analogy with Eq. (13.21),

$$E = \frac{h^2}{8m_e a^2}\ (n_x{}^2 + n_y{}^2 + n_z{}^2) = \frac{h^2}{8m_e a^2}\ n_T{}^2 \qquad (13.30)$$

where n_x, n_y, and n_z are positive integers. Using the exclusion principle, one can then fill energy levels using the three quantum numbers n_x, n_y, and n_z plus the spin quantum numbers $m_s = \pm \frac{1}{2}$. The number of states with a particular value of E depends on how many combinations of the quantum numbers result in the same value of n_T. Since we are dealing with almost a continuum of energy levels, we may construct a three-dimensional space with the coordinates n_x, n_y, and n_z and let each point with integer values of the coordinates represent an energy state. A radius vector n_T, from the origin, may then be drawn to point (n_x, n_y, n_z) in this space, and all points on the surface of a sphere of radius n_T must have the same energy. The number of available states within a sphere of radius n_T is then $\frac{1}{8} \times 2 \times \frac{4}{3}\pi n_T{}^3$. (The factor $\frac{1}{8}$ accounts for the fact that only positive integers are allowable and thus only one octant of the sphere is available. The factor of 2 accounts for the fact that there are two states per unit volume in the space ($m_s = \pm\frac{1}{2}$).) The number of states within a sphere of radius $n_T + dn_T$ is $\frac{1}{3}\pi(n_T + dn_T)^3$, and thus the number of states in the energy range dE is $\frac{1}{3}\pi(n_T + dn_T)^3 - \frac{1}{3}\pi n_T{}^3$.

$$s(E)\ dE = \pi n_T^2\ dn_T \qquad (13.31)$$

or combining with Eq. (13.30):

$$s(E)\ dE = \frac{\pi}{2} \left(\frac{8m_e a^2}{h^2}\right)^{3/2} E^{1/2}\ dE \qquad (13.32)$$

From Eq. (13.29) the number of electrons in the energy range E to $E + dE$ is

$$N(E)\ dE = \frac{\pi}{2} \left(\frac{8m_e a^2}{h^2}\right)^{3/2} E^{1/2} \frac{dE}{1 + \exp\left[(E - E_F)/kT\right]} \qquad (13.33)$$

where

$$\int_0^\infty N(E)\ dE = Na^3 \qquad (13.34)$$

N is the number of electrons *per unit volume*, and a^3 is the volume of the solid. At absolute zero, the Fermi function $\mathfrak{W}(E)$ is zero above E_F and 1 below E_F, so that Eq. (13.34) may be written as

$$N = \int_0^{E_F} \frac{\pi}{2} \left(\frac{8m_e}{h^2}\right)^{3/2} E^{1/2}\ dE$$

$$= \frac{\pi}{3} \left(\frac{8m_e}{h^2}\right)^{3/2} E_F^{3/2} \qquad (13.35)$$

The Fermi level E_F is thus

$$E_F = \frac{h^2}{2m_e} \left(\frac{3N}{8\pi}\right)^{2/3} \qquad (13.36)$$

The electron densities at absolute zero and at a finite temperature are plotted as a function of energy in Fig. 13.11. The distribution of free electrons at absolute zero is parabolic up to a cutoff point at the Fermi level. At higher tempera-

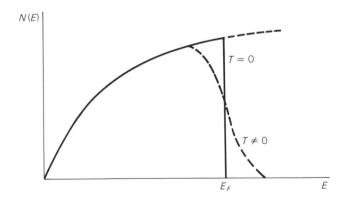

Fig. 13.11 The population density for a free-electron gas is parabolic in energy at low energies. The relationship is sensitive to temperature near the Fermi level for the material.

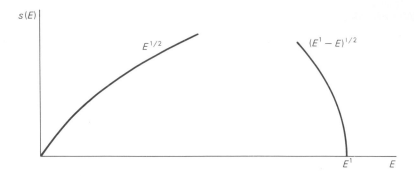

Fig. 13.12 The electronic state distribution is a parabolic function of energy at the top and bottom of a valence band in a solid.

tures a tailing effect develops, the extent of which depends on the temperature level.

In the region of the Brillouin zones where the energy contours are spherical (or circular for a two-dimensional lattice, Fig. 13.8), the distribution of energy states, $s(E)$, is approximately parabolic, as shown in Fig. 13.12. Likewise, at the corners of the zones (see Fig. 13.8) the energy contours again appear as spheres with centers at the corners. Thus, the distribution curve drops parabolically at the top of the band. The distribution in the central region of the band is a complex function of energy, and it has been found that the function has a cusplike shape, as shown in Fig. 13.13. When energy bands overlap, the distribution of states is the sum of the two bands in the overlap region (Fig. 13.14).

The Fermi surface (surface of constant E_F) marks the boundary of filled energy states at absolute zero. This Fermi surface may be confined to a single Brillouin zone or may penetrate across boundaries into the second, third, and even higher zones. The nature of the surface is important in determining the electronic properties of materials.

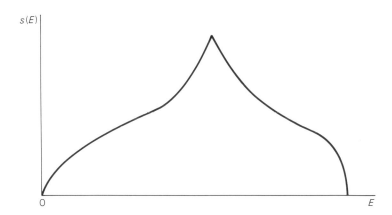

Fig. 13.13 The complete electronic state distribution function is characterized by a cusplike shape at the center.

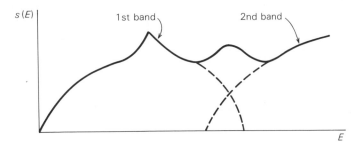

Fig. 13.14 The electronic state distribution function is continuous when the bands overlap.

13.5
Electrical conductivity — Zone concepts

The initial part of the band structure for the simple alkali and alkaline-earth metals (Li, Na, K and Be, Mg, Ca) is shown in Fig. 13.14. The complete structure is a complex overlapping of all of the bands right up to the zero point of energy. This means that there is an almost continuous range of energy states available to the valence electrons of these metals. The electron density at $T = 0°K$ is determined by filling the bands starting at the lowest energy and remembering that $2N$ electrons will fill one band. The alkali metals have one valence electron per atom and thus possess a half-filled band, as shown schematically in Fig. 13.15. The alkaline-earth metals have two valence electrons per atom. This would be enough to completely fill the first band if it were not for the overlapping of the second. Since the lowest energy states of the second are filled before the top of the first, the Fermi surface penetrates the second band, leaving a continuous range of states above the surface as shown schematically in Fig. 13.16.

The band structures of the group IV elements [C (diamond), Si, Ge, Sn (gray)], are very difficult to obtain, since the electrons in the outer shell, forming highly directional covalent bonds, do not conform to the simple pictures we have developed here. We may, however, still retain the concept of allowable

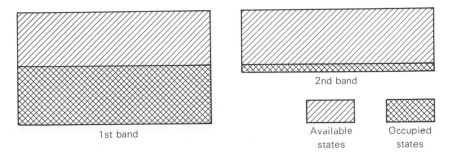

Fig. 13.15 The first band is only half-filled in the alkali metals.

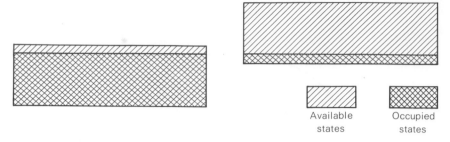

Available
states

Occupied
states

Fig. 13.16 The first two overlapping bands are only partially filled in the alkaline-earth metals.

energy bands separated by forbidden zones, as shown schematically in Fig. 13.17. The four valence electrons per atom thus completely fill the first two energy bands (i.e., the valence bands) at absolute zero.

A qualitative description of electrical conductivity can be given in terms of these models. When an electric field is imposed on the solid, an electron will *tend* to drift toward the positive pole of the field, thereby gaining energy. Whether or not an electron *can* gain energy, however, depends upon whether there is an available energy level to occupy. If a level is available, the electron can interact with the field and be accelerated. If there is no energy level available, the electron cannot be excited, will not interact with the field, and thus will not be carried with the electric current.

In terms of band structure, the criterion for electron conduction is that the electrons at the *top* of the band must have energy states available to them that are within the very small excitation energies involved in most conduction phenomena. Since the alkali metals have only half-filled bands, there is an almost continuous distribution of available states above the Fermi surface. Electrons at the top of the band can be excited to higher states, leaving empty states or "holes" below the Fermi surface and thus making it possible for electrons

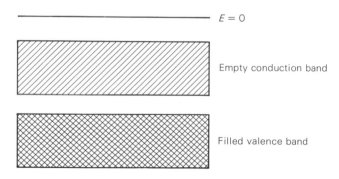

$E = 0$

Empty conduction band

Filled valence band

Fig. 13.17 In the group IV elements the empty conduction band is separated from the filled valence band by a finite energy gap.

deeper in the band to be excited also. The conclusion is that electrical conduction is relatively easy in materials with partially filled bands. The situation is the same in the alkaline metals, since the first two bands overlap. Thus a material will be a good electrical conductor when the energy bands are partially filled or when there is an overlapping of consecutive bands.

The insulating properties of diamond structures are also explainable on this basis. At $T = 0$, the four valence electrons completely fill the first two bands of the structure. Excitation can occur only if the electrons at the Fermi surface absorb enough energy to jump the large forbidden zone between the second and third bands. In diamond, this energy gap is 6.0 ev (9.6×10^{-19} joules per particle), which is considerably more energy than is normally associated with thermal or electrical excitation. The electrons are not free to accelerate in the electric field, thus making diamond a good insulator. By the same token, we know that all systems have a wide distribution of energies and there is always a small probability of a particle being in a much higher energy state than average. This means that there is a finite probability of an electron jumping the energy gap between the *valence band* and the *conduction band,* thereby promoting some conductivity.

The electrons in the conduction band are free to move in the field, and the newly formed holes in the valence band are free to accept excited electrons. This is the situation in semiconductors, which will be discussed in section 13.8. If this line of reasoning is correct, the resistivity (i.e., the reciprocal of conductivity) of an insulator or a semiconductor should increase with an increasing energy gap. The energy gap and resistivity at $T = 300°K$ of diamond are 6.0 ev and 10^{14} ohm-m, of silicon are 1.1 ev and 3×10^3 ohm-m, and of germanium are 0.7 ev and 0.50 ohm-m. Materials with resistivities greater than about 10^{10} ohm-m are generally classed as insulators; materials with resistivities smaller than about 10^{-8} ohm-m are called metallic conductors; and materials in the intermediate range of about 10^{-4} to 10^7 ohm-m are called semiconductors.

Since an electron in a periodic lattice is not really free, Newton's laws cannot be legitimately applied to calculate its acceleration and velocity in the lattice. The energy-momentum relationship, rather than being parabolic, is a complex function of the wave number k, as shown in Fig. 13.5. The "velocity" of a De Broglie wave can be obtained from Eqs. (13.19) and (13.20):

$$v = \frac{2\pi}{h} \frac{dE}{dk} \tag{13.37}$$

The acceleration in the electric field is thus

$$\frac{dv}{dt} = \frac{2\pi}{h} \frac{d}{dt} \frac{dE}{dk}$$

$$= \frac{2\pi}{h} \frac{d^2E}{dk^2} \frac{dk}{dt} \tag{13.38}$$

The change in energy dE when the electron moves $v\, dt$ units of distance in a field of strength $\mathscr{E}$ is

$$dE = e\mathscr{E}v\,dt$$

$$= e\mathscr{E}\,\frac{2\pi}{h}\,\frac{dt}{dk}\,dE \tag{13.39}$$

so that the time derivative of the wave number is

$$\frac{dk}{dt} = \frac{2\pi e\mathscr{E}}{h} \tag{13.40}$$

Substituting Eq. (13.40) into (13.38) gives one the acceleration of the electron:

$$\frac{dv}{dt} = \frac{4\pi^2}{h^2}\,\frac{d^2E}{dk^2}\,e\mathscr{E} \tag{13.41}$$

This expression for the acceleration is identical with Newton's second law if an *effective mass m** is defined as

$$m^* = \frac{h^2/4\pi^2}{d^2E/dk^2} \tag{13.42}$$

Since the second derivative of energy with respect to the wave number is not constant (except for the free electron), the effective mass will be a function of position in the Brillouin zones. Near the center of a zone the De Broglie wavelength is very large relative to the lattice spacing (that is, $k \doteq 0$) and the electron motion approaches that of a free electron. Farther out in a zone the De Broglie wavelength approaches the dimensions of the lattice and the behavior is modified because of interferences and reflections of the electron waves when they interact with the ion cores of the lattice. Under certain conditions an increase in energy could conceivably *reduce* the electron momentum because of interference between advancing and reflecting waves, which gives a *negative* effective mass. This simply means that momentum transfer to the lattice is larger than the momentum transfer to the electron. It is obvious that Newtonian concepts cannot be applied to describe the wave-mechanical nature of the electron, but nevertheless it is generally satisfactory to retain the visual picture of classical motion and merely substitute *effective mass m** for m_e. Remember, however, that we must now accept the fact that m^* is a quantity that varies from one point to the next and may in fact become negative at certain points in the Brillouin zones.

13.6
Evaluation of the conductivity of metals

By analogy with Eq. (13.9) we may express the conductivity as

$$\sigma = \frac{Ne^2 l_p}{m^* \mathbf{u}_F} \tag{13.43}$$

In the simple alkali and alkaline-earth metals, the number of electrons participating in the conduction process, N, is about equal to the number of valence electrons.   For the more complicated atoms, the band structures are more complex and the actual number of "effective" valence electrons is difficult to specify.   Even though all electrons in a valence band can participate in conduction, one may use the velocity of the electrons near the Fermi surface, $\mathbf{u}_F$, as being characteristic of the valence electrons.   The thermal velocity may then be estimated from the Fermi energy for the system Eq. (13.36).   The "mean free path" l_p in the wave-mechanical picture takes on a completely different meaning.   It can be rigorously shown that in an ideal, perfectly periodic lattice, an electron wave can propagate through the solid without any interference.   This means an infinite relaxation time or an infinite path length. A real crystal, however, departs from perfect periodicity because of lattice vibrations, vacancies, dislocations, alloying elements, grain boundaries, and, in fact, any kind of crystal defect.

Figure 13.18 shows the temperature dependence of the resistivity $\mathscr{R} = 1/\sigma$ for a number of metals.   At high temperatures the resistivity increases linearly with temperature, while at very low temperatures ($T < 0.1\Theta_D$) it becomes ap-

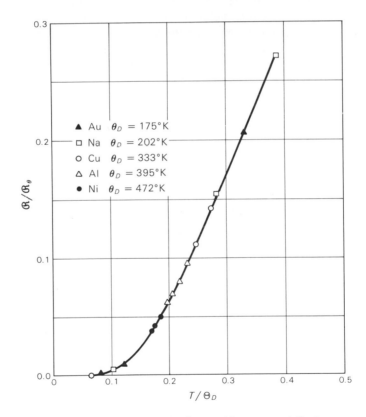

Fig. 13.18   A single curve may be used to represent the temperature variation of electrical resistance for various metals using the resistance at the Debye temperature as a reducing parameter.   [By permission from J. Bardeen, *J. Appl. Phys.,* **11:** 88 (1940).]

proximately constant. The high-temperature behavior is associated with changes in lattice vibrations, while the "residual" resistance at low temperature is associated with the other structural defects. At very high temperatures, the temperature dependence again diverges from linearity, as is shown in Fig. 13.19.

The total resistivity of a metal may be expressed as the sum of two parts:

$$\frac{1}{\sigma} = \mathscr{R} = \mathscr{R}_i + \mathscr{R}_T \qquad (13.44)$$

where $\mathscr{R}_i$ is the residual resistivity and $\mathscr{R}_T$ is the contribution from lattice vibrations. It can be shown that the probability of electron scattering from a harmonically vibrating atom is proportional to the square of the displacement, or, for a classical harmonic oscillator, proportional to the kinetic energy kT:

$$\mathscr{R}_T = KT \qquad (13.45)$$

where K is a characteristic constant for a given material. At low temperatures, quantum effects cause the resistance to vary with approximately the fifth power of the temperature. At very high temperatures, the lattice vibrations become anharmonic, causing deviations from the linear law.

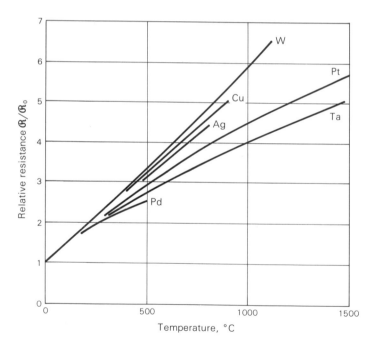

Fig. 13.19 The electrical resistance of metals at high temperature does not vary linearly with temperature. (By permission from N. F. Mott and H. Jones, "The Theory of the Properties of Metals and Alloys," p. 269, Dover Publications, Inc., New York, 1958.)

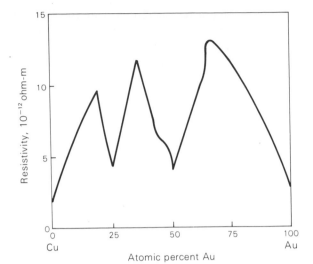

Fig. 13.20 The resistivity of copper-gold alloys decreases sharply at compositions corresponding to ordered solid solutions.

The major contribution to the residual resistivity of an annealed metal is from the presence of impurities in the lattice. At low impurity concentration, the residual resistivity is independent of temperature and, obviously, the higher the impurity content, the greater the resistivity. Other point defects, dislocations, and grain boundaries have less of an effect unless severe cold-working promotes very high concentrations of lattice defects.

Alloying has a very complicated effect on resistivity. In general, anything that promotes lattice disorder will increase resistivity, while an ordering of the structure will decrease it. This is illustrated in Fig. 13.20 with copper-gold alloys. The pure materials have the lowest resistivity, and a steady increase occurs upon addition of alloying element. When the ordered solid solutions Cu_3Au and $CuAu$ are formed, the resistivity takes a sharp drop because of the development of a more regular lattice.

13.7
Thermal properties of electrons

Valence electrons are the primary carriers of thermal energy in conductors, and thus the mobility of the electrons is the prime factor in determining the magnitude of the thermal conductivity. If we consider the valence electrons as perfectly free, the thermal conduction is analogous to the thermal conduction in an ideal gas. From Eq. (2.87), the thermal conductivity will be

$$\kappa = \frac{1}{3}c_v \mathbf{u} l_p \qquad (13.46)$$

where c_v is the heat capacity, $\mathbf{u}$ is the average thermal velocity, and l_p is the mean free path between collisions. If the electrons truly behaved as gas particles, the specific heat per particle would be $\frac{3}{2}k$. In the Fermi-Dirac distribution, however, only a few electrons near the Fermi surface can actually be excited to carry energy. An estimate of the true specific heat may be obtained by assuming that only the electrons in the region E_F to $E_F - kT$ can carry energy. The fraction of valence electrons that carry energy is thus about kT/E_F. The specific heat of the electron gas is thus roughly

$$c_v \doteq \frac{3}{2} Nk \frac{kT}{E_F} \qquad (13.47)$$

A more detailed analysis gives the same result but with a different proportionality constant:

$$c_v = \frac{\pi^2}{2} \frac{Nk^2 T}{E_F} \qquad (13.48)$$

Using the effective mass m^* and the thermal velocity at the Fermi surface, $\mathbf{u}_F$, gives

$$\kappa = \frac{\pi^2}{3} \frac{Nk^2 l_p}{m^* \mathbf{u}_F} T \qquad (13.49)$$

The ratio of thermal to electrical conductivity is obtained by combining Eqs. (13.43) and (13.49):

Table 13.1

Selected values of thermal conductivity

Material	κ, watts/m-°K	
	−190°C	0 or 20°C
Al	256	226
Cd ‖	92	84
Cd ⊥	113	105
Fe	184	92
Au		306
Cu	578	394
Mg	189	172
Ni	113	84
Na	155	138
Ag	427	419
Zn		113
NaCl	26.8	7.1
KCl	21.0	7.1
Brass (70-30 Cu-Zn)		96.0
Steel		44.8
Nickel steel, 2.0% Ni, 0.7% Mn	26.7	
Manganese steel	7.0	
Iron alloy, 4% Al	12.2	

$$\frac{\kappa}{\sigma} = \frac{\pi^2}{3} \left(\frac{k}{e}\right)^2 T \tag{13.50}$$

or

$$\frac{\kappa}{\sigma T} = 2.45 \times 10^{-8} \text{ watt-ohm/°K}^2 \tag{13.51}$$

This equation, known as the Wiedemann-Franz law, holds reasonably well for metals in the temperature range where the electrical resistivity is directly proportional to the temperature. This means that, in the range $T > \Theta_D$, the electron thermal conductivity is independent of temperature. When $T < \Theta_D$, the thermal conductivity varies rapidly with temperature, generally increasing to a maximum as the temperature decreases and then decreasing toward zero at absolute zero. Lattice vibrations also contribute to thermal conductivity, but electron transfer is the dominant mechanism in metals. Selected values of the thermal conductivity of a number of materials are given in Table 13.1.

13.8
Semiconductors

Materials with resistivities on the order of 10^{-4} to 10^7 ohm-m are called *semiconductors*. An *intrinsic semiconductor* is a pure crystal with the band structure shown in Fig. 13.17. At absolute zero the valence band is completely filled and the conduction band is empty, so the material acts as an insulator. At finite temperatures, some of the more energetic electrons can jump the energy gap and carry current in the conduction band. When this occurs, "holes" are left in the valence band which behave in every way as particles of positive charge $(+e)$. If an electric field is imposed, a drift of electrons in the $-x$ direction promotes a positive flow of current in the $+x$ direction. The holes, behaving as positive charges, drift in the $+x$ direction, thus promoting an additional positive current. From Eq. (13.2), the total conductivity will be the sum of effects from the electrons and the holes:

$$\sigma = N_e e \eta_e + N_h e \eta_h \tag{13.52}$$

The problem is to then calculate the number and mobility of the electrons and the holes.

The number of electrons excited to the conduction band at temperature T may be estimated. Let the energy at the top of the valence band be the reference state $E_v = 0$ and let the energy gap equal E_g. The number of electrons *per unit volume* above energy E_g is then obtained by using Eq. (13.33) and (13.34):

$$N_e = \int_{E_g}^{\infty} \frac{\pi}{2} \left(\frac{8m_e}{h^2}\right)^{3/2} (E - E_g)^{1/2} \exp\frac{E_F - E}{kT} \, dE \tag{13.53}$$

where it is assumed that $E - E_F \gg kT$. The integration yields

$$N_e = 2 \left(\frac{2\pi m_e kT}{h^2}\right)^{3/2} \exp \frac{E_F - E_g}{kT} \qquad (13.54)$$

The probability of finding a hole at energy E is related to the probability of finding an electron by

$$\mathfrak{W}_h = 1 - \mathfrak{W}_e$$

$$= 1 - \frac{1}{1 + \exp\left[(E - E_F)/kT\right]} \doteq \exp \frac{E - E_F}{kT} \qquad (13.55)$$

where it is assumed that $E_F - E \gg kT$. The number of holes in the valence band from energy 0 to $-\infty$ is then

$$N_h = \int_{-\infty}^{0} \frac{\pi}{2} \left(\frac{8m}{h^2}\right)^{3/2} (-E)^{1/2} \exp \frac{E - E_F}{kT} \, dE$$

$$= 2 \left(\frac{2\pi m_h kT}{h^2}\right)^{3/2} \exp \left(-\frac{E_F}{kT}\right) \qquad (13.56)$$

In an intrinsic semiconductor, the number of electrons in the conduction band is equal to the number of holes in the valence band, so that Eqs. (13.54) and (13.56) may be combined to yield

$$N = (N_e N_h)^{1/2} = 2 \left(\frac{2kT}{h^2}\right)^{3/2} (m_e m_h)^{3/4} \exp \left(-\frac{E_g}{2kT}\right) \qquad (13.57)$$

and

$$E_F = \frac{E_g}{2} + \frac{3}{4} kT \ln \frac{m_h}{m_e} \qquad (13.58)$$

Combining with the conductivity equation (13.52), one gets

$$\sigma = 2e \left(\frac{2\pi kT}{h^2}\right)^{3/2} (m_e m_h)^{3/4} (\eta_e + \eta_h) \exp \left(-\frac{E_g}{2kT}\right) \qquad (13.59)$$

If $m_e = m_h$, $E_F = E_g/2$, which means that the Fermi level at any temperature T is in the middle of the forbidden gap. Since the preexponential factor in Eq. (13.59) does not vary markedly with temperature, compared with the exponential factor, the log of σ should be proportional to $1/T$, with the slope determined by the energy gap E_g. Figure 13.21 is a plot of the resistivity ($\mathcal{R} = 1/\sigma$) of several semiconductors as a function of temperature and shows that Eq. (13.59) is of the correct form. Table 13.2 gives values for the energy gaps between valence and conduction bands for a number of semiconductors, and Table 13.3 gives values for the mobilities of the electrons and the holes at room temperature. From these data, one may then calculate the conductivity of intrinsic semiconductors.

Small amounts of impurities are always present in semiconducting materials. When the concentration of impurity is high enough to have an effect on the conductivity, the material is called an *extrinsic semiconductor*. When a small amount of impurity of valence $n + 1$ or greater is added to a semicon-

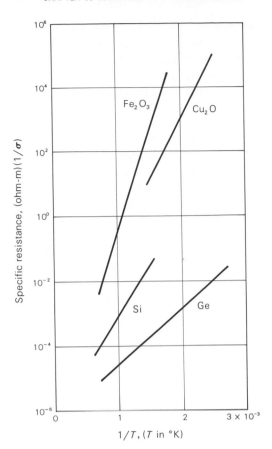

Fig. 13.21 The specific resistance of many intrinsic semiconductors varies with temperature according to an Arrhenius-type relation.

ductor of valence n, additional electrons that cannot fit into the valence band are added to the system. They must therefore reside in higher energy states. This is called an n-type semiconductor. When the impurity has a valence of $n - 1$ or less, there is a deficiency of electrons which promotes holes in the valence band. These are known as p-type semiconductors. A simple calculation will show that a very small trace of impurity can have a very large effect on the conductivity. The conductivity of pure germanium at room temperature, for example, is about 2.0 $(\text{ohm-m})^{-1}$. Suppose x percent of arsenic atoms replace germanium atoms in the crystal lattice. Since each arsenic atom has five valence electrons, there will be one extra valence electron per atom that must be placed in the conduction band of the structure. If these are free electrons, their contribution to the conductivity is

$$\sigma \doteq N_e e \eta$$

$$\doteq \left(N_e \frac{\text{electron}}{\text{m}^3}\right)\left(1.6 \times 10^{-19} \frac{\text{amp-sec}}{\text{electron}}\right)\left(0.3800 \frac{\text{m}^2}{\text{volt-sec}}\right)$$

$$\doteq 6.08 \times 10^{-20} N_e \ (\text{ohm-m})^{-1} \tag{13.60}$$

An electron density of only 3.3×10^{21} electrons/m³ will give a conductivity of 200 (ohm-m)⁻¹ or, in other words, will increase the conductivity of pure germanium by a factor of 100. This is equivalent to a 7.4×10^{-8} mole fraction of arsenic atoms. Thus, an extraordinarily small amount of impurity has a very marked effect on the conductivity. It is clear that the purification of semiconductor crystals is very important in the production of semiconductor devices.

When an atom such as arsenic replaces a germanium atom in a crystal lattice, the local available energy states in the vicinity of the impurity will be somewhat different than in the pure crystal because of the difference in electrostatic field created by the As^{5+} nucleus. Four of the electrons form primary bonds with the surrounding germanium atoms, leaving a fifth electron relatively free to migrate through the metal. The allowable energy states for these extra electrons are called *donor states,* and their level depends on the energy required to remove the electron from the ionic core in the presence of surrounding germanium atoms. In most cases the experimental values of these "ionization" energies lie in the range of 0.01 to 0.02 ev and are thus of the order of magnitude of normal thermal excitation. The donor states are thus of the order

Table 13.2

Values of the energy gap between the valence and conduction bands in semiconductors, at room temperature *

Crystal	E_g, ev	Crystal	E_g, ev
Diamond	6	ZnSb	0.56
Si	1.10	GaSb	0.78
Ge	0.68–0.72	PbS	0.34–0.37
Sn (gray)	0.08	PbSe	0.27
InSb	0.18	PbTe	0.30
InAs	0.33	CdS	2.42
InP	1.25	CdSe	1.74
GaAs	1.4	CdTe	1.45
AlSb	1.6–1.7	ZnSe	2.60
InSe	(1)	AgI	2.8
GaP	2.25	Ag_2Te	0.17
α-Mg_3Sb_2	0.82	Cu_2O	2.1
Ca_2Si	0.9	Mg_2Si	0.7
Ca_2Sn	0.9	Mg_2Ge	0.7
Ca_2Pb	0.46	Mg_2Sn	0.3

* By permission, from C. Kittel, "Introduction to Solid State Physics,"; p. 351. John Wiley & Sons, Inc., New York, 1959.

Table 13.3

Carrier drift mobilities at room temperature *

Crystal	Mobility, $m^2/volt\text{-}sec$	
	Electrons	Holes
Diamond	0.1800	0.1200
Si	0.1600	0.0400
Ge	0.3800	0.1800
InSb	7.7000	0.1250
InAs	2.3000	0.0100
InP	0.3400	0.0650
GaSb	0.2500–0.4000	0.0650
PbS	0.0600	0.0200
PbSe	0.0900	0.0700
PbTe	1.7000	–
AgCl	0.0050	–

* By permission from C. Kittel, "Introduction to Solid State Physics," John Wiley & Sons, Inc., New York, 1959.

of 0.01 to 0.02 ev below the bottom of the conduction band (Fig. 13.22). Above $T = 0°K$ donor electrons are easily excited into the conduction band and therefore are able to carry current. By analogy with Eq. (13.58), the Fermi level at absolute zero is halfway between the donor level and the bottom of the conduction band. As the temperature increases, however, an increasing fraction of electrons from the valence band also may be excited into the conduction band and the relative effect of the impurity is decreased. The Fermi level thus decreases with temperature, approaching $E_g/2$ as a limit (Fig. 13.23).

An analogous argument can be used when an impurity such as a gallium

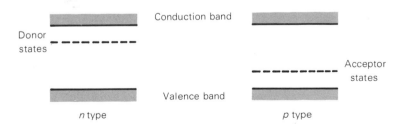

Fig. 13.22 Extrinsic semiconductors have acceptor and donor states within the forbidden zones of the corresponding intrinsic semiconductors.

atom replaces a germanium atom. In this case, the nucleus has a charge Ga^{3+} and there is a deficiency of one electron in the primary bonds formed with the germanium neighbors. One may visualize this deficiency as a localized hole bound to the impurity with a certain ionization energy. This produces localized "acceptor" states on the order of 0.01 to 0.02 ev above the valence band. The electron deficiency causes holes in the valence band, which then allows for a higher conductivity. The Fermi level at $T = 0°K$ is midway between the acceptor levels and the top of the valence band and increases with temperature to a limiting value of $E_g/2$.

Commercial semiconducting materials would probably contain both donors and acceptors. If there were an excess of donors, the donor electrons would tend to fill the empty states in the valence band and the acceptor levels before filling donor levels. The electron distributions and Fermi levels would thus be a bit more difficult to analyze.

The conductivity of extrinsic semiconductors is calculated with Eq. (13.52), but this time it must be recognized that the number of electrons and the number of holes are not the same, as in an intrinsic semiconductor. Also, the relative effectiveness of the impurities will vary with temperature as shown in Fig. 13.24. In the intrinsic range, the slope is equal to $E_g/2k$, while in the extrinsic range it is approximately $E_i/2k$, where E_i is the binding energy of the electron or hole.

The production and use of semiconductor devices have had a tremendous impact on the electronics industry. Miniaturization, computing devices, and information-processing systems are all outgrowths of developments in the

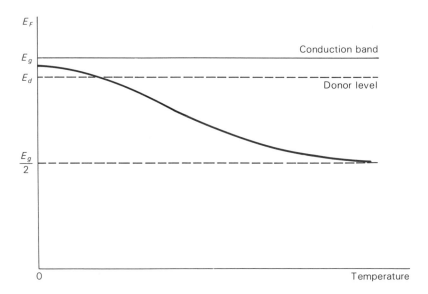

Fig. 13.23 The Fermi level in an *n*-type extrinsic semiconductor is a function of temperature.

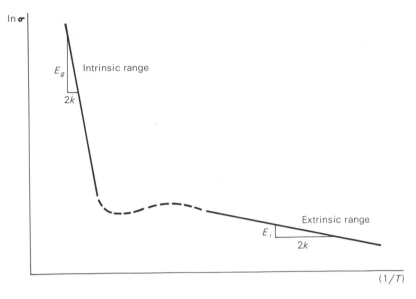

Fig. 13.24   The conductivity of an impurity semiconductor passes through three distinct regions of behavior.

semiconductor field.   Although it is not the purpose of this text to discuss products and devices, it is strongly recommended that one of the references listed at the end of this chapter be read for a description of transistors, rectifiers, and the like.

References

1   Azároff, L. V.: "Introduction to Solids," McGraw-Hill Book Company, New York, 1960. *Chapters 10, 12, and 13 cover the material in this chapter at about the same level but in much greater detail.*

2   Bardeen, J.: Electrical Conductivity of Metals, *J. Appl. Phys.,* **11:** 88 (1940).

3   Coblenz, A., and H. L. Owens: "Transistors: Theory and Applications," McGraw-Hill Book Company, New York, 1955. *Treats the application and manufacture of transistor devices. Necessary reading supplementary to this chapter.*

4   Dekker, A.: "Solid State Physics," Prentice-Hall, Inc., Englewood Cliffs, N.J., 1957. *A general reference text written at the graduate level.*

5   Greiner, R. A.: "Semiconductor Devices and Applications," McGraw-Hill Book Company, New York, 1961. *Thorough discussions of the properties of semiconductor devices. Necessary reading supplementary to this chapter.*

6   Hutchison, T. S., and D. C. Baird: "The Physics of Engineering Solids," John Wiley & Sons, Inc., New York, 1963. *Chapters 7 to 11 present the material of this chapter at an elementary level but in greater detail than here.*

7 Kittel, C.: "Introduction to Solid State Physics," 2d ed., John Wiley & Sons, Inc., New York, 1959. *A graduate-level text on all aspects of solid-state physics. Chapters 10 to 13 cover free-electron models, band theory, and application of band theory to alloys in great detail. Chapter 14 discusses transistors and rectifiers. Highly recommended to those who want a fuller understanding of electronic properties.*

8 Mott, N. F., and H. Jones: "The Theory of the Properties of Metals and Alloys," Dover Publications, Inc., New York, 1958. *This is a soft-covered reprint of a classic reference work on the properties of metals. Major emphasis is placed on relationship between electronic properties and lattice structure.*

9 Shockley, W.: "Electrons and Holes in Semiconductors," D. Van Nostrand Company, Inc., Princeton, N.J., 1950. *A complete text on the theory and applications of semiconductor devices.*

10 Wert, C. A., and R. M. Thomson: "Physics of Solids," McGraw-Hill Book Company, New York, 1964. *A general undergraduate text on the physics of solids. Chapters 9 and 11 to 13 cover the material of this chapter in an elementary fashion.*

Questions

13.1 The resistance of a homogeneous body varies directly with length in the direction of current flow and inversely with the cross section normal to the current flow. Calculate the resistance in ohms of a copper rod which is 10.40 mm in diameter and 100 cm long. If the rod is drawn down to a diameter of 5.2 mm, what will be the new resistance? (Assume no volume change on drawing.)

13.2 Determine the allowed energy states for an electron in a one-dimensional box of length L. Assume a constant potential, $\psi = 0$, inside the box, and an infinite potential outside the box.

13.3 Plot the predicted electronic distribution for the model of Question 13.2 for the ground state, $n = 1$, and the first excited state, $n = 2$. Why is it apparent that this oversimplified model will not accurately describe the nature of simple metals?

13.4 It is possible to remove electrons from a metal surface by the action of an electric field. This phenomenon is called *field emission*. Show how this phenomenon can be described using the simplified free-electron model of Fig. 13.1. Show the effect of a constant external field $\mathscr{E}$ on the potential outside the metal. (Assume there is no voltage drop within the metal.) Indicate how the Schrödinger equation gives the electron concentration outside the metal surface. (Outline—do not solve.)

13.5 Use Eq. (13.26) to build up the first three Brillouin zones in a two-dimensional lattice. Plot your results. Calculate the electron momenta at the boundaries of the Brillouin zones if the lattice parameter is 3 Å.

13.6 Develop equations for the surfaces of the first and second Brillouin zones in a simple cubic lattice.

13.7 Derive an equation for the kinetic energy of a free-electron gas at 0°K in terms of the Fermi level of the solid. Answer: $U(0) = \frac{3}{2}NE_F(0)$.

13.8 Calculate the Fermi energies of sodium and lithium. Determine the temperature at which there is a 1 percent probability $\mathfrak{W}(E)$ of finding an electron 0.05 ev above the Fermi level of Na. Determine the temperature at which there is a 1 percent probability of finding an electron 0.5 ev above the Fermi level of Na.

13.9 Calculate the electron density in copper if the Fermi energy is 7.1 ev. Compare this with the electron density calculated from simple valence concepts. (The crystal density is 8.92 g/cm^3.)

13.10 Estimate the thermal conductivities of the following metals from the following values of electrical resistivity at 20°C.

Metal	Ag	Al	Cu	Fe	Hg	Ni
$\mathscr{R}_{20}10^{-12}$ ohm-m	1.6	2.83	1.69	8.85	95.8	7.24

13.11 Calculate and plot the intrinsic conductivity of germanium as a function of temperature, using data given in this chapter. What fraction of the valence electrons are in the conduction band at 300 and 800°K?

13.12 Calculate the conductivity of a germanium crystal containing 5×10^{16} arsenic atoms/cm^3. Also make the calculation for a germanium crystal containing 5×10^{16} gallium atoms/cm^3. Qualitatively discuss the effects on conductivity and Fermi level if a germanium crystal is doped with equal amounts of the n- and p-type impurities.

14
Dielectric properties

14.1
Introduction

In the preceding chapter it was shown that the electrical resistivity of a semiconductor is proportional to the exponent of the energy gap between the conduction and the valence bands [Eq. (13.59)]. When the energy gap is of the order of several electron volts, the resistivity is generally of the order of 10^{14} ohm-m or higher; materials with this high a resistivity are called insulators. The effects of impurities on insulators are the same as on semiconductors, but in this case the acceptor and donor states are so far removed from the conduction and valence bands that the decrease in resistivity is relatively small. Electrons are thus not free to accelerate in an electric field but rather remain tightly bound to a particular ionic core (or nucleus). The very small amount of direct current that does pass through the solid is carried by a combination of electronic and ionic migration. The rate of ionic migration can be analyzed in a fashion similar to that used in Sec. 13.2 to describe the migration of small particles that follow Newton's laws of motion. The ionic conductivity may be calculated with Eq. (13.2), where the mobility of an ion as given by Einstein is

$$\eta_{\text{ionic}} = \frac{e\mathscr{D}}{kT} \qquad (14.1)$$

where $\mathscr{D}$ is the coefficient of self-diffusion of the ion. If the migration occurs by a thermally activated jump into vacant lattice sites (as discussed in Sec. 6.6), the temperature dependence of the diffusion coefficient may be given by

$$\mathscr{D} = \mathscr{D}_0 \exp\left(-\frac{\Delta E_D}{RT}\right) \qquad (14.2)$$

where $\mathscr{D}_0$ is a constant and ΔE_D is the activation energy. The ionic conductivity is thus

$$\sigma_{\text{ionic}} = \frac{e^2 N \mathscr{D}_0}{kT} \exp\left(-\frac{\Delta E_D}{RT}\right) \qquad (14.3)$$

The temperature dependence of the conductivity is thus the same as for semiconductors, but with the slope of a log σ versus $1/T$ plot being proportional to the activation energy for ionic migration. At ordinary temperatures, the number of electrons in the conduction band and the number of vacant lattice sites are so small that the conductivity is negligible.

In describing insulators it is important to measure the properties that are associated with polarizability. When an electric field is applied to a material, the electrons are attracted to the positive pole while the positively charged particles are attracted to the negative pole. The total induced dipole moment per unit volume is defined as the *polarization* $\mathscr{P}$ of the material. If each particle acts independently, the polarization is just the sum of the induced dipole moments for each atom in the unit of volume. The magnitude of an atomic dipole moment may be characterized by the *polarizability* α_a, as defined in Chap. 1. An additional polarization effect is encountered in polar materials. In the absence of an electric field, the permanent dipoles are randomly oriented because of Brownian motion (except for highly directional bonds such as hydrogen bonds). When an electric field is applied, the rotating dipoles are partially oriented in the direction of the field. This is called *orientation polarization.*

In the following sections the dielectric constant, the susceptibility, the loss angle, and other measurable dielectric properties will be discussed in terms of the molecular structure of a variety of materials.

14.2
General definitions

Figure 14.1 shows a voltage $\mathbf{V}$ across a pair of flat metal plates. If the gap w between the plates is completely evacuated, the total charge q_T on the plates is related to the electric field by

$$q_T = \frac{A\epsilon_0}{4\pi} \mathscr{E} = \frac{A\epsilon_0}{4\pi w} \mathbf{V}$$

$$= C_{\text{vac}} \mathbf{V} \qquad (14.4)$$

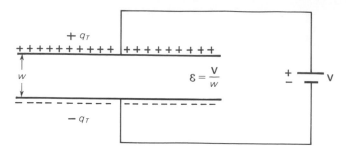

Fig. 14.1   A parallel-plate capacitor.

The quantity A is the total area of one plate; ϵ_0 is defined as the *permittivity of empty space;* and C_{vac} is the capacitance of the circuit. The permittivity has the units of charge per meter per unit potential. In cgs-esu units, $\epsilon_0 = 1.0$ escoul/cm-esvolt, while in mks units $\epsilon_0 = \frac{1}{9} \times 10^{-9}$ farad/m. (See Appendix E for the proper conversion units.) Capacitance has the units of charge per unit potential, or coulombs per volt in mks units.

When the volume between the plates is filled with a nonconducting material, a polarization $\mathscr{P}$ is induced in the material. The polarization, being the total dipole moment per unit volume, produces a polarization charge on the positive face of the capacitor of $q/A = -\mathscr{P}$ and on the negative face of the capacitor of $q/A = +\mathscr{P}$. If the external electric field remains constant at $\mathscr{E}$, this extra charge density must be neutralized by a flow of charge through the external circuit. The charge on the positive capacitor plate must therefore increase to $(A\epsilon_0/4\pi)\mathscr{E} + A\mathscr{P}$ and on the negative plate to $-(A\epsilon_0/4\pi)\mathscr{E} - A\mathscr{P}$. Equation (14.4) can then be written as

$$q_T = \frac{A}{4\pi}\,(\epsilon_0\mathscr{E} + 4\pi\mathscr{P}) = \frac{A}{4\pi}\,D = \frac{A}{4\pi}\,\epsilon_0\kappa_e\mathscr{E} \tag{14.5}$$

where D is the *electric displacement* and κ_e is the *static dielectric constant* for the material. The dielectric constant expresses the increase in capacitance caused by the insulating material, and values for several materials are listed in Table 14.1. Because of the low density of particles, the dielectric constants of gases are close to 1.0, while for liquids and solids the numbers are much higher. Equation (14.5) may be rewritten to give

$$\kappa_e = \frac{D}{\epsilon_0\mathscr{E}} = 1 + \frac{4\pi}{\epsilon_0}\frac{\mathscr{P}}{\mathscr{E}} \tag{14.6}$$

and

$$\kappa_e - 1 = \frac{4\pi}{\epsilon_0}\frac{\mathscr{P}}{\mathscr{E}} = 4\pi\chi_e \tag{14.7}$$

where χ_e is the *electric susceptibility* of the material. Since $\mathscr{P} = \epsilon_0\chi_e\mathscr{E}$, the electric susceptibility is a measure of the polarizability of the substance.

When there is negligible interaction between the molecules of a substance, as in dilute gases, each molecule responds independently to the electric field $\mathscr{E}$. The susceptibility is then proportional to the atomic polarizability α. If there are N particles per unit volume and the induced dipole moment per particle in the direction of $\mathscr{E}$ is μ^{ind}, then

$$\mathscr{P} = N\mu^{ind} \tag{14.8}$$

Combining Eqs. (14.7) and (14.8), one gets

$$\mu^{ind} = \frac{\epsilon_0 \chi_e}{N} \mathscr{E} \tag{14.9}$$

From the definition of polarizability, $\mu^{ind} = \alpha_T \epsilon_0 \mathscr{E}$, the polarizability of a dilute gas is

$$\alpha_T = \frac{\chi_e}{N} = \frac{\kappa_e - 1}{4\pi N} \tag{14.10}$$

The polarization of individual particles is caused by deformation of the electron distribution (induction polarization), deformation of charged ions relative to one another (ionic polarization), and by the orientation of permanent dipoles in the molecule (orientation polarization). We shall next discuss each of these phenomena.

Table 14.1

The static dielectric constants for several materials *

Material	κ_e
Vacuum	1.000000
Air, 1 atm	1.000590
Air, 100 atm	1.05480
CO_2, 1 atm	1.000985
H_2, 1 atm	1.000264
H_2O vapor, 1 atm	1.00705
H_2O liquid	81.0
Ice, $-5°C$	2.9
Ethyl alcohol, liquid, 0°C	28.4
Ethyl alcohol, solid	2.7
Glass	5.0 to 10.0
Rubber	2.5 to 35.0
Wood	2.5 to 8.0

* From several sources, notably from "The Handbook of Chemistry and Physics," Chemical Rubber Publishing Co., Cleveland, Ohio.

14.3
Polarization of atoms and molecules

The total polarizability of a particle is the sum of the three contributions:

$$\alpha_T = \alpha_{\text{elec}} + \alpha_{\text{ionic}} + \alpha_{\text{orient}} \qquad (14.11)$$

The electronic or induction polarizability of a spherical, nonpolar atom may be estimated by assuming that the electron cloud is bound harmonically to the nucleus. The polarizability of a linear oscillator in the field direction is related to the force constant by

$$\alpha_{\text{elec}} = \frac{e^2}{\epsilon_0 k_f} = \frac{e^2}{4\pi^2 m\nu^2 \epsilon_0} \qquad (14.12)$$

For a hydrogen atom in its ground state, $E_1 = -2\pi^2 e^4 m_e / h^2 = h\nu/2$, or

$$\alpha_{\text{elec}} \doteq \frac{h^6}{64\pi^6 e^6 m^3} = a_0^3 \epsilon_0 \qquad (14.13)$$

Since a_0 is the radius at which the electron cloud has its maximum density, the induced polarizability of a nonpolar atom is seen to be proportional to the atomic radius. Several values are listed in Table 1.2. It should be noted that the induced polarizability is truly scalar only for spherical molecules.

When a molecule is composed of ions, an ionic polarization can develop from the displacement of ions of opposite charge in the electric field. A diatomic molecule like HCl, for example, can be considered as a hydrogen cation harmonically bound to a chloride anion. The ionic polarizability in the field direction is also

$$\alpha_{\text{ionic}} = \frac{e^2}{\epsilon_0 k_f} \qquad (14.14)$$

where k_f is the force constant for the HCl bond. From the spectroscopic data given in Question 4.17, $k_f \doteq 50 \text{ kg}_w/\text{m}$ (4.8×10^5 dynes/cm) and $\alpha_{\text{ionic}} \doteq 4.8 \times 10^{31}$ m³. This is of the order of about one-fifth of the induced polarizability given in Table 1.2. Actually, the calculation probably gives too high a value, and the true ionic contribution is probably no more than 10 percent of the electronic portion.

Since the electron distributions in atoms and ions are insensitive to temperature, the induced and ionic polarizabilities are also independent of temperature. Figure 14.2 shows that the molar polarizability $4/_3\pi N\alpha$ is independent of temperature for spherical nonpolar molecules. This is because the only contribution is from the displacement of the electron cloud (that is, $\alpha_T = \alpha_{\text{elec}}$). For polar molecules, on the other hand, the polarizability increases linearly with $1/T$. The temperature dependence arises from the partial orientation of permanent dipoles in the direction of the electric field.

In the absence of an electric field, all the permanent dipoles in a dilute gas

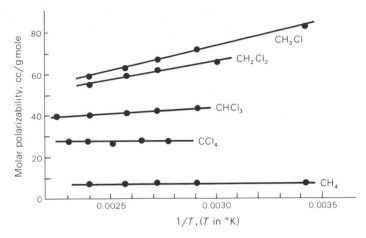

Fig. 14.2   The effect of temperature on the molar polarizability of vapors is determined by the magnitude of the dipole moment. [R. Sanger, *Physik. Z.,* **27:** 556 (1926).]

are randomly oriented owing to the thermal, rotational motion of the particles. When an electric field is imposed, there is a tendency for the dipoles to line up in the direction of the field (Fig. 14.3), but this tendency is partially compensated for by the randomizing influence of thermal motion. The net result is that the dipoles are, on the average, at an angle θ to the field. The angle, and thus the orientation polarizability, is a function of temperature. If one assumes a free rotation of dipoles and a Maxwell-Boltzmann energy distribution, one may derive an expression for the orientation polarizability as follows:

The energy of the dipole in the field is given as

$$\psi = -(\mu \cos \theta)\mathscr{E} \tag{14.15}$$

The minimum potential-energy state is $\theta = 0$, which can be approached only at very low temperature, and the zero potential-energy state is $\theta = 90°$, which can be approached only at very low field strength.

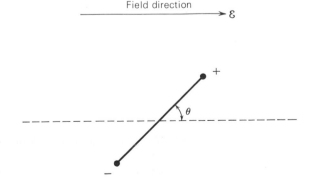

Fig. 14.3   The orientation of a dipole in an electric field.

If the distribution of energy states follows Maxwell-Boltzmann statistics, the average value of the dipole moment in the direction of the field, $\langle \mu \cos \theta \rangle$, is

$$
\langle \mu \cos \theta \rangle = \frac{\int_0^{2\pi} \int_0^{\pi} \mu \cos \theta \left(\exp \frac{\mu \mathscr{E} \cos \theta}{kT} \right) \sin \theta \, d\theta \, d\phi}{\int_0^{2\pi} \int_0^{\pi} \exp \frac{\mu \mathscr{E} \cos \theta}{kT} \sin \theta \, d\theta \, d\phi}
$$

$$
= \frac{\mu \int_{-1}^{1} x \exp ax \, dx}{\int_{-1}^{1} \exp ax \, dx}
$$

$$
= \mu \left(\text{ctnh } a - \frac{1}{a} \right)
$$

$$
= \mu L(a) \tag{14.16}
$$

where $x = \cos \theta$, $a = \mu \mathscr{E}/kT$ and, $L(a)$ is the *Langevin function*. For most materials, μ is of the order of 10^{-30} coulomb-m (see Table 1.1), so that μ/kT is generally of the order of 10^{-9} m/volt. For field strengths below 10^8 volts/m, $a \ll 1$ and the Langevin function reduces to $L(a) \doteq a/3$. Under these conditions, Eq. (14.16) reduces to

$$
\langle \mu \cos \theta \rangle = \frac{\mu a}{3} = \frac{\mu^2 \mathscr{E}}{3kT} \tag{14.17}
$$

or in terms of an orientation polarizability, $\alpha_{\text{orient}} = \langle \mu \cos \theta \rangle / \epsilon_0 \mathscr{E}$,

$$
\alpha_{\text{orient}} = \frac{\mu^2}{3kT\epsilon_0} \tag{14.18}
$$

Combining the induced and ionic polarizability into a single temperature-independent term α_0, one can then express the total polarizability as

$$
\alpha_T = \alpha_0 + \frac{\mu^2}{3kT\epsilon_0} \tag{14.19}
$$

The slope of an α_T versus $1/T$ plot is thus proportional to the square of the permanent dipole moment of the substance. The experimental measurement of electric susceptibility is one way of determining the dipole moment of the molecules.

With dilute gases, there is negligible interaction between particles and the full force of the external electric field is felt by each. With liquids and solids, each particle is surrounded by many neighbors that are within a few atomic diameters. The molecular interactions have two effects. First of all, the electric fields of the surrounding particles create a force on the particle in question, thus making the *local* electrical field at each point different from the external field. Thus, the force per unit charge felt by each particle is *not* $\mathscr{E}$, but rather is a different value, $\mathscr{E}_{\text{local}}$. Second, the presence of other particles within an atomic radius has an effect on both the distortion of the electron cloud and the freedom of the permanent dipoles to rotate. This means that the calculation of the various components of polarizability is more complex than is shown above. One can, however, define a total polarizability in terms of the polarization and the local electric field and then calculate a value for $\mathscr{E}_{\text{local}}$. The basic equation is thus

$$\mathscr{P} = N\alpha_T \mathscr{E}_{\text{local}} \qquad (14.20)$$

In the next section we shall consider the evaluation of the local electric field.

14.4
Electric fields within dielectrics

Figure 14.4 shows the charge densities at various places in a capacitor containing a condensed dielectric material. Consider a particular point in the dielectric, a, and imagine that it is inside a spherical cavity that has a radius which is large compared with the interatomic spacing. Within the sphere are all the dipoles that are near enough to have a measurable effect on the particle at point a, and outside the sphere is a homogeneous material with a dielectric constant κ_e. The electric field at a arises from the combined effects of the charge density on the surface of the capacitor, $D/4\pi$, the charge density on the surface of the dielectric due to polarization, $-\mathscr{P}$, the charge density on the surface of the spherical cavity, $(q_T/A)_L$, and the net charge density of the dipoles within the spherical cavity. The electric field at point a due to the charge on the surface of the sphere is evaluated as follows: The surface element dA at an angle θ from the field direction has a total charge equal to the normal component of the polarization times the surface area (that is, $dq = \mathscr{P} \cos \theta \, dA$). The electric field at the center of the cavity due to this element of charge is, from Coulomb's law:

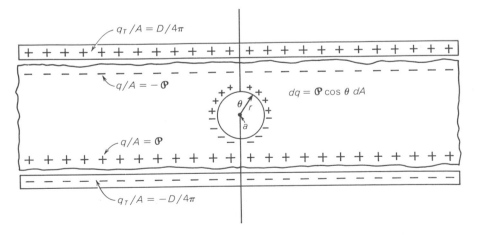

Fig. 14.4 The charge distribution within a capacitor.

$$(d\mathscr{E}_L)_r = \frac{\mathscr{P}\cos\theta\,dA}{r^2} \tag{14.21}$$

If the element of area is a spherical ring of area $2\pi r \sin\theta\,(r\,d\theta)$, the force per unit charge in the direction of the field due to the charge on the whole surface, $(\mathscr{E}_L)_x$, is

$$(\mathscr{E}_L)_x = \int_0^\pi 2\pi r^2 \sin\theta\,d\theta\,\frac{\mathscr{P}\cos\theta}{r^2}\cos\theta$$

$$= 2\pi\mathscr{P}\int_0^\pi \cos^2\theta \sin\theta\,d\theta$$

$$= \frac{4}{3}\pi\mathscr{P} \tag{14.22}$$

$(\mathscr{E}_L)_x$ is called the *Lorentz field.* The electric field due to the dipoles from within the cavity must be calculated by adding the effects of all the points in the cavity. This could become a very tedious task for complex geometries, but it can be shown that for isotropic materials, simple cubic, body-centered cubic, and face-centered cubic crystals, the net electric field at the center of the cavity is zero (Ref. 5, p. 160).

The local electric field at point a is then the sum of the four contributions from these charged surfaces:

$$\mathscr{E}_{\text{local}} = D - 4\pi\mathscr{P} + {}^4\!/_3\pi\mathscr{P} + 0$$

$$= \epsilon_0\mathscr{E} + {}^4\!/_3\pi\mathscr{P} \tag{14.23}$$

The total polarization of a dielectric containing N atoms per unit volume is, from Eqs. (14.20) and (14.23):

$$\mathscr{P} = N\alpha_T(\epsilon_0\mathscr{E} + {}^4\!/_3\pi\mathscr{P}) \tag{14.24}$$

which may be rearranged to give

$$\frac{\mathscr{P}}{\epsilon_0\mathscr{E}} = \frac{N\alpha_T}{1 - {}^4\!/_3\pi N\alpha_T} \tag{14.25}$$

The dielectric constant may then be written in terms of the polarizability by combining with Eq. (14.7) and rearranging to give

$$\frac{\kappa_e - 1}{\kappa_e + 2} = \frac{4}{3}\pi N\alpha_T \tag{14.26}$$

Equation (14.26), called the Clausius-Mossotti equation, shows the relationship between the measurable dielectric constant of a material and the polarizability of the molecules. For a dilute gas, $\kappa_e \doteq 1$, $\kappa_e + 2 \doteq 3$, and $\kappa_e - 1 \doteq 4\pi N\alpha_T$, in agreement with Eq. (14.10).

The relative magnitude of the different contributions to α_T depends upon temperature, state of the system, and the frequency of the external field (for the case of alternating fields). Nitromethane, CH_3NO_2, for example, is a polar material. At 300°K it is a liquid with a molar polarizability of about 143 cm³/g mole. Upon cooling to 244°K, the polarizability increases linearly to about 179 cm³/g mole. This indicates that $\alpha_T = \alpha_0 + b/T$ and all three contributions are present in the liquid state. Upon freezing at 244°K, the molar polarizability decreases abruptly to about 13 cm³/g mole and does not change upon further cooling. This indicates that the molecules are not free to rotate in the crystalline state and thus there is no orientation polarization. The quantity 13 cm³/g mole is the sum of the electronic and ionic polarizabilities, while the difference $179 - 13 = 166$ cm³/g mole is equal to the orientation polarizability at 244°K.

Very often, especially with spherical or nearly spherical molecules, the dipoles are partially free to rotate in the solid state and thus the constant b may not necessarily go to zero. If a glass transition occurs below the melting point, however, rotation can be further hindered, with subsequent decrease in polarizability.

The effects of frequency are especially important because dielectrics are often used in alternating fields. The polarization depends on the ability of the fundamental particles to move relative to each other. At high field frequencies the more massive molecular particles cannot move rapidly enough to follow the direction of the electric field. Thus, at high frequencies, dipoles cannot rotate rapidly enough to contribute to the polarization and remain, on the average, at a 90° angle to the field direction. Since the electrons are capable of "relaxing" very rapidly, the electron cloud distortions more readily follow the field direction at high frequency. Figure 14.5 schematically shows how the total polarizability

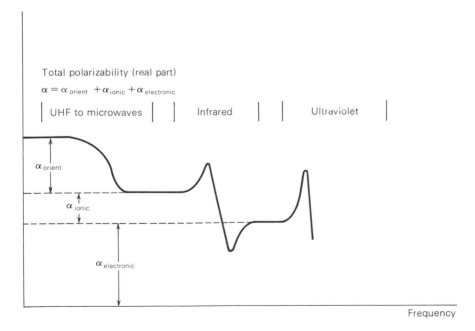

Fig. 14.5 The frequency dependence of the polarizability can be explained in terms of the molecular structure of a material.

might vary with frequency. The maximum or "static" polarizability occurs at zero frequency. At radio-wave frequencies the effective orientation polarizability begins to drop; at infrared frequencies the ionic contribution drops off, leaving only the electronic contribution at the optical frequencies.

When a dielectric is in an alternating field, the displacement current D does not remain in phase with the electric field $\mathscr{E}$. Equation (14.5) may, in general, be written in terms of a complex dielectric constant κ_e^* as

$$D = \kappa_e^* \epsilon_0 \mathscr{E} \qquad (14.27)$$

The dielectric constant may be divided into a real and an imaginary component. The existence of an out-of-phase component leads to an energy dissipation in the dielectric that is a function of the frequency. The analysis of the power loss is analogous to our treatment of power dissipation in viscoelastic materials under vibration. In the next section we shall consider dielectric losses due to both dipole relaxation and resonance absorption by vibrating particles.

14.5
Power losses in dielectrics

When a static field $\mathscr{E}_0$ is suddenly applied across a capacitor, an instantaneous charge density $D(0)/4\pi$ develops on the capacitor plates. If the voltage is kept constant, the dipoles of the dielectric will orient in the field, causing a buildup of the charge, with time, to the steady value of $(\kappa_e)_s \epsilon_0 \mathscr{E}_0/4\pi$. Figure 14.6 shows the displacement D as a function of time when the electric field strength is constant. This is analogous to a retarded elastic deformation and can be represented by

$$D(t) = (\kappa_e)_s \epsilon_0 \mathscr{E}_0 - [(\kappa_e)_s \epsilon_0 \mathscr{E}_0 - D(0)] \exp\left(-\frac{t}{\lambda_{R1}}\right) \qquad (14.28)$$

where λ_{R1} is a *retardation time* for the rotating dipoles. Another possible experiment is to impose an electric field $\mathscr{E}(0)$ which produces a displacement D_0 and

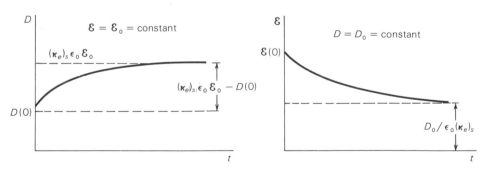

Fig. 14.6 The variations of displacement current and electric field with time are analogous to retarded elasticity and stress relaxation, respectively.

then maintain the charge on the capacitor constant at $D_0/4\pi$ by lowering the electric field with time. This is analogous to stress relaxation and can be represented by

$$(\kappa_e)_S\epsilon_0\mathscr{E}(t) = D_0 + [(\kappa_e)_S\epsilon_0\mathscr{E}(0) - D_0]\exp\left(-\frac{t}{\lambda_{R2}}\right) \qquad (14.29)$$

where λ_{R2} is a *relaxation time* for the rotating dipoles (Fig. 14.6).

By analogy with viscoelastic behavior, if one wishes to study the response of a dielectric in oscillating electric fields, an *equation of state* that expresses both the retardation and relaxation effects must be developed. It can be shown that the following equation satisfies both (14.28) and (14.29):

$$D + \lambda_{R1}\frac{dD}{dt} = (\kappa_e)_S\epsilon_0\mathscr{E} + (\kappa_e)_S\epsilon_0\lambda_{R2}\frac{d\mathscr{E}}{dt} \qquad (14.30)$$

Suppose an alternating electric field $\mathscr{E} = \mathscr{E}_0\cos\omega t$ is applied to the capacitor. The electric field may also be expressed as the real part of the complex number $\mathscr{E} = \mathscr{E}_0\exp i\omega t$. Substituting this into (14.30), one can get an expression for the displacement current as a function of time:

$$\frac{dD}{dt} + \frac{1}{\lambda_{R1}}D = \frac{(\kappa_e)_S\epsilon_0\mathscr{E}_0(1 + i\omega\lambda_{R2})}{\lambda_{R1}}\exp i\omega t \qquad (14.31)$$

The first-order linear differential equation can be solved to give

$$D - (\kappa_e)_S\frac{1 + i\omega\lambda_{R2}}{1 + i\omega\lambda_{R1}}\epsilon_0\mathscr{E} + K\exp\left(\frac{t}{\lambda_{R1}}\right) \qquad (14.32)$$

where K is a constant of integration. After an initial transient period $t \gg \lambda_{R1}$, the electric displacement may be expressed in terms of a complex dielectric constant $D = \kappa_e^*\epsilon_0\mathscr{E}$, where

$$\kappa_e^* = \kappa_e' - i\kappa_e''$$

$$= (\kappa_e)_S\frac{1 + i\omega\lambda_{R2}}{1 + i\omega\lambda_{R1}}$$

$$\doteq (\kappa_e)_S\frac{1 + \omega^2\lambda_{R1}\lambda_{R2} + i\omega(\lambda_{R2} - \lambda_{R1})}{1 + \omega^2\lambda_{R1}^2} \qquad (14.33)$$

At zero frequency, $\omega = 0$, $\kappa_e^* = (\kappa_e)_S$, while at very high frequencies:

$$\kappa_e^* \doteq (\kappa_e)_S\frac{\lambda_{R2}}{\lambda_{R1}} = (\kappa_e)_\infty \qquad (14.34)$$

Substitution of Eq. (14.34) into (14.33) gives the complex dielectric constant κ_e^* in terms of a static constant $(\kappa_e)_S$, a constant for high frequency $(\kappa_e)_\infty$, and a single-dipole retardation time λ_{R1}:

$$\kappa_e^* = \left[(\kappa_e)_\infty + \frac{(\kappa_e)_S - (\kappa_e)_\infty}{1 + \omega^2\lambda_{R1}^2}\right] - i\frac{(\kappa_e)_S - (\kappa_e)_\infty}{1 + \omega^2\lambda_{R1}^2}\omega\lambda_{R1} \qquad (14.35)$$

or from Eq. (14.33):

$$\frac{(\kappa_e)_S - \kappa_e'}{(\kappa_e)_S - (\kappa_e)_\infty} = \frac{(\omega\lambda_{R1})^2}{1 + (\omega\lambda_{R1})^2} \qquad (14.36)$$

$$\frac{\kappa_e''}{(\kappa_e)_S - (\kappa_e)_\infty} = \frac{\omega\lambda_{R1}}{1 + (\omega\lambda_{R1})^2} \qquad (14.37)$$

These equations are identical with those obtained for the storage and loss moduli of a Maxwell fluid [Eqs. (12.75) and (12.76)]. Figures 14.7 and 12.17 are also identical except for the properties plotted on the ordinates. The power dissipation per unit volume of dielectric is the product of the electric field and the current density in phase with the field $\mathscr{I}''$:

$$P_L \frac{\text{watts}}{\text{m}^3} = \mathscr{E} \frac{\text{volts}}{\text{m}} \mathscr{I}'' \frac{\text{amp}}{\text{m}^2} \qquad (14.38)$$

From the definition of D, Eq. (14.5):

$$\mathscr{I} = \frac{1}{4\pi} \frac{dD}{dt} = \frac{\kappa^*\epsilon_0}{4\pi} \frac{d\mathscr{E}}{dt}$$

$$= (\kappa_e'' + i\kappa_e') \frac{\omega\epsilon_0}{4\pi} \mathscr{E}$$

$$= \mathscr{I}'' + i\mathscr{I}' \qquad (14.39)$$

The power loss is then

$$P_L = \frac{\kappa_e''\omega\epsilon_0\mathscr{E}^2}{4\pi}$$

$$= \frac{[(\kappa_e)_S - (\kappa_e)_\infty]\epsilon_0\mathscr{E}^2}{4\pi\lambda_{R1}} \frac{(\omega\lambda_{R1})^2}{1 + \omega^2\lambda_{R1}{}^2} \qquad (14.40)$$

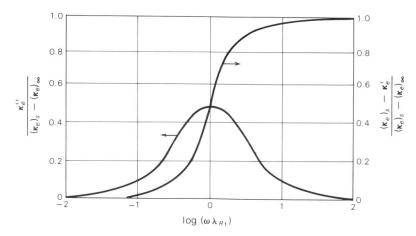

Fig. 14.7 The frequency dependence of the dielectric properties of an insulator is analogous to the mechanical response of a Maxwell fluid.

The power loss may also be expressed in terms of the *power factor* (sin δ) or the *dissipation factor* (tan δ) as

$$\tan \delta = \frac{\kappa_e''}{\kappa_e'}$$

$$= \frac{[(\kappa_e)_S - (\kappa_e)_\infty]\omega\lambda_{R1}}{(\kappa_e)_S + (\kappa_e)_\infty\omega^2\lambda_{R1}{}^2} \tag{14.41}$$

or

$$P_L = \frac{\omega\epsilon_0}{4\pi} \mathscr{E}^2\kappa_e' \tan \delta \tag{14.42}$$

When the *loss angle* δ is small, the power factor and dissipation factor are about equal. Some typical values of dielectric constants and power factors are given for various materials in Table 14.2.

It has been assumed that the response to a suddenly applied field $\mathscr{E}$ was an instantaneous displacement $D(0)$ followed by a time-dependent displacement associated with dipole relaxation. Actually, the displacement of an electron cloud also has a time constant whose magnitude is controlled by the strength of the electrostatic bond between the electrons and the nucleus. If we again represent the behavior by a linear oscillator, one can imagine the electron cloud oscillating about the nucleus in harmonic motion. The displacement of the cloud in an alternating field can be calculated using Newton's second law:

$$m \frac{d^2x}{dt^2} = -4\pi^2 m\nu_0{}^2 x + q\mathscr{E}_0 (\exp i\omega t) - m\beta \frac{dx}{dt} \tag{14.43}$$

The left side of Eq. (14.43) is the acceleration of the charge cloud. The first term on the right is the harmonic force tending to restore the cloud to its equilibrium position; the second term is the force due to the electric field acting on the net effective charge q; and the third term is a frictional resistance caused by interaction of the cloud with its surroundings. The general solution of Eq. (14.43) is

$$x = \frac{q}{m} \mathscr{E} \left[\frac{\omega_0{}^2 - \omega^2}{(\omega_0{}^2 - \omega^2)^2 + \beta^2\omega^2} - \frac{i\beta\omega}{(\omega_0{}^2 - \omega^2)^2 + \beta^2\omega^2} \right] \tag{14.44}$$

where ω_0 is the natural vibration frequency of the oscillator, $2\pi\nu_0$, ω is the frequency of the field, and β is a frictional constant for the material. The displacement of the electron cloud, and thus the polarization $\mathscr{P}$, has a real part in phase with $\mathscr{E}$ and an imaginary part out of phase with $\mathscr{E}$. The total polarization is Nqx, and combining with Eq. (14.6) gives

$$\kappa_e^* = \frac{D}{\epsilon_0 \mathscr{E}} = 1 + \frac{4\pi Nq^2}{m\epsilon_0} \frac{\omega_0{}^2 - \omega^2}{(\omega_0{}^2 - \omega^2)^2 + \beta^2\omega^2} - i \frac{4\pi Nq^2}{m\epsilon_0} \frac{\beta\omega}{(\omega_0{}^2 - \omega^2)^2 + \beta^2\omega^2} \tag{14.45}$$

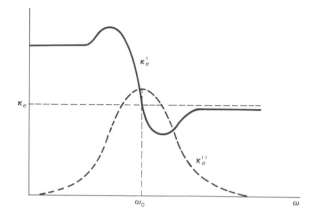

Fig. 14.8 Resonance absorption in dielectric materials.

The real and imaginary parts of the dielectric constant are plotted in Fig. 14.8. The power loss, using Eq. (14.40), is

$$P_L = \frac{Nq^2}{m} \frac{\beta\omega^2 \mathscr{E}^2}{(\omega_0^2 - \omega^2)^2 + \beta^2\omega^2} \tag{14.46}$$

The power loss has a maximum at a field frequency of ω_0; the phenomenon is called *resonance absorption*.

14.6
Dielectric losses in polymers

In the preceding section we derived equations for the dielectric properties in terms of either a single relaxation time or a single vibration frequency. As was the case with mechanical properties, polymers behave as if they possessed a distribution of relaxation times. Thus rather than conforming to Eq. (14.37), for example, the out-of-phase portion of the dielectric constant more nearly conforms to

$$\frac{\kappa_e''}{(\kappa_e)_S - (\kappa_e)_\infty} = \omega \sum_i \frac{\lambda_{Ri}}{1 + (\omega\lambda_{Ri})^2} \tag{14.47}$$

The effect of using a distribution spectrum is to broaden the frequency band over which the changes occur, as is shown in Fig. 14.9. The distribution functions developed in Chap. 12 may also be used to describe dielectric measurements, and in particular it has been found that the time-temperature superposition factor a_T is the same. Thus, dielectric measurements may also be correlated with glass transitions and other phase changes.

The relationship between structure and dielectric properties can be seen by examining Fig. 14.10. The glass-transition temperature of polyvinylacetate is about 29°C. Below this temperature, the relaxation times for dipole move-

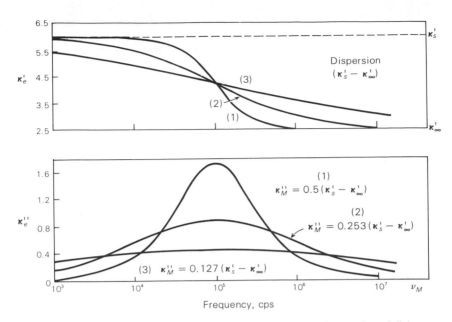

Fig. 14.9 Typical frequency variation of dielectric properties in a region of dielectric absorption. Curve 1: single relaxation time. Curve 2: moderate distribution of relaxation times. Curve 3: broad distribution of relaxation times. (By permission from A. X. Schmidt and C. A. Marlies, "Principles of High-polymer Theory and Practice," McGraw-Hill Book Company, New York, 1948.)

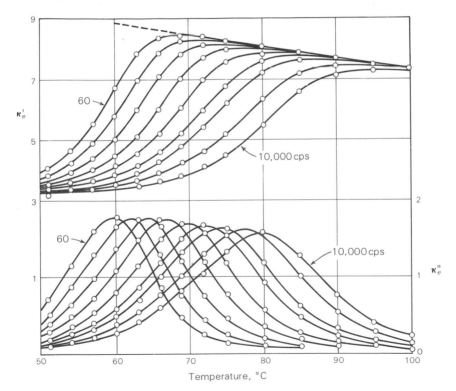

Fig. 14.10 Dielectric properties of polyvinylacetate as a function of frequency and temperature. [D. J. Mead and R. M. Fuoss, *J. Am. Chem. Soc.*, **63:** 2832 (1941).]

ment are very high and the dielectric constant is low and is associated only with electronic polarizability. As the temperature is increased at a constant frequency, say 60 cycles/sec ($\omega = 377$ rad/sec), the time for dipole relaxation decreases, which causes κ'_e to increase toward the static value $(\kappa_e)_S$. The static value must decrease with increasing temperature, since the polarizability of the dipole moments is smaller at higher temperature. If the temperature is held constant and the field frequency is increased, κ'_e decreases toward $(\kappa_e)_\infty$, since the effective polarization must become relatively smaller. Thus, Eq. (14.36) qualitatively describes the shape of the curves for the dielectric constant κ'_e in Fig. 14.10. The out-of-phase portion of the dielectric constant κ''_e is characterized by a maximum at $\omega\lambda_{R1} = 1.0$ [Eq. (14.37)]. As the frequency increases, the value of λ_{R1} at the maximum must decrease in proportion, which means that the temperature at which the maximum occurs increases. The actual magnitude of κ''_e at the maximum decreases with increasing temperature, since the dipolar polarizability decreases.

Dissipation factors for a number of nonpolar polymers are given as a function of frequency in Fig. 14.11. In general, one can see that the dissipation factors are very low and show maxima at certain frequencies. The behavior, however, is much more complicated than the simple descriptions presented previously, and large changes can develop because of subtle structural changes. Note, for example, that the dissipation factor of polyethylene is increased an order of magnitude by milling the material at elevated temperature. This is probably due to the formation of carbonyl groups along the polymer chains as a result of oxidation. A similar plot is given for polar materials in Fig. 14.12. In this case, the dissipation factors can be several orders of magnitude larger, because of the presence of dipoles, and in general the behavior is very complex. It should be clear that it is very difficult to predict the behavior of a dielectric unless a wide range of experimental data are available on the specific materials being used.

When a high polymer is placed in an alternating field, the power dissipation causes a rise in temperature. Since the mechanical, as well as the electrical, properties are strongly dependent upon temperature, it is important to know precisely how much the material heats up. The maximum temperature rise occurs when the dielectric is thermally insulated from its surroundings and all of the heat generated in dissipation is used to heat the material:

$$\rho_v c_p \frac{dT}{dt} = P_L = \frac{0.239\epsilon_0}{4\pi} \omega\kappa''_e\mathscr{E}^2 \qquad \frac{\text{kcal}}{\text{m}^3\text{-sec}} \qquad (14.48)$$

where ρ_v is density in units of kg_m/m^3 and c_p is specific heat in units of kcal/kg-°K. Equation (14.48) may be solved for temperature as a function of time at constant frequency if the dielectric constant κ''_e is a known function of temperature. In general, at any given frequency, κ''_e will first increase with temperature and then decrease, causing the rate of temperature change to go through a maximum and then decrease toward zero. This results in time-temperature curves that plateau to a steady-state temperature.

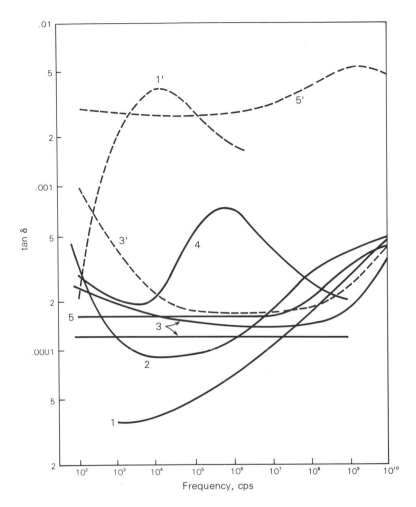

Fig. 14.11 Dissipation factor vs. frequency for nonpolar polymers:
1. Polystyrene at 25°C, 1'-polystrene at 134.5°C
2. Polyisobutylene at 25°C
3. Polytetrafluoroethylene at 23°C (two sources); 3'-polytetrafluoroethylene at 100°C
4. Polyfluoroethylene-propylene at 23°C (DuPont FEP)
5. Polyethylene at 25°C; 5'-polyethylene at 25°C after milling at 190°C for 30 min.
(By permission from E. Baer (ed.), "Engineering Design for Plastics," p. 545, Reinhold Publishing Corporation, New York, 1964.)

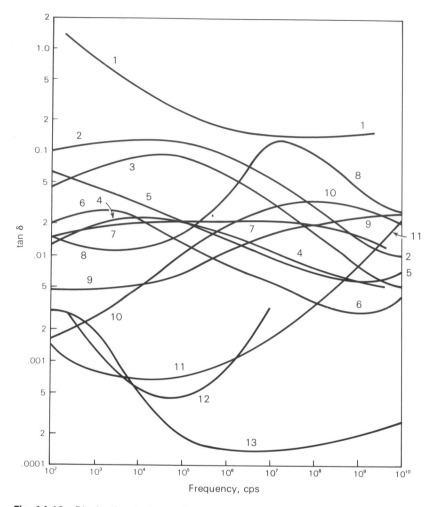

Fig. 14.12   Dissipation factor vs. frequency at 25°C for polar polymers:
1. Clear cast phenolic resin
2. Plasticized polyvinyl chloride
3. Copolymer-polyvinyl and vinylidene chloride (Dow's Saran)
4. Unplasticized polyvinyl chloride
5. Polymethylmethacrylate
6. Polychlorotrifluoroethylene
7. Hexamethylene-adipamide (nylon)
8. Compounded poly-2-chlorobutadiene-1,3 (neoprene)
9. Plasticized ethyl cellulose
10. Epoxy casting resin (Ciba's Araldite B)
11. Silicone rubber (GE's SE-550)
12. Polyurethane foam (density = 0.033)
13. 50-50 polystyrene–chlorinated diphenyl
(By permission from E. Baer (ed.), "Engineering Design for Plastics," p. 548, Reinhold Publishing Corporation, New York, 1964.)

14.7
The resistivity of insulators

One may learn a great deal about the molecular structure of a dielectric by examining its resistance characteristics. In the preceding few sections we have assumed that the leakage of direct current was negligible and furthermore that the electrical forces did not cause any irreversible changes in the molecular structure.

Under most conditions, the resistivities of dielectrics are in the range of 10^6 to 10^{16} ohm-m, while circuit leakage-resistance requirements in most electronic applications are generally less than 10^6 ohm-m. Table 14.2 gives some average values for a number of important insulating materials. This means that, from the point of view of applications, the resistivity is not an important variable. On the other hand, the resistivity of a material is very sensitive to temperature, moisture, the degree of cure of a resin, and the presence of impurities in the material or on the surface. As a result, measuring the change of resistivity with time is a sensitive indication of subtle changes in structure that could lead to failure of other properties. It has been found, for example, that a large decrease in resistivity is often accompanied by electric breakdown, and in some cases there is correlation between mechanical failure and sudden changes in resistance. From this point of view, resistivity measurements are important as nondestructive tests for functioning parts.

Inorganic insulators, especially crystalline materials, have ionic and metallic impurities, lattice vacancies, porosity, and other impurities that are capable of promoting direct currents. Organic polymers have fewer defects of this type, but they are highly sensitive to absorption of moisture and instabilities of the chemical structure. As is the case with most nonconducting materials, the volume resistivity decreases with increasing temperature. Figure 14.13 shows the behavior of a variety of commercial materials. Some, like nylon, are extremely temperature-sensitive, while others, like silicones, are relatively insensitive to temperature. Over restricted temperature ranges, the volume resistivity $\mathscr{R}_v$ varies exponentially with temperature:

$$\mathscr{R}_v = A \exp \frac{\Delta E_R}{RT} \qquad (14.49)$$

where A is a constant and ΔE_R is the activation energy. The conduction processes may thus be considered as thermally activated, but since there are a number of sources of electric current, one cannot associate ΔE_R with one specific mechanism.

The absorption of water has a profound effect on the resistivity of a material. Water will generally bring in electrolytes such as carbon dioxide from the air and traces of salts from the surroundings. It will also tend to dissolve soluble impurities in the insulator. Nonpolar materials such as polyethylene, polystyrene, and quartz are less sensitive to humidity or water immersion, since

Table 14.2

Electrical insulating properties of materials *
(Average properties at room temperature)

Material	Log volume resistivity, ohm-m	Log surface resistivity, ohms, at 100% RH	Dielectric strength, short time, ⅛ in. thick, volts/mil	Dielectric constant at 1 mc	Power factor at 1 mc	Arc resistance, sec †
Silica, fused	17	8	3,500 ‡	4.7	0.0001	
Polystyrene	16	10	600	2.5	0.0002	60–80
Hydrocarbon wax (paraffin)	15	10	750 ‡	2.3	0.0004	
Styrene rubber	14		700	2.6	0.001	> 200
Polytetrafluoroethylene	14	12	500	2.0	0.0002	
Mica	14	9	1,000 ‡	7	0.0002	135–235
Polyethylene	13	9	450	2.3	0.0003	
Butyl rubber, unfilled vulcanizate	13		500	2.2	0.004	
Hevea rubber, unfilled:						
Soft vulcanizate	13		450	2.5	0.007	
Hard vulcanizate	13		500	3.0	0.008	
Methyl methacrylate	13		500	3	0.025	No track
Polyvinylidene chloride	13		400	4	0.04	
Buta S, unfilled vulcanizate	12		500	2.5	0.01	
Silicone oils and paste	12		600 ‡	2.8	0.0004	200–500

Material						
Silicone rubbers	12	13	600‡	3–11	0.003–0.04	200–500
Polyvinyl formal	12	9	450	3	0.02	
Polyvinyl chloride-acetate, sheet	11	9	400	3	0.02	
Aniline formaldehyde	11	9	600	4	0.007	130–140
Nylon, molding	11	8	400	4	0.06	
Phenol-formaldehyde, mineral-filled	11	9	450	5	0.007	
Phenol-formaldehyde, cast unfilled	10		400	6	0.04	
Neoprene, unfilled vulcanizate	10					
Ethyl cellulose	10	10	500	4	0.03	60–80
Silicone-glass-fiber laminate	9	7	270	4	0.005	250–300
Glass-bonded mica	9	7		8	0.002	250–300
Melamine-formaldehyde	9	9	350	7	0.04	95–200
Phenol-formaldehyde, paper-filled, XX	9	8	400	5	0.04	
Phenol-formaldehyde, cellulose-fabric-filled, LE	9	9	300	5	0.05	180–200
Cellulose acetate, sheet	9	9	325	4	0.04	
Cellulose acetate-butyrate	9	13	325	5	0.03	
Vulcanized fiber	8	8	200	5–8	0.04–0.08	80–150
Urea-formaldehyde, molding	7		350	7	0.03	
Buta N, unfilled vulcanizate	6		300	11	0.03	

* Reproduced from A. X. Schmidt and C. A. Marlies, "Principles of High-polymer Theory and Practice," p. 430, McGraw-Hill Book Company, New York, 1948, except for arc-resistance data. Data from various sources, notably American Society for Testing Materials, "Standards,"; Plastic Materials Manufacturers' Association, "Technical Data on Plastics," Washington, D.C.; R. F. Field, *J. Appl. Phys.*, **17:** 318 (1946); A. J. Warner, *Elec. Commun.*, **22:** 70 (1944).

† Arc-resistance data from Plastics Properties Charts, "Modern Plastics Encyclopedia."

‡ 1 mm thick (40 mils).

they do not absorb very much water. Polar materials such as nylon, epoxies, and polyesters, on the other hand, are highly sensitive owing to the relatively high degree of water absorption. Water sensitivity is especially important when a polymer is used with a fibrous filler such as cotton or paper. Then the porosity of the filler and the tendency for a high degree of water absorption can create tremendous changes in resistivity. Figure 14.14 shows the effect of relative humidity on the resistivity of a series of fiber-filled phenolic resins. In general, the higher the humidity, the higher the degree of water absorption

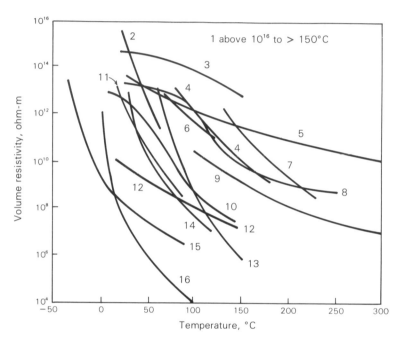

Fig. 14.13 Effect of temperature on volume resistivity for various plastics:

  1. Polytetrafluoroethylene (Dupont Teflon)
  2. Low-density polyethylene [66]
  3. Polycarbonate foil (Bayer Makrafol N) [36]
  4. Polyester–glass fabric laminate [67]
  5. Solventless silicone resin [68]
  6. Epoxy casting resin (Furane Epocast No. 3) [69,70]
  7. Polyethylene terephthalate (Dupont Mylar)
  8. Silicone rubber
  9. Molded silicone resin [67]
  10. Plasticized cellulose acetate butyrate foil (Bayer Triafol, BW) [36]
  11. Plasticized vinyl chloride [67]
  12. Soft polyurethane foam (Bayer Moltoprene, density 30 kg/m³)
  13. Epoxy resin [67]
  14. Cast epoxy resin (Ciba Araldite 502) [69]
  15. Polyurethane elastomer (Bayer Vulkollan 18) [71]
  16. Polyamide resin (nylon)
  (By permission from E. Baer (ed.), "Engineering Design for Plastics," p. 507, Reinhold Publishing Corporation, New York, 1964.)

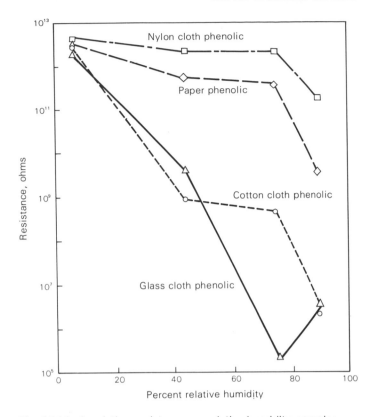

Fig. 14.14 Insulation resistance vs. relative humidity; samples conditioned 35 days. (By permission from E. Baer, (ed.), "Engineering Design for Plastics," p. 524, Reinhold Publishing Corporation, New York, 1964.)

and the lower the resistivity. Because of the extremely low rate of water absorption in solids, it can take a long time before an "equilibrium" resistivity is attained. Figure 14.15 shows the effect of time at a constant 100 percent humidity on a few epoxy and polyester materials. In some cases it may take months to even approach an equilibrium state.

With such high volume resistivities, the conduction of electricity along the surfaces of an insulator is an important factor. Surface breakdown can occur when any conducting material, particularly water, is adsorbed. When water can wet the surface, a continuous low-resistance layer forms, which promotes a low surface resistivity. On the other hand, materials like silicones and polystyrene do not wet easily, but rather develop discrete droplets on the surface. In these cases, high surface resistivities exist. For this reason, the leakage characteristics of polar insulators (e.g., ceramic-type insulators) can be improved by coating them with silicones, wax, polystyrene, and the like. Surface resistivity also decreases with temperature, but the effects of moisture and other surface contaminants are by far the most important. In general, a

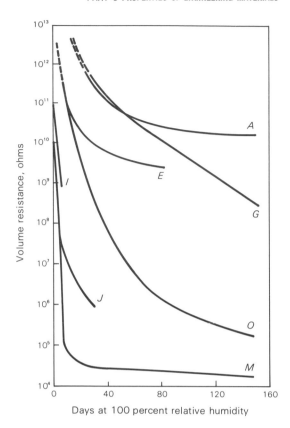

Fig. 14.15 Volume resistance vs. time at 100 percent RH; casting resins: A and I, unfilled epoxy; E and G, filled epoxy; J, unfilled modified polyester; M and O, filled polyester. (By permission from E. Baer (ed.), "Engineering Design for Plastics," p. 526, Reinhold Publishing Corporation, New York, 1964.)

small increase in the amount of adsorbed water can decrease the surface resistivity several orders of magnitude.

14.8
Electric breakdown of insulators

At low voltages the electric displacement D is directly proportional to the product of the dielectric constant and the electric field strength. Beyond a critical value of the electric field, an *electric breakdown* will occur, with an excessive flow of current through the dielectric and a physical destruction of the material. The *dielectric strength* is defined as the breakdown voltage per unit thickness of dielectric specimen and is generally reported in units of *volts per mil*. In a sense, the electrical failure of a substance is analogous to mechanical failure in that it is a phenomenon which is associated with the presence or formation of flaws in the structure. Like yield stress, tensile stress, and fatigue strength, the measured dielectric strength of a material is highly dependent on the method of measurement. It is not a static property of the material, but rather depends upon the thickness of the test piece, the frequency of the applied voltage, the rate of application of voltage, the duration of the test, the size and shape of the electrodes, and environmental variables such as temperature, pressure, and surrounding fluid. In order to get relative information on different materials, very carefully standardized tests have been developed (ASTM standard tests). The most common method of measuring dielectric strength is to place a specimen between two electrodes and increase the voltage from zero to breakdown either at a uniform rapid rate or by a step-by-step method in which the voltage is increased by increments, being held at each level for a fixed period of time. (See ASTM test D 149–55T.)

A second measure of insulator resistance to electric breakdown is *arc resistance.* In this test (ASTM D 495–56T), point electrodes are placed at two points on the surface of the material and an electric arc is passed between the electrodes. As the arc passes through the air, it will, in time, cause a degradation of the surface and a transfer of the arc to a path along the surface. When the decomposition is permanent, a "track" forms on the surface which permits subsequent discharges to take place at lower potentials. The arc resistance is the number of seconds that a material can withstand a standard arc without the current transferring to the surface. As yet, the electric breakdown of dielectric solids is not well understood, but several types have been recognized and classified. The classifications are intrinsic breakdown, thermal breakdown, defect breakdown, and discharge breakdown.

In insulators, the energy gap between the valence and conduction band is so large that the number of electrons in the conduction band is negligible. When excessively high electric fields are present, the atoms can absorb sufficient energy to be excited or ionized, thus producing other conducting electrons. By an unknown mechanism, a cataclysmic flow of electrons, probably from impurity levels in the band structure, induces an electric breakdown of the structure. Ideally, this is a property which is independent of electrode size, geometry, and other test variables and is therefore an intrinsic property of the material; thus the name *intrinsic breakdown.* The "true" intrinsic breakdown is extremely hard to measure, but experiments at low temperature and with direct-current voltage applied for very short periods of time are thought to give approximate values of this quantity.

From Eq. (14.42) we see that the power dissipation in an alternating field is $P_L = (\omega \epsilon_0 / 4\pi) \mathscr{E}^2 \kappa'_e \tan \delta$. Thus, the higher the frequency in a breakdown test, the higher the rate of heating of the specimen. High temperature can cause a number of different physical changes in a sample which could lead to a premature electric breakdown. Figures 14.16 and 14.17 show that generally the dielectric strength of a material will decrease as both the frequency of the applied voltage and the thickness of the sample increase. Both of these effects can, at least in part, be related to the greater tendency for the material to attain a high temperature. Thermal effects are often cumulative. Since both the dielectric constant and the dissipation factor increase with temperature, a temperature increase causes a greater amount of dissipation, which in turn leads to a still higher temperature. When electrical failure is preceded by excessive heating, it is called *thermal breakdown.*

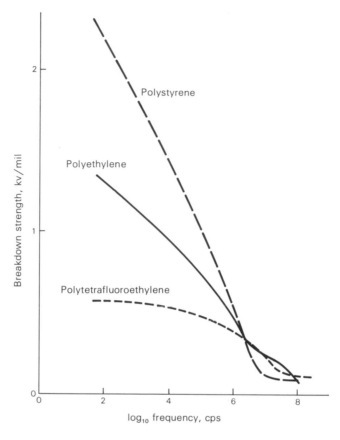

Fig. 14.16 The breakdown strength of polymers generally decreases with increasing frequency.

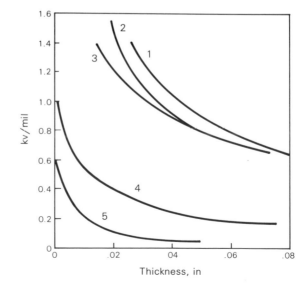

Fig. 14.17 Short-time breakdown strength vs. thickness comparison of materials:
1. Annealed polystyrene
2. Polyfluoroethylene-propylene (DuPont FEP)
3. Polyethylene
4. Paper-phenolic laminate
5. Wet paper–phenolic laminate
(Reproduced from E. Baer (ed.), "Engineering Design for Plastics," p. 452, Reinhold Publishing Corporation, New York, 1964.)

The presence or formation of physical defects such as cracks, voids, and impurities will also limit the dielectric strength of a material. Dirt and moisture can collect at such defects and promote failure at extremely low voltages. This type of breakdown, called *defect breakdown,* is especially troublesome in applications that involve mechanical stresses and vibrations, since these conditions promote the formation of such defects. A particularly important problem is that gases can collect in voids and fissures and be subject to voltage breakdown. Such breakdowns can lead to ionization-induced failure or a slow chemical and thermal degradation of the material. This type of failure, called a *discharge breakdown,* is a very complex phenomenon which has not been extensively studied.

The complexity of electric breakdown cannot be overemphasized. The actual behavior of a given material in service depends on a large number of interacting physical and environmental factors. The results of standard ASTM tests under controlled conditions can only be used for screening and comparative purposes. The response under service conditions must be studied carefully and in great detail. Some values of dielectric strength and arc resistance for a number of materials are given in Table 14.2.

14.9
Magnetic properties of materials

Magnetism is not restricted to dielectric materials and is, by itself, a very broad area of materials science. A number of magnetic properties, however, are defined in the same way that dielectric properties are, and many of the electronic and atomic phenomena are similar.

A magnetic field of intensity $\mathfrak{H}$ amp/m is analogous to an electric field of intensity $\mathscr{E}$ volts/m. The field may be produced by either permanent magnets or by conductors carrying an electric current. The flux density $\mathscr{B}$ exerts a force on an element of conductor which is normal to both the electric current $\mathscr{I}$ and the magnetic flux density $\mathscr{B}$. It thus has the units of force per ampere per unit length of conductor. It is related to the magnetic field by

$$\mathscr{B} = (\pmb{\mu}_0)_M \mathfrak{H} \qquad\qquad (14.50)$$

Analogous to ϵ_0, the quantity $(\pmb{\mu}_0)_M$ is the "permeability of empty space" with units of force per ampere squared. In mks units it has the value of 10^{-7} kg$_m$-m/coul^2 or 10^{-7} henry/m. The magnetic field $\mathfrak{H}$ has the units of amperes per meter [or ampere-turns per meter where the current is given for a single conductor and the total force is obtained by multiplying by the number of conductors (or turns) in the magnetic coil]. The flux density $\mathscr{B}$, in mks units, is given in terms of webers per square meter, where a weber is a volt-second. The relations between various systems of units are shown in Appendix E. The *relative permeability* of a material, $(\pmb{\mu}_e)_M$, is then defined analogously to the static dielectric constant as

$$\mathscr{B} = (\pmb{\mu}_e)_M (\pmb{\mu}_0)_M \mathfrak{H} \qquad\qquad (14.51)$$

Since both permanent and induced magnetic dipoles exist in materials, one can also define a total magnetic moment per unit volume, or a *magnetic polarization* $\mathcal{M}$, as

$$\mathcal{B} = (\mu_0)_M(\mathfrak{H} + 4\pi\mathcal{M}) \tag{14.52}$$

or, in terms of a *magnetic susceptibility* χ_M, as

$$(\mu_e)_M - 1 = 4\pi\,\chi_M = 4\pi\,\frac{\mathcal{M}}{\mathfrak{H}} \tag{14.53}$$

The magnetic character of a material may then be classified according to the sign, magnitude, and temperature dependence of the magnetic susceptibility.

An external magnetic field can induce a magnetic dipole moment in an atom much the same way that an electric field can induce an electric moment. This effect is called *diamagnetism*. The origin of the effect can best be seen by considering the classical picture of a hydrogen atom. The electron charge, orbiting the proton at a radius a_0 and a frequency $2\pi\nu_0 = \omega_0$, produces an orbital magnetic dipole moment μ_M which is equal to the product of the current carried in the loop and the area swept out by the loop:

$$\mu_M = -\frac{e\omega_0}{2\pi}\,\pi a_0^2 = -\frac{ea_0^2\omega_0}{2}. \tag{14.54}$$

The direction of the moment is normal to the plane of the loop. When an external magnetic field causes an increase in the flux density to $\mathcal{B}$, the electron acts like an inductance in that a counter electromotive force is produced in accordance with Lenz's law. The electromotive force will cause an increase in the angular momentum to $\omega_0 + (e/2m_e)\mathcal{B}$, which will remain constant as long as $\mathcal{B}$ does not change. The additional angular momentum gives rise to an induced magnetic moment of

$$(\mu_M)_{\text{ind}} = -\frac{ea_0^2}{2}\,\frac{e}{2m_e}\,\mathcal{B}$$

$$= -\frac{e^2a_0^2\mathcal{B}}{4m_e} \tag{14.55}$$

The magnetization is directly opposing $\mathfrak{H}$ which, from Eq. (14.52), causes a decrease in $\mathcal{B}$ and thus gives rise to a negative susceptibility [Eq. (14.53)]. For a dilute gas with N atoms/m³ and n electrons/atom, the *diamagnetic susceptibility* is

$$(\chi_M)_{\text{dia}} = -\frac{e^2a_0^2 nN}{4m_e}\,(\mu_e)_M(\mu_0)_M \tag{14.56}$$

If $n \doteq 10$ and $a_0 \doteq 0.5$ Å, $(\chi_M)_{\text{dia}} \doteq -\text{⁴/₅} \times 10^{-34}\,N$. For a typical dilute gas $N \doteq \text{¼} \times 10^{26}$ atoms/m³ and $(\chi_M)_{\text{dia}} \doteq -2 \times 10^{-9}$, while for a typical solid $N \doteq 5 \times 10^{28}$ atoms/m³ and $(\chi_M)_{\text{dia}} \doteq -4 \times 10^{-6}$. Measured values of diamagnetic susceptibility are generally of this order of magnitude. As with induced electric susceptibility, the diamagnetic susceptibility is independent of temperature under most conditions.

Atoms and molecules may also possess permanent magnetic moments. In the absence of a magnetic field, the atomic moments of a material are randomly oriented, producing no net magnetization. In the presence of a magnetic field, the moments tend to line up in the field direction, enhancing the field intensity with a net orientational magnetization. This effect, called *paramagnetism,* is analogous to orientation polarization.

Permanent magnetic moments are associated with three structural factors: the orbital magnetic moment of the electrons, the spin magnetic moment of the electrons, and the spin magnetic moment of the nucleus.

The orbital magnetic dipole moment of a single electron is given by Eq. (14.54) as $-\frac{1}{2}ea_0^2\omega_0$, or in terms of orbital angular momentum $\mathscr{L} = mr^2\omega_0$,

$$(\mu_M)_{\text{ind orbit}} = -\frac{e}{2m_e} \cdot \mathscr{L} \qquad (14.57)$$

The wave-mechanical angular momentum of an atom is related to the shape of the electron charge distribution, which, in turn, is related to the azimuthal quantum number l (see Sec. 3.2). It can be shown that

$$\mathscr{L}^2 = l(l+1)\frac{h^2}{4\pi^2} \qquad (14.58)$$

with the component of $\mathscr{L}$ in the field direction related to the orientational quantum number m_l:

$$\mathscr{L}_z = m_l \frac{h}{2\pi} \qquad (14.59)$$

The net magnetic dipole moment in the field direction for a multielectron atom is then the vector sum of the moments for the individual electrons. The true moment for a single s electron is thus zero, since $m_l = 0$. The H atom, H_2, and He, therefore, do not have an orbital magnetic moment. Also, all atoms or ions with closed electronic shells will have a zero orbital magnetic moment, since m_l will take on all values between $\pm l$ (that is, $m_l = 0, \pm 1, \pm 2, \ldots, \pm l$). In general, a resultant orbital magnetic moment can be attained only in atoms that have partially filled electronic shells. In a dilute gas, the net effect is calculated from the resultant sum of its atoms. In solids, however, strong interactions between neighboring lattice atoms influence the net moment.

The spin magnetic moment of an electron is associated with the spin quantum numbers. Similar to the orbital contribution, it can be shown that the spin magnetic moment in the direction of the field is

$$(\mu_M)_{z\,\text{spin}} = -\frac{e}{m_e}\frac{h}{2\pi}m_s \qquad m_s = \pm\frac{1}{2} \qquad (14.60)$$

The net spin magnetic moment of atoms containing paired electrons, as in atoms with filled electronic shells, is thus zero. The net spin magnetic moment of atoms with partially filled shells can be obtained from Hund's rule, which states that electron spins always add together in such a way as to give a maximum spin angular momentum. Thus, the first five electrons in the d level of an atom have the same spin, giving a maximum moment of $5eh/4\pi m_e$. Additional electrons add to the shell with opposite spin, and when a total of 10 electrons fill the shell, the moment reduces to zero.

The nuclear magnetic dipole moment is associated with nuclear spin and can be described by an equation analogous to (14.60). The moment is proportional to $h/2\pi m_n$, but since the mass of a nuclear particle is of the order of 3,600 times greater than the mass of the electrons, the nuclear moment is smaller by the same amount.

The temperature dependence of the paramagnetic effect is the same as that of orientation polarization, namely, that the magnetization $\mathscr{M}$ is proportional to the Langevin function:

$$\mathscr{M} = N(\mu_M)_{\text{para}}L(a) \tag{14.61}$$

where $a = (\boldsymbol{\mu}_0)_M(\mu_M)_{\text{para}}\mathfrak{H}/kT$ and $L(a)$ is defined in Eq. (14.16). For small values of a, the paramagnetic susceptibility reduces to

$$(\chi_M)_{\text{para}} = \frac{N(\boldsymbol{\mu}_0)_M(\mu_M)_{\text{para}}^2}{3kT}$$

$$= \frac{C}{T} \tag{14.62}$$

where the quantity C is called the *Curie constant* for the material.

The magnetic behavior of a few elements, the most important being iron, cobalt, and nickel, is characterized by a very high susceptibility which is both field- and temperature-dependent below a characteristic temperature Θ_c, called the Curie temperature. These materials are termed *ferromagnetic*. Above the Curie temperature, the susceptibility has a temperature dependence similar to paramagnetic materials:

$$\chi_{\text{ferro}}_{\substack{T > \Theta_c}} = \frac{C}{T - \Theta_c} \tag{14.63}$$

Below Θ_c, however, the relationship between flux density and field intensity, and consequently the susceptibility, is nonlinear and may be represented by the hysteresis curve shown in Fig. 14.18. The area inside the hysteresis loop is related to the energy losses in alternating fields.

The cause of ferromagnetism is closely associated with the electron-spin contributions to the paramagnetic effect. In paramagnetism the magnetization $\mathscr{M}$ reaches a saturation value of $N(\mu_M)_{\text{para}}$ in the limit when $(\boldsymbol{\mu}_0)_M(\mu_M)_{\text{para}}\mathfrak{H} \gg kT$. [The Langevin function in Eq. (14.61) goes to 1.] This implies that all the magnetic moments are lined up parallel to the magnetic field. This can occur only near absolute zero or with very high field strengths, generally of the order of 10^9 amp/m. A ferromagnetic material is one in which complete alignment can occur at ordinary temperatures and relatively low field strengths, generally of

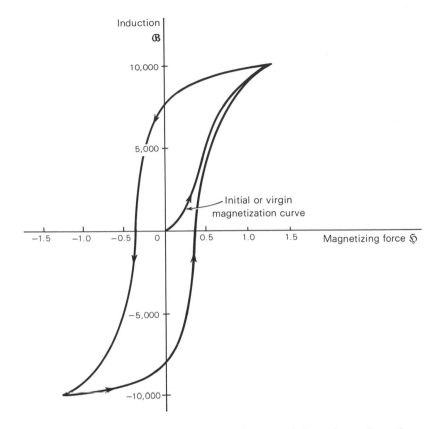

Fig. 14.18 Energy losses in a ferromagnetic material placed in an alternating field are related to the area inside the hysteresis loop.

the order of 10^6 amp/m. The explanation of this lies in the existence of an internal molecular field which is proportional to the magnetization:

$$\mathfrak{H}_e = b\mathcal{M} \tag{14.64}$$

The field strength $\mathfrak{H}$ in Eq. (14.61) is then replaced by an effective local field $\mathfrak{H} + \mathfrak{H}_e$. For small values of the Langevin function (i.e., at very high temperatures):

$$\mathcal{M} = \frac{N(\mu_M)^2_{\text{para}}(\boldsymbol{\mu}_0)_M(\mathfrak{H} + b\mathcal{M})}{kT} \tag{14.65}$$

or, in terms of the susceptibility,

$$\chi_{\text{ferro}} = \frac{N(\mu_M)^2_{\text{para}}(\boldsymbol{\mu}_0)_M}{kT - N(\mu_M)^2_{\text{para}}(\boldsymbol{\mu}_0)_M b} \tag{14.66}$$

Combining with Eq. (14.63) gives

$$C = \frac{N(\mu_M)_{\text{para}}^2(\mu_0)_M}{k} \tag{14.67}$$

$$\Theta_c = bC \tag{14.68}$$

Data show that the susceptibility of iron is given by Eq. (14.66) when $\Theta_c = 1043°K$ and $C \doteq 1$. This means that the proportionality constant b is of the order of 10^3 and that the internal field strength must be extremely high. The source of this internal field is a spin-dependent electrostatic interaction between the electrons in partially filled bands. It can be shown quantum-mechanically that under certain conditions an exchange interaction (Chap. 3) occurs if the spins of the electrons are all lined up in the same direction. This extra exchange energy stabilizes a spin-aligned state and promotes a magnetization even in the absence of an external field. It has been shown that the atomic spacing and the width of the $3d$ band in iron, cobalt, and nickel favor a high exchange energy and thus a stable magnetized state.

In the absence of an external magnetic field, $\mathfrak{H} = 0$ and Eq. (14.61) reduces to

$$
\begin{aligned}
\mathscr{M} &= N(\mu_M)_{\text{para}} L \left(\frac{(\mu_0)_M (\mu_M)_{\text{para}} b \mathscr{M}}{kT} \right) \\
&= N(\mu_M)_{\text{para}} L \left(\frac{\mathscr{M}/N(\mu_M)_{\text{para}}}{T/\Theta_c} \right) \\
&= \mathscr{M}_{\text{sat}} L \left(\frac{\mathscr{M}/\mathscr{M}_{\text{sat}}}{T/\Theta_c} \right)
\end{aligned}
\tag{14.69}
$$

where $\mathscr{M}_{\text{sat}}$ is the maximum or the saturation value for the magnetization. The relative magnetization $\mathscr{M}/\mathscr{M}_{\text{sat}}$ is plotted as a function of reduced temperature T/Θ_c in Fig. 14.19. One can see that the magnetization remains high to about three-fourths of the Curie temperature and then drops very sharply toward zero. Above the Curie temperature the substances are paramagnetic. The Curie temperatures of iron, cobalt, and nickel are 1043, 1404, and 631°K, respectively, so that all are strongly ferromagnetic at room temperature.

The implication of the above arguments is that a ferromagnetic material should have its maximum magnetization at any given temperature below Θ_c. However, it is experimental fact that these materials can exist in an unmagnetized state. This is explained by assuming that a ferromagnetic material is made up of many small domains within which the material is magnetized to saturation. In the absence of external fields, these domains are oriented in a random fashion and are separated from one another by domain boundaries. The overall net magnetization of a material then depends upon the degree to which the domains can be oriented in the field direction. Figure 14.20a is a schematic drawing of an arrangement of domains in a single crystal (or even a single grain of a polycrystalline material) which gives a net magnetic moment of zero. The moment is determined by the vector sum of the moments in the domains. The moment of any one domain is proportional to its volume, which is a

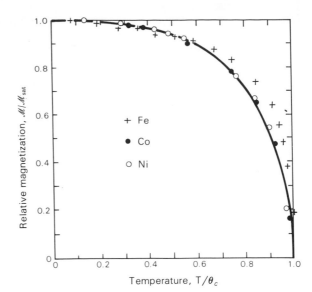

Fig. 14.19 The relative magnetization of ferromagnetic materials drops sharply on approaching the Curie temperature.

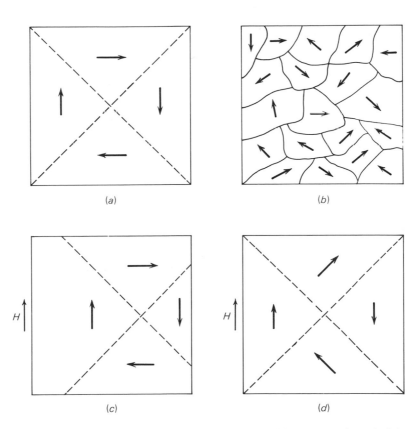

Fig. 14.20 The magnetization characteristics of ferromagnetic materials can be explained in terms of domain theories. (*a*) Unmagnetized; (*b*) polycrystal unmagnetized; (*c*) magnetized by domain growth (boundary displacement); (*d*) magnetized by domain rotation.

function of the material and its prior history. Typical sizes for single domains may vary from 10^{-6} to 10^{-15} cm^3. A single grain in a polycrystalline material may thus contain one or many domains. In the unmagnetized state, the domains are oriented to produce a net moment of zero. The application of a weak magnetic field can cause a growth of favorably oriented domains at the expense of unfavorably oriented ones, as shown in Fig. 14.20c. The displacement of the boundary may be either reversible or irreversible. The initial part of the magnetization curve corresponds to reversible boundary displacements; when the field is removed, the boundaries return to their initial positions and the material remains demagnetized. At intermediate field strengths, where the flux density varies more rapidly, the boundary displacements are irreversible and a net magnetization remains upon removal of the external field. In strong fields, the domains can be permanently rotated to line up in the field direction (Fig. 14.20d) to produce a saturation. On reversal of a strong field, the reorientation does not follow the same path, but rather the demagnetization lags behind the field. This results in the hysteresis curve shown in Fig. 14.18, and thus there is always an energy loss in alternating fields.

The purpose of this chapter has been to examine the molecular phenomena responsible for the electromagnetic responses of materials. The information presented here should be sufficient to acquaint the reader with some of the ideas that are presented in great detail in the many excellent treatises that are available on these subjects. Some of these texts are listed in the bibliography.

References

1   Bates, L. F.: "Modern Magnetism," 3d ed., Cambridge University Press, London, 1951.

2   Bozorth, R. M.: "Ferromagnetism," Bell Laboratory Series, D. Van Nostrand Company, Inc., Princeton, N.J., 1951.

3   Debye, P.: "Polar Molecules," Dover Publications, Inc., New York, 1929. *A classic reference work on the nature of electric dipoles, polarizability, and the effects of molecular structure.*

4   Goodenough, J. B.: "Magnetism and the Chemical Bond," John Wiley & Sons, Inc., New York, 1963. *Detailed description of the concepts of magnetism and the interrelation with atomic structure.*

5   Kittel, C.: "Introduction to Solid State Physics," 2d ed., John Wiley & Sons, Inc., New York, 1959. *Chapter 7 is a clear discussion of electric fields and the polarization of matter. Chapter 9 considers diamagnetism and paramagnetism, while chaps. 8 and 15 are concerned with ferromagnetism. An advanced, but easy-to-read, text.*

6   Mathes, K. N.: Electrical Properties, in E. Baer (ed.): "Engineering Design for Plastics," Reinhold Publishing Corporation, New York, 1964. *A comprehensive source of data and testing methods for dielectric materials, primarily polymers.*

7   Peck, E. R.: "Electricity and Magnetism," McGraw-Hill Book Company, New York, 1953.

An intermediate physics text which provides detailed discussions of electrostatic fields, dielectrics, and magnetic properties.

8 Smythe, W. R.: "Static and Dynamic Electricity," 2d ed., McGraw-Hill Book Company, New York, 1950. *An undergraduate text on electrostatics, magnetostatics, and electromagnetic theory.*

9 Van Vleck, J. H.: "The Theory of Electric and Magnetic Susceptibilities," Oxford University Press, London, 1932.

10 von Hippel, A. R.: "Dielectrics and Waves," John Wiley & Sons, Inc., New York, 1954. *An authoritative text on dielectric materials covering the field from both a macroscopic and a molecular viewpoint. Essential reading for those doing research in the area.*

11 von Hippel, A. R.: "Dielectric Materials and Applications," John Wiley & Sons, Inc., New York, 1954. *Extensive data on dielectric constants and dissipation factors over a wide range of frequencies.*

12 Wert, C. A., and R. M. Thomson: "Physics of Solids," McGraw-Hill Book Company, New York, 1964. *Chapters 16 to 21 cover the material of this chapter in much greater detail but at approximately the same level of sophistication. Recommended for supplementary reading.*

13 Whitehead, S.: "Dielectric Breakdown of Solids," Oxford University Press, London, 1951.

Questions

14.1 A flat-plate air capacitor has a capacitance of 1,000 $\mu\mu$f.
(a) If the plates are 0.01 cm apart, what is the cross-sectional area of the capacitor?
(b) If the potential across the capacitor is 250 volts, what is the charge?
(c) How much work is required to separate the plates of the capacitor?

14.2 A 2-mm-ID 5-mm-OD glass capillary tube which is 12 in. long is vacuum-metalized on the outside. The inside of the tube is then filled with mercury. Calculate the total capacitance if the dielectric constant of the glass is 8.0.

14.3 (a) A 5-μf capacitor and a 10-μf capacitor are connected together in series across a 250-volt line. Calculate the charge on each and the voltage across each.
(b) The same two capacitors are connected in parallel across a 250-volt line. Calculate the charge on each and the voltage across each.

14.4 The electronic polarizability of argon gas is 16.5×10^{-31} m³. What are the dielectric constant and electric susceptibility of argon?

14.5 The induced polarization of dichloromethane vapor is 51×10^{-6} m³, and its permanent dipole moment is 1.59 debyes. Calculate its polarization at 350°K.

14.6 Prove that the orientation polarizability of a molecule is $\mu^2/3kT\epsilon_0$. State all your assumptions.

14.7 A dielectric has a static dielectric constant of 4.0. Calculate the ratio of the local field intensity within the dielectric to the applied field. If its measured dielectric strength is 10^7 volts/m, what is the actual field intensity in the material at breakdown?

14.8 The dielectric constant and the dissipation factor in Table 14.3 are given as functions of temperature for Delrin Acetal Resin 500 NC-10. Find the temperature at which one gets a maximum power dissipation. What is the maximum power dissipation if the electric field strength is 10,000 volts/mm?

Table 14.3 *

Temp, °C	κ'_e, (ASTM D 150–54T) at 10^3 cps	tan δ (ASTM D 150–54T) at 10^3 cps
−170	2.76	0.0007
−140	2.77	0.0020
−100	2.82	0.0080
−80	2.91	0.0118
−60	3.15	0.0225
−50	3.30	0.0260
−40	3.36	0.0150
−30	3.38	0.0030
−20	3.40	0.0011
−10	3.41	0.0007
10	3.41	0.0007
25	3.44	0.0007
60	3.58	0.0035
100	3.74	0.0059
120	3.83	0.0130

* From Delrin, Design & Engineering Data, Plastics Dept., E. I. du Pont de Nemours & Co.

14.9 The dielectric properties of polyvinylacetate are given as a function of temperature and frequency in Fig. 14.10. Suppose a 0.02-cm sheet of PVA is used as a dielectric between two flat electrodes across which is imposed an alternating field of 1,000 volts at 1,000 cycles/sec. Calculate the maximum temperature that the film can reach as a function of time. The density of PVA is 1.25 g/cm³, and the specific heat is 0.46 cal/g-°K.

14.10 The magnetic susceptibility of silicon is -0.4×10^{-5}. Calculate the flux density and the total magnetic moment per unit volume in a magnetic field of 10^5 amp/m.

14.11 Estimate the diamagnetic susceptibility of silicon if the electron radius of an atom is of the order of 1 Å. Compare your calculation with the experimental value of -0.4×10^{-5}.

14.12 The following data are for annealed iron:

$\mathfrak{H}$, amp/m	0	10	20	50	100	150	200	500	10^3	10^4	10^5
$\mathscr{B} \times 10^5$, webers/m²	0	1.3	2.5	6.3	13	19	25	63	130	1,300	13,000

Calculate the maximum permeability $(\mu_e)_M$, the maximum magnetic susceptibility χ_M, and the maximum magnetic moment per unit volume $\mathscr{M}$. What is the permeability in the limit of $\mathfrak{H} = 0$?

15
Chemical resistance
of materials

15.1
Introduction

The term *corrosion* is very widely used to denote the destruction of a metallic material by water, the atmosphere or, for that matter, any other *corrosive* medium. In general, the destruction involves a chemical change in the material, and thus *corrosion resistance* may be categorized as an aspect of *chemical resistance.* In general usage, the two terms are often used interchangeably, with people referring to "different kinds" of corrosion. Since we have been considering a wide variety of both metallic and nonmetallic materials, it is more convenient to define these terms separately.

The *chemical resistance* of a material is defined as the ability of the material to resist destruction through either a physical or a chemical change starting at its exposed surfaces. The destruction thus occurs by any kind of an interaction between the surface and the environment.

Oxidation (or more generally, dry corrosion) involves the reaction of the material with oxygen (or more generally, any gas) to form oxide compounds. With metals, the oxides that form at the surface may be either undesirable, as is the case with rust formation on iron, or desirable, as is the case with the passivation of stainless steel. In some cases, the oxidation will lead to a steady deterioration of the material, while in other cases a protective coating improves the chemical resistance. Oxygen, especially at slightly elevated temperatures, almost always has adverse effects on the properties of organic solids. Most commonly, oxygen or an oxygen compound will interact with polymer chains to cause both chain scission and cross-linking.

In some cases softening will result, while in other cases embrittlement will result. The thermal instability of polymers is, in general, one of their weakest characteristics.

We shall reserve the term *corrosion* (often called wet corrosion) for the electrochemical reaction that takes place on the surface of a material in the presence of a conducting fluid. When a conducting solid comes in contact with water or solutions of acids, bases, or salts, there is a tendency for the metal to be dissolved into the solution. The prime prerequisites are the presence of two points with different *electrode potentials* and the ability to conduct electricity in a closed circuit through the two points. Differences in potential can be caused by differences in composition, differences in internal stress, anisotropic conditions, or several other sources, while the ability to conduct electricity merely depends on the formation of an electrolyte solution. In many instances the moisture of the air is sufficient to create this latter condition.

Permeation and mutual compatibility can be responsible for the dissolution of a material. Although metals are not usually thought of as soluble substances, special conditions, such as the use of liquid metals at high temperature, for example, can lead to the partial dissolving of a structural unit. Mutual compatibility also means the possibility of alloy or intermetallic formation. Organic materials are especially sensitive to permeation by organic fluids or, for that matter, almost any environmental substance. Thermoplastic materials can be totally destroyed by dissolution in the proper solvent, while thermosetting materials can be so badly swelled that they lose all of their desirable characteristics.

In the next few sections we shall discuss and explain these phenomena from a molecular point of view.

15.2
Oxidation of metallic materials

If a perfectly clean metal surface is exposed to the atmosphere, it will adsorb gases almost instantaneously. The adsorbed oxygen will then combine with the metal through a sharing of valence electrons to form a monolayer of metal oxide on the surface. Further adsorption occurs, and a thin film of oxide begins to develop. Since intermolecular forces are relatively short-range, this surface film takes on the characteristics of a pure oxide compound after a relatively few atomic layers have formed. Further buildup of the film is then no longer controlled by adsorption of gas, but rather is controlled by the diffusion of metal, oxygen, and electrons through the oxide layer. Since diffusion is a relatively slow process in solids, this initial film is in a sense protective.

The oxides of metals such as gold are unstable, and no further change in surface occurs under normal conditions. Certain other oxides, such as molybdenum oxide, are volatile, and the oxidation proceeds very rapidly with the continual volatilization of the surface. Most frequently, the film thickens into an oxide layer called *scale.* If the molar volume of the scale is greater than that of the parent metal, the oxide forms a continuous, protective layer which limits further oxidation. If the molar volume is less than that of the parent metal, the oxide layer becomes nonadherent and porous, generally having little effect on the rate of oxidation.

Figure 15.1 schematically shows the course of oxidation when an adherent, continuous oxide layer is formed. Oxidation is normally controlled by the ionic mobility, except in certain cases when the electronic conductivity of the metal oxide is unusually low. When ion diffusion through the protective oxide layer controls, the rate of growth of the oxide layer, dx/dt, is inversely proportional to the scale thickness:

$$\frac{dx}{dt} = \frac{k_R(T)}{x} \qquad (15.1)$$

where $k_R(T)$ is a temperature-dependent rate constant:

$$k_R(T) = k_0 \exp\left(-\frac{\Delta E_D}{RT}\right) \qquad (15.2)$$

On integration at constant temperature,

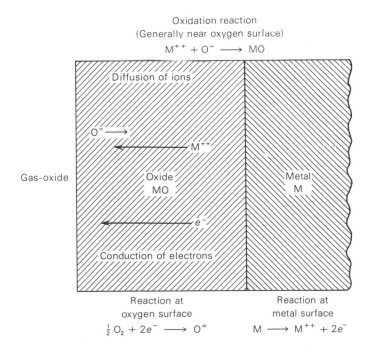

Oxidation reaction
(Generally near oxygen surface)
$$M^{++} + O^= \longrightarrow MO$$

Diffusion of ions

$O^= \longrightarrow$

$\longleftarrow M^{++}$

Gas-oxide

Oxide
MO

Metal
M

$\longleftarrow e^-$

Conduction of electrons

Reaction at
oxygen surface
$$\tfrac{1}{2} O_2 + 2e^- \longrightarrow O^=$$

Reaction at
metal surface
$$M \longrightarrow M^{++} + 2e^-$$

Fig. 15.1 The oxidation of a metal is sometimes controlled by the mobility of ions in a protective oxide layer on the surface.

$$x^2 = 2k_R(T)t \qquad (15.3)$$

This is known as the parabolic growth law.

Certain other oxides, such as those of aluminum and beryllium, have such low electronic conductivities that a deficiency of electrons occurs at the gas-oxide interface. This causes a deficiency of anions in the oxide and a buildup of a space charge that retards the mobility of the cations. The thickness of the oxide layer tends to approach a limiting value asymptotically, and the time dependence can be represented by a logarithmic growth law:

$$x = k_R(T) \log (at + 1) \qquad (15.4)$$

where $k_R(T)$ and a are constants that depend on the temperature and the type of oxide.

When a nonprotective porous oxide layer is formed, the rate of oxidation is controlled by the rate of flow of gaseous oxygen through the pores and fissures of the oxide. For all practical purposes, the gas flow is independent of the oxide layer thickness and the rate of oxidation is dependent only on the temperature:

$$\frac{dx}{dt} = k_L(T) \qquad (15.5)$$

A linear growth law is obtained on integration:

$$x = k_L(T)t \qquad (15.6)$$

The temperature dependence of the constant $k_L(T)$ is not exponential in this case, but rather depends on the properties of the gas and the change in porosity of the scale. Obviously, those metals that follow logarithmic growth laws, such as aluminum and its alloys and chromium and its alloys, are most resistant to oxidation.

The oxidation of alloys is a little more complex than the oxidation of a pure metal. If both components of a binary alloy oxidize, a two-component oxide layer results. The oxides may or may not form a single-phase solid solution, and two-phase alloys may or may not form protective films. Copper-zinc alloys, for example, form discontinuous pockets of ZnO in a continuous matrix of Cu_2O. The rate of oxidation is primarily controlled by the rate of diffusion through the Cu_2O. If one element of an alloy oxidizes much more rapidly than the others, *selective oxidation* occurs. The selective oxidation of carbon in steel, for example, leads to the formation of gaseous carbon monoxide and the subsequent decarburization of the steel. Selective oxidation can also be beneficial, as in the case of chromium-rich stainless steels. The selective formation of a protective film of chromium oxides produces a highly oxidation-resistant surface on the steel. The same effect occurs on the preferential oxidation of silicon in cast iron, where a highly resistant silica surface protects the iron from rapid deterioration.

Since oxidation is primarily a surface phenomenon, it can be minimized by modifying either the solid surface or its environment. Paints, pitch, porcelain, plastics of various types, and other nonmetallic materials can be coated on a metal surface in order to provide a continuous barrier between the metal and the environment. Zinc and cadmium coatings on steel are examples of metallic coatings that afford both a mechanical and a galvanic (Sec. 15.4) protection to steel, while tin, nickel, and chromium coatings on steel are examples of metallic coatings that form a mechanical oxide barrier between the steel and the environment. *Painting, spraying, dipping,* and *electroplating* are all widely used techniques for producing an adhering coating on a metallic surface. The heating of steel in the presence of powdered aluminum, chromium, or zinc is an example of the *diffusion coating* of metals. The casting of pure aluminum on a sheet of less-resistant alloy, followed by a hot-working operation to firmly bond the two layers (Al-clad alloys), is an example of *metal cladding* for oxidation protection. There are a great many combinations of materials and types of fabricating techniques, and we cannot hope to cover the subject here.

15.3
Oxidation of organic materials

The thermal instability of organic polymers is one of their weakest characteristics. The maximum temperature for continuous use of most thermoplastics is 150 to 250°F, with the fluorocarbons, the silicones and some of the newer aromatic polymers as exceptions: they have good properties to 450 to 550°F. The thermosetting materials do not have softening points, but they do have a maximum temperature for continuous use of 300 to 500°F. Almost all polymers will degrade or generally change their properties at these elevated temperatures. In the presence of oxygen, degradation will occur relatively fast even at lower temperatures. The oxidative aging of rubber is a typical example of the effects of oxidation. It has been found that the property changes are accompanied by the formation of carbonyl, hydroxyl, carboxy, and peroxy groups along the polymer chain. Often there is a sharp decrease in molecular weight accompanied by softening and increased solubility, while other times there is an increase in molecular weight accompanied by embrittlement and decreased solubility. These phenomena are quite common to all organic polymers to varying degrees.

Although the actual mechanisms for oxidative degradation have not been completely worked out (and probably differ from one material to the next), it is generally agreed that the presence of molecular oxygen probably leads to the formation of unstable hydroperoxides which decompose to yield free radicals. The free radicals may then participate in further polymerization, depolymerization, scission, cross-linking, or any other free-radical-catalyzed organic reaction. The following set of reactions illustrates how a variety of free radicals might form in the presence of oxygen:

$$\sim\!\!\sim\!-CH_2-\!\!\sim\!\!\sim + O_2 \;\rightarrow\; \sim\!\!\sim\!-\overset{\cdot}{C}H-\!\!\sim\!\!\sim + \cdot OOH$$

$$\sim\!\!\sim\!-\overset{\cdot}{C}H-\!\!\sim\!\!\sim + O_2 \;\rightarrow\; \sim\!\!\sim\!-\underset{\underset{\displaystyle O}{\overset{\displaystyle |}{\underset{\displaystyle O}{|}}}}{CH}-\!\!\sim\!\!\sim$$

$$\sim\!\!\sim\!-\underset{\underset{\displaystyle O}{\overset{\displaystyle |}{\underset{\displaystyle O}{|}}}}{CH}-\!\!\sim\!\!\sim + \sim\!\!\sim\!-CH_2-\!\!\sim\!\!\sim \;\rightarrow\; \sim\!\!\sim\!-\underset{\underset{\displaystyle O}{\overset{\displaystyle |}{\underset{\displaystyle H}{\underset{\displaystyle O}{|}}}}}{CH}-\!\!\sim\!\!\sim + \sim\!\!\sim\!-\overset{\cdot}{C}H-\!\!\sim\!\!\sim$$

$$\sim\!\!\sim\!-\underset{\underset{\displaystyle O}{\overset{\displaystyle |}{\underset{\displaystyle H}{\underset{\displaystyle O}{|}}}}}{CH}-\!\!\sim\!\!\sim \;\rightarrow\; \text{free radicals of hydroperoxides}$$

The active species $R\cdot$, $RO\cdot$, $RO_2\cdot$, and $ROOH$ (where R is the organic chain) may then participate in a number of different reactions that can explain the physical changes that occur. These reactions may be classified as either aggregative reactions such as branching and cross-linking, which increase molecular weight, or disaggregative reactions such as chain scission, which decrease molecular weight. The following reactions are typical of these:

Aggregative reactions

$$R\cdot + R\cdot \rightarrow RR$$
$$RO_2\cdot + R\cdot \;\rightarrow\; RO_2R$$

$$RO_2\cdot + RO_2\cdot \;\rightarrow\; RO_2R + O_2$$

$$R\cdot + \sim\!\!\sim\!-C\!=\!C-\!\!\sim\!\!\sim \;\rightarrow\; \sim\!\!\sim\!-\underset{\displaystyle R}{\overset{\displaystyle |}{C}}-\overset{\displaystyle \cdot}{C}-\!\!\sim\!\!\sim$$

$$RO_2\cdot + \sim\!\!\sim\!-C\!=\!C-\!\!\sim\!\!\sim \;\rightarrow\; \sim\!\!\sim\!-\underset{\underset{\displaystyle R}{\overset{\displaystyle |}{\underset{\displaystyle O}{\overset{\displaystyle O}{|}}}}}{C}-\overset{\displaystyle \cdot}{C}-\!\!\sim\!\!\sim$$

Disaggregative reactions

$$\sim\!\!\sim\!-CH_2-CHXCH_2\cdot CXCH_2CHX-\!\!\sim\!\!\sim \;\rightarrow$$

$$\sim\!\!\sim CH_2CHX\cdot + CH_2\!=\!CX-CH_2CHX-\!\!\sim\!\!\sim$$

$$\sim\!\!\sim\!-CHXOOCH_2-\!\!\sim\!\!\sim \;\rightarrow\; \sim\!\!\sim CHXO\cdot + \cdot OCH_2\!\sim\!\!\sim$$

$$\sim\!\!\sim\!-CH_2CHXO\cdot \;\rightarrow\; \sim\!\!\sim CH_2\cdot + HXC\!=\!O$$

Under most conditions, aggregative and disaggregative reactions will occur simultaneously. The relative rates will depend on the concentrations of the various active species. There are considerable data available on the effects of aging of specific materials, but each material must be investigated in the environment in which it is used.

15.4
Corrosion — Electrode reactions

In this section we shall discuss the electrochemical decomposition of a metal. There are generally a great many variables that influence the rate and extent of a corrosion reaction, and an analysis of a specific situation must be conducted in light of information about the corroding material and its environment.   In other words, as in the cases of mechanical fatigue and dielectric breakdown, the behavior of a particular system strongly depends on the fine details of the interaction between the structure and its environment and is not a static property of the material.   On the other hand, it is possible to rationalize the corrosion of a metal in terms of basic electrochemical principles.

When a metal comes in contact with a conducting fluid, such as water, there is a tendency for the metal to dissolve in the fluid in the form of ions. This dissolution can be illustrated by zinc:

$$Zn \rightleftarrows Zn^{++} + 2e \qquad (15.7)$$

When the ions leave the surface of the metal, the equivalent number of excess electrons accumulate on the surface. The electrostatic field created by the interaction of the electrons with the ions tends to hold the ions in the solution in a thin layer near the surface. This film of high ion concentration is called the *electric double layer* for the electrode. The greater the tendency of the metal to dissolve, the greater the accumulation of charge at the surface and thus the greater the potential drop through the double layer. Every metal surface in contact with a conducting fluid thus has an *electrode potential* associated with it.

Suppose two different metals are immersed in aqueous solutions and are connected externally by a wire, as shown in Fig. 15.2. The zinc electrode is immersed in an aqueous zinc sulfate solution, while the copper electrode is immersed in an aqueous copper sulfate solution. The two solutions are physically (but not electrically) separated by a porous barrier which prevents convective mixing but still allows ionic diffusion.

The dissolving tendency at each electrode can be represented by the following reactions:

$$Zn \rightleftarrows Zn^{++} + 2e \qquad (15.8)$$

$$Cu \rightleftarrows Cu^{++} + 2e \qquad (15.9)$$

The copper, however, is less easily ionized than the zinc, which means that there is less of an electrode potential drop and a smaller electron concentration at the copper surface. When the two electrodes are connected externally by a conductor, there is an electron flow from the zinc electrode (with high electron con-

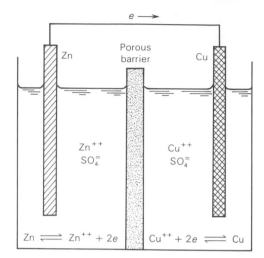

Fig. 15.2 The Daniell cell is an illustration of a galvanic cell.

centration) to the copper electrode (with low electron concentration). The disruption of the electric charges at the two surfaces destroys the equilibrium in the two electric double layers and promotes changes that will restore equilibrium. Since the zinc electrode is losing electrons, it is driven toward equilibrium by dissolving more zinc, while the copper electrode is gaining electrons and must therefore use them by combining with copper ions from the solution to form metallic copper. By convention, the electrode that supplies electrons is called the *anode,* while the electrode that accepts electrons is called the *cathode.* The reaction at the anode, $M \rightarrow M^{n+} + ne$, is called *oxidation,* while the reaction at the cathode, $M^{n+} + ne \rightarrow M$, is called *reduction.* This illustrates *galvanic corrosion;* the anodic portion of this cell is continually dissolving as long as it is electrically connected to the cathode. A galvanic cell can be formed whenever there is a potential difference between two points connected by an electrical conductor. The potential difference can arise because of contact between dissimilar metals, heterogeneities in the surface of a single metal, differences in environment from one point to the next, and many other factors. The occurrence of this type of electrochemical reaction, regardless of source, is called *wet corrosion.*

The tendency for a given electrode to dissolve is measured by the change in free energy that accompanies the ionization reaction. The free-energy change ΔG of a process taking place in a cell, such as the one shown in Fig. 15.2, may be related to the reversible emf, $\mathscr{E}_R$, by the equation

$$-\Delta G = nF\mathscr{E}_R \qquad (15.10)$$

where nF is the number of coulombs passing through a reversible cell, n is the number of faradays passing through the cell, and F is the factor 96,500 coul/faraday. A reversible cell is one that satisfies the following conditions: When it is connected to a source of emf that is equal but opposite to that of the cell, all chemical reactions stop and the cell stays at equilibrium. When the external emf is decreased by an infinitesimal amount, the anode dissolves; and when the external emf is increased by an infinitesimal amount, the anode gains mass. That is to say that the electrode reactions are completely reversible at $\mathscr{E}_R$. When the emf of the cell is positive (that is, ΔG is negative), a spontaneous flow of current is possible with, by convention, oxidation occurring at the left-hand electrode and reduction occurring at the right-hand electrode. The complete cell reaction is obtained by adding the separate electrode reactions. The conventional symbolism is as follows (for the Daniell cell):

$$Zn \mid ZnSO_4 \text{ sol} \vdots CuSO_4 \text{ sol} \mid Cu$$

$$Zn + Cu^{++} \rightleftarrows Zn^{++} + Cu \tag{15.11}$$

The overall reaction for the cell is represented by Eq. (15.11), and the free-energy change for the isothermal reaction is

$$\Delta G = \Delta G^0 + RT \ln \frac{[Zn^{++}][Cu]}{[Zn][Cu^{++}]} \tag{15.12}$$

where ΔG^0 is the standard free-energy change for the reaction and is related to the equilibrium constant K for the reaction by $\Delta G^0 = -RT \ln K$. The bracketed quantities in the logarithmic term are the activities of the different species. (Activity can be defined in a number of ways, but usually it is defined as the product of an activity coefficient β and the concentration: $[A] = \beta_A C_A$. For pure liquids and solids $[A] = 1$, and for dilute solutions $\beta_A \to 1$ and $[A] = C_A$.)

The emf of a cell can be obtained by combining Eqs. (15.10) and (15.12):

$$\mathscr{E} = \mathscr{E}_0 - \frac{RT}{nF} \ln \frac{[Zn^{++}]}{[Cu^{++}]} \tag{15.13}$$

where

$$\mathscr{E}_0 = \frac{RT}{nF} \ln \mathscr{K} \tag{15.14}$$

The quantity $\mathscr{E}_0$ is the *standard emf* for a given cell and is constant for a given temperature and pressure. The actual emf of the cell also depends on the activities of the substances involved in the cell reaction.

The electrode potential of a single electrode may be defined in a similar fashion:

Reduced state $\rightleftarrows$ oxidized state + electrons

$$M \rightleftarrows M^{n+} + ne$$

$$\mathscr{E}_M = (\mathscr{E}_0)_M - \frac{RT}{nF} \ln [M^{n+}] \tag{15.15}$$

The quantity $(\mathscr{E}_0)_M$ is the *standard electrode potential* for the given electrode and is a constant at a given temperature. By convention, these are referred to as *oxidation potentials* when the oxidized state is on the right side of the reaction equation. The overall emf of a cell is obviously the *difference* of the oxidation potentials at the two electrodes (since reduction occurs at the cathode). For the Daniell cell:

$$\mathscr{E} = \mathscr{E}_{Zn} - \mathscr{E}_{Cu} \tag{15.16}$$

There is no method known for reliably measuring the absolute potential of a single electrode. In order to catalog the relative tendency of different metals for oxidation, each electrode is combined in a cell with a standard reference electrode whose electrode potential is arbitrarily chosen as zero. The measured emf of the cell is then taken to be the electrode potential of the unknown. The most widely used standard is a reversible hydrogen electrode, with gas at 1 atm pressure and 25°C, in a solution of hydrogen ions of unit activity:

$$H_2(\text{gas 1 atm}) \mid H^+ \text{ sol } [H^+] = 1$$

From Eq. (15.15), one can see that the emf of any given cell will still be a function of the metal-ion activity. A table of standard electrode potentials is derived by arbitrarily choosing an ion concentration of $C = 1$ g-ion/liter and assuming that the logarithmic term is zero (i.e., assuming a unit activity coefficient). The standard electrode potentials of metals, relative to a standard hydrogen electrode at 25°C and at a unit activity of metal ions, are given in Table 15.1. The sign convention is arbitrary and is in accordance with the

Table 15.1

Standard electrode potentials of metals
(Relative to a standard hydrogen
electrode at 25°C
and unit activity of ions)

Element	Electrode	Electrode potential, volts	Element	Electrode	Electrode potential, volts
Lithium	Li^+, Li	2.959	Cadmium	Cd^{++}, Cd	0.42
Rubidium	Rb^+, Rb	2.925	Nickel	Ni^{++}, Ni	0.23
Potassium	K^+, K	2.924	Tin	Sn^{++}, Sn	0.14
Calcium	Ca^{++}, Ca	2.763	Lead	Pb^{++}, Pb	0.13
Sodium	Na^+, Na	2.714	Iron	Fe^{3+}, Fe	0.045
Magnesium	Mg^{++}, Mg	2.37			
Beryllium	Be^{++}, Be	1.85	Hydrogen	H^+, $H_2(g)$	0.000
Aluminum	Al^{3+}, Al	1.69	Copper	Cu^{++}, Cu	−0.337
Titanium	Ti^{++}, Ti	1.63	Copper	Cu^+, Cu	−0.522
Zinc	Zn^{++}, Zn	0.761	Silver	Ag^+, Ag	−0.797
Chromium	Cr^{++}, Cr	0.71	Mercury	Hg^{++}, Hg	−0.798
Chromium	Cr^{3+}, Cr	0.50	Platinum	Pt^{++}, Pt	−1.20
Iron	Fe^{++}, Fe	0.44	Gold	Au^{3+}, Au	−1.50

recommendations of the American Chemical Society. The values given are for pure, oxide-free metals in cells that are very close to equilibrium (i.e., the current passing through the cell is negligible). In a galvanic cell, under these ideal conditions, a metal higher on the scale will be anodic relative to one lower on the scale. Thus, the standard potential of the Daniell cell is $0.761 - (-0.337) = 1.098$ volts; the anode is zinc and the cathode is copper.

15.5
Corrosion — Specific causes

The standard electrode potentials listed in Table 15.1 give one an idea of the relative oxidation tendency of different metals. Thus, if two metals are in a galvanic couple, one would expect the metal with the higher electrode potential to dissolve (i.e., corrode). In actual practice the environmental conditions are extremely important and the relative positioning of the elements may shift somewhat, depending on the specific conditions. Materials that readily oxidize, for example, can be strongly affected by the presence of oxygen. Chromium, for example, is anodic relative to iron, yet the chromium-iron stainless steels are cathodic relative to iron in normal environments. This is attributable to the oxidizing tendency of chromium:

$$Cr + 2O_2 + 2e \rightarrow CrO_4^{--} \qquad (15.17)$$

A layer of adsorbed chromate anion on the surface of a metal will isolate it from its environment so that further reaction is retarded. A metal under these conditions is said to be *passivated*. The effects of passivation on commercially important materials are shown in Table 15.2. This table is based on the behavior of electrodes in environments that more closely approach those met in practice and is thus of great value from an engineering point of view. It must be emphasized that this table is still for a rather specific set of conditions and that, in any given situation, metals might shift their position in the series. Practical experience and simulated environmental testing are essential parts of corrosion engineering.

On the basis of the electrochemical principles stated in the preceding section, we see that wet corrosion will occur whenever a potential difference exists between two points in a closed electrical circuit. There are many subtle differences in structure and environment that can create galvanic currents. We shall classify these in terms of three basic types: compositional differences, energetic differences, and environmental differences.

Compositional cells are established between any two dissimilar metals in a closed electrical circuit. Figure 15.3 illustrates the corrosion of a tin-plated steel. The tin plate acts as a protective covering for the steel as long as it is a continuous barrier. When a scratch is deep enough to expose steel, a galvanic couple is set up with the tin as the cathode and the steel as the anode. The iron dissolves in a typical anodic reaction:

$$Fe \rightleftarrows Fe^{++} + 2e \qquad (15.18)$$

Table 15.2

Electromotive series of common alloys *

Anodic ↑	Magnesium	
	Magnesium alloys	
	Zinc	
	Aluminum, 2S	
	Cadmium	
	Aluminum alloy 17S-T	
	Carbon steel	
	Copper steel	
	Cast iron	
	4 to 6% Cr steel	Active
	12 to 14% Cr steel	Active
	16 to 18% Cr steel	Active
	23 to 30% Cr steel	Active
	Ni-resist	
	7% Ni, 17% Cr steel	Active
	8% Ni, 18% Cr steel	Active
	14% Ni, 23% Cr steel	Active
	20% Ni, 25% Cr steel	Active
	12% Ni, 18% Cr, 3% Mo steel	Active
	Lead-tin solder	
	Lead	
	Tin	
	Nickel	
	60% Ni, 15% Cr	Active
	Inconel	Active
	80% Ni, 20% Cr	Active
	Brasses	
	Copper	
	Bronzes	
	Nickel-silver	
	Copper-nickel	
	Monel metal	
	Nickel	Passive
	60% Ni, 15% Cr	Passive
	Inconel	Passive
	80% Ni, 20% Cr	Passive
	12 to 14% Cr steel	Passive
	16 to 18% Cr steel	Passive
	7% Ni, 17% Cr steel	Passive
	8% Ni, 18% Cr steel	Passive
	14% Ni, 23% Cr steel	Passive
	23 to 30% Cr steel	Passive
	20% Ni, 25% Cr steel	Passive
	12% Ni, 18% Cr, 3% Mo steel	Passive
↓	Silver	
Cathodic	Graphite	

*C. A. Zapffe, "Stainless Steels," ASM, Cleveland, 1949.

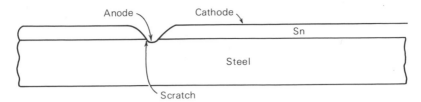

Fig. 15.3 When a tin-plated steel is scratched, exposing iron, a galvanic coupling action will cause corrosion of the steel.

In a neutral or slightly alkaline aqueous environment, in the presence of oxygen, the electrons flow to the cathodic tin plate, where they react with oxygen:

$$\tfrac{1}{2}O_2 + 2e + H_2O \rightleftarrows 2OH^- \tag{15.19}$$

Since the anode area is very small relative to the cathode area, a high current density is concentrated in a small region of the steel. This leads to a strong attack on the exposed area, the extent of corrosion depending on the amount of oxygen available. The iron cations and the hydroxyl anions migrate and react to form iron hydroxides:

$$Fe^{++} \rightarrow Fe^{3+} + e \tag{15.20}$$

$$Fe^{3+} + 3OH^- \rightarrow Fe(OH)_3 \tag{15.21}$$

The ferric hydroxide, or rust, is generally deposited at the cathode surface because of the greater mobility of the ferric ions. In the presence of an acidic environment, a hydrogen evolution can occur at the cathode surface. With excess acid:

$$Fe. \rightleftarrows Fe^{++} + 2e \tag{15.22}$$

$$2H^+ + 2e \rightleftarrows H_2 \tag{15.23}$$

Thus, metals above hydrogen in the electrochemical series tend to dissolve in acids.

These principles are taken *advantage* of in the galvanizing of steel with zinc. A pure zinc coating of steel will be protective even when iron is exposed. Zinc, having a higher electrode potential, acts as an anode, making the exposed iron cathodic. As long as zinc is present, it will be an anode and prevent dissolution of an iron surface. Thus, we see that galvanic corrosion can be either advantageous or undesirable.

Galvanic couples can also occur in heterogeneous alloys. Pearlite, for example, is a two-phase eutectoid of ferrite and iron carbide. The ferrite is slightly more anodic than the iron carbide, and thus a multitude of tiny galvanic cells exist in the material, causing a corrosion of the ferrite. This effect is seen in Fig. 15.4, which shows the corrosion rate of a quenched steel after tempering at various temperatures. At low tempering temperatures, single-phase martensite is maintained and the corrosion rate is low. At intermediate

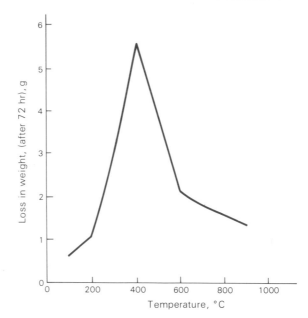

Fig. 15.4 The effect of temperature on the corrosion rate of a quenched steel can be explained in terms of the microstructure of the steel. (Data from F. N. Speller, "Corrosion: Causes and Prevention," McGraw-Hill Book Company, New York, 1935.)

temperatures, a very fine grained pearlite is formed which leads to a relatively high corrosion rate, while at higher temperatures a coarser-grained pearlite exhibits a lower corrosion rate. This effect is quite general in that multiphase alloys are more subject to corrosion than single-phase alloys of the same composition.

There are a number of forms of corrosion that are associated with differences in energy from one point on a surface to another. These differences arise from grain boundaries, heterogeneities in composition, and, very importantly, from internal stresses.

Grain boundaries are considerably different from the material within the crystals. Differences in atomic arrangement and composition give them a higher free energy than the surrounding material and usually a greater chemical activity. Boundaries are generally anodic relative to grains, which leads to dissolving at the grain boundary, or *intergranular corrosion.* A striking example of intergranular corrosion occurs in multiphase alloys such as the austenitic stainless steels. Austenitic steels tend to precipitate complex chromium carbides at grain boundaries, which leaves adjacent areas with a lower than average chromium content. These areas are thus anodic relative to their surroundings. Intergranular corrosion can be quite severe in certain environments, unless the precipitation reactions are suppressed. This phenomenon occurs with many alloys which tend to precipitate intermetallic compounds. It should be obvious from the above discussion that fine-grained materials will corrode at a faster rate than coarse-grained materials.

Closely associated with intergranular corrosion is stress corrosion. The presence of residual or externally applied tensile stress will greatly accelerate the rate of corrosion of certain materials. In general, pure materials are relatively insensitive to stress corrosion, while almost all alloys will exhibit it under certain conditions. Stress corrosion is characterized by a localized attack at points of high stress concentration. Areas of stress concentration, such as those that appear because of phase transformations, precipitation reactions, cold working, welding, cooling operations, and the like, act as anodes relative to unstressed portions and tend to dissolve. This causes voids and fissures in the material which, in the presence of a tensile stress, can start a crack propagating in the material. The result is a premature brittle fracture, which may be either intergranular or transgranular. The magnitude and distribution of stress, the nature of the environment, the microstructure of the material, and the geometry of the crystal structure all interact in a very complex fashion to produce a problem which is difficult to treat analytically. Each alloy must be studied individually in an environment similar to the one expected in practice. There are also standardized tests which may be used to predict the relative stress-corrosion resistance of materials, but these are used only as an initial guide because of the many unknown factors involved.

The third factor causing galvanic action is differences in environment from one point to another on a surface. "Concentration cells" are usually the result of differences in electrolyte concentration. Equation (15.15) shows that the electrode potential is dependent on the ion concentration; in very dilute solutions the electrode becomes more anodic. Thus, if the electrolyte concentration at the surface of a metal varies, the surface in contact with the most dilute solution becomes anodic relative to its surroundings and tends to dissolve. The most important type of concentration cell is that caused by variations in oxygen concentration. When a portion of a surface is inaccessible to oxygen, as, for example, under a film of dirt, under a scale deposit, in the interstices of a crack, under wood (as the shank of a nail), or beneath the surface of a fluid, it becomes anodic relative to the accessible areas. The reason for this is that the oxygen consumes electrons as was shown in Eq. (15.19). Thus, hydroxyl ions are formed at the cathodic areas, causing an electron deficiency. An electrode potential difference exists between these areas and the oxygen-deficient ones, creating a free flow of electrons through the metal and a dissolving of the metal at the anodes. This type of corrosion is often characterized by a highly localized attack called *pitting,* as shown in Fig. 15.5.

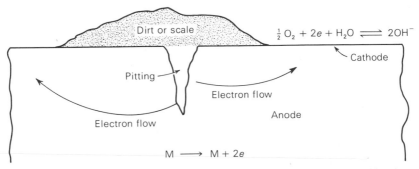

Fig. 15.5 The inaccessibility of oxygen beneath a film of dirt or scale will lead to pitting through the action of an oxygen concentration cell.

15.6
Compatibility and dissolution of materials

Another form of destruction of materials is by permeation and dissolution. These are rarely problems with solid metals, since diffusion rates are usually very small. When liquid metals come into contact with solids, however, a number of forms of attack are possible. Solid solution formation, intermetallic compounding, and selective extraction of the various components of alloys can occur when mutually compatible metals come in contact. The erosion of copper and iron tubes in heat exchangers carrying liquid-metal coolants is an example of dissolution and precipitation reactions (at the hot and cold ends of the exchanger, respectively) causing eventual destruction. The formation of amalgams when mercury contacts silver, tin, and copper alloys is an example of structural change due to intermetallic formation.

Of considerably greater importance are the effects of solvents and plasticizers on organic structures. Polymeric solids are, to one degree or another, mutually compatible with a wide variety of liquids. Thermoplastic materials can be completely dissolved by the proper solvent and can be strongly modified by absorption of nonsolvents. Nylon, for example, can be completely dissolved by cresol and can have many of its physical properties markedly changed by the absorption of a percent or two of water. Mutual compatibility is utilized in plasticizer technology when low-molecular-weight materials are used to make rigid plastics more pliable and extensible. Pure polyvinylchloride, for example, is a hard, brittle solid, but when mixed with 10 to 30 percent tricresylphosphate, it becomes a soft, pliable material. Insoluble, thermosetting materials have a tendency to absorb a compatible fluid and become highly swelled. Although they do not completely lose their cohesion, very drastic property changes result.

The mutual compatibility of two materials is determined by the thermodynamic properties of the resulting solutions. Two very useful criteria for solubility (or plasticizer compatibility) are the Hildebrand solubility parameter δ_S and the Flory interaction parameter χ_S. Both of these will be discussed in this section.

In the "mechanistic" concept of dissolution, one visualizes a dynamic equilibrium between aggregative and disaggregative processes. In a pure material, the molecules are at lattice sites with a specific number of nearest neighbors. The cohesion of the material is primarily from the valence bonding between nearest neighbors. Since the particles are in continuous Brownian motion, these bonds are being simultaneously broken and reformed. The condensed state may be visualized as a dynamic system of aggregates of molecules that are continually being formed and broken up. The cohesiveness and the life of a given aggregate will depend on the strength of the valence bonding and the temperature of the material. Likewise, a pure solvent may be visualized in the same manner. When a polymer (or any other material) is mixed with a solvent, polymer-polymer, polymer-solvent, and solvent-solvent interactions are possible. The most stable aggregates are those that are energetically most favorable. Thus, when polymer-solvent interactions are as strong, or stronger, than either polymer-polymer or solvent-solvent interactions, there will be a tendency for dissolution. When polymer-polymer and/or solvent-solvent interactions are strongest, immiscibility results.

The two critical molecular characteristics for determining which type of interaction predominates are molecular geometry and intermolecular forces. When there is similarity in size and shape between two different molecules, they tend to replace each other in a lattice network without serious distortion of the lattice (recall the Hume-Rothery rules in Chap. 7), and they tend to form homogeneous solutions. (The molecular similarity might refer to whole molecules, as in the case of mixtures of small molecules, or it might refer to the repeating unit in a polymer chain, as in polymer-solvent mixtures.) When there are differences in size and shape, lattice distortion causes an increase in free energy and promotes immiscibility. When the cohesive energies of the separate materials are similar, the chances of polymer-solvent interactions are improved. An "ideal" solution is most easily formed by materials with same-size molecules and equal cohesive energy densities. This is the basis for the old rule of thumb—like dissolves like, but the problem is to make sure that the degree of "likeness" is clearly stated, since very subtle changes in molecular factors can grossly change the compatibility of two substances.

The thermodynamic criterion for dissolution is that the free-energy change on mixing is negative:

$$\Delta G_M = \Delta H_M - T \, \Delta S_M < 0 \tag{15.24}$$

Since the entropy change on mixing, ΔS_M, is always positive, the sign and magnitude of the heat of mixing is the critical factor.

By using a statistical theory, Flory [4] calculated the entropy of mixing of solvent and large polymer molecules as

$$\Delta S_M = -R(n_S \ln \phi_S + n_P \ln \phi_P) \tag{15.25}$$

where n_S and n_P are moles of solvent and polymer, respectively, and ϕ_S and ϕ_P are volume fractions of solvent and polymer, respectively. When the molecules involved are almost identical in size, shape, and the nature and magnitude of their intermolecular forces, the heat of mixing is zero, the volume fractions equal mole fractions ($\phi_1 = N_1$), and an "ideal solution" is formed. When the molecules are nonpolar and similar in shape, but have different cohesive energies, an enthalpy change occurs on mixing. Hildebrand [6] has calculated the enthalpy of mixing by visualizing the mixing process in the following way. A molecule from each of two pure materials free themselves from the condensed state by evaporation and then exchange positions by condensation. The difference in energy results because the evaporation involves the breaking of solvent-solvent and solute-solute bonds, while the condensation involves the formation of solvent-solute bonds. For the random mixing of two species, it can be shown that

$$\Delta H_M = V_M \left[\left(\frac{\Delta U_S}{V_S}\right)^{1/2} - \left(\frac{\Delta U_P}{V_P}\right)^{1/2} \right]^2 \phi_S \phi_P \tag{15.26}$$

where ΔH_M is the total energy of mixing in units of energy, V_M is the volume of the mixture, and $(\Delta U_i/V_i)$ is the energy of vaporization per unit volume of component i (i.e., the cohesive energy density of i). Then

$$\Delta H_M = V_M[(E_{CD})_S^{1/2} - (E_{CD})_P^{1/2}]^2\phi_S\phi_P$$

$$= V_M(\delta_S - \delta_P)^2\phi_S\phi_P \tag{15.26a}$$

The quantities δ_S and δ_P are the solubility parameters for the solvent and polymer (solute), respectively. The solubility parameter for the solvent is obtained from the latent heat of vaporization,

$$\delta_S = \left(\frac{\Delta H_v - R}{V_S}\right)^{1/2} \tag{15.27}$$

while the solubility parameter for the nonvolatile polymer must be estimated by empirical methods. From Small's results, presented in Eq. (8.17),

$$\delta_P = (E_{CD})_P^{1/2} = \frac{\Sigma\Delta_i}{Mv} \tag{15.28}$$

The free energy of mixing is thus:

$$\Delta G_M = RT(n_S \ln \phi_S + n_P \ln \phi_P) + V_M(\delta_S - \delta_P)^2\phi_S\phi_P \tag{15.29}$$

Equation (15.29) must usually be modified by an empirical correction factor β_c in order to predict correctly the entropy and free energy of mixing:

$$\frac{\Delta G_M}{RT} = n_S \ln \phi_S + n_P \ln \phi_P + \left[\beta_c + \frac{V_M}{RTn_S}(\delta_S - \delta_P)^2\phi_S\right]n_S\phi_P$$

$$= n_S \ln \phi_S + n_P \ln \phi_P + \chi_S n_S\phi_P \tag{15.30}$$

where χ_S is the *interaction parameter* for the polymer-solvent system. Replacing $\phi_S V_M/n_S$ by the molar volume of the solvent in the solution, v_S,

$$\chi_S = \beta_c + \frac{v_S}{RT}(\delta_S - \delta_P)^2 \tag{15.31}$$

Both ϕ_S and ϕ_P are fractions, so the first two terms in Eq. (15.30) are negative. Since compatibility increases as ΔG_M becomes more negative, small or negative values of χ_S lead to greater compatibility. The maximum compatibility occurs when the solubility parameters are equal, since $(\delta_S - \delta_P)^2$ is then zero. It should be noted, however, that equal solubility parameters does not in itself guarantee compatibility, since the factor $\beta_c n_S\phi_P$ could still counterbalance the other two terms. Nevertheless, equal solubility parameters are often used as a practical criterion of mutual compatibility. Since solubility parameters are easily obtained, this is a very useful tool for predicting the best solvent for a given material or, conversely, to decide whether a material is chemically resistant to a given environment.

The solubility parameters for a variety of simple liquids are given in Table 15.3. To a rough order of approximation, the solubility parameter of a mixture

Table 15.3

Solubility parameters of selected solvents *   δ (cal/cm³)^{1/2}

Aliphatic hydrocarbons

Isobutylene	6.7	VM&P	7.6
Low-odor mineral spirits	6.9	Methylcyclohexane	7.8
Pentane	7.0	Turpentine	8.1
Hexane	7.3	Cyclohexane	8.2
Heptane	7.4	Dipentene	8.5
Octane	7.6		

Aromatic hydrocarbons

Solvesso 150	8.5	Toluene	8.9
Solvesso 100	8.6	Benzene	9.2
Ethylbenzene	8.8	Tetralin	9.5
Xylene	8.8		

Chlorinated

2,2-Dichloropropane	8.2	Tetrachloroethylene	9.4
Carbon tetrachloride	8.6	Chlorobenzene	9.5
1,2-Dichloropropane	9.0	Methylene chloride	9.7
Chloroform	9.3	Ethylene dichloride	9.8
Trichloroethylene	9.3	o-Dichlorobenzene	10.0

Ethers

Diethyl	7.4	Dioxan	9.9
Dimethyl	8.8	Cellosolve	9.9
Dichloroethyl	9.8		

Esters

Isobutyl n-butyrate	7.8	Propyl acetate	8.8
Isopropyl isobutyrate	7.9	Butyl Cellosolve	8.9
Methylamyl acetate	8.0	Ethyl acetate	9.1
Butyl butyrate	8.1	Propyl formate	9.2
sec-Butyl acetate	8.2	Dibutyl phthalate	9.4
sec-Amyl acetate	8.3	Methyl acetate	9.6
Isobutyl acetate	8.3	Ethyl lactate	10.0
Isopropyl acetate	8.4	Butyronitrile	10.5
Amyl acetate	8.5	Acetonitrile	11.9
Butyl acetate	8.5	Propylene carbonate	13.3
Cellosolve acetate	8.7	Ethylene carbonate	14.7

Ketones

Diisobutyl	7.8	Diacetone alcohol	9.2
Diisopropyl	8.0	Methyl cyclohexanone	9.3
Methyl isobutyl	8.4	Methylethyl	9.3
Methylamyl	8.5	Cyclohexanone	9.9
Methyl propyl	8.7	Acetone	10.0
Diethyl	8.8	Cyclopentanone	10.4
Isophorone	9.1	Cyclobutandione	11.0

Alcohols

Butyl Carbitol	8.9	sec-Butanol	10.8
Butyl Cellosolve	8.9	n-Pentanol	10.9
Diethylene glycol	9.1	n-Butanol	11.4
2-Ethylene glycol	9.1	Cyclohexanol	11.4
Carbitol	9.6	Isopropanol	11.5
Cellosolve	9.9	n-Propanol	11.9
Methylisobutyl carbinol	10.0	Ethanol	12.7
n-Octanol	10.3	Ethylene glycol	14.2
2-Ethylbutanol	10.5	Methanol	14.5
n-Hexanol	10.7	Glycerol	16.5
		Water	23.4

* By permission, from H. Burrell, "Official Digest," p. 744, Interchemical Corporation, October, 1955.

may be estimated as additive in proportion to the mole fraction of the components:

$$(\delta_S)_{\text{mix}} = \sum_i N_i(\delta_S)_i \qquad\qquad (15.32)$$

The interaction parameter χ_S is more difficult to obtain, is less available, but is probably a better indication of compatibility. Some typical values are given in Table 15.4.

In general, a polymer and a solvent are compatible if $-1.1 \leq (\delta_S - \delta_P) \leq 1.1$ and $\chi_S < 0.5$. Outside these limits one would expect only limited compatibility with the degree of immiscibility increasing with an increasing difference between solubility parameters.

There are two very important limitations to the above equations. First, the solubility parameters are based on dispersion forces and spherically symmetric molecules. The theory appears to work for a variety of different-shaped molecules, but very strong electrostatic forces, such as hydrogen bonding, invalidate the equations. Second, a major assumption in developing these equations is that the pure materials are amorphous and isotropic. With crystalline polymers, the latent energy of fusion must also be overcome before dissolution can occur. Thus, a high degree of crystallinity generally leads to insolubility and a high degree of chemical resistance.

The concept of solubility parameters has also been extended to metallic solutions. Table 15.5 gives the solubility parameters for a variety of metals at 25°C. Since metals have relatively small expansion coefficients and δ is a measure of cohesive energy, the solubility parameter is relatively insensitive to temperature. The small changes that do occur are predictable; they decrease with increasing temperature and show discontinuities at phase transitions as illustrated by the data on iron, shown in Fig. 15.6. As with nonmetallic systems, the greater the difference $\delta_1 - \delta_2$, the less the compatibility of the two metals. As a rough rule of thumb, two metals are miscible if

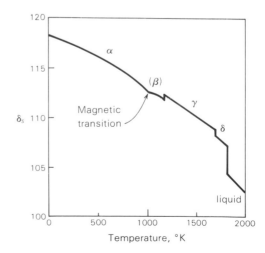

Fig. 15.6 The solubility parameter of iron is a function of temperature. (By permission from J. H. Hildebrand and R. L. Scott, "The Solubility of Nonelectrolytes," 3d ed., p. 325, Dover Publications, Inc., New York, 1964.)

Table 15.4

Values for χ_S for various polymer-solvent systems *

Components	χ_S	Temp, °C
Cellulose acetate–tetrachloroethane	−1.8	24.4 [a]
Cellulose nitrate–acetone	0.19	20 [a]
Cellulose nitrate–acetone	0.26	22 [a]
Cellulose nitrate–acetone	0.30	27 [a]
Cellulose nitrate–cyclohexanone	0.15	25 [a]
Gutta percha–benzene	0.52	25 [a]
Gutta percha–carbon tetrachloride	0.28	27 [a]
Polydichlorostyrene–butanone	0.50	27 [a]
Polyisobutylene–benzene	0.50	27 [b]
Polyisobutylene–cyclohexane	0.44	27 [b]
Polystyrene–benzene	0.20	25 [a]
Polystyrene–butanone	0.48	5 [a]
Polystyrene–ethyl laurate	0.47	25 [a]
Polystyrene–isoamyl laurate	0.91	25 [a]
Polystyrene–toluene	0.44	27 [a]
Polyvinyl acetate–acetone	0.44	27 [c]
Polyvinyl chloride–trioctyl phosphate	−0.76	53 [c]
Polyvinyl chloride–trioctyl phosphate	−0.65	76 [c]
Polyvinyl chloride–dibutyl phthalate	−0.04	53 [c]
Polyvinyl chloride–dibutyl phthalate	−0.01	76 [c]
Polyvinyl chloride–butyl acetate	0.40	53 [c]
Polyvinyl chloride–butyl acetate	0.41	76 [c]
Polyvinyl chloride–acetone	0.63	27 [c]
Polyvinyl chloride–acetone	0.60	53 [c]
Polyvinyl chloride–benzene	0.77	76 [c]
Polyvinyl chloride–dioctyl ether	2.6	53 [c]
Polyvinyl chloride–dioctyl ether	2.8	76 [c]
Rubber–benzene	0.44	25 [a]
Rubber–benzene–10% methanol	0.26	25 [a]
Rubber–benzene–15% methanol	0.50	25 [a]
Rubber–carbon disulfide	0.49	25 [a]
Rubber–carbon tetrachloride	0.28	15–20 [a]
Rubber–chloroform	0.37	15–20 [a]
Rubber–cumene	0.38	15–20 [a]
Rubber–cyclohexane	0.33	6 [a]
Rubber–ether	0.51	15–20 [a]
Rubber–light petroleum	0.43	25 [a]
Rubber–tetrachloroethane	0.36	15–20 [a]
Rubber–toluene	0.43	27 [a]

* By permission, from H. Mark and A. V. Tobolsky, "Physical Chemistry of High Polymeric Systems," p. 265, Interscience Publishers, Inc., New York, 1950.

[a] M. L. Huggins, *Ann. N.Y. Acad. Sci.,* **44:** 431 (1943).

[b] P. J. Flory, *J. Am. Chem. Soc.,* **65:** 372 (1943).

[c] P. M. Doty and H. S. Zable, *J. Polymer Sci.,* **1:** 90 (1946).

Table 15.5

Solubility parameters of the metals at 25°C *

	ΔH_S, kcal	V, cm³	δ, $(cal/cm^3)^{1/2}$		ΔH_S, kcal	V, cm³	δ, $(cal/cm^3)^{1/2}$
Re	189	8.9	146	Al	75.0	10.0	86
W	201.6	9.6	145	Ag	69.1	10.3	82
B	90	(4.3)	145	Sc	93	14.5	80
Os	174	8.4	144	Ge	78.4	13.7	76
Ir	165	8.6	139	Ga	65	11.8	74
Ru	160	8.3	139	Y	103	(19)	72
Ta	200	10.8	136	As	58	13.1	66
Rh	138	8.3	129	β-Sn	70.0	16.3	65
Be	80	4.9	129	α-La	88	22.4	63
Mo	156.0	9.4	128	In	57.4	15.7	60
Cb	175.6	10.8	127	Sb	* 63	18.2	59
α-Co	105	6.6	126	Zn	31.2	9.2	58
Ni	101.8	6.6	124	Li	37.0	13.0	54
Pt	135	9.1	121	Pb	48.5	18.3	51
V	120	8.5	119	Mg	35.9	14.0	50
α-Fe	96.7	7.1	117	α-Tl	42.8	17.3	49
α-Hf	170	13.5	112	Bi	49	21.3	48
Cr	84.5	7.3	108	Cd	26.8	13.0	45
Cu	81.5	7.2	107	α-Ca	42.6	26.0	40
Pd	93	8.9	102	α-Sr	39.2	32.9	34
U	128	12.7	100	Ba	42	37	33
α-Mn	68.6	7.6	95	Na	26.0	23.7	33
α-Zr	125	14.0	94	Hg	14.5	14.8	31
α-Ti	95	10.7	94	K	21.5	45.4	21
Au	90.5	10.3	93	Rb	20.5	56	19
Si	90	11.7	88	Cs	18.8	70	16

* From J. H. Hildebrand and R. L. Scott, "The Solubility of Non-electrolytes," 3d ed., p. 323, Dover Publications, Inc., New York, 1964.

$$\frac{v_1 + v_2}{2}(\delta_1 - \delta_2)^2 < 2RT \qquad (15.33)$$

Since the atomic volumes of most metals are near 10 cm³/g atom, $\delta_1 - \delta_2$ must be less than about $\frac{2}{3}\sqrt{T}$ for complete miscibility or about 15 to 30 $(cal/cm^3)^{1/2}$ for most metals below 2000°K. Recalling the empirical Hume-Rothery rules stated in Sec. 7.2, we now have an additional criterion for determining mutual compatibility. Table 15.6 shows the behavior of a number of binary solid solutions of face-centered cubic transition metals. In general, complete miscibility occurs when $\delta_1 - \delta_2$ is less than 25, and mutual compatibility becomes less and less as $\delta_1 - \delta_2$ becomes larger and larger. Furthermore, when two metals have differences in size, valency, or crystal structure, but similar solubility parameters, a large measure of compatibility may exist. These factors have been discussed qualitatively in Chap. 7.

Table 15.6

Solid solutions of face-centered cubic transition metals *

System	$\delta_1 - \delta_2$	Solubility limits, mole %	System	$\delta_1 - \delta_2$	Solubility limits, mole %
Ir-Pt	18 [a]	Completely miscible	Ni-Au	31 [a]	Completely miscible above 1120°K
Ir-γFe	22 [a]	Completely miscible			
Ir-Cu	32 [a]	0.5% Ir	Ni-Ag	42 [a]	0.1% Ni (two liquids)
Ir-Au	46 [a]	2.8% Ir	Pt-γFe	7 [b]	Completely miscible
Ir-Ag	57 [a]	Virtually zero solubility	Pt-Cu	16 [b]	Completely miscible
			Pt-Pd	19 [a]	Completely miscible
Rh-Ni	5 [a]	Completely miscible	Pt-Au	29 [b]	Completely miscible above 1430°K
Rh-Pt	8 [a]	Completely miscible			
Rh-γFe	12 [a]	Completely miscible	Pt-Ag	41 [b]	40% Pt, 20% Ag
Rh-Cu	22 [a]	20% Rh, 10% Cu	γFe-Cu	9 [b]	4% Fe, 8% Cu
Rh-Pd	27 [a]	Completely miscible	γFe-Cu	15 [a]	Completely miscible
Rh-Au	36 [a]	3% Rh, 2% Au	γFe-Mn	20 [c]	Completely miscible(?)
Rh-Ag	47 [a]	<0.1% Ag	γFe-Au	22 [b]	60% Fe, 5% Au
βCo-Ni	2 [a]	Completely miscible	γFe-Ag	34 [b]	0.001% (two liquids)
βCo-Pt	3 [b]	Completely miscible	Cu-Pd	5 [a]	Completely miscible
βCo-γFe	10 [b]	Completely miscible	Cu-γMn	12 [a]	Completely miscible(?)
βCo-Cu	19 [b]	8% Co, 12% Cu	Cu-Au	13 [b]	Completely miscible
βCo-Pd	24 [a]	Completely miscible	Cu-Ag	25 [b]	12% Cu, 5% Ag
βCo-γMn	31 [a]	Completely miscible(?)	Pd-Au	9 [a]	Completely miscible
βCo-Au	32 [b]	15% Co, 3% Au	Pd-Ag	20 [a]	Completely miscible
βCo-Ag	44 [b]	0.001% Co (two liquids)	† γMn-Au	2 [a]	Intermediate phases or compounds
Ni-Pt	3 [a]	Completely miscible			
Ni-γFe	7 [a]	Completely miscible	γMn-Ag	13 [a]	35% Mn
Ni-Cu	17 [a]	Completely miscible	Au-Ag	12 [b]	Completely miscible
Ni-Pd	22 [a]	Completely miscible			
Ni-γMn	29 [a]	30% Ni, 55% Mn			

* From J. H. Hildebrand and R. L. Scott, "The Solubility of Non-electrolytes," 3d ed., p. 337, Dover Publications, Inc., New York, 1964.

[a] At 298°K; [b] at 1000°K; [c] at 1500°K.

† Intermediate phases or compounds

15.7
Permeability and chemical resistance

As stated previously, the term chemical resistance can have many shades of meaning ranging from the resistance of a material to total destruction to the resistance of a material to solvent absorption. We have already discussed several types of chemical and electrochemical reactions that can cause destruction of a material. Also, we have considered the principles of solvent compatibility.

Whenever the bulk of a material, rather than merely the surface, is involved in an interaction with its environment, molecules of the environment must permeate the mass of the material. The chemical resistance is thus closely related to the rate and magnitude of permeation of the environmental substance. The permeation is, in turn, a function of both the thermodynamic behavior of the system (i.e., the solution compatibility of the involved substances) and the diffusional properties of the permeating materials.

The transmission of a substance through a material that is free of porosity or other flaws can be considered as a thermally activated process. The net rate of unidirectional transport of the diffusing substance can be expressed as the product of a diffusion coefficient and a concentration gradient [cf. Eq. (2.89)]:

$$j_x = -D_{12} \frac{\partial c}{\partial x} \qquad (15.34)$$

This is called Fick's first law of diffusion. Consider a unit area of a material l units thick, Fig. 15.7, exposed to an environmental substance at concentration c_1^0 on one side and c_2^0 on the other. The equilibrium concentration of the penetrant in the surface layers of the material can be expressed as

$$c = \mathscr{S} c^0 \qquad (15.35)$$

where $\mathscr{S}$ is the *solubility coefficient* of the penetrant in the material. When the penetrant is a gas, c^0 may be replaced by the partial pressure p, $\mathscr{S}$ is a constant,

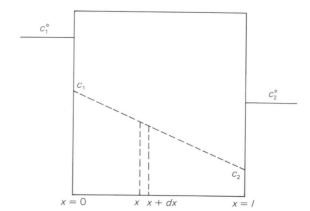

Fig. 15.7 Permeation through a solid results from a concentration gradient in the solid.

and Eq. (15.35) is called *Henry's law.* If the rate of transport is j_x at position x and $j_x + (\partial j_x/\partial x)\, dx$ at position $x + dx$, the rate of accumulation of penetrant at position x, $\partial c/\partial t$, is

$$\frac{\partial c}{\partial t} = -\left(\frac{\partial j_x}{\partial x}\right)$$

$$= \frac{\partial}{\partial x} D_{12} \frac{\partial c}{\partial x} \tag{15.36}$$

When the diffusion coefficient is independent of position, this reduces to Fick's second law of diffusion:

$$\frac{\partial c}{\partial t} = D_{12} \frac{\partial^2 c}{\partial x^2} \tag{15.37}$$

If, however, D_{12} is not constant but varies as a function of concentration, one must know the functional form of $D_{12}(c)$ to solve Eq. (15.36). For small concentration gradients or for a moderate concentration dependence, Fick's second law can be used with a mean value of D_{12} defined by

$$\langle D_{12} \rangle = \frac{\displaystyle\int_{c_1}^{c_2} D_{12}(c)\, dc}{\displaystyle\int_{c_1}^{c_2} dc} \tag{15.38}$$

For the special case of steady-state transport and constant D_{12}, $\partial c/\partial t = 0$, the flux is constant and Eq. (15.34) may be integrated to give

$$j_x \int_0^l dx = -D_{12} \int_{c_1}^{c_2} dc \tag{15.39}$$

$$j_x = D_{12} \frac{c_1 - c_2}{l} \tag{15.40}$$

and from Eq. (15.35)

$$j_x = D_{12}\mathscr{S} \frac{c_1{}^0 - c_2{}^0}{l} = P_c \frac{c_1{}^0 - c_2{}^0}{l} \tag{15.41}$$

The product $P_c = D_{12}\mathscr{S}$ is defined as the permeability constant for a given penetrant-material system and is generally reported in units of volume of penetrant passing through the material per unit time per unit area per unit concentration gradient. For gas transmission, for example, P_c can have units of cm³ STP/sec-cm²-mm Hg/mm thickness. Selected values of permeability constants and permeation rates for a few polymer-penetrant systems are given in Tables 15.7 to 15.9.

The temperature dependence of the solubility coefficient generally follows an Arrhenius-type relationship:

$$\mathscr{S} = \mathscr{S}_0 \exp\left(-\frac{\Delta H_s}{RT}\right) \tag{15.42}$$

where ΔH_s is the apparent heat of solution. The sorption process may be visualized as consisting of two stages: (1) A vacancy or "hole" must be formed on the surface of the material, which requires an absorption of energy. (2) A molecule from the environment must be transferred to the hole, with a subsequent release of energy when the Van der Waals bonds form between the penetrant molecule and the material. The heat of solution is the sum of these two effects. The amount of energy required for the first stage increases approximately in proportion to the cohesive energy density of the material and the volume of the hole required to accept the penetrant molecule. The energy given off in the second stage increases in proportion to the strength of the Van der Waals bonds that are formed. The light nonpolar gases such as He and H_2 thus have positive heats of solution, since the first-stage endothermic process outweighs the second-stage exothermic process (Table 15.10). For such gases, solubility increases with temperature. As the penetrant molecules become more polar and more polarizable, the second-stage interactions predominate, the heats of solution become negative (Table 15.10), and the solubilities decrease with increasing temperature. The magnitude of the solubility coefficient also depends on the properties of both the material and the penetrant. In general, it has been found that, for a given material, the logarithm of the

Table 15.7

Gas permeability through selected polymers *

P in cm³ STP/cm²-sec-cm Hg/mm $\times$ 10^{10}; ΔE_p in kcal/g mole; T in °C

Polymer	Hydrogen			Nitrogen			Oxygen			Carbon dioxide		
	T	P	ΔE_p	T	P	ΔE_p	T	P	ΔE_p	T	P	ΔE_p
Polybutadiene	25	420	6.6	25	64.5	8.2	25	191	7.1	25	1,380	5.2
Natural rubber	25	500	6.9	25	84.0	9.0	25	230	7.1	25	1,330	6.1
Polychloroprene	25	136	8.1	25	11.8	10.6	25	40	9.9	25	250	8.5
Butyl rubber	25	73	8.7	25	3.2	12.5	25	13	10.7	25	52	9.9
Polyethylene 0.922, g/cm³	25	86	8.2	30	20	11.7	30	55	10.3	30	265	8.2
Polyvinylchloride	30	36	1.9	30	0.4		30	1.2		30	10.2	0.99
Polyvinylidene chloride	28	0.76		30	0.01	16.8	30	0.05	15.9	30	0.29	12.3
Polyvinyl fluoride	25	3.5		25	0.042		25	0.2		25	0.9	
Polytrifluorochloro- ethylene	25	9.5	7.1	30	1.3	12.5	30	5.6	10.9	30	12.5	7.4
Polystyrene				25	3–80		25	15–250		25	75–370	
Acetal				30	0.22		30	3.8		30	19	
Nylon	25	10	8.1	30	0.2	11.2	30	0.38	10.4	30	1.6	9.7
Mylar	25	6	5.5	25	0.05	7.5	25	0.30	6.4	25	1.0	6.2
Polycarbonate	20	136		20	3		25	20		25	85	
Silicon rubber							25	5,000		25	28,000	

* Data from E. Baer (ed.), "Engineering Design for Plastics," p. 682, Reinhold Publishing Corporation, New York, 1964.

Table 15.8

Sorption and transmission of water in selected polymers [*]

Polymer	Percent H$_2$O 24-hr immersion, $\frac{1}{8}$-in. sample	T, °C	Transmission rate 90–95% RH, g/m²/24 hr/mil
Polybutadiene	0.05–0.5	40	680
Natural rubber	0.06–0.3	39	390
Polychloroprene	0.05–0.35	39	240
Butyl rubber	0.04–0.18	39	26
Polyethylene, 0.92 g/cm³	<0.01	39	28
Polyethylene, 0.96 g/cm³	<0.01	37	4
Polypropylene	0.005–0.03	38	8.7
Polyvinylchloride	0.03	38	32
Polyvinylidene chloride	<0.01	39	1.5–7
Polyvinylfluoride	<0.5	40	46
Polytrifluorochloroethylene	<0.01	40	5
Polytetrafluoroethylene	0.00	40	5
Polystyrene	0.03–0.3	39	133
Nylon 6-6	1.6–3.0	39	225
Mylar	0.03–2.5	39	30
Polycarbonate	0.35	20	31
Silicon rubber	0.1–0.15		
Cellophane	45–115	38	1,870

[*] Data from E. Baer, "Engineering Design for Plastics," p. 684, Reinhold Publishing Corporation, New York, 1964.

Table 15.9

Transmission rate of organic substances through selected polymers [*]
Transmission rate in gm/m²/24 hr/mil; T in °C

Polymer	Benzene		Carbon tetrachloride		Methanol		Acetone	
	T	j_x	T	j_x	T	j_x	T	j_x
Polyethylene, 0.92 g/cm³	23	7,700	21	9,500	23	20	24	300
Polyethylene, 0.96 g/cm³			23	1,500	23	3.3	23	5.3
Polychloroprene	25	550,000	25	335,000	25	2,710		
Mylar	35	4.3	35	1.7			35	20
Nylon 6-6			23	8.5	23	590		
Teflon FEP	40	8.6	40	0.43			25	13
Polyvinylacetate	20	23,000	30	9,000	20	11,000		
Cellophane MSAT	35	6.5	35	9.4			35	580

[*] Data from E. Baer, "Engineering Design for Plastics," p. 686, Reinhold Publishing Corporation, New York, 1964.

solubility coefficients increase linearly with the boiling points of the penetrants:

$$\log \mathscr{S} = A + BT_b \qquad (15.43)$$

where the constants A and B are functions of the material and the temperature.

The temperature dependence of the diffusion coefficient also follows an Arrhenius-type relationship:

$$D_{12} = D_0 \exp\left(-\frac{\Delta E_D}{RT}\right) \qquad (15.44)$$

where ΔE_D is the activation energy for the thermally activated diffusion of the penetrant from one position in the material to another. It should be related to the energy required to produce a large enough hole in the structure to permit the penetrant molecule to diffuse. The activation energy should thus be approximately proportional to the product of cohesive energy density and the volume of the penetrant molecule. As shown in Table 15.11, the activation energy for diffusion of a given molecule is higher in materials with higher cohesive energy density; also, the activation energy in a given material increases as the size of the penetrant molecule increases. There have been a number of theories relating activation energy to the properties of a material-penetrant system, but they are beyond the scope of this chapter.

The absolute magnitude of the diffusion coefficient also depends on the preexponential factor D_0. It has been shown by the theory of rate processes that this factor is related to the entropy change in going from the stable state to the activated state:

$$D_0 \doteq \frac{ekT}{h} l_0{}^2 \exp\frac{\Delta S_D}{R} \qquad (15.45)$$

Table 15.10

Solubility coefficients and heats of solution at 25°C *

($\mathscr{S}$ in cm^3 (STP)/cm^3 polymer-atm $\times 10^2$; ΔH_s in kcal/g mole)

Gas	Natural rubber $\mathscr{S}$	ΔH_s	Polyisobutylene $\mathscr{S}$	ΔH_s
He	1.1	1.8	1.1	1.8
H_2	3.9	0.8	3.4	0.6
O_2	9.9	−0.8	10.7	−1.2
CO_2	90	−2.8	69	−2.1
C_2H_2	162	−2.2	63	−1.2

* Data from G. J. Van Amerongen, *J. Polymer Sci.*, **5:** 307 (1950); *J. Appl. Phys.*, **17:** 972 (1946).

where l_0 is the length of the diffusion path and ΔS_D is the entropy of activation. In Table 15.11, one may observe that D_0 generally increases with the size of the penetrant molecule. This may be interpreted as the penetrant molecule causing a greater disturbance of the surrounding molecules when it is activated for a diffusional jump.

The temperature dependence of the permeability constant may also be expressed as an Arrhenius-type relationship:

$$P = P_0 \exp\left(-\frac{\Delta E_P}{RT}\right) = D_0 \mathcal{S}_0 \exp\left(-\frac{\Delta E_D + \Delta H_s}{RT}\right) \qquad (15.46)$$

Since the heat of solution can be either positive or negative, the permeability coefficient could either increase or decrease with temperature; usually the activation energy for diffusion predominates and the permeation increases with temperature.

Equation (15.46) implies that a plot of $\log P$ versus $1/T$ would be a straight line. This is normally the case when D_{12} and $\mathcal{S}$ are independent of the concentration of the penetrant in the material, such as for noncondensable, nonpolar gases in organic polymers. On the other hand, condensable gases and liquids often have a high solubility in organic polymers and do not conform to Fickian diffusion [Eq. (15.34)] or Henry's law [Eq. (15.35)]. In these cases the behavior is highly nonlinear. Under certain conditions $d \log P/d(1/T)$ might even change sign.

Permeability is an important factor in the chemical resistance of polymers. From the experimental data presented in Tables 15.7 to 15.11, one can develop a physical picture of the permeation process. The surface of the polymer is exposed to a penetrating substance. Sorption of the penetrant occurs until an equilibrium is established at the interface. The penetrant molecules then diffuse into the bulk of the material by a series of thermally activated jumps. A trapped penetrant molecule has a tendency to vibrate about a fixed position in the material. It is held in this position by the surrounding polymer chains. The polymer chains are also in a continual state of vibration, oscillation, and

---

Table 15.11

Diffusion coefficients and activation energies at 30°C
(D_0 in cm^2/sec; ΔE_D in kcal/g mole)

Polymer	He D_0	He ΔE_D	N$_2$ D_0	N$_2$ ΔE_D	CO$_2$ D_0	CO$_2$ ΔE_D	n-Butane D_0	n-Butane ΔE_D	n-Pentane D_0	n-Pentane ΔE_D
Natural rubber			2.9	8.7	3.6	8.9	7.4	10.8	174	12.5
Polyisobutylene			18	11.7	2.2	11.7	250	16.7	63	16.0
cis-4 Polybutadiene	0.017	4.14	0.076	5.98						
Ameripol 1502	0.23	5.66	2.3	8.60						
(86 mole % butadiene, 14% styrene)										

rotation. When the chains surrounding a penetrant molecule coordinate their motion in such a way as to open up a "hole" in the structure, the penetrant molecule is freed for motion to another point in the structure. When the chains come back to a closer-packed arrangement, the penetrant molecule could be trapped at a different lattice site. This random thermal process continues until the penetrant molecule is transported out of the material. Any molecular properties that inhibit the thermal motion of the polymer chains or make it difficult for the penetrant molecule to move freely in the material or limit the solubility of the penetrant will tend to improve the resistance of the material to the permeating substance.

From this physical picture it is easier to rationalize the behavior of polymer-penetrant systems. Permeability generally increases with similarity between components, since solubility increases. Nonpolar hydrocarbons, for example, have a higher permeability through polyethylene than polar materials. Chemical modification of a polymer can also affect the permeability of a given substance. Thus, the introduction of polar groups on a rubber molecule reduces permeability by virtue of increasing the cohesive energy density. Increased cross-link density or crystallinity will almost always lead to greater permeation resistance by making it less likely that coordinated motion of polymer chains will lead to the formation of a large enough hole for a diffusion jump of the penetrant. High cross-link density and crystallinity can also restrict segment mobility, thereby increasing the activation energy. There is a great deal of experimental data in the literature on specific systems, but no general theory which successfully ties together all of these factors.

References

1 Bruins, P. F. (ed.): "Plasticizer Technology," vol. 1, Reinhold Publishing Corporation, New York, 1965. *Chapters 1 and 2 are excellent surveys of compatibility and plasticization.*

2 Ehlers, G. F. L.: Thermal Stability, in E. Baer (ed.): "Engineering Design for Plastics," chap. 6, Reinhold Publishing Corporation, New York, 1964.

3 Evans, U. R.: "An Introduction to Metallic Corrosion," Edward Arnold (Publishers) Ltd., London, 1963. *A concise, easily read presentation of the subject. An excellent introduction for both students and researchers.*

4 Flory, P. J.: "Principles of Polymer Chemistry," Cornell University Press, Ithaca, N.Y., 1953. *Chapters 12 and 13 are discussions of the statistical thermodynamics of polymer solutions and the origin of the interaction parameter.*

5 Guy, A. G.: "Elements of Physical Metallurgy," Addison-Wesley Publishing Company, Inc., Reading, Mass., 1959. *Chapters 10 and 11 are discussions of corrosion and oxidation at about the same level as this text.*

6 Hildebrand, J. H., and R. L. Scott: "The Solubility of Nonelectrolytes," 3d ed., Dover Publications, Inc., New York, 1964. *A standard reference text on solution theory. Contains discussions on solubility parameters, interaction parameters, simple solutions, metallic solutions, and polymer solutions.*

7 Jastrzebski, Z. D.: "Nature and Properties of Engineering Materials," John Wiley & Sons, Inc., New York, 1959. *Chapter 9 gives an unusually clear and concise discussion of corrosion principles. An excellent introduction for undergraduates.*

8 Kubaschewski, O., and B. Hopkins: "Oxidation of Metals and Alloys," Butterworth & Co. (Publishers), Ltd., London, 1953.

9 LaQue, F. L. (supervisor): "Corrosion in Action," The International Nickel Co., New York, 1955. *A well-illustrated, easily read introduction to corrosion. It is the narrative for a motion picture of the same name.*

10 Uhlig, H. H.: "Corrosion and Corrosion Control," John Wiley & Sons, Inc., New York, 1963. *A comprehensive text on corrosion principles and their application to engineering problems.*

11 Uhlig, H. H.: "Corrosion Handbook," John Wiley & Sons, Inc., New York, 1948. *Presents detailed information on all aspects of corrosion for a wide variety of engineering materials.*

Questions

15.1 Fick's first law of diffusion states that the steady flux of a given component in a homogeneous medium is directly proportional to the concentration gradient of the component in the medium: $j_A = \mathscr{D}_A \, dc_A/dx$. Suppose an adherent, continuous oxide film is being formed on the surface of a metal. Assume that metal ions diffuse in steady state (the concentration gradient is linear) through the oxide layer and instantly react when they reach the air-oxide interface. Further assume that the ion concentration is c_0 at the metal-oxide interface and zero at the oxide-air interface. Show that at constant temperature a parabolic growth law is followed.

15.2 In terms of atomic and ionic radii, explain why magnesium, potassium, and sodium form nonprotective, porous oxide films.

15.3 Explain why aluminum is more resistant to oxidation than iron.

15.4 Short-time data are given for the thickness of an adherent oxide film for the oxidation of a metal (Table 15.12).

Table 15.12

Time, min	Oxide layer thickness, Å	Time, min	Oxide layer thickness, Å
0	0	120	1,230
10	230	150	1,370
30	540	180	1,480
60	850	240	1,660
90	1,050		

Calculate the thickness of the layer after 1 day, 1 month, 1 year, and 10 years.

15.5 If polyethylene is held at 120°C for a period of time, its maximum viscosity decreases with time and infrared analysis shows the presence of carbonyl, carboxyl, and hydroxyl units. Describe the chemical processes that are occurring. Continued exposure causes the material to become partially insoluble. Explain.

15.6 Natural rubber and polybutadiene are considerably more susceptible to oxidation than polyethylene. Explain.

15.7 Calculate the electromotive force in a Daniell cell when the activities of both the zinc and copper ions are 1.000. What is the electromotive force when the copper-ion concentration is decreased to 0.01 normal?

15.8 Chromates, tungstates, and other complex ions of the transition elements are used as inhibitors in radiators and boilers. Explain why they are effective in inhibiting corrosion.

15.9 Stainless steel is highly resistant to atmospheric corrosion but rapidly deteriorates in the presence of HCl or HF. Explain.

15.10 The most corrosion-resistant stainless steels are those with high chromium and very low carbon content. Explain.

15.11 Sodium sulfite (Na_2SO_3) is frequently added to aqueous solutions in order to make them less corrosive. Explain why it works.

15.12 A magnesium bar is often submerged in water tanks or condensers in order to protect the structure from corrosion. Explain why it works. Can you suggest other methods for accomplishing the same thing?

15.13 Wire screen will corrode at the points of contact between the wires. Explain why.

15.14 Derive an expression [Eq. (15.26)] for the heat of mixing of two similar species. Assume random mixing.

15.15 Table 15.13 gives the volume of solvent imbibed per unit volume of lightly cross-linked polymer (i.e., the degree of swelling) for natural rubber and polyethylene in a variety of solvents. Calculate the solubility parameters and compare with the results using the empirical method of Small. Discuss the results. Why does polyethylene swell to such a small extent relative to natural rubber?

Table 15.13

Solvent	δ_S, $(cal/cm^3)^{1/2}$	Q, $\dfrac{volume\ solvent}{volume\ polymer}$	
		Natural rubber	Polyethylene
n-Pentane	7.05	1.12	0.21
n-Hexane	7.30	1.18	0.28
n-Heptane	7.45		0.31
Cyclohexane	8.20		0.40
Limolene	8.50	4.00	
Carbon tetrachloride	8.65		0.40
m-Xylene	8.80	4.15	0.29
Toluene	8.90	4.10	0.25
Benzene	9.15	3.90	0.22

15.16 Ether-alcohol mixtures are good solvents for nitrocellulose. What would probably be the best combination of diethylether ($\delta_S = 7.4$) and ethanol ($\delta_S = 12.7$) for a nitrocellulose polymer with $\delta_P = 11.5$?

16
Surface properties

16.1
Introduction

At an interface between two phases or between two grains of a crystalline material, the atomic arrangement changes abruptly. The mass of material within a few atomic layers on either side of the interface is not in a state of minimum free energy and, therefore, is not in a true equilibrium state. This excess free energy, termed surface energy, causes the atoms in these areas to behave quite differently from the rest of the material. Many examples of the behavior of both external and internal (i.e., grain boundaries) surfaces have been qualitatively discussed in prior chapters. Nucleation, solid-state transformations, intergranular corrosion, fatigue strength, and dielectric strength are characteristics that are all, in one way or another, influenced by the nature of surfaces in the material. To this list we may add other properties which are determined completely by the nature of the surface. Two of these, frictional resistance and adhesive character, will be discussed in this chapter.

There are two kinds of characteristics that determine surface properties. On a microstructural level, the shape and contour of the surface are important. One may visualize even the smoothest of surfaces as a continuous plane of hills and valleys, the dimensions of which may vary from hundreds to thousands of angstroms. Properties such as frictional resistance depend on the fine details of the shape and contour. On an atomic level, it is the surface energy or "surface tension" that is of major importance. At a solid-gas interface, for example, the atoms on the surface of the solid are strongly attracted to the dense array of atoms in the solid phase but are weakly attracted to the atoms in the dilute-gas phase. This imbalance of forces causes the surface atoms to be pulled toward the solid in such a way that the surface energy is minimized. Since the crystal structure is different at the surface, and since the lattice within the material is already in its equilibrium state, the minimum energy state for the surface is higher than that for the lattice. This excess energy, called *surface energy* or *surface tension,* is a function of the molecular orientation on both sides of the interface. Of course, considerable surface energy can also exist at liquid-solid, liquid-gas, liquid-liquid, and solid-solid (grain boundary) interfaces.

In this chapter we shall discuss the nature of these characteristics and consider the effects on two very important properties of materials, namely, frictional resistance and adhesion.

16.2
Surface energy

Surface energy is related to the work required to increase the area of a surface. Consider a unit area of soap film on a movable wire frame as shown in Fig. 16.1. In order to hold the movable wire in place, a force $2\gamma_{SV}$ newtons/m (dynes/cm) of wire must be applied. In order to move the 1-m wire a distance dx to the left, an energy $2\gamma_{SV} \times 1 \, dx$ joules must be expended. Since there are two air-soap interfaces, this increases the total interfacial area by an amount $2 \times 1 \, dx$ m². The total energy expended per unit area of new interface is thus $2\gamma_{SV} \, dx/2 \, dx = \gamma_{SV}$ joules/m². The total force on the movable wire results from a tension between the air-soap interface so that a surface tension of γ_{SV} newtons/m is associated with each unit area of surface. This illustrates the numerical equivalence of surface tension in newtons per meter (dynes per centimeter) and "free" surface energy in joules per square meter (ergs per square centimeter). The numerical equivalence is important, since surface tension is

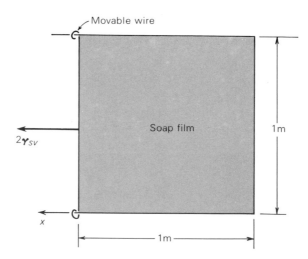

Movable wire

$2\gamma_{SV}$

Soap film

1m

x

1m

Fig. 16.1 The surface tension of the soap film causes a resistance to the motion of the movable wire.

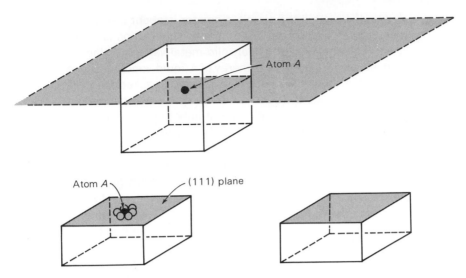

Fig. 16.2   The formation of a solid-vapor interface with the (111) plane is equivalent to a cleavage along that plane.

generally measured experimentally, while surface-free energy is the important quantity in making thermodynamic calculations.

Since the equilibrium state at constant temperature and pressure is the one with the lowest free energy, a system will always tend to minimize its surface area. The formation of spherical drops of mercury is an example of this. While these conclusions are generally true for isotropic fluids, they are not necessarily true for solid surfaces. The atoms of crystalline solids, for example, are constrained to a specific lattice geometry. The surface tension is then an anisotropic quantity which is dependent upon the types of crystallographic planes that make up the interface. Since a small extension of a solid interface may change the geometry, the surface tension may not be independent of the surface area. This means that surface tension and surface energy are not always numerically equal. Generally, this reservation is important only at very low temperatures.

The magnitude of the surface tension may be roughly estimated by considering the atomic structure on either side of the interface. Consider the unit cube of a face-centered cubic crystal shown in Fig. 16.2. An atom A in the center of the cube has 12 nearest neighbors. If the cube is split in the close-packed (111) plane containing atom A, two unit surfaces will be formed. Atom A will then be bonded to only nine nearest neighbors in the solid phase and to approximately none in the vapor phase. Thus, three chemical bonds per atom are broken in forming the surfaces. Since there are two unit areas formed, there are three-halves of a broken bond per atom per unit area of surface. Similarly, sublimation of atom A from the surface requires the breaking of the remaining nine nearest-neighbor bonds. Thus, the surface energy per atom should be of the order of three-eighteenths of the heat of sublimation per atom.

For a typical strongly bonded crystal, the atomic diameter is about 3 Å, giving about 9×10^{-20} m² of surface per atom, and the heat of sublimation is about 80 kcal/g mole. The surface energy of a typical solid metal-vapor interface is thus of the order of 1.0 joule/m². The surface energy of a liquid-vapor interface must be less than this, since the liquid phase is less closely packed than the crystalline solid. For many crystals, the density decreases 5 to 10 percent on melting. This means that the average coordination number in the liquid is of the order of eleven-twelfths of that for the crystal. The surface energy of the liquid surface is thus of the order of 0.9 joule/m².

Similarly, the formation of a solid-liquid interface involves a transition from a coordination number of 12 to 11. The solid-liquid interface thus has a surface energy of about one-twelfth of that of the solid-vapor interface, or, for the typical strongly bonded material, of the order of 0.10 joule/m². These estimates are generally of the right order for most simple crystals which are bonded by short-range, high-energy chemical bonds.

A more exact calculation of surface energy may be made if the potential energy of interaction between two particles is known. Then, the total surface energy may be equated to the work W done in mechanically separating a crystal into two parts:

$$W = \int_{a_0}^{\infty} F \, da = \int_{a_0}^{\infty} \frac{d\psi_T}{da} \, da$$

$$= (\psi_T)_{a=\infty} - (\psi_T)_{a=a_0}$$

$$= (-\psi_T)_{a=a_0} \qquad (16.1)$$

where a_0 is the equilibrium separation between the cleaved planes and ψ_T is the potential energy of interaction per unit area between the two planes. As was shown in Chap. 11, the potential energy is related to the elastic modulus of the solid [Eqs. (11.3) to (11.6)]. If the total work in separating a unit cross section results in two unit surfaces,

$$\gamma_{SV} = \frac{W}{2} \doteq \frac{E_{[hkl]} a_0}{2mn} \qquad (16.2)$$

For most crystals, $9 < m < 18$, $1 < n < 6$,

$$\gamma_{SV} \doteq \left(\frac{1}{20} - \frac{1}{200} \right) E_{[hkl]} a_0 \qquad (16.3)$$

Since Young's modulus and the interplanar distance are known from other sources, the surface tension can be estimated. Table 16.1 shows a comparison of theoretical and experimental values for a variety of ionic and metallic materials, using a numerical constant of ¼₀. In general, the agreement is good.

The surface energy has been equated to the mechanical work required to form a surface at constant temperature and pressure. Thermodynamically speaking, this is numerically equal to the Gibbs free energy of the surface:

Table 16.1

Comparison of theoretical and experimental values of surface energies

Crystal	Experimental * γ_{SV}, joules/m^2	Calculated γ_{SV}, joules/m^2
NaCl	0.300	0.310
LiF	0.340	0.370
MgO	1.200	1.300
CaF_2	0.450	0.540
BaF_2	0.280	0.350
$CaCO_3$	0.230	0.380
Si	1.240	0.890
Zn	0.105	0.185
Fe (3% Si)	1.360(?)	1.400

*From J. J. Gilman, *J. Appl. Phys.*, **31:** 2208 (1960).

$$\gamma_{SV} = \Delta G_{SV} = \Delta H_{SV} - T \, \Delta S_{SV}$$

$$= \Delta H_{SV} + T \left(\frac{\partial \Delta G_{SV}}{\partial T} \right)_p$$

$$= \Delta H_{SV} + T \left(\frac{\partial \gamma_{SV}}{\partial T} \right)_p \tag{16.4}$$

In general, surface tension decreases with increasing temperature, since $-(d\gamma_{SV}/dT)_p = \Delta S_{SV}$. A particle on the surface, having fewer chemical bonds than within the crystal lattice, tends to vibrate with a lower characteristic frequency. Since the number of vibrational levels is roughly $3RT/h\nu$, there are more vibrational states on the surface, more ways of randomly distributing the states, and therefore, a higher entropy. Typically, $\Delta S_{SV} \doteq 4 \times 10^{-4}$ joules/°K-m^2 for a solid-vapor interface. The surface enthalpy is thus somewhat higher than the surface tension.

16.3
Shape and contour of solid surfaces

Certain properties, such as frictional resistance, adsorption, and adhesion, are strongly dependent on the contours of the contacting surfaces. Even the most highly polished surfaces are extremely rough on an atomic scale. A finely ground, superfinished silver plate, for example, may have surface asperities of the order of 100 to 1,000 Å, while a finely ground steel surface may have asperities of the order of 1,000 to 10,000 Å. Since the distance between atomic planes is generally of the order of 2 to 5 Å, this corresponds to some pretty large irregularities. When two such surfaces are placed together (Fig. 16.3), contact occurs only at the tips of the matching asperities, while over the remainder of the surfaces there may be gaps of hundreds to thousands of angstroms. Since intermolecular forces are very short-range, generally effective over about 10 Å or less, there is molecular interaction between surfaces only at these points of contact. Various experimental measurements have shown that intimate contact occurs over only a minute fraction of the apparent area [2,10].

An estimate of the real area of contact can be made by a very simple analysis. Assume that a typical point of contact can be represented by a portion of a sphere of radius r resting on a locally flat surface, as shown in Fig. 16.4a. When a load is applied, the contacting surfaces first elastically deform until a certain yield stress is reached, and then plastic deformation occurs. The final geometry might look like Fig. 16.4b. On a macroscopic scale, this is almost identical with the geometry that prevails in a Brinell hardness test, in which a hardened steel or tungsten carbide ball is placed on the surface of a sample. A load is chosen to produce an indentation that can be conveniently measured under a microscope, and the area of the indentation is calculated. A hardness test measures the resistance of a material to plastic yielding in compression, and it is reported in units of force per unit area, or *yield pressure.* The yield pressure of a ductile material in a Brinell hardness test is approximately constant (i.e., independent of total deformation) and is approximately equal to three times the 0.2 percent yield stress of a standard tension test [10].

$$s_H \doteq 3s_y \tag{16.5}$$

For a number of commercially important alloys it is also about 0.9 percent of the Young's modulus:

$$s_H \doteq 0.009E_Y \tag{16.6}$$

Thus, we assume that when two asperities on adjacent surfaces come together,

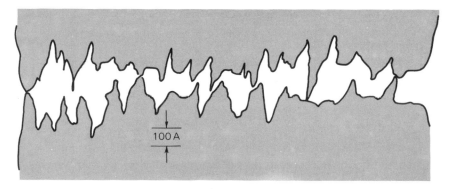

Fig. 16.3 Because of roughness on a submicroscopic scale, only a small fraction of the contacting surfaces exhibit solid-to-solid contact, even on finely ground surfaces.

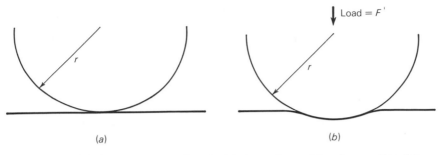

Fig. 16.4 A model for the points of contact between two solid surfaces. Also, the geometry of a Brinell hardness test. (a) Sphere resting on flat surface; (b) sphere pressed into surface by a force F.

they plastically deform until the area of contact is sufficient to support the yield pressure of the material. The real area of contact of a single junction, a_R, is then

$$a_R \doteq \frac{F_1}{s_H} \tag{16.7}$$

where F_1 is the load on the single junction. If there are n such junctions per unit area of apparent surface, the total real area of contact, A_R, is then

$$na_R = A_R \doteq \frac{nF_1}{s_H} - \frac{F_T}{s_H} \tag{16.8}$$

where F_T is the total load on the surface. Since the yield pressure is approximately constant, the real area of contact between two surfaces is directly proportional to the load and is independent of the apparent size and shape of the contacting surfaces. These two facts will be important in our discussion of frictional laws in the next section.

One can see from Eq. (16.8) that only a minute fraction of the total surface is actually in contact for reasonable loadings. For example, an alloy steel has a Young's modulus of about 2.1×10^{10} kg$_w$/m² (30×10^6 psi) and a yield pressure of about $0.009E_Y$ or $s_H = 1.9 \times 10^8$ kg$_w$/m² (2.7×10^5 psi). A 1- by 1- by 1-in. cube, weighing about 0.27 lb, exerts 0.27 psi on the flat surface. The real area of contact is $0.27/2.7 \times 10^5 = 10^{-6}$ in.² per square inch of apparent contact area. Thus, only a minute fraction of the surface is actually supporting the load. Even when the cube is pressed against the flat surface with a pressure of 2,700 psi, the actual contact area is only one-hundredth of the total surface.

The above arguments have been well substantiated in experiments on ductile materials. When the solid surfaces either are unusually smooth or do not plastically deform, however, the real area of contact is often considerably higher than predicted by Eq. (16.8) and is not always proportional to the load. This is the case with ultra-highly polished surfaces of metals, with hard, nonyielding materials such as diamond, and with elastomers, which show very large elastic deformation. Such materials also show unusual frictional properties.

The surface roughness may either be defined as the average distance between high and low points on a surface (Fig. 16.3) or as the ratio of the true overall area to the nominal projected area. We shall next consider two measuring techniques that are commonly used to determine the surface roughness.

One method of determining the average height of ridges and visually examining the surface contours is the use of a needle profile meter. A diamond stylus with a rounded tip (the radius of curvature is typically 0.001 mm or 100 μin.) is moved across a surface and its vertical movements are amplified electrically and recorded. A pen recording will give a picture of surface undulations with a resolution of about 10^{-5} mm (1μ in.) in the vertical direction. Because the tip is relatively large, however, its horizontal resolution is poor, in that it cannot detect very sudden sharp irregularities.

The adsorption of gases on a solid surface is a method of determining the true overall area of the solid. When gas molecules are adsorbed, the process occurs in such a way that a complete monolayer, covering every site on the surface, forms before a second layer starts. Subsequent layers build on top of the first in a somewhat different manner. It is possible to determine when adsorption of the first layer is complete and thus how many gas molecules are required to form the monolayer. Since the gas molecules have diameters of the order of 3 to 5 Å, they can penetrate into every crevice and microcrack on the surface. Since the molecular diameter is known and the weight of the monolayer can be measured, the total overall area can be calculated. It has been found that a rough metal surface may have a total area that is as much as three times as great as its projected area.

16.4
Frictional resistance

Friction is the resistance to motion which exists when two contacting surfaces move relative to each other. The force necessary to start the motion is called *static friction,* while the force necessary to maintain a steady relative motion is called *kinetic friction.* There are two aspects of friction that are important in engineering practice. One is the fact that energy must be expended to overcome frictional losses. The reduction of friction through the use of suitable materials and lubricants is a continuing engineering problem. The second aspect is that friction generally leads to wear and sometimes leads to seizure and extensive damage. This is one of the limiting factors in determining the useful life of a machine with moving parts.

Frictional resistance can be quantitatively described by the following three laws:

1. The total frictional force F_f tangential to a surface is directly proportional to the force normal to the surface.

$$F_f = \beta_{sf} F \qquad\qquad (16.9)$$

The coefficient of friction, β_{Sf}, is a constant which is also equal to the tangent of the frictional angle θ:

$$\beta_{Sf} = \tan \theta \qquad (16.10)$$

The frictional angle is the maximum angle of an inclined plane such that an object, regardless of its weight, placed on the plane will remain stationary (Fig. 16.5).

2. The frictional force is independent of the apparent area of contact. Thus, a multisided object has the same coefficient of friction regardless of which of its surfaces it is lying on, and, likewise, large and small objects of the same material have the same coefficient of friction.

3. Kinetic friction is very nearly independent of the relative velocity of the two surfaces.

The first two laws are followed very closely by most ductile materials. Exceptions occur with very hard, clean surfaces and with elastomers. In these cases the deformation at the points of contact is elastic, rather than plastic, and the real area of contact is not proportional to the load [Eq. (16.8)]. An analysis based on elastic deformation shows that the frictional force will depend on the load in the following way:

$$F_f = \beta_{Sf} F^x \qquad (16.11)$$

where x is generally in the range of $2/3$ to 1. Another way to look at this is to say that the coefficient of friction is a function of the load:

$$\beta_{SF} = \beta_{Sf} F^{x-1} = \frac{F_f}{F} \qquad (16.12)$$

Viscoelastic solids also tend to follow Eq. (16.12) for similar reasons. Another

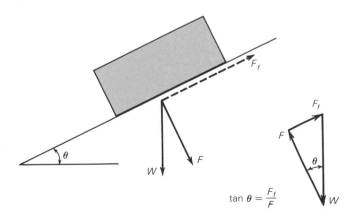

Fig. 16.5 Equilibrium diagram for an object of weight W on an inclined plane.

exception occurs when hard, friable surface oxides are formed on soft metals. With copper, for example, the oxide on oxide has a coefficient of friction of about 0.4, while the pure metal on metal has a coefficient of about 1.6. At small loads the oxide layer remains protective and the friction is low, while at higher loads the oxide layer is penetrated and the friction approaches that of the pure metal on metal. Thus, the frictional coefficient varies with the load.

The third law is a little less specific than the first two. In general, it is found that the kinetic friction tends to be lower than the static friction and for high sliding speeds tends to decrease with increasing velocity. The effect is usually mild with metals, the frictional coefficient decreasing with the $1/10$ to $1/20$ power of the sliding velocity. The mechanism is more complex with polymers, since the deformation of the surface is highly viscoelastic. The friction thus varies with geometry, load, and rate of loading.

The laws of friction are qualitatively explained by recognizing that two solid surfaces are in contact only on a minute fraction of the total surface. These points of contact form adhering junctions through plastic deformation. Since the yield pressure of the junctions is relatively constant, the real area of contact is proportional to the load [Eq. (16.8)]. If one visualizes the resistance to friction as the shearing of these junctions, the shear strength being approximately the bulk shear strength of the softest material making up the junction, then the frictional resistance should be proportional to the real area of contact and thus proportional to the load. If the bulk shear strength is τ_y,

$$F_f = \tau_y A_R = \frac{\tau_y}{s_H} F \qquad\qquad (16.13)$$

or

$$\beta_{Sf} = \frac{\tau_y}{s_H} \qquad\qquad (16.14)$$

For most materials, the yield strength in shear is one-half the yield strength in tension, and since $s_H \doteq 3s_y$,

$$\beta_{Sf} \doteq \frac{1/2 s_y}{3 s_y} \doteq 1/6$$

$$\doteq 0.167 \qquad\qquad (16.15)$$

which says that all ductile materials should have a coefficient of friction of about $1/6$. As shown in Table 16.2, this is not nearly true, but it is significant that a wide variety of materials, whose strength and hardness vary over orders of magnitude, have similar coefficients of friction. The independence of the frictional force on the apparent area of contact is clear, since it is the real area of contact that controls the interaction. As was discussed previously, the real area of contact is a function of load and yield pressure but is independent of the apparent area of contact. The weak dependence of kinetic friction on sliding

Table 16.2

Static friction of materials *

Material	β_{sf}
Metals, pure, sliding in a vacuum of $<10^{-6}$ mm Hg:	>100
In air, unlubricated	1
Lubricated with animal, vegetable oil	0.1
Alloys, sliding on steel:	
Copper-lead unlubricated	0.2
Copper-lead lubricated	0.1
Phosphor bronze, brass, unlubricated	0.35
Phosphor bronze, brass, lubricated	0.15–0.20
Cast iron unlubricated	0.4
Cast iron lubricated	0.1–0.2
Hard steel surfaces with lubricants:	
Unlubricated	0.6
Vegetable and animal oils	0.08–0.10
Mineral oils	0.14–0.20
Graphitized oils	0.12
Molybdenum disulfide	0.1
Glass on glass:	
Clean	1.0
Liquid hydrocarbons	0.3–0.6
Solid hydrocarbons	0.1
Tungsten carbide on self:	
Clean	0.20–0.25
Lubricated	0.1–0.2
Plastics:	
Polythene on self, clean	0.8
Polythene on steel, clean	0.3–0.5
Nylon on self	0.5
Polytetrafluoroethylene on self	0.04–0.1
Polytetrafluoroethylene on steel	0.04–0.1
Wood on self, clean, dry	0.25–0.5
Wood on self, clean, wet	0.2
Leather on metal, clean, dry	0.6
Leather on metal, clean, greasy	0.2
Brake material on cast iron:	
Clean	0.4
Wet	0.2
Greasy	0.1

* Data from Ref. 3.

velocity is expected, since the bulk shear strength of most solids is relatively insensitive to rate of loading. Viscoelastic solids, whose strength is more strongly dependent on rate of strain, also exhibit a more pronounced dependence of the frictional force on sliding velocity.

The main contribution to frictional resistance comes from the shearing of the contact junctions. Two other factors, however, have a noticeable effect on the overall resistance. One factor is that of surface roughness. When two very rough surfaces slide past one another, an additional frictional resistance is encountered because of the need to lift one surface over an asperity on the other. This is equivalent to sliding a body up an incline and is thus proportional to the tangent of the angle of incline. Since a given junction will go down inclines as well as go up them as it slides along a surface, the roughness effect does tend to cancel itself. Although the frictional force is relatively insensitive to roughness, very rough surfaces do show a higher coefficient of friction. At the other end of the roughness spectrum, very smooth surfaces have much greater coefficients of friction because the real area of contact becomes greater than would be expected from Eq. (16.8). Then the friction mechanism is strongly influenced by the elastic properties as well as by the plastic properties of the solid.

The second factor involves the "plowing" out of a softer material by the asperities of a harder one. When the sharp edge of a hard asperity slides over a soft surface, it tends to dig into the softer surface and produce a groove. The required energy of deformation causes the frictional force to be larger. Generally, the combination of these two factors rarely exceeds 10 percent of the total frictional resistance, the remainder being true shearing of the junctions. Under certain conditions, however, as in the sanding of a surface, the roughness and plowing effects can become much larger.

It is common knowledge that it is much easier to roll a spherical or cylindrical surface over a flat one than it is to slide one past the other. The frictional resistance to rolling (i.e., *rolling friction*) is normally orders of magnitude less than sliding friction, corresponding to coefficients of rolling friction of the order of 10^{-3} to 10^{-5}. The frictional resistance is a function of load and the diameter of the rolling surface d:

$$F_R = \beta_{SR} \frac{F^n}{d^m} = \frac{(\beta_{SR})_0 F^{n-1}}{d^m} F \qquad (16.16)$$

where n is a constant which normally ranges from 1.2 to 2.4 and m is a constant which normally ranges from 1.5 to 1.7. Generally, the coefficient of rolling friction is lower for smoother surfaces than for rougher ones and the static friction force is greater than the kinetic. Rolling friction is caused by elastic deformation of the contacting surfaces, with the major portion of the energy dissipation arising from elastic hysteresis. Thus, materials with high damping capacities, such as rubber, have high coefficients of rolling friction.

16.5
Wear

The most important consequence of the continual moving of one surface over another is wear. Wear is defined as the removal of material from a solid surface as the result of mechanical action. In many instances very minute amounts of wear can totally disable a complex piece of machinery. The cylinders in an automobile engine, for example, are generally machined to within $\frac{1}{50}$ mm. The continual relative motion of the piston in the cylinder will, in time, wear away the cylinder walls. When the dimensions have changed by about $\frac{1}{4}$ mm, the engine will not operate properly. This means that the loss of only a couple of grams of mass from an object that weighs a thousand or more kilograms can disable it. Fortunately, when properly designed equipment is functioning well, the rates of wear can be very low. Wear in useful machines is, in fact, characterized by small changes at very low rates.

There are a number of operations, such as the polishing of surfaces and the sharpening of tools, that utilize the wear phenomenon in a useful way. Generally, however, wear is thought of as an *unintentional* removal of material from a surface and harmful to the material.

There is no direct relationship between frictional properties and the amount of wear. There are four main processes causing wear, and each conforms to its own laws. The usual situation is that several processes interact in a complex fashion, so that it is often impossible to sort out the individual effects. Needless to say, there are no generally accepted laws of wear at present, but some work has been done to untangle the picture.

The four main types of wear are classified as adhesive, abrasive, corrosive, and surface fatigue wear. *Adhesive wear* occurs when two surfaces slide over each other and fragments are pulled off one surface and adhere to the other. These fragments can either be transferred back to the original surface or else fall off. This generally occurs because of the strong adhesion at the interface of a junction. When a junction forms, strong interactions between atoms on adjacent surfaces reduce the surface energy sufficiently to form a cohesive mass. When the contact is broken, there is always a small but finite chance that the break will occur within one of the materials rather than at the interface. Thus, adhesive wear is the fragmentation of the tips of asperities on the surface. It can be shown that the volume of material fragmented by adhesive wear when sliding through a distance x is given by

$$V_{AW} = \frac{k_{AW}Fx}{3s_H} \qquad (16.17)$$

Thus, the amount of wear is directly proportional to the load and amount of sliding and is inversely proportional to the yield pressure of the material. The constant k_{AW} is a measure of the rate at which wear occurs at a pair of surfaces. Values of k_{AW} are given in Table 16.3 for a few combinations. In general, the lowest rate of wear is obtained by using dissimilar materials with hard surfaces. This tends to minimize the adhesive interaction and make fragmentation more difficult.

Abrasive wear occurs when a hard, rough surface slides against a softer one and removes material by plowing and gouging. This is called two-body abrasion. Abrasive wear may also occur when hard abrasive particles are introduced between two softer sliding surfaces and the abrasive grains gouge both sliding surfaces. This is called three-body abrasion.

Two-body abrasion can be described by Eq. (16.17). The abrasive wear constant is strongly dependent on the roughness of the hard surface and for most metals is of the order of 10^{-6} to 10^{-3}. This type of wear has been practically eliminated in machinery by using smooth finishes on hard surfaces. Two-body abrasion is, of course, *utilized* in files, abrasive paper, and abrasive wheels.

Three-body abrasion may also be described by Eq. (16.17). The wear constant, in this case, is strongly dependent on the amount, size, shape, and hardness of the abrading particles and is generally of the order of 10^{-3}. This type of wear is almost impossible to eliminate completely, since dust and oxidized debris cannot be totally eliminated from a machine or its environment. The extent of abrasive damage, however, is generally much less severe than adhesive wear. Three-body abrasion is utilized in lapping and polishing operations.

Corrosive wear occurs when the sliding surfaces chemically interact with the environment, and the sliding action wears off the reaction products. The formation of protective oxide layers on exposed metal surfaces is typical. In the

Table 16.3

Wear constants for various surfaces *

Combination	$k_{AW} \times 10^3$
Zinc on zinc	160
Low-carbon steel on low-carbon steel	45
Copper on copper	32
Stainless steel on stainless steel	21
Copper on low-carbon steel	1.5
Low-carbon steel on copper	0.5
Bakelite on bakelite (phenolic)	0.02

* Ref. 10, p. 139.

absence of sliding, the protective oxide forms and the rate of oxidation drops off according to a parabolic or a logarithmic rate law (Chap. 15). When sliding occurs, the (usually) brittle oxide layer has the chance of being broken by adhesion and abrasion, thus destroying the protective layer and causing an increase in oxidation rate.

Surface fatigue wear is primarily observed in rolling applications such as encountered in gears and rolling contact bearings. This form of wear is related to the bulk fatigue of materials, and many variables are common to both phenomena. In the usual application, the surfaces are highly polished and interfacial contact is primarily rolling, with very little sliding. The interfacial deformation is primarily elastic under these conditions, and adhesive, abrasive, and corrosive wear are negligible. As the mechanism continues, the material at the surface is continually stressed and unstressed. The cyclic stressing may continue for millions of cycles with no apparent damage, but after a certain period small fatigue cracks will form slightly below the surface. The cracks will then propagate parallel to the surface, causing a spalling and flaking of material from the surface. The particles which flake off tend to be much larger than for other forms of wear, being of the order of 1,000 Å or more as compared with the order of 30 Å for adhesive wear. As with other forms of fatigue, the surface-wear fatigue life of a material varies inversely with a high power of the surface stress (usually about the ninth power). Surface fatigue wear, however, does not show an endurance limit, so failure can occur even at very low stresses. The variation of fatigue life under apparently identical conditions is enormous, in many cases by factors of 100 or more to 1. Thus, it is always difficult to predict the life of a device with much certainty. High surface hardness, highly polished surfaces, and imperfection-free surfaces will reduce surface fatigue wear.

16.6
Lubrication

Lubrication is the interposing of a film of material between two contacting surfaces for the purpose of reducing friction and wear on the rubbing surfaces. Fluid lubricants operate by either of two mecnanisms: *fluid lubrication* or *boundary lubrication*. In fluid lubrication the moving surfaces are separated by a continuous, thick layer of lubricant so that there is no direct solid-to-solid contact. The resistance to motion arises solely from the viscosity of the lubricant. Under ideal conditions, the coefficient of friction can be reduced several orders of magnitude to the range of 0.001 to 0.01 and wear can be reduced to negligible amounts. In boundary lubrication, the moving surfaces are separated by lubricant films which are only a few molecular layers thick. In this case, the chemical constitution of the lubricant molecules and the nature of the underlying surfaces, rather than the fluid viscosity, determine the properties of the system. Under ideal conditions, the coefficient of friction can be reduced an order of magnitude to the range of 0.05 to 0.15 and wear can be reduced significantly.   Between these two extremes, there is an intermediate type of lubrication in which part of the surface is in boundary contact while the remainder is separated by a fluid film.   Another type of lubrication, closely related to boundary lubrication, utilizes a soft solid film between two hard surfaces. Films of this type may be mechanically or electrolytically applied, or they may result from a chemical reaction between the surfaces, the environment, and special additives.   These solid lubricants are often referred to as "extreme-pressure lubricants" and are generally required for unusual environmental conditions (such as extremely high temperatures, for example).

The resistance to motion in the presence of fluid lubrication can be estimated by calculating the viscous resistance of the fluid.   Consider the ideal bearing shown in Fig. 16.6.   Suppose the shaft is rotating in the bearing so that

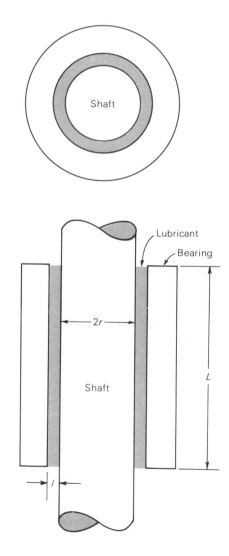

Fig. 16.6 A hydrodynamic bearing for a vertical shaft.

the lubricant film has a uniform thickness. The surface velocity of a shaft of radius rm, rotating $\mathfrak{N}_R$ rps, is $2\pi r \mathfrak{N}_R$ m/sec. If there is no slip at the fluid-solid interface and if the film is very thin (that is, $l \ll r$), the rate of shear of the film is approximately uniform and is roughly $2\pi r \mathfrak{N}_R/l$. If the viscosity of the fluid is η_v, the shearing stress is $2\pi r \mathfrak{N}_R \eta_v/l$ kg$_w$/m². If the length of the bearing is L, the sheared area is $2\pi r L$ and the total viscous force is $4\pi^2 r^2 \mathfrak{N}_R L \eta_v/l$. The resisting torque for the shaft is then $\mathbf{T} = rF$, or

$$\mathbf{T} = \frac{4\pi^2 r^3 \mathfrak{N}_R L \eta_v}{l} \tag{16.18}$$

Equation (16.18) is found to predict resisting torque very well for lightly loaded bearings or vertically running shafts at low rotational speeds. In any other situation, however, the shaft does not run in a central position but rather runs eccentrically relative to the bearing, squeezing the lubricant through the converging gap between the surfaces. Furthermore, non-Newtonian flow and thermal effects make this an extremely complex fluid dynamical problem. Nevertheless, one may still say that the resisting torque is directly proportional to the product of a characteristic viscosity and a rotational speed:

$$\mathbf{T} = K\eta_{v0}\mathfrak{N}_R \tag{16.19}$$

If the apparent pressure on the bearing is s_P (i.e., load divided by projected bearing area), the apparent frictional coefficient, β_{Sf}, is proportional to the ratio of the torque and the bearing pressure:

$$\beta_{Sf} = K_1 \frac{\eta_{v0}\mathfrak{N}_R}{s_P} \tag{16.20}$$

Figure 16.7 shows the coefficient of friction as a function of the parameter $\eta_{v0}\mathfrak{N}_R/s_P$. In general, high loads, low viscosity, and low speeds lead to a breakdown of fluid lubrication and a sharp increase in β_{Sf}. Above a critical value of the parameter $\eta_{v0}\mathfrak{N}_R/s_P$, Eq. (16.20) for fluid lubrication is valid. Thus, for a minimum of frictional resistance, a fluid with as low a viscosity as possible, while still maintaining fluid lubrication, is desirable.

As $\eta_{v0}\mathfrak{N}_R/s_P$ approaches a small number, the lubricant film becomes thinner and thinner until the surface asperities start penetrating the fluid. Portions of the surface then show boundary lubrication. As shown in Fig. 16.7, a region of mixed mechanisms occurs over a range of variables. When $\eta_{v0}\mathfrak{N}_R/s_P$ is small enough, boundary lubrication predominates. Since different material characteristics control the two main types of lubrication, a material that is a good fluid lubricant is not necessarily a good boundary lubricant. A good fluid lubricant must have a low vapor pressure, a low freezing point, good oxidation resistance, noncorrosive properties, an adequate viscosity, and the proper viscosity-temperature characteristics.

The viscosity characteristics of a fluid lubricant are especially important, since they essentially determine the operating characteristics of the lubricant. If the viscosity is too low, fluid lubrication cannot be maintained and partial or

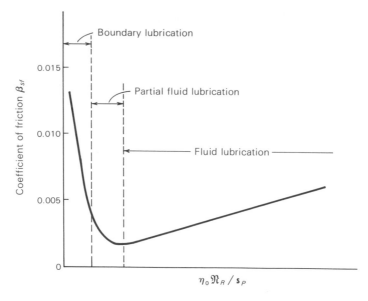

Fig. 16.7 The coefficient of friction is a measure of the lubricating characteristics of a material.

total boundary lubrication will control. This means higher frictional resistance and excessive wear. If the viscosity is too high, excessive friction and power dissipation will result. The effects of temperature on the lubricant are álso important, since viscous dissipation in the lubricant will always cause an appreciable temperature rise. Since viscosity decreases exponentially with the temperature rise, relatively small temperature increases can make the oil too "thin" to be an effective lubricant. From Chap. 12 we recall that the viscosity is proportional to $\exp(\Delta E_v/RT)$, where ΔE_v is the activation energy. A low activation energy promotes a relative insensitivity to temperature changes. The molecular structure of a material determines ΔE_v. Thus, linear molecules with a high degree of chain flexibility and strong intermolecular forces have a high activation energy and high temperature sensitivity. Highly branched molecules, containing rings and nonpolar groups, have a low activation energy and thus low temperature sensitivity. The organic silicones with the general structures

for example, are widely used as special lubricants because they have thermal stability, chemical resistance, and very low viscosity change with temperature and may be obtained over a wide range of viscosity (by choosing the proper molecular weight).

Because of economics, the majority of fluid lubricants are obtained by distilling crude petroleum. These do not necessarily have the best combination of properties, but the addition of oxidation inhibitors, viscosity improvers, detergents, and wetting agents make them suitable for general use at a reasonable price.

In boundary lubrication, a one- or two-molecule-layer film is formed by a surface reaction between the lubricant and the material. For the lubricant to be effective, the surface compound that forms must be a cohesive mass that readily shears but is strong enough to maintain a separation between the contacting materials. Two requirements of a boundary lubricant are that they can react with the materials to form surface compounds and that the shapes of the lubricant molecules are such that strong intermolecular forces can set up a dense, protective film on the surface. It is seldom possible to develop perfect protection with a boundary lubricant. The total load will always be supported by both lubricant-lubricant contacts and metal-metal contacts. With a good lubricant, the number of metal-metal contacts is reduced sufficiently to make metallic friction negligible, so that the frictional resistance of the surface is controlled by the boundary film. As long as there are metal-to-metal contacts, however, there will be a measurable amount of surface wear.

The effectiveness of a boundary lubricant depends on the magnitude of the interaction between its molecules and the metal surface. If there is a tendency for chemical reaction with the surface, the monomolecular lubricating layer will be more permanent. Thus fatty acids that tend to form metallic soaps are generally good boundary lubricants. Very highly polar molecules also tend to be good lubricants, since strong electrostatic bonding can develop with the metal surface. Molecular geometry is also important, since a dense, thick monomolecular layer will be more effective. Thus, long straight-chain molecules are superior to branched and ring types because they can align into a high packing density. Superior boundary lubrication is obtained with compounds such as long-chain alcohols and fatty acids, since they are linear, have dimensions of the order of asperities on a surface and have polar end groups that can react with the metal. Silicones, which are good fluid lubricants, are very poor boundary lubricants because of their inability to react with metals, their branched, nonlinear structures, and their relatively weak intermolecular forces.

Since dense packing in the boundary film is desirable, it follows that *solid-lubricant films* are useful. Various chlorine, sulfur, and phosphorus compounds react with metals to form complex solids which coat the surface and act as lubricating films. Rather than the metal wearing at metal-metal junctions, the film-to-film junctions cause friction and undergo wear. Such compounds are often used as additives, with sufficient material to continually form a protective film as fast as it is worn away. The mode of action is often extremely complex, and other factors, such as oxidation effects, are very important. The problem of wear in solid films is sometimes overcome by combining a good lubricant in an adhesive binder. Thus, Teflon and graphite imbedded in epoxy adhesive produces a wear-resistant film.

For detailed information on the wide variety of lubricants that are commercially available, the reader is referred to the references at the end of the chapter.

16.7
Adsorption and adhesion

When two absolutely clean metal surfaces are placed together in a very high vacuum ($<10^{-6}$ mm Hg), they tend to adhere strongly to one another. A coefficient of friction is not really measurable under seizure conditions, but it would probably be of the order of 100 or so. When two clean iron surfaces are placed together in an environment of 10^{-4} mm Hg of pressure, a frictional coefficient of about 2.5 exists, and under several millimeters of mercury the frictional coefficient reduces to about 1.0. These phenomena are indicative of the strong adsorption and adhesion tendencies of surfaces. In the absence of a gas, metal atoms in one surface come in direct contact with metal atoms of the other surface and strong primary bonds form, joining the two surfaces together. This is similar to the adhesive nature of a grain boundary in holding two grains of a polycrystalline material together. Indeed, grain boundaries are often referred to as internal surfaces. While the strength of a grain boundary is often greater than the strength within the crystals, the adhesive strength between two surfaces is usually only a small fraction of the tensile strength of the bulk material. The reasons for this are that the real area of contact is actually very small, joints that are formed in compression often break when the load is removed because of elastic recovery of the surfaces, and impurities, such as gas molecules, have a strong tendency to adsorb on a clean metal surface, thereby cutting down the number of actual metal-to-metal bonds across the interface.

One of the more important aspects of adhesion between surfaces is the strength of the bond between an initially fluid surface and a solid surface. *Adhesives,* for example, are applied in a fluid form so as to attain a maximum contact to the two surfaces being bonded together. After application, the fluid becomes more viscous and tacky until it is finally converted to a hard solid by either physical or chemical reaction. Extrusion coating, laminating, and heat sealing are examples of techniques that are used to join two surfaces.

There are many factors which affect the measured strength of the bond between two substances. The maximum theoretical strength across the interface is determined by the strength of the intermolecular bonding. This full strength is rarely attained because of inability of a fluid to perfectly wet a solid surface. Also, when the fluid adhesive sets to a solid, residual stresses will always be left in the adhesive, which further decreases the bond strength. The final residual strength of a bond across an interface may be orders of magnitude less than the maximum. If the residual strength is greater than the bulk strength of either the adhesive or the bonded materials, failure will occur in the weakest constituent. If the residual strength is less than the bulk strength of the weakest constituent, failure will occur across the interface. A satisfactory theory for predicting the true strength of an adhesive bond must take into account intermolecular forces, the thermodynamic wetting characteristics of the surfaces, and the mechanical properties of the constituents.

There has been considerable effort expended in calculating the intermolecular attractions that exist at an interface [5]. One cannot verify these calculations experimentally, since the bond cannot be ruptured without bringing in all other factors. The following simple approximation, however, shows that the intermolecular attraction is probably orders of magnitude greater than the strength of the adhesive bond.

Consider an adsorbed molecule at a distance d from a plane solid surface of adsorbent, which has a molecular density of N_A molecules/m³ (Fig. 16.8). In order to estimate the total molecular interaction between the adsorbed molecule and the adsorbent, one may express the interaction between the molecule and an annular ring below the solid surface as (refer to Fig. 16.8) $N_A 2\pi r \, dr \, dz$ $\psi(a)$, where $\psi(a)$ is the intermolecular potential energy between a pair of particles. The total interaction energy for a single adsorbed molecule is then

$$\psi_{AT} = 2\pi N_A \int_{a=z}^{\infty} \int_{z=d}^{\infty} \psi(a) \, dz \, a \, da \qquad (16.21)$$

where $2\pi r \, dr = 2\pi a \, da$, and

$$\psi(a) = (\psi_{a=r*}) \left[2 \left(\frac{r^*}{a} \right)^n - \left(\frac{r^*}{a} \right)^m \right] \qquad (16.22)$$

On integrating Eq. (16.21), we have

$$\psi_{AT} = 2\pi (r^*)^3 N_A (\psi_{a=r*}) \left[\frac{2}{(n-2)(n-3)} \left(\frac{r^*}{d} \right)^{n-3} - \frac{1}{(m-2)(m-3)} \left(\frac{r^*}{d} \right)^{m-3} \right] \qquad (16.23)$$

Equation (16.23) is the potential energy of interaction between a single adsorbed molecule at a distance d from a plane surface and the adsorbent material. If $N_L^{2/3}$ molecules are adsorbed in a monomolecular layer, the total interaction between the monomolecular layer and the adsorbent is $N_L^{2/3}$ times Eq. (16.23). Succeeding layers at distances $2d$, $3d$, etc., will strengthen the interaction further, but the first monomolecular layer is the primary source of bonding. A rough estimate of the total energy of adhesion per unit area of contact (assuming a 50 percent increase in energy due to non-nearest neighbors) is thus

$$(\psi_T)_{\text{adhes}} \doteq 3\pi r^{*3} N_A N_L^{2/3} \, \psi_{a=r*} \left[\frac{2}{(n-2)(n-3)} \left(\frac{r^*}{d} \right)^{n-3} - \frac{1}{(m-2)(m-3)} \left(\frac{r^*}{d} \right)^{m-3} \right]$$

$$(16.24)$$

where N_L is the density of the adsorbed layer. If the equilibrium separation is d_0 (that is, $\partial \psi_T / \partial d = 0$ at $d = d_0$):

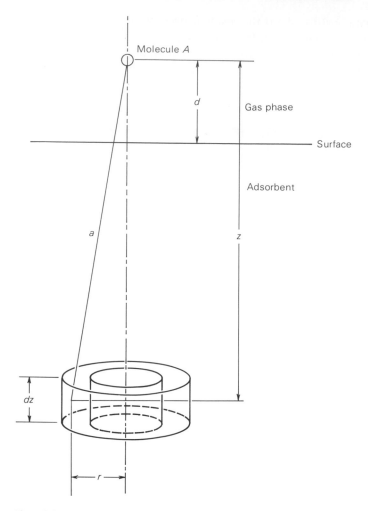

Fig. 16.8 A coordinate system for the interaction of a molecule with a plane surface.

$$(\psi_T)_{\text{adhes}} \doteq 6\pi r^{*3} N_A N_L^{2/3} \, \psi_{a=r*} \left(\frac{r^*}{d_0}\right)^{n-3} \frac{1}{n-2} \frac{m-n}{(n-3)(m-3)} \qquad (16.25)$$

Equation (16.25) is also an alternative expression for the cohesive energy (when $N_A = N_L$). As long as we are considering dispersion forces (n and $m > 3$), it is equivalent to Eq. (11.3). If $n = 6$, $m = 12$, $r^* \doteq d_o \doteq 3$ Å, $N_A \doteq N_L \doteq 4 \times 10^{28}$, and $\psi \doteq 1$ to 10 kcal/g mole,

$$(\psi_T)_{\text{adhes}} \doteq 0.09 \text{ to } 0.9 \text{ joules/m}^2 \qquad (16.26)$$

Experimental data show [5] that energies of adhesion of 0.2 to 0.3 joules/m² are typical for dispersion-bonded materials, while energies of adhesion of 0.7

to 1.0 joules/m² are typical for hydrogen-bonded materials. Thus our calculations give reasonable values for the energy of adhesion. The theoretical mechanical strength of the bond is obtained by differentiating Eq. (16.24) and finding the maximum force of attraction:

$$s_{max} = 6\pi(r^*)^2 N_A (N_L)^{2/3} \psi_{a=r*} \left(\frac{r^*}{d_{max}}\right)^{n-2} \frac{m-n}{(n-2)(m-2)} \qquad (16.27)$$

Equation (16.27) is also an alternate expression for the theoretical tensile strength of a material if $N_A = N_L$. As long as we are considering dispersion forces only (n and $m > 2$), it is equivalent to Eq. (11.4). Using the same values of the constants as before, we obtain

$$s_{max} \doteq 7.6 - 76 \times 10^7 \ kg_w/m^2 \qquad (16.28)$$

Experimental values for the tensile strength of adhesive bonds vary over wide ranges, but generally they are of the order of 10^5 to $10^6 \ kg_w/m^2$ (200 to 2,000 psi). Thus our theoretical maximum is a few orders of magnitude higher than our actual bond strength.

One reason for a low adhesive strength is that the real area of contact between surfaces is small (e.g., as with contacting solid surfaces). When a liquid contacts a solid, the contact area can be limited by the inability of the liquid to perfectly wet the solid. When a liquid is dropped on a solid surface, it will spread along the surface and completely wet only if the net free energy of the system is decreased by replacing a solid-vapor interface with a solid-liquid and a liquid-vapor interface. The condition for complete wetting is thus

$$\gamma_{SL} + \gamma_{LV} < \gamma_{SV} \qquad (16.29)$$

On the other hand, if the replacing of the solid-vapor interface involves an increase in free energy, complete wetting cannot be spontaneous. Under these conditions a liquid droplet will spread until a balance of surface forces establishes an equilibrium. This is "partial wetting," and the angle that the liquid hemispherical top makes with the solid surface is called the "contact angle" (Fig. 16.9). When the surface tensions are in equilibrium,

$$\gamma_{SL} + \gamma_{LV} \cos \theta = \gamma_{SV} \qquad (16.30)$$

When the contact angle is 180°, a spherical droplet is formed and no wetting occurs. The condition for no wetting is thus

$$\gamma_{SL} \geqslant \gamma_{SV} + \gamma_{LV} \qquad (16.31)$$

A liquid material is a good adhesive only if it can extensively wet the surface (that is, $\cos \theta \doteq 1$). The contact angle will depend on the nature of the contacting materials, the condition and cleanliness of the surfaces, and the nature of adsorbed gases or oxide films on the surfaces. Degreased metal surfaces, for example, are easily wetted by epoxy adhesives (giving good adhesive bonds), while greasy surfaces cannot be wetted (giving poor bond strengths).

Finally, the inherent strength of an adhesive bond can be greatly reduced

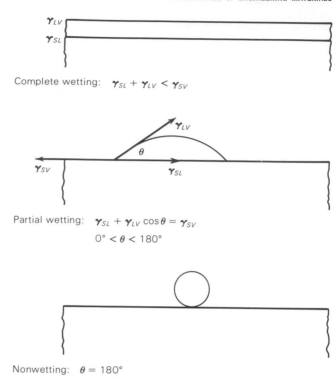

γ_{LV}

γ_{SL}

Complete wetting: $\gamma_{SL} + \gamma_{LV} < \gamma_{SV}$

γ_{LV}

θ

γ_{SV} γ_{SL}

Partial wetting: $\gamma_{SL} + \gamma_{LV} \cos \theta = \gamma_{SV}$

$0° < \theta < 180°$

Nonwetting: $\theta = 180°$

$\gamma_{SL} > \gamma_{SV} + \gamma_{LV}$

Fig. 16.9   The contact angle is a measure of the wetting characteristics of a surface by a liquid.

because of internal stresses that build up at the interface and within the bulk of the material. When a liquid adherent is converted to a solid, for example, the change will involve either a chemical reaction, such as polymerization, or a physical change, such as solvent evaporation. Accompanying volume changes can set up internal stresses at the interface which greatly decrease the strength. Internal stresses can also build up because of temperature differentials, crystallization, surface orientation, oxidative aging, moisture absorption, leaching effects, surface imperfections, and other such characteristics. In general, besides the surface properties of the materials and the topography of the surfaces, moduli of elasticity, plasticity, differential thermal expansion, and joint design are all important variables in determining the strength of adhesion.

References

1   Adam, N. K.: "The Physics and Chemistry of Surfaces," Oxford University Press, London, 1941. *An advanced reference text on the physical chemistry of surfaces.*

2 Bowden, F. P., and D. Tabor: "The Friction and Lubrication of Solids," 2d ed., Oxford University Press, London, 1954. *A detailed and expert account of these subjects. Necessary reading for those doing research in these areas.*

3 Bowden, F. P., and D. Tabor: "Friction and Lubrication," John Wiley & Sons, Inc., New York, 1956. *A condensed version of Ref. 2. A nonmathematical analysis of the mechanisms of friction and lubrication.*

4 Braithwaite, E. R.: "Solid Lubricants and Surfaces," Pergamon Press, New York, 1964. *Detailed account of solid-film lubricants and their properties.*

5 Clark, F., J. E. Rutzler, and R. L. Savage (eds.): "Adhesion and Adhesives: Fundamentals and Practice," John Wiley & Sons, Inc., New York, 1954. *A series of papers presented at a symposium at Case Institute and a conference in London covering the theory of intermolecular forces, the thermodynamics of adhesion, and adhesives technology.*

6 Davies, J. T., and E. K. Rideal: "Interfacial Phenomena," Academic Press Inc., New York, 1961. *A detailed, readable text on all aspects of surface phenomena.*

7 Freeman, P.: "Lubrication and Friction," Sir Isaac Pitman & Sons, Ltd., London, 1962. *Detailed information on lubricants and their properties.*

8 Gomer, R., and C. S. Smith (eds.): "Structure and Properties of Solid Surfaces," The University of Chicago Press, Chicago, 1953. *A series of research papers on surfaces.*

9 Moelwyn-Hughes, E. A.: "Physical Chemistry," 2d ed., The Macmillan Company, New York, 1961. *Chapter XIX, on the interfacial state, is an easily read survey of the physical chemistry of surfaces, with an emphasis on the relationship between surface properties and intermolecular forces.*

10 Rabinowicz, E.: "Friction and Wear of Materials," John Wiley & Sons, Inc., New York, 1965. *A very readable, authoritative text on friction, wear, and lubrication. Highly recommended as supplementary reading and as a starting text for researchers in the field.*

11 Swalin, R. A.: "Thermodynamics of Solids," John Wiley & Sons, Inc., New York, 1962. *Chapter 12 gives a readable survey of the thermodynamics of surfaces.*

Questions

16.1 Show that the close-packed planes in face-centered cubic structures have the lowest surface energy.

16.2 The solid-vapor surface tension of $NaCl$ is 0.300 joules/m². Estimate the modulus of elasticity and compare with experimental values.

16.3 The ratio of the surface tension to the Brinell hardness is given roughly by the equation:

$$\frac{\gamma_{SV}}{s_H} = 3.37 \times 10^{-3} \, s_H^{-2/3}$$

where γ_{SV} is in joules/per square meter and s_H is in kilograms weight per square meter. Explain why this simple relationship is reasonable. Estimate the surface energy of potassium, tin, aluminum, copper, and nickel. Compare your estimates with experimental values.

Material	Potassium	Tin	Aluminum	Copper	Nickel
Brinell hardness, kg_w/m^2	3.9×10^4	5.83×10^6	2.68×10^7	7.50×10^7	2.35×10^8

16.4 Estimate the real areas of contact when two 1 by 1 by 1-cm cubes of the materials listed in Question 16.3 are placed in contact under their own weight.

16.5 Explain the mechanism of friction between two moving ductile surfaces.

16.6 Explain why elastomers do not exactly follow the same laws of friction as ductile metals.

16.7 Why is the coefficient of rolling friction much lower than the coefficient of sliding friction? Would you expect lubricants to affect rolling friction?

16.8 What methods are used for improving the wear resistance of metals? Explain why the different methods are effective.

16.9 Two stainless-steel surfaces are rubbing against each other at the rate of 1 cm/ second under a load of 70 kg_w/m^2. Estimate the adhesive wear loss per square centimeter of surface per year.

16.10 Explain why a fluid lubricant is not necessarily a good boundary lubricant.

16.11 Why are polar compounds added to lubricating oils?

16.12 Why is it desirable to maintain fluid lubrication in operating equipment?

16.13 What molecular and physical properties are desirable for fluid lubricants and for boundary lubricants?

16.14 Estimate the surface tension of liquid mercury at 0°C if $d_0 = 1.944$ Å, $n = 6$, and $m = 9$. Compare your calculation with the experimental value of 0.463 joules/m².

16.15 A fine powdered solid is sealed in an evacuated glass cylinder and submerged in a calorimeter filled with a liquid. The seal is broken, the liquid wets the solid, and a temperature rise occurs because of the heat of wetting ΔH_W. Show that the work of adhesion may be calculated from the equation

$$W_A = \Delta H_W + \gamma_{LV} - T \frac{d\gamma_{LV}}{dT}$$

where γ_{LV} is the surface tension of the liquid in contact with its own vapor.

16.16 Discuss the factors that control the actual strength of an adhesive joint.

Appendixes

Appendix A
Atomic weights of the elements

Element	Symbol	Atomic number	Atomic weight
Actinium	Ac	89	[227]
Aluminium	Al	13	26.98
Americium	Am	95	[243]
Antimony	Sb	51	121.76
Argon	Ar	18	39.944
Arsenic	As	33	74.91
Astatine	At	85	[210]
Barium	Ba	56	137.36
Berkelium	Bk	97	[245]
Beryllium	Be	4	9.013
Bismuth	Bi	83	209.00
Boron	B	5	10.82
Bromine	Br	35	79.916
Cadmium	Cd	48	112.41
Cesium	Cs	55	132.91
Calcium	Ca	20	40.08
Californium	Cf	98	[248]
Carbon	C	6	12.011
Cerium	Ce	58	140.13
Chlorine	Cl	17	35.457
Chromium	Cr	24	52.01
Cobalt	Co	27	58.94
Copper	Cu	29	63.54
Curium	Cm	96	[245]
Dysprosium	Dy	66	162.51
Einsteinium	Es	99	
Erbium	Er	68	167.27
Europium	Eu	63	152.0
Fermium	Fm	100	
Fluorine	F	9	19.00
Francium	Fr	87	[233]
Gadolinium	Gd	64	157.26
Gallium	Ga	31	69.72
Germanium	Ge	32	72.60
Gold	Au	79	197.0
Hafnium	Hf	72	178.50
Helium	He	2	4.003
Holmium	Ho	67	164.94
Hydrogen	H	1	1.0080
Indium	In	49	114.82
Iodine	I	53	126.91
Iridium	Ir	77	192.2

Element	Symbol	Atomic number	Atomic weight
Iron	Fe	26	55.85
Krypton	Kr	36	83.80
Lanthanum	La	57	138.92
Lawrencium	Lw	103	[257]
Lead	Pb	82	207.21
Lithium	Li	3	6.940
Lutecium	Lu	71	174.99
Magnesium	Mg	12	24.32
Manganese	Mn	25	54.94
Mendelevium	Md	101	
Mercury	Hg	80	200.61
Molybdenum	Mo	42	95.95
Neodymium	Nd	60	144.27
Neon	Ne	10	20.183
Neptunium	Np	93	[237]
Nickel	Ni	28	58.71
Niobium (Columbium)	Nb (Cb)	41	92.91
Nitrogen	N	7	14.008
Nobelium	No	102	
Osmium	Os	76	190.2
Oxygen	O	8	16.0000
Palladium	Pd	46	106.4
Phosphorus	P	15	30.975
Platinum	Pt	78	195.09
Plutonium	Pu	94	[242]
Polonium	Po	84	[210]
Potassium	K	19	39.100
Praseodymium	Pr	59	140.92
Promethium	Pm	61	[145]
Protactinium	Pa	91	[231]
Radium	Ra	88	[226.05]
Radon	Rn	86	[222]
Rhenium	Re	75	186.22
Rhodium	Rh	45	102.91
Rubidium	Rb	37	85.48
Ruthenium	Ru	44	101.1
Samarium	Sm	62	150.35
Scandium	Sc	21	44.96
Selenium	Se	34	78.96
Silicon	Si	14	28.09
Silver	Ag	47	107.880
Sodium	Na	11	22.991

Element	Symbol	Atomic number	Atomic weight
Strontium	Sr	38	87.63
Sulfur	S	16	32.066
Tantalum	Ta	73	180.95
Technetium	Tc	43	[99]
Tellurium	Te	52	127.61
Terbium	Tb	65	158.93
Thallium	Tl	81	204.39
Thorium	Th	90	232.05
Thulium	Tm	69	168.94
Tin	Sn	50	118.70
Titanium	Ti	22	47.90
Tungsten	W	74	183.86
Uranium	U	92	238.07
Vanadium	V	23	50.95
Xenon	Xe	54	131.30
Ytterbium	Yb	70	173.04
Yttrium	Y	39	88.92
Zinc	Zn	30	65.38
Zirconium	Zr	40	91.22

Appendix B
Nomenclature

Symbol	Definition	Typical unit or unit abbreviation	Page
A	Helmholtz free energy	joules/kg$_m$ mole	29
A_f	Frequency factor in the rate equation	sec^{-1}	49
$\mathfrak{A}$	Madelung constant	Dimensionless	136
a_T	Shift factor in superposition principle	Dimensionless	379
$\mathscr{B}$	Magnetic flux density	webers/m^2	451
$\mathbf{b}$	Length of a Burger's vector	Å	166
C	Number of components in Gibbs phase rule		185
C_{vac}	Capacitance	farads	425
c	Speed of light	m/sec	529
c_v	Specific heat at constant volume	joules/kg$_m$ mole–°K	269
c_p	Specific heat at constant pressure	joules/kg$_m$ mole–°K	269
D	Dielectric displacement	coul/m^2	426
D_p	Degree of polymerization		235
D_{12}	Binary diffusion coefficient	m^2/sec	43
$\mathscr{D}$	Self-diffusion coefficient	m^2/sec	43
d_1	Diameter of particle 1	m	43
d	Distance between planes (in Bragg's law)	Å	124
E_{CD}	Cohesive energy density	cal/cm^3	229
ΔE_D	Activation energy for diffusion	kcal/kg$_m$ mole	47
E_Y	Young's modulus of elasticity	kg$_w$/m^2	290
$E(t)$	Tensile relaxation modulus	kg$_w$/m^2	366
E	Total energy content	joules/kg$_m$ mole	25
$\mathfrak{E}$	Electron affinity	electron volts	61
$\mathscr{E}$	Electric field	volts/m	15
e	A unit of electric charge	coulombs	12
F	Force	kg$_w$	10
F_D	Degrees of freedom (Gibbs phase rule)		185
$\mathfrak{F}$	Faraday constant	$\dfrac{coul}{equivalent}$	468
$\mathscr{F}(t)$	Percent transformation during nucleation		199
f	Functionality of a monomer		235
f_{12}	Frequency of binary collisions	$\dfrac{collisions}{sec\text{-}m^3}$	39
f_T	Tensile force	kg$_w$	352
G	Gibbs free energy	joules/kg$_m$ mole	29
G_S	Shear modulus	kg$_w$/m^2	292
$G(t)$	Relaxation modulus in shear	kg$_w$/m^2	366
$\mathscr{G}_r$	Rate of grain growth during freezing	mm/sec	199
h	Planck's constant	joule-sec	29
h_c	Heat-transfer coefficient	joules/sec-m^2–°K	341
H	Enthalpy	joules/kg$_m$ mole	155
$\mathscr{H}$	The Hamiltonian in the Schrödinger wave equation	kcal/kg$_m$ mole	56

Symbol	Definition	Typical unit or unit abbreviation	Page
$\mathfrak{H}$	Magnetic field intensity	amp/m	451
I	Moment of inertia	kg_m-m^2	31
$\mathfrak{I}$	Ionization potential	electron volts	54
$\mathbf{I}$	Intensity of scattered radiation	joule/sec-m^2	122
$\mathscr{I}$	Current density	amp/m^2	393
j_P	Flux of property P	units of P/m^2-sec	41
$J(t)$	Compliance	m^2/kg_w	365
J	An integer representing a specific rotational quantum state	Dimensionless	31
k_f	Force constant for a harmonic oscillator	newtons/m	101
k_R	Rate constant		248
k	Boltzmann constant	joules/°K-molecule	27
K	Bulk modulus	kg_w/m^2	292
$\mathscr{K}$	Equilibrium constant		469
$\mathfrak{K}_{AA}$	The coulombic integral	electron volts	66
l	Distance between centers of gravity of charges in a molecule	Å	14
l_p	Mean free path of a gas molecule	Å	40
L_A	Electronegativity of atom A	Dimensionless	73
$\mathscr{L}$	Orbital angular momentum	kg_m-m^2/sec	453
$L(a)$	The Langevin function	Dimensionless	430
m	Mass	kg_m	30
m_R	Reduced mass	Dimensionless	101
M	Molecular weight	kg_m/kg_m mole	241
$\mathscr{M}$	Magnetic polarization	amp/m	452
n_1	Number of type 1 particle		25
N	Total number of atoms	atom/unit mass or atoms/unit volume	25
N_1	Mole fraction of type 1 particles		164
$\mathfrak{N}$	Revolutions per second		509
$\mathscr{N}$	Rate of nucleation	nuclei/cm^3-sec	156
p	Pressure	kg_w/m^2	29
p_1	Momentum of particle 1	kg_m-m/sec	29
$\mathfrak{p}$	Extent of reaction		235
P	Number of phases		185
P_c	Permeability coefficient	cm^3/sec/cm^2/mm Hg/mm	485
P_L	Power loss	watts or watts/cycle	374
$\mathscr{P}$	Polarization	coul/m^2	426
q_a	Net charge of molecule a	coulombs	13
q_x	Energy flux	joules/m^2-sec	42
Q_a	Quadrupole moment of molecule a	coul-m^2	13
$\mathfrak{Q}_{AB}$	Exchange integral	electron volts	66
$\mathscr{Q}$	Configurational partition function		30
r	Radius of atom	Å	7

Symbol	Definition	Typical unit or unit abbreviation	Page
$\langle r^2 \rangle$	Average of the square of the end-to-end distance for a polymer chain	Å^2	219
R	The gas constant	joules/kg$_m$ mole–°K	529
$\mathscr{R}$	Electrical resistivity	ohms	412
s_j	Number of jth energy states		27
s_a and s_b	Geometric lattice constants		135
S	Entropy	joules/kg$_m$ mole–°K	28
$\mathscr{S}$	Solubility coefficient		484
t	Time	sec	527
T	Temperature	°K	—
$\mathbf{T}$	Resisting torque	kg$_w$-m	509
$\mathbf{u}$	Absolute electron velocity	m/sec	395
u	Internal energy per molecule	joules/molecule	42
U	Internal energy	joules/kg$_m$ mole	28
v	Velocity	m/sec	37
V	Volume	cm^3/g	28
$\mathbf{V}$	Voltage	volts	425
$\mathfrak{w}_1$	Number of distinguishable arrangements of particles in state 1		26
W_1	Weight of component 1	kg$_w$	182
W_{el}	Elastic work of stretching	joules	352
$\mathfrak{W}$	Probability of finding a system in a given state		26
x_v	Fractional free volume in WLF equation		363
X_w	Weight-average degree of polymerization		364
$\mathfrak{z}$	Number of nearest neighbors in a crystal lattice		135
z	Molecular partition function		29
Z	Total partition function		28
α_a	Polarizability of molecule a	Å^3	15
$\boldsymbol{\alpha_v}$	Volume coefficient of thermal expansion	°K^{-1}	267
β	Frictional constant		437
β_{SF}	Static coefficient of friction		500
$\boldsymbol{\beta}$	Activity coefficient		469
γ_s	Strain energy	joules/cm^3	304
γ	Surface tension	joules/cm^2	496
Γ	Grain boundary energy	joules/cm^2	172
Γ_s	Total strain energy	joules	304
Γ	Total surface energy	joules	496
δ	Loss angle	degrees	437
$\tan \delta$	Dissipation factor		437
δ_s	Solubility parameter	(cal/cm^3)$^{1/2}$	478
Δ	Excess bond energy	kcal/g mole	73
Δ	Small's molar attraction constants		231
ϵ_1	Energy of particle 1	joules	25

Symbol	Definition	Typical unit or unit abbreviation	Page
ϵ^*	Energy parameter in a potential energy function	joules/molecule	44
ϵ	Energy difference between trans and gauche states in a polymer	joules	219
ϵ_{xx}	Strain due to the x tensile component of stress	m/m	290
ϵ_s	Strain	m/m	290
ϵ_0	Permittivity of empty space	farads/m	425
η_v	Viscosity coefficient	g-cm/sec or poise	42
η_e	Electron mobility	m/sec-volt/m	393
ϑ_p	Poisson ratio	Dimensionless	292
θ	Angle		10
Θ_D	Debye characteristic temperature	°K	270
Θ	Time of flight between collisions	seconds	393
Θ_c	Curie temperature	°K	454
κ	Thermal conductivity	watts/m-°K	42
κ_e	Dielectric constant	Dimensionless	426
κ_T	Isothermal compressibility	m^2/kg_w	269
λ	Wavelength	Å	54
λ_R	Relaxation time	seconds	368
μ_a	Electric dipole moment of molecule a	debyes	13
μ_M	Magnetic dipole moment	coul-m^2/sec	452
μ_0	Permeability of empty space	henrys/m	451
$(\mu_e)_M$	Relative magnetic permeability	Dimensionless	451
ν	Natural vibration frequency	sec^{-1}	32
π	Internal pressure	kg_w/m^2	282
π_x	A molecular orbital formed by overlapping p-type atomic orbitals		68
ρ_s	Surface density	particles/m^2	289
ρ_v	Volume density	g/cm^3	276
σ	Range parameter in Lennard-Jones potential	Å	44
σ_s	Sigma-type molecular orbital		68
σ	Electrical conductivity	ohm^{-1}	393
ς	Tensile stress	kg_w/m^2	289
τ_{xz}	Shear stress in x direction normal to yz plane	kg_w/m^2	294
ϕ	An angle		10
ϕ_i	Volume fraction of component i		477
χ_e	Electric susceptibility	Dimensionless	426
χ_M	Magnetic susceptibility	Dimensionless	452
χ_S	Flory interaction parameter	Dimensionless	476
ψ	Potential energy	kcal/kg_m mole	10
Ψ	Wave function		55
ω	Frequency of oscillation	sec^{-1}	435
Ω_v	Parameter used in dilute-gas theory	Dimensionless	44

Index